Foreword

Formerly known as the CESMM3 Price Database, the Institution of Civil Engineers' CESMM3 Carbon & Price Book is now in its seventh edition. Building upon its standard in the provision of civil engineering cost information, in this latest edition the name has changed to reflect the inclusion of estimates of embodied carbon for every work activity.

The CESMM3 Price Database evolved from a document known as the Wessex Database for Civil Engineering. The originator of this publication was Richard McGill, who was a partner of EC Harris at the time. Richard not only developed the Wessex Database of Civil Engineering in 1985, but also led the team that produced the first edition of the CESMM3 Price Database in 1992. As such, he can be considered the original author of this publication and the ICE would like to express its gratitude in recognition of his contribution.

The seventh edition has built upon these strong foundations and been thoroughly updated to reflect information accurate at the second quarter of 2010. This new publication has been compiled using the unparalleled industry knowledge and expertise of Franklin and Andrews, one of the UK's foremost whole life cost and carbon advisers. In particular their dedicated Economic Research Unit (www.economic-research-unit.com) produces high quality cost and carbon data for many price books and databases for all sectors of the construction industry.

Once again it has been structured in line with the requirements of CESMM3 to enable users familiar with the class structure of the CESMM to go directly to the section they require. As before, an additional section has also been included to cover alteration works. In this edition, improvements have been made to the structures of the items in a number of classes to more closely accord with the measurement rules of CESMM3.

In order to accurately estimate the levels of embodied carbon, over 2,000 specialist lump-sum prices have been broken down into labour, materials and plant, giving you the reader a greater degree of detail on the accuracy of the data provided.

The CESMM3 Carbon & Price Book should be on the desk of every contractor, specifier, estimator, engineer, quantity surveyor and project manager actively involved in civil engineering work. It is the only definitive guide to publish estimates of cost and carbon emissions, allowing reference to both to enable the optimum design solution.

The information will undoubtedly be used for appraisal purposes at various stages in civil engineering contracts and will be an invaluable cost and carbon management tool. However, whilst every effort has been made to ensure the accuracy of the data, it must be borne in mind that resource availability, location, procurement nature and size of project etc. will all have a bearing on the cost or carbon values recorded for any individual project. The CESMM3 data may only be regarded as 'typical' under 'normal conditions' and are current the second quarter of 2010. Prices exclude Value Added Tax.

The data provided here should be substituted with actual data where available, functionality that is available through CapIT, the online version of the database (see back cover advert).

Thomas Telford welcomes comments from users on changes or amendments which would further enhance the usefulness of the publication. Please address any correspondence to:

Thomas Telford Ltd., 40 Marsh Wall, London E14 9TP, UK.
Telephone +44 (0)20 7987 6999 Fax +44 (0)20 7538 4101
email publishing@thomastelford.com Internet http://www.icevirtuallibrary.com/cesmm

Acknowledgements

The publishers wish to acknowledge the invaluable assistance given by the following individuals, organisations, manufacturers, contractors, suppliers and associations, including those who have given their kind permission for the reproduction and publication of copyright material.

Editing Authors:
Franklin + Andrews Ltd
St Anne House
Wellesley Road
Croydon
Surrey CR9 2UL
Tel (0207) 633 9966
Email: eru@franklinandrews.com

Editorial Staff:
James Fiske BSc, MQSi, MACostE
Nang Vo Kham Murng MRICS, MSc, BSc
Karl Horton BSc (Hons)
Aaron Wright BSc (Hons)
Sean O'Halloran
Jingxin Shen MSc, BSc (Hons)
Emma Will
Rachael Ogden
Sam Wenham BA (Hons) PG.Dip
Terry J Ellis MSc, BSc (Hons)
Sue Ellis BSc (Hons)

All queries should be made in email to Franklin + Andrews for the attention of Nang Murng

CLASS B - GROUND INVESTIGATION

Geotechnics Ltd
The Geotechnical Centre
203 Torrington Avenue
Tule Hill
Coventry CV4 9AP
Tel (024) 7669 4664
Fax (024) 7669 4642

CLASS C - GEOTECHNICAL AND OTHER SPECIALIST PROCESSES

Kvaemer Cementation Foundations Ltd
Maple Cross House
Denham Way
Rickmansworth
Herts WD3 2SW
Tel (01923) 423100
Fax (01923) 777934

CLASS E - EARTHWORKS

Clive Scott Landscapes
3 Coral Road
Cheadle Hulme
Cheadle
Cheshire SK8 6HQ
Tel (0161) 485 4932
Fax (0171) 276 3000

CLASS F - IN SITU CONCRETE

Tilcon (North) Ltd
PO Box 5
Birtley
Chester le Street
County Durham
DH3 2ST
Tel (0191) 492 2400
Fax (0191) 492 1353

Karrimix Concrete
82 Runwell Road
Construction House
Wickford
Essex SSll 7HJ
Tel (01268) 733421
Fax (01268) 560537

CLASS G - CONCRETE ANCILLARIES

Hy-Ten Reinforcement Company
Bridle Road
Bootle
Liverpool L30 4UG
Tel (0800) 037 1506
Fax (0151) 523 2252
Email: liverpool@hy-ten.co.uk

Ancon CCL Ltd
President Way
President Park
Sheffield
S47UR
Tel (0114) 2755224
Fax (0114) 2768543

Fosroc Ltd
Coleshill Road
Tamworth
Staffordshire B78 3TL
Tel (01827)262222
Fax (01827) 262444

CLASS H - PRECAST CONCRETE

FC Precast Concrete Ltd
Alfreton Road
Derby DE214BN
Tel (01332) 364314
Fax (01332) 372208
email sales@fcprecast.co.uk

CLASS I - PIPE WORK and CLASS J - PIPE WORK FITTINGS AND VALVES

ARC Pipes
Mells
Frome
Somerset BAll 3PD
Tel (0117) 9812791
Fax (0117) 9814516
email sales@arc-pipes.co.uk

Johnston Pipes Ltd
Doseley
Telford
Shropshire TF4 3BX
Tel (01952) 630300
Fax (01952) 503833

Duropipe - S & LP
Walsall Road
Norton Canes
Cannock
Staffordshire WS 11 3NS
Tel (01543) 279909
Fax (01543) 279450

Stanton PLC
Lows Lane
Stanton by Dale
Ilkeston
Derbyshire DE7 4QW
Tel (0115) 930 5000
Fax (0115) 932 9513

Hepworth Building Products
Edlington Lane
Edlington
Doncaster
South Yorkshire
DN12 1BY
United Kingdom
Tel (0170) 985 6300
Fax (0170) 985 6301

Marley Extrusions Ltd
Dickley Lane
Lenham
Maidstone
Kent
ME17 2DE
Tel (0162) 285 8888
Fax (0162) 285 8725

CLASS K - PIPEWORK - MANHOLES AND PIPEWORK ANCILLARIES

Albion Concrete Products Ltd
Station Road
Llangadog
Carmarthenshire
SA19 9LT
Tel (01550) 776508
email sales@albion.co.uk

J & J W Longbottom Ltd
Bridge Foundry
Holmfirth
Nr Huddersfield HD9 7AW
Tel (01484) 692141
Fax (01484) 681513

CLASS M - STRUCTURAL METALWORK

Severfield-Reeve Structures Ltd
Dalton Airfield Industrial Estate
Dalton
Thirsk
North Yorkshire Y07 3JN
Tel (01845) 577896
Fax (01845) 577411
email info@sfrplc.com

CLASS N - METALWORK

Edgeguard Safety Systems Ltd
Edgeguard Place
Trad Wharf
Knights Road
Silvertown
London E16 2AT
Tel (0207) 540 5212
Fax (0207) 540 5218

CLASS P - PILES and
CLASS Q - PILING ANCILLARIES

Kvaemer Cementation Foundations Ltd
Maple Cross House
Denham Way
Maple Cross
Rickmansworth
Herts WD3 2SW
Tel (01923) 423100
Fax (01923) 777834

CLASS R - ROADS AND PAVINGS

AAC (Road Markings) Ltd
Unit 2
Granby Business Park
Granby Avenue
Garretts Green
Birmingham
West Midlands B33 OTJ
Tel(0121)2441121
Fax (0121) 244 2212

CAMAS Building Materials
Bardon Hill
Coalville
Leicestershire LE67 1TL
Tel (01530) 510066

Norman Smith (Congleton) Ltd
Sunny Bank
Somerford, Booths
Congleton
Cheshire CW12 2LX
Tel (01260) 224444

Shap Concrete Products Ltd
Shap, Penrith
Cumbria CA 10 3QQ
Tel(01931)716444
Fax (01931) 716617

CLASS T - TUNNELS

AMEC Civil Engineering Ltd
Booths Park
Chelford Road
Knutsford
Cheshire
WA16 8QZ
Tel (01565) 652100
Fax (01565) 683200

CLASS V - PAINTING

Dacrylate Paints Ltd
Lime Street
Kirby in Ashfield
Nottingham NG17 8AL
Tel (01623) 753845
Fax (01623) 757151
Email sales@dacrylate.co.uk

CLASS X - MISCELLANEOUS WORK

J B Corrie & Co Ltd
Fencing Contractors and Manufacturers
Frenchmans Road
Peterfield
Hants GU32 3AP
Tel (01730) 237100
Fax (01730) 264915
Email fencing@jbcorrie.co.uk

Jacksons Fencing
Ashford
Kent
TN25 6BN
Tel (0123) 3750393
Fax (0123) 3750403
Email sales@jacksons-fencing.co.uk

CLASS Y - SEWER AND WATER MAIN RENOVATION & ANCILLARY WORKS

Lanes for Drains (NW) Ltd
Landsdowne Road
Monton, Eccles
Manchester M30 9PJ
Tel (0161) 788 2222

PLANT HIRE

John Davies Plant Hire
61 Waterloo Road
Liverpool L3 7BE
Tel (0151) 2275728
Fax (0151) 2550652
email johndavies@btintemet.com

HSS Hire Service Group Ltd
25 Willow Lane
Mitcham
Surrey
CR4 4TS
Tel (0845) 7282828

Jewson Ltd
Merchant House
Binley Business Park
Coventry CV3 2TT
Tel (0247) 643 8400

CONTENTS

Introduction

This is the seventh edition of what was formerly know as the CESMM3 Price Database. Completely redesigned and updated for 2011, this new edition still follows the same structure and presentation as earlier editions, the bulk of the book consisting of pricing information covering all aspects of civil engineering activity. It is structured in accordance with the requirements of CESMM3 and broken down into the 26 classes of CESMM3, with an additional section, Class ZZ, which covers alteration works.

This exciting new edition sets a standard in the construction industry. This is the first civil engineering price book to include an estimate of Carbon Dioxide (CO_2) emissions for all activities of work – as well as retaining the accurate pricing that has made this price book a definitive guide for civil engineering professionals. To reflect this change in content the name has been changed to the CESMM3 Carbon & Price Book.

The information provided is complemented by sections covering approximate estimating, plant hire rates and outputs, economic forecasts, the Working Rule Agreement, professional, government and trade bodies and, finally, a section of technical information useful for those preparing estimates for civil engineering projects.

It is generally accepted in the construction industry that unit costs and carbon quantities for civil engineering works are more profoundly influenced by such factors as the scale, nature and characteristics of the project than the similar units for building works. The reasons for this are many and varied but the greater opportunity for the contractor to exercise his expertise and ingenuity in arriving at the optimum solution to a particular problem, combined with the wide variety of available plant with its different outputs and applications, must be major factors.

Consequently the build up of the civil engineering unit rate is of particular significance and it is for this reason that the book provides detailed information on how the rates have been derived in order to enable users to make adjustments to allow for the various factors affecting a particular project.

The information contained in this book will have many applications, including providing valuable data for use in the preparation of budget estimates at the various stages of civil engineering projects from inception to completion, supplementing the information already in Contractors' estimating departments and forming a basis for the negotiation of new rates within existing contracts. However, rates, prices and discounts can fluctuate dramatically over short periods of time and between various regions of the country. The costs shown are second quarter 2010. Prices exclude Value Added Tax, general items, contractor's profit and overheads (see Section 1, Unit Pricing).

Whilst it has been our intention throughout the preparation of this book to be factual and accurate, neither the Editing Authors nor the Publishers can in any way accept liability for any loss, direct or otherwise, of any kind arising out of the use or application of the contents of this book.

CapIT: Online Carbon & Cost Estimator

CapIT is a powerful online estimating tool and the only such system to offer comprehensive and detailed embodied CO_2 data for civil engineering works. Fully customisable, it enables users to build up cost and carbon estimates using the data found in this book, but also their own items, carbon values, unit rates, and plant or material costs.

The cost and carbon data is updated quarterly and users can select specific regional settings as well as dates in the past or future for ever greater accuracy in their estimates. (For a full listing of the many benefits of CapIT: Online Carbon & Cost Estimator, readers are encouraged to visit: www.capit-online.com).

As a purchaser of the book, you are entitled to a 3-month period of access to CapIT. Please refer to the back page for instructions on activating your user account.

SECTION 1:
UNIT PRICING

SECTION 1 - UNIT PRICING

Introduction to Unit Pricing Section

Prices used have been calculated as at the second quarter of 2010.

The price shown is the net cost to the contractor for the activity and does not include preliminaries and general items, head office overheads and profit, nor VAT.

Coherence has been maintained throughout the Unit Pricing section by basing the construction activities on a typical civil engineering contract, with pricing levels applicable to a UK average location. Access to the site is free from restraint. The total value of the construction works being £8 to £10m.

Our unit pricing assumes a general average level of conditions and circumstances. You should modify the appropriate parts of a unit price in line with your own knowledge and experience of the factors which may affect them. Prices and rates can fluctuate considerably, so any application other than a broad, approximate estimate requires up-to-date quotations for the constituent parts of a unit price.

Unless shown otherwise a percentage addition has been made to the supply cost of the materials to cover unloading, storing and rehandling as well as wastage. A small general purpose gang has been allowed for in the general items which will assist with unloading. Where unloading and stacking are a significant part of the activity, such as pipe stringing in a pipe laying contract, the activity has been separately priced and included in the total cost of the activity. The percentage addition to reinforcing steel covers stools, spacers, binding wire as well as wastage.

It is common practice in Civil Engineering estimating to build up a price for an activity on a weekly gang cost of labour and plant and this has been adopted here, the weekly cost of the gang being divided by 39 to arrive at an hourly cost.

Many contractors these days sub-let non-specialist as well as specialist activities according to their current commitments; for instance, there has been a move by contractors to favour sub-letting major elements of a contract to obtain low competitive sub-contract quotes so enabling them to make low tender submissions.

The hire rates used for the plant can be improved upon if a firm quote is called for. The rates include fuel and consumables and driver where appropriate. Fuel consumptions have been averaged out for each broad sector of machine. Particular attention has to be paid to the cost of fuel which can fluctuate widely.

All gang hours have been calculated to 3 decimal places but, due to printing requirements, we can only show the quantity to 2 decimal places. Thus, where an hourly quantity is less than one hundredth part of an hour, although the calculation has been correctly inserted into the net price, it will appear in the labour gang hours column at the 'rounded-up' value of 0.01 (but in the calculation of the NET UNIT PRICE the 'rounding-up' has been ignored).

If the reader wishes to determine the actual quantity of hours, this can be derived by dividing the relevant gang cost given at the front of the section into the net labour or plant price of the item.

Guidance Notes to Use of Pricing Section

At the beginning of each pricing section the cost of the labour and plant gangs respectively has been shown, with the details of the gang make up.

The hours shown in the 'labour hours' column have to be multiplied by the appropriate hourly cost to arrive at the 'labour net' which, in turn have to be added to the 'materials net' and 'plant net' to give the total 'unit net'.

UNIT PRICING

PRICING EXAMPLE

A typical unit price build-up is shown here, followed by a detailed analysis to explain how the price is built-up.

CLASS G - CONCRETE ANCILLARIES

G5 REINFORCEMENT

		Unit	Labour Gang Hours	Plant Gang Hours	Labour Net Price £	Plant Net Price £	Material Net Price £	Unit Net PRICE £
G5.2	**Deformed high yield steel bars, BS 4449; bent and cut to length**							
G5.2.4	Nominal size: 12mm							
G5.2.4.01	Generally	t	11.82	11.82	542.89	127.77	648.27	**1,318.94**

1) LABOUR GANGS, PLANT GANGS AND MATERIAL BUILD-UPS

Labour Cost Analysis

Labour gangs		
Steel fixing gang		
Craftsman WRA	2 x £16.68	= £33.37
Labourer (standard rate)	1 x £12.56	= £12.56
Total hourly cost of gang		**= £45.93**

Plant Cost Analysis		
Plant gangs		
Steel fixings gang		
NCK 305B 20t	0.25 x £41.48	= £10.81
Total hourly cost of gang		**= £10.81**

Materials Cost Analysis

Reinforcement
NOTE: The waste factor of 5% is inclusive of offloading, tying wire, chairs and spacers.
Grade 460 deformed type 2 high tensile reinforcing bars, BS 4449

	Supply Price £	Waste Factor %	Unloading Labour £	Unloading Plant £	TOTAL UNIT COST £	Unit
Cut, bent and bundled: 12mm	617.40	5	-	-	**648.27**	t

2) PRICE BUILD-UP SUMMARY

Net Labour Price:	
Labour gang hours x Total hourly cost of gang = 11.82 x £45.93	542.89
Net Plant Price:	
Plant gang hours x Total hourly cost of gang = 11.82 x £10.81	127.77
Net Material Price:	
12mm reinforcement bar	648.27
Net Unit Price	£1,318.94 t

The reader may adjust any of the variables in the resource build-ups to suit his own requirements e.g. size of labour gang, plant type, material costs or wastage on materials.

UNIT PRICING

Coding System

The codes used to identify items refer to the coding structure of the Civil Engineering Standard Method of Measurement, 3rd Edition, 1991. Each item and each group of items has been allocated a unique code.

The codes used in the pricing example for reinforcement on page 104, are defined below:

CODE	**CESMM, 3rd Edition, 1991 Reference**
G	Class G: Concrete Ancillaries

5.2.4.02
524 - This is an item build-up from the divisions of the SMM

t .02 - Is a secondary code, giving the item a unique identity (i.e. as opposed to .01, .03, etc.)

5 - The first numerical digit refers to the First Division within Class G: Concrete Ancillaries. In this case;
5 - Reinforcement

2 - The second numerical digit refers to the Second Division within Class G appertaining to reinforcement;
2 - Deformed high yield steel bars to BS 4449

4 - The third numerical digit refers to the Third Division within Class G appertaining to Deformed high yield steel bars to BS 4449; 4 - Nominal size 12mm

t - Contrary to CESMM3 section 4 paragraph 4.7 two numerical digits have been used to clarify secondary coding.

Units Used in Pricing Section

The following units have been used in the pricing sections:

Kg - kilogramme	m - linear metre	Nr - number
t - tonne	m^2 - square metre	h - hour
ha - hectare	m^3 - cubic metre	l - litre

Introduction to Carbon Dioxide Emission Factors

Climate change is considered to be one of the greatest environmental threats facing the world today. Carbon Dioxide (CO_2) is the most significant of the greenhouses gases contributing to this threat and the construction industry is one of the most significant contributors to the creation of it.

Simplistically speaking there are two measures of CO_2 emissions, embodied and direct. Embodied relates to the CO_2 emissions made during the production of something, direct is that which is produced physically during a process or activity.

Materials used in the construction industry will generally have an embodied CO_2 measure. This demonstrates the CO_2 emissions during the extraction of the material and the production of the component. Plant will have a direct CO_2 impact during the running of the plant and burning of the fuel.

Study Boundaries

It is essential to understand the boundaries of any study, and it is important to understand what boundaries the data that you are using has if you want to ensure that you are not double counting or missing elements of the measure.

Generally, published embodied CO_2 data will have one of four boundaries:

1) Cradle to Gate
2) Cradle to Site
3) Cradle to Grave
4) Cradle to Cradle

Cradle to gate measures all of the CO_2 emissions relating to the material to get it to factory gate ready for transportation to site. Cradle to site also contains an estimate of the transport. Cradle to grave also makes an allowance for its final disposal, and cradle to cradle also includes elements of recycling.

As the latter three boundaries make allowances for project specific issues such as how for to transport to site, the authors only use the Cradle to Gate boundary for the materials. Further allowances can then be made by the user for transport and if needed disposal and recycling.

UNIT PRICING

Labour

The CO_2 impact of labour is not included within the calculations as these impacts would occur regardless of undertaking construction activity. Allowances for hand tools are made within the plant totals. Please see the Transportation section below with regard to quantification of labour transportation.

Materials

The authors have developed their own estimates of embodied CO_2 data for materials with a Cradle to Gate boundary. Reference was been made to published UK CO_2 figures for materials from a variety of sources in order to achieve this.

In particular, the publishers wish to acknowledge the research carried out by Professor Geoff Hammond and Craig Jones from the Department of Mechanical Engineering (University of Bath) on the embodied energy and carbon of a large number of building materials. The research publication, Inventory of Carbon and Energy (ICE), which is publicly available for download from the University web site has been an invaluable source of data used to verify and supplement the primary research and composite item build-ups.

With any material the embodied CO_2 figures will be different for each material supplier depending on the manufacturing process adopted e.g. a supplier adopting a renewable energy source will have a lower figure than another. The figures used therefore represent an estimate of likely embodied CO_2 for materials. As with any estimate the figures should be superseded with actual manufacturer data when available.

The use of recycling or reuse of materials will also have an impact on the embodied CO_2 for materials. For these estimated guides typical recycled content has been used but allowances or adjustments should be made in the instances of specific data being known. For materials that may be reused, as the potential number of reuses can not be determined, the full impact of the embodied carbon is taken within the rate. Users will need to make amendments to any subsequent work activities where materials have been reused or recycled.

As with the estimates of cost, elements of waste have been included, but additional allowance would need to be made for any project-specific issues.

Please see the Transportation section below with regard to quantification of material transportation.

Plant

The embodied CO_2 of the production and maintenance of plant is not included within the guide figures. The plant elements are therefore quantified using the fuel consumption. The plant selected for the guide uses what the author considers the more traditional sources. Reductions will be recorded if alternate sources of renewable energy or biofuels are used.

As with the estimates of cost, elements of non-productive standing time have been included, but additional allowance would need to be made for project specifics such as ground conditions and weather.

Please see the Transportation section below with regard to quantification of the transportation of plant.

Specialist

Although very few in number, the embodied CO_2 of specialist items can not be quantified and included within this book due to the uncertainty of their detailed nature.

Transportation

The CO_2 impact for transporting labour, materials and plant resources has not been included within the unit rate data. This is due to the levels of disparity that will be recorded on projects. It is recommended that this is either excluded from the studies or quantified additionally.

It is important that quantification of transport is included when you are considering procurement options for locations with variations in transportation distance as this will have a significant impact on the final result, especially when quantifying international procurement options.

To quantify the transport of labour additionally the following table has been included to allow estimates of the kilograms of CO_2 produced per kilometre travelled:

Method	CO_2 emissions (kg/km)
Train	0.0400
Underground	0.0560
Bus	0.0930
Aeroplane: Short Haul	0.1800
Aeroplane: Long Haul	0.1120
Water	0.0755
Hatchback: Petrol	0.1750
Hatchback: Diesel	0.1350
Saloon: Petrol	0.2050
Saloon: Diesel	0.1580
People carrier: Petrol	0.2420
People carrier: Diesel	0.1960
SUV: Petrol	0.2910
SUV: Diesel	0.2380
Smaller Van	0.1430
Transit Van	0.2090
Motorbike	0.1000
Bicycle	0.0000

To quantify the transport of materials and plant additionally the following table has been included to allow estimates of the kilograms of CO_2 produced per tonne of weight transported per kilometre travelled:

Method	CO_2 emissions (kg/t/km)
Road	0.32
Rail	0.04
Water	0.01

Both tables above have been provided to allow estimates only, actual data will vary depending on age and state of repair of vehicle, weather conditions and numbers of people being transported.

CLASS A:
GENERAL ITEMS

CLASS A – GENERAL ITEMS

Build Up of Labour Rates

The following is an abridged extract from the Working Rule Agreement for the Building and Civil Engineering Industry:

Rule WR.3 The normal working hours in the industry shall generally be:

Monday to Thursday	8 hrs per day
Friday	7 hrs
Total for week	39 hrs

Rule WR.4 Overtime shall be calculated as follows:

- Monday to Friday
  For the first four hours after the completion of the normal working hours of the day time and a half; thereafter at the rate of double time until the starting time the following day.
- Saturday
  Time and a half, until the completion of the first four hours, and thereafter at double time.
- Sunday
  At the rate of double time, until the starting time on Monday morning.

Overtime shall be calculated on the normal hourly rate. Additional payments for intermittent skill or responsibility or adverse conditions and bonus shall not be included when calculating overtime payments.

In practice the working week is commonly five days of 9.5 hours in the summer and five days of 8.5 hours in the winter. The following calculation is used to determine the actual cost of productive hours.

Summertime Production hours			
5 days @ 9.5 hours =	47.5 x 35.0wks =	1,662.50 hours	
Non-Productive hours			
4 days @ 0.75 hours =	3.00		
1 day @ 1.25 hours =	1.25		
	4.25 x 35 wks =	148.75 hours	**1,811.25 hours**
Wintertime Production hours			
5 days @ 8.5 hours =	42.5 x 11.2wks =	476.00 hours	
Non-Productive hours			
4 days @ 0.25 hours =	1.00		
1 day @ 0.75 hours =	0.75		
	1.75 x 11.2wks =	19.60 hours	
		495.60 hours	
			2,306.85 hours
Total number of paid hours =			
Total number of production hours = (1662.50 + 476.00) =		2,138.50	
Allow 5% wet time = (say)		106.93	
			2,031.60 hours

Basic wage rates: on 30 June 2010

General Operative =	£302.25 for 39 hour week: £7.75 per hour
Craft Rate =	£401.70 for 39 hour week: £10.30 per hour
Average paid hours/week =	2,306.85 divided by 46.2 = 49.93
Average production hours/week =	2,031.60 divided by 46.2 = 43.97

GENERAL ITEMS - A

Build Up of Labour Rates continued...

		General Operative	Skill Rate 4	Skill Rate 3	Skill Rate 2	Skill Rate 1
Total paid hours 49.93 @	£	7.75	8.35	8.85	9.46	9.82
per week	£	386.97	416.93	441.90	472.36	490.33
Overtime payment at premium rate: (49.93 -39) = 10.93 hrs		42.35	45.63	48.37	51.70	53.67
Service allowance @ 5 hours per week		-	-	-	-	-
Gross weekly wage (A)	**£**	**429.33**	**462.56**	**490.26**	**524.05**	**544.00**
Employers liability and public liability insurance at 2.5% of labour content (A)		10.73	11.56	12.26	13.10	13.60
Construction industry training board levy @ 0.50% of (A)		2.15	2.31	2.45	2.62	2.72
Daily travel allowance (say 5 days x 25km one way per day)		10.35	10.35	10.35	10.35	10.35
Annual holiday allowance		39.03	42.05	44.57	47.64	49.45
Public holidays with pay		14.87	16.02	16.98	18.15	18.84
National Insurance contributions based on 12.8% of gross weekly wage above earnings threshold (ET) of £110.00 per week		40.87	45.13	48.67	53.00	55.55
B&CE EasyBuild Stakeholder pension contribution (say)		5.00	5.00	5.00	5.00	5.00
Total weekly cost	£	552.33	594.99	630.54	673.91	699.51
Total Lablour cost per Hour	**£**	**12.56**	**13.53**	**14.34**	**15.33**	**15.91**

		Craftsman	Plant Operator SR 4	Plant Operator SR 3	Plant Operator SR 2	Plant Operator SR 1
Total paid hours 49.93 @	£	10.30	8.35	8.85	9.46	9.82
per week	£	514.30	416.93	441.90	472.36	490.33
Overtime payment at premium rate: (49.93 -39) = 10.93 hrs		56.29	45.63	48.37	51.70	53.67
Service allowance @ 5 hours per week		-	41.75	44.25	47.30	49.10
Gross weekly wage (A)	**£**	**570.59**	**504.31**	**534.51**	**571.35**	**593.10**
Employers liability and public liability insurance at 2.5% of labour content (A)		14.26	12.61	13.36	14.28	14.83
Construction industry training board levy @ 0.50% of (A)		2.85	2.52	2.67	2.86	2.97
Daily travel allowance (say 5 days x 25km one way per day)		10.35	10.35	10.35	10.35	10.35
Annual holiday allowance		51.87	45.85	48.59	51.94	53.92
Public holidays with pay		19.76	17.47	18.51	19.79	20.54
National Insurance contributions based on 12.8% of gross weekly wage above earnings threshold (ET) of £110.00 per week		58.96	50.47	54.34	59.05	61.84
B&CE EasyBuild Stakeholder pension contribution (say)		5.00	5.00	5.00	5.00	5.00
Total weekly cost	£	733.64	648.58	687.34	734.63	762.53
Total Lablour cost per Hour	**£**	**16.68**	**14.75**	**15.63**	**16.71**	**17.34**

GENERAL ITEMS - A

Build Up of Labour Rates continued...

NOTES: There has been an allowance included for daily fare and travel allowances as required under WR.5 on the assumption that sites will be away from major conurbations, entailing the provision of transport or travel allowances to operatives (which will not always be the case) and that craftsmen, in particular, will in some cases require subsistence payments, as required under WR.15. These allowances should be reviewed when considering the labour costs for specific sites.

Other 'Labour cost per hour' rates have been similarly calculated and applied in this book to the following classes of operatives:

Banksman	£13.53	Ganger	£16.99	Pipelayer (standard)	£14.34
Pipelayer (large pipes)	£15.91	Driller	£14.34	Shot Firer	£14.34
Fitters & Welders	£16.68	Timbermen	£14.34	Piling Hand	£13.53
Painter	£16.68	Painter (chargehand)	£17.93	Brush Hand	£12.56
Spray Painter	£16.68	Asphalt Layer	£14.34	Plasterer	£16.68
Tiler	£16.68	Bricklayer (chargehand)	£17.93	Waller	£16.68
Miner*	£39.89	Carpenter (chargehand)	£17.93		

* Not based on WRA

PRICING EXAMPLE

Generally

The figures used in this section are based on a typical civil engineering project of value £8.50m, located on the fringe of a large conurbation with reasonable access to the resources necessary for the project.

Principal quantities

Clear and level site	300,000m^2
Excavation	130,000m^3
Concrete	17,000m^3
Formwork	28,000m^2
Reinforcement	1,700t

Tender build-up

General items	1,562,900
Profit and H.O overheads	510,000
Labour (including Labour only Subcontractors)	1,487,500
Materials	2,092,640
Plant and fuel	629,000
Direct Sub-contractors	920,100
Nominated Sub-contractors	1,211,160
Engineers contingencies	86,700
Contract value	£8,500,000

Cost analysis of General Items

The total cost of the General Items represents 24.32% of the net cost of the works calculated as follows:

Total tender cost	8,500,000
Less Profit and H.O. Overheads (say 6.0%)	510,000
Net tender cost	7,990,000
Less General Items	1,562,908
	6,427,092

Total cost of General Items as a percentage of net cost of the works

$$\frac{1,562,908}{6,427,092} \times 100 = 24.32\%$$

The following table shows a cost analysis of the General Items with reference to the General Items section of the Civil Engineering Standard Method of Measurement.

CESMM Class 'A' Code	CESMM Class 'A' First division Section	Amount £	% of General Items	% of net Cost of Works
1	Contractual Requirements	111,136	7.11%	1.73%
2	Specified Requirements	220,652	14.12%	3.43%
3	Method-Related Charges	1,231,895	78.77%	19.16%
4-	Provisional Sums	excl	-	-
5	Nominated Sub-contracts	excl	-	-
6	nominated Sub-contracts	excl	-	-
1-6	All Sections	1,562,908	100.00%	24.32%

GENERAL ITEMS - A

EXAMPLE continued/ ....

NOTES: Performance Bond
It is usual for a local authority to call for a performance bond from the Contractor. This is normally a percentage of the tender sum (0.25%) and will vary according to the nature of the work and the standing of the Contractor. An estimator will be required to obtain firm quotations from an insurance company or bank. The percentage sum will be levied on an annual basis for the actual duration of the contract, that is until the issue of a completion certificate and thereafter at a reduced percentage from the period of maintenance. It is important to have the details fixed before the final tender figure is submitted.

Insurance of the Works
The premium will depend on the nature of the work and the insurance experience of the Contractor. Normally this will form part of an insurance package which will include public liability, fire and theft and possibly professional indemnity (Employers liability is dealt with in the labour rate build-up).

Provisional Sums and Nominated Sub-contracts
Provisional Sums and Nominated Sub-contracts have been excluded from the General Items.

A1 Contractual Requirements

A1.1	**Performance Bond**			
	Not normally requested from the Contractor for this type of Contract			
A1.2	**Insurance of the Works (in accordance with Clause 21)**			
	Allow 1.00% of total contract value			
			£	
	Contract Value	=	8,500,000	
	Inflation Allowance 2.0%	=	170,000	
			8,670,000	
	Additional costs including professional fees 8%	=	693,600	
			9,363,600	
	1.00% of £9,363,600			93,636
A1.3	**Third party insurance (in accordance with Clause 23)**			
	Allow lump sum			17,500
	TOTAL FOR CONTRACTUAL REQUIREMENTS			**£111,136**

A2 Specified Requirements

A2.1 Accommodation for the Engineer's Staff (R.E. and staff - 78 wks)

A2.1.1 **Offices**			
A2.1.1.01 Establish and remove			
	Transport, erect and dismantle		595
A2.1.1.02 Maintain and operate			
	40m² @ £3.25 per m² x 78wks	10,140	
	Heat, light and clean: £87 per week x 78wks	6,786	
			16,926
A2.1.2 **Laboratories**			
A2.1.2.01 Establish and remove			
	Transport, erect and dismantle		595
A2.1.2.02 Maintain and operate			
	20m² @ £3.25 per m² x 78wks	5,070	
	Heat, light and clean: Included with offices		5,070
A2.1.3 **Cabins**			
A2.1.3.01 Establish and remove Ablution Block			
	Connect to cesspit or town sewer		1,480
A2.1.3.02 Maintain and operate Ablution Block			
	£107 per wk x 78wks		8,346
A2.1.3.03 Establish and remove Inspectors Hut			
	Mobile: on/off charges		245
A2.1.3.04 Maintain and operate Inspectors Hut			
	8m² @ £3.25 per wk x 78 wks		2,028

A2.2 Services for the Engineer's staff

A2.2.1 Transport vehicles			
A2.2.1.01 Maintain and operate			
	2000cc car - £ 216 per wk x 78wks	16,848	
	Landrover - £405.00 per wk x 78wks	31,590	
	Petrol - 120 litres per wk @ £0.90 per litre x 78 wks	8,424	
			56,862
A2.2.2 Telephones			
A2.2.2.01 Establish and remove			
	Installation: BT charges		330
A2.2.2.02 Maintain and operate			
	Calls and rental: £107 per wk x 78wks		8,346
	Carried forward		£100,823

A2 Specified Requirements continued/...

	Brought forward		£100,823
A2.3	**Equipment for use by the Engineer's staff**		
A2.3.1	**Office equipment**		
A2.3.1.01	Establish and remove		400
A2.3.1.02	Maintain and operate	2 PC's, 4 desks, 4 tables, 1 conference table, 6 chairs, 2 cabinets: £110 per wk x 78wks	8,580
A2.3.2	**Laboratory equipment**		
A2.3.2.01	Establish and remove		400
A2.3.2.02	Maintain and operate	£90 per wk x 78 wks	7,020
A2.3.3	**Surveying equipment**		
233.1	Establish and remove		400
233.2	Maintain and operate	£90 per wk x 78wks	7,020
A2.4	**Attendance upon the Engineer's staff**		
A2.4.1	**Drivers**		
A2.4.1.01	Establish and remove	Recruitment - included	-
A2.4.1.02	Maintain and operate	£12.56 per hr x 39 x 78wks	38,208
A2.4.2	**Chainmen**		
A2.4.2.01	Establish and remove	Recruitment - included	-
A2.4.2.02	Maintain and operate	£12.56 per hr x 39 x 78wks	38,208
A2.4.3	**Laboratory assistants**		
A2.4.3.01	Establish and remove	Recruitment - included	-
A2.4.3.01	Maintain and operate	£12.56 per hr x 39 x 40wks	19,594
A2.5	**Testing of materials**		
	Included -		
A2.6	**Testing of the Works**		
	Included -		
		TOTAL FOR SPECIFIED REQUIREMENTS	**£220,652**

A3 Method-Related Charges

A3.1 Accommodation and buildings

A3.1.1 Offices

A3.1.1.01	Establish and remove		
	Transport	1,650	
	Erect and dismantle	600	
	Telephone installation: BT charges	600	
	Furniture, PC's, etc.	6,600	9,450.00
			(Fixed)
A3.1.1.02	Maintain and operate		
	Mobile offices: 10 staff x 8m2 each = $80m^2$		
	Conference room = $20m^2$		
	$100m^2$		
	100m2 @ £2.00 per m2 x 60wks	12,000	
	Heat, light and clean: £140 per wk x 60wks	8,400	
	Telephone calls and rental: £120 per wk x 60wks	7,200	
	Stationery £125 per wk x 60wks	7,500	35,100.00
			(Time Related)

A3.1.3 Cabins

A3.1.3.01	Establish and remove Ablution Blocks		
	Connect to cesspit or town sewer		1,500.00
			(Time Related)
A3.1.3.02	Maintain and operate Ablution Blocks		
	£100 per wk x 78wks	7,800	7,800.00
			(Time Related)
A3.1.3.03	Supply, maintain and operate Toilet Blocks		
	Inr @ £100 per wk x 60wks	6,000	
	Maintain: 0.5 man @ £12.56 per man per hr x 39 x 60wks	14,695	20,695.20
			(Time Related)
A3.1.3.04	Supply, maintain and operate Drying Room		
	£33 per wk x 60wks		1,980.00
			(Time Related)

A3.1.4 Stores

A3.1.4.01	Establish and remove		
	Erect and dismantle		600.00
			(Fixed)
A3.1.4.02	Maintain and operate		
	£30 per wk x 60wks		1,800.00
			(Time Related)

A3.1.5 Canteens and Messrooms

A3.1.5.01	Maintain and operate		
	4nr mobiles @ £ 25 each per wk x 60wks	6,000	
	Heat, light and clean: £ 28 per wk x 60wks	1,680	7,680.00
			(Time Related)

A3.2 Services

A3.2.1 Electricity

A3.2.1.01	Establish and remove		
	Electricity to compound and batching plant:		
	Cable and switches	3,000	3,000.00
	(Time Related)		

A3.2.2 Water

A3.2.2.01	Establish and remove		
	Water main to compound and batching plant:		
	50mm dia. UPVC - 600m @ £13.33 including fittings	7,998	7,998.00
			(Fixed)
Carried forward			£97,603

A3 Method-Related Charges continued/ ...

	Brought forward		97,603

A3.3 Plant

A3.3.5 Concrete Mixing

A3.3.5.01	Establish and remove		
	Transport, erect and dismantle: concrete batching plant, aggregate bins, cement silos and concrete pump.		
	Site preparation: level area, spread hardcore, lay concrete:		
	Plant:		
	Dresser 1004 - 2 days @ £28.68 per hr	459	
	Labour:		
	4 labourers - 2 days @ £12.56 per hr	804	
	Carpenter -1 day @ £17.93 per hr	143	
	Material:		
	Hardcore - 400m2 x 0.25m deep @ £23.90 per m^3	2,390	
	Concrete - 50m3 @ £87.88 per m^3	4,394	
	Carried forward	8,190	
	Transport batcher and erect:		
	Plant:		
	2nr flat top lorries - 1 day @ £42.63 each per hr	682	
	Inr crane - 3 days @ £42.28 per hr	1,015	
	Labour:		
	4 labourers - 5 days @ £12.56 per hr	2,010	
	Supervision	340	
	Timber for bins - £1,350 less residual value	675	
	Dismantle and reinstate	1,390	
		6,112	
	Brought forward		
			14,302
			(fixed)
	Carried forward		£111,905

A3 Method-Related Charges continued/ ...

	Brought forward		111,905
A3.5	**Temporary Works**		
A3.5.3	**Access roads**		
A3.5.3.01	Establish and remove access roads 1000 x 6m wide = 6000m^2 Construct 100m run per day		
	Plant:		
	Dresser 1004 - 10 days @ £28.68 per hr	2,294	
	Vibratory roller - 5 days @ £2.04 per hr	82	
	JCB 3CX - 5 days @ £27.01 per hr	1,080	
	Labour:		
	2 labourers -10 days @ £12.56 per hr	2,010	
	Materials:		
	Hardcore or ballast - 6000m2 x 0.20m deep = 1200m^3 @ £23.90 per m^3	28,680	
	Lotrak - 6000m^2 @ £0.93 per m^2	5,580	39,726 *(Fixed)*
A3.5.3.02	Maintain access roads Dresser 1004 - 0.5 days per wk: 60 wks x 4hrs @ £28.68 per hr		6,883 *(Time Related)*
A3.6	**Temporary Works**		
A3.6.6	**Hardstandings**		
A3.6.6.01	Establish and remove administration and storage compound hardstanding Allow 5 days for the operation		
	Plant:		
	Dresser 1004 - 3 days @ £28.68 per hr	688	
	Vibratory roller - 3 days @ £2.04 per hr	49	
	JCB 3CX - 2 days @ £27.01 per hr	432	
	Labour:		
	Tradesman - 5 days @ £17.93 per hr	717	
	2 labourers - 5 days @ £12.56 per hr	1,005	
	Materials:		
	Sub-base - spread, level 1000m^2 x 0.20m deep = 200m^3 @ £24.03 per m^3	4,806	
	Concrete - 600m2 x 0.15m deep = 90m^3 @ £87.88 per m^3	7,909	
	Drainage - septic tank or connection into main sewer	2,000	17,606 *(Fixed)*
	Carried forward		£176,120

A3 Method-Related Charges continued/ ...

	Brought forward		176,120
A3.7	**Supervision and Labour**		
	Regional/Area Manager - Incl. in H.O. Overheads		
	Regional/Area Q.S. - Incl. in H.O. Overheads		
	Planning Engineer - Incl. in H.O. Overheads		
	Trade Foremen - Incl. in rates		
	Staff subsistence - Incl. in weekly charges		
	Overtime - Incl. in weekly charges		
NOTE:	* weekly rate includes allowance for Company car		
A3.7.1	**Supervision**		
	Agent/Senior Engineer - 60wks @ £1,776 per wk*	106,560	
	Section Engineer: Tanks - 60wks @ £1,247 per wk*	74,820	
	Section Engineer: Wharf - 40wks @ £1,247 per wk*	49,880	
	Section Engineer: Excavating Roads, etc. 60wks @ £1,247 per wk	74,820	
	Assistant Engineer - 50wks @ £975 per wk	48,750	
	Technicians - 60wks @ £585 per wk	35,100	
	Senior Quantity Surveyor - 78wks @ £1,550 per wk x 50%*	60,450	
	Assistant Quantity Surveyor - 50 wks @ £1,260 per wk*	63,000	
	General Foreman -78wks @ £1,535 per wk (Landrover incl.)	119,730	
	Sectional Foreman: Concrete - 50wks @ £1,404 per wk	70,200	
	Sectional Foreman: Excavating Roads etc. - 60wks @ £1,536 per wk (Landrover incl.)	92,160	795,470 *(Time Related)*
A3.7.2	**Administration**		
	Office Manager - 60wks @ £773 per wk	46,380	
	Wages Clerk - 60wks @ £514 per wk x 50%	15,420	
	Timekeeper - 60wks @ £500 per wk	30,000	
	Storekeeper - 10wks @ £585 per wk	5,850	
	Typist/Receptionist/Telephonist - 60wks @ £463 per wk	27,780	
	Office cleaners/tea - 60wks @ £104 per wk (part time)	6,240	
	Security man - 60wks @ £803 per wk	48,180	179,850 (Time Related)
A3.7.3	**Labour teams**		
	Offloading materials and maintaining services gang		
	Plant:		
	Tractor and trailer - 40wks @ £1,125 per wk	45,000	
	NCK 305 - 10wks @ £1,524 per wk	15,240	
	Labour:		
	1.5 labourers - 40wks @ £486 per wk	19,440	79,680 (Time Related)
			1,231,121

TOTAL FOR METHOD-RELATED CHARGES

SUMMARY OF GENERAL ITEMS

CONTRACTUAL REQUIREMENTS	£111,136
SPECIFIED REQUIREMENTS	£220,652
METHOD-RELATED CHARGES	£1,231,121
TOTAL GENERAL ITEMS	£1,562,908

CLASS B:

GROUND INVESTIGATION

Calculations used throughout Class B - Ground Investigation

Labour

		Qty		Rate		Total
L B0001ICE	**Cable Percussion Borehole Labour Gang**					
	Craftsman WRA	1	x	16.68	=	£16.68
	Labourer (General Operative)	1	x	12.56	=	£12.56
	Total hourly cost of gang				=	**£29.24**
L A0120ICE	**General Earthworks Labour Gang**					
	Ganger	1	x	16.99	=	£16.99
	Labourer (General Operative)	1	x	12.56	=	£12.56
	Banksman	1	x	13.53	=	£13.53
	Total hourly cost of gang				=	**£43.08**
L B0004ICE	**Rotary Bored Borehole Labour Gang**					
	Craftsman WRA	1	x	16.68	=	£16.68
	Labourer (General Operative)	2	x	12.56	=	£25.12
	Total hourly cost of gang				=	**£41.80**
L A0331ICE	**Trial Hole Labour Gang**					
	Ganger	1	x	16.99	=	£16.99
	Labourer (Skill Rate 4)	1	x	13.53	=	£13.53
	Labourer (General Operative)	2	x	12.56	=	£25.12
	Plant Operator (Class 3)	1	x	15.63	=	£15.63
	Total hourly cost of gang				=	**£71.27**

Plant

P A1333ICE	**Trial holes excavation Plant Gang**					
	Hydraulic Excavator - JCB 3CX Sitemaster	1	x	27.01	=	£27.01
	Dumper - 3.0t 4WD	1	x	23.77	=	£23.77
	Compressor - 180 cfm	1	x	7.15	=	£7.15
	Hydraulic Breaker (Independant) -					
	Two Tool Towable Breaker	1	x	2.75	=	£2.75
	Hose & Breaker & 3 Steels	1	x	0.35	=	£0.35
	Vibrating Plate Diesel 24kN	1	x	2.36	=	£2.36
	Total hourly cost of gang				=	**£63.39**
P B0001ICE	**Cable Percussion Borehole Plant Gang**					
	Cable Percussion Rig	1	x	8.06	=	£8.06
	Landrover 4WD	1	x	15.10	=	£15.10
	Bowsers (250 gallon water / fuel)	1	x	0.88	=	£0.88
	Total hourly cost of gang				=	**£24.04**
P B0003ICE	**Rotary Bored Borehole Plant Gang**					
	Rotary Borehole Rig	1	x	12.31	=	£12.31
	Landrover 4WD	1	x	15.10	=	£15.10
	Bowsers (250 gallon water / fuel)	1	x	0.88	=	£0.88
	Bowsers (250 gallon water / fuel)	1	x	0.88	=	£0.88
	Compressor - 480 cfm	1	x	18.85	=	£18.85
	Grouting Rig (Anchorage Items)	1	x	9.84	=	£9.84
	Total hourly cost of gang				=	**£57.86**

Class B - Ground Investigation

Note(s): The rates in this section have been provided by a specialist sub-contractor and are supplied without prejudice as guide prices only.

B1 Trial Pits and Trenches

Note(s): The prices under Trial Pits and Trenches assume that the pits and trenches are inspected and backfilled the same day.

		Unit	Labour Hours	Labour Net £	Plant Net £	Materials Net £	Unit Net £	CO_2 Kg
B1.1	**Number in material other than rock**							
B1.1.1	Maximum depth not exceeding 1m							
B1.1.1.01	plan area at bottom of pit 2 x 1m	Nr	0.22	15.68	13.95	-	**29.63**	*6.15*
B1.1.1.02	as above; excavated by hand	Nr	1.00	71.27	1.42	-	**72.69**	*0.37*
B1.1.2	Maximum depth 1 - 2m							
B1.1.2.01	plan area at bottom of pit 2 x 1m	Nr	0.43	30.65	27.26	-	**57.91**	*12.02*
B1.1.3	Maximum depth 2 - 3m							
B1.1.3.01	plan area at bottom of pit 2 x 1m	Nr	0.46	32.78	29.16	-	**61.94**	*12.86*
B1.1.4	Maximum depth 3 - 5m							
B1.1.4.01	plan area at bottom of pit 2 x 1m	Nr	0.52	37.06	32.97	-	**70.03**	*14.54*
B1.2	**Number in material which includes rock**							
B1.2.1	Maximum depth not exceeding 1m							
B1.2.1.01	plan area at bottom of pit 2 x 1m	Nr	0.24	17.10	15.22	-	**32.32**	*6.71*
B1.2.2	Maximum depth 1 - 2m							
B1.2.2.01	plan area at bottom of pit 2 x 1m	Nr	0.45	32.07	28.53	-	**60.60**	*12.58*
B1.2.3	Maximum depth 2 - 3m							
B1.2.3.01	plan area at bottom of pit 2 x 1m	Nr	0.49	34.92	31.07	-	**65.99**	*13.70*
B1.2.4	Maximum depth 3 - 5m							
B1.2.4.01	plan area at bottom of pit 2 x 1m	Nr	0.58	41.34	36.77	-	**78.11**	*16.21*
B1.3	**Depth in material other than rock**							
B1.3.1	Maximum depth not exceeding 1m							
B1.3.1.01	plan area at bottom of pit 2 x 1m	m	0.24	17.10	15.22	-	**32.32**	*6.71*
B1.3.1.02	as above; excavated by hand	m	1.00	71.27	1.42	-	**72.69**	*0.37*
B1.3.2	Maximum depth 1 - 2m							
B1.3.2.01	plan area at bottom of pit 2 x 1m	m	0.50	35.63	31.70	-	**67.33**	*13.98*
B1.3.3	Maximum depth 2 - 3m							
B1.3.3.01	plan area at bottom of pit 2 x 1m	m	0.56	39.91	35.50	-	**75.41**	*15.65*
B1.3.4	Maximum depth 3 - 5m							
B1.3.4.01	plan area at bottom of pit 2 x 1m	m	0.64	45.61	40.58	-	**86.19**	*17.89*
B1.4	**Depth in rock**							
B1.4.1	Maximum depth not exceeding 1m							
B1.4.1.01	plan area at bottom of pit 2 x 1m	m	0.32	22.81	20.29	-	**43.10**	*8.94*
B1.4.2	Maximum depth 1 - 2m							
B1.4.2.01	plan area at bottom of pit 2 x 1m	m	0.59	42.05	37.41	-	**79.46**	*16.49*
B1.4.3	Maximum depth 2 - 3m							
B1.4.3.01	plan area at bottom of pit 2 x 1m	m	0.67	47.54	42.29	-	**89.83**	*18.64*

B1 Trial Pits and Trenches continued...

		Unit	Labour Hours	Labour Net £	Plant Net £	Materials Net £	Unit Net £	*CO_2 Kg*
B1.4	**Depth in rock**							
B1.4.4	Maximum depth 3 - 5m							
B1.4.4.01	plan area at bottom of pit 2 x 1m	m	0.79	56.30	50.09	-	106.39	*22.08*
B1.5	**Depth supported**							
B1.5.1	Maximum depth not exceeding 1m							
B1.5.1.01	plan area at bottom of pit 2 x 1m; in soft ground	m	0.43	18.48	-	7.33	25.81	*5.77*
B1.5.1.02	as above; in hard ground	m	0.10	4.18	-	0.77	4.95	*1.84*
B1.5.2	Maximum depth 1 - 2m							
B1.5.2.01	plan area at bottom of pit 2 x 1m; in soft ground	m	0.51	21.84	-	10.73	32.57	*8.02*
B1.5.2.02	as above; in hard ground	m	0.12	5.04	-	1.02	6.06	*2.45*
B1.5.3	Maximum depth 2 - 3m							
B1.5.3.01	plan area at bottom of pit 2 x 1m; in soft ground	m	0.62	26.88	-	17.54	44.42	*12.55*
B1.5.3.02	as above; in hard ground	m	0.16	6.72	-	3.62	10.34	*8.70*
B1.5.4	Maximum depth 3 - 5m							
B1.5.4.01	plan area at bottom of pit 2 x 1m; in soft ground	m	0.90	38.64	-	27.24	65.88	*18.12*
B1.5.4.02	as above; in hard ground	m	0.23	10.08	-	8.17	18.25	*19.61*
B1.6	**Depth backfilled, material stated**							
B1.6.1	Materials arising from excavation							
B1.6.1.01	In soft ground	m	0.65	8.79	0.35	-	9.14	*0.09*
B1.6.1.02	In hard ground	m	1.71	84.34	67.89	-	152.23	*30.72*

B2 Light Cable Percussion Boreholes

		Unit	Labour Hours	Labour Net £	Plant Net £	Materials Net £	Unit Net £	*CO_2 Kg*
B2.1	**Number**							
B2.1.1	including transport, erection, dismantling							
B2.1.1.01	Diameter at base 150mm	Nr	1.00	29.24	30.85	-	60.09	*26.42*
B2.3	**Depth**							
B2.3.1	In soft ground; borehole at base; 150mm diameter							
B2.3.1.01	In holes of maximum depth 5 - 10m	m	0.50	14.62	12.03	-	26.65	*9.14*
B2.3.1.02	In holes of maximum depth 10 - 20m	m	0.70	20.47	16.84	-	37.31	*12.79*
B2.3.1.03	in holes of maximum depth 20 - 30m	m	1.40	40.94	33.67	-	74.61	*25.59*

B3 Rotary drilled boreholes

		Unit	Labour Hours	Labour Net £	Plant Net £	Materials Net £	Unit Net £	*CO_2 Kg*
B3.1	**Number**							
B3.1.1	including transport, erection, dismantling							
B3.1.1.01	Diameter at base 150mm	Nr	1.00	41.80	64.66	-	106.46	*51.72*
B3.3	**Depth without core recovery**							
B3.3.1	In holes of maximum depth: not exceeding 5m							
B3.3.1.01	150mm diameter	m	1.00	41.80	57.86	-	99.66	*43.58*

B3 Rotary drilled boreholes continued...

		Unit	Labour Hours	Labour Net £	Plant Net £	Materials Net £	Unit Net £	CO_2 Kg
B3.3	**Depth without core recovery**							
B3.3.2	In holes of maximum depth 10 - 20m							
B3.3.2.01	150mm diameter	m	1.00	41.80	57.86	-	99.66	*43.58*
B3.3.3	In holes of maximum depth 20 - 30m							
B3.3.3.01	150mm diameter	m	1.10	45.98	63.65	-	109.63	*47.93*
B3.4	**Depth; with core recovery**							
B3.4.1	In holes of maximum depth: not exceeding 5m							
B3.4.1.01	Maximum 76mm diameter	m	1.15	48.07	66.54	-	114.61	*50.11*
B3.4.2	In holes of maximum depth 10 - 20m							
B3.4.2.01	Maximum 76mm diameter	m	1.15	48.07	66.54	-	114.61	*50.11*
B3.4.3	In holes of maximum depth 20 - 30m							
B3.4.3.01	Maximum 76mm diameter	m	1.25	52.25	72.33	-	124.58	*54.47*
B3.5	**Depth cased**							
B3.5.1	Additional cost of casting in drift deposits							
B3.5.1.01	Additional cost of casting in drift deposits	m	0.15	6.27	8.68	-	14.95	*6.54*
B3.5.2	Additional cost of casing rock							
B3.5.2.01	Additional cost of casing rock	m	0.15	6.27	8.68	-	14.95	*6.54*
B3.7	**Core boxes, length of core stated**							
B3.7.1	3m capacity							
B3.7.1.01	to be retained until 1 month after submission of report	Nr	0.20	8.36	11.57	-	19.93	*8.72*
B3.7.1.02	to be retained by client	Nr	0.40	16.72	23.14	-	39.86	*17.43*

B4 Samples

		Unit					Specialist Net £	CO_2 Kg
B4.2	**From boreholes**							
B4.2.1	Open tube							
B4.2.1.01	Undisturbed sample; 102 x 450mm long	Nr	-	-	-	-	22.18	-
B4.2.2	Disturbed							
B4.2.2.01	Bulk disturbed samples	Nr	-	-	-	-	4.88	-
B4.2.3	Groundwater							
B4.2.3.01	Jar samples of soil or ground water	Nr	-	-	-	-	3.99	-

B5 Site Tests and Observations

B5.1	**Site Tests and Observations**							
B5.1.3	Standard penetration							
B5.1.3.01	maximum 75 nr. blows	Nr	-	-	-	-	22.18	-

B7 Laboratory tests

B7.1	**Classification**							
B7.1.1	Moisture content							
B7.1.1.01	Moisture content	Nr (per test)	-	-	-	-	5.77	-
B7.1.3	Specific gravity							
B7.1.3.01	Bulk density	Nr (per test)	-	-	-	-	18.63	-
B7.1.4	Particle size analysis by sieve							
B7.1.4.01	P.S.D. sieve analysis	Nr (per test)	-	-	-	-	60.34	-
B7.1.5	Particle size analysis by pipette or hydrometer							
B7.1.5.01	P.S.D. sedimentation analysis	Nr (per test)	-	-	-	-	84.30	-
B7.2	**Chemical content**							
B7.2.1	Organic matter							
B7.2.1.01	Organic content	Nr (per test)	-	-	-	-	26.62	-
B7.2.2	Sulphate							
B7.2.2.01	Quantitive estimation of sulphate content of water or soil	Nr (per test)	-	-	-	-	17.75	-
B7.2.3	pH value							
B7.2.3.01	pH determination of water or soil	Nr (per test)	-	-	-	-	10.65	-
B7.3	**Compaction**							
B7.3.1	Standard							
B7.3.1.01	Density/water content relationship	Nr (per test)	-	-	-	-	106.49	-

B7 Laboratory tests continued...

		Unit					Specialist Net £	CO_2 Kg
B7.3	**Compaction**							
B7.3.2	Heavy							
B7.3.2.01	Density/water content relationship	Nr (per test)	-	-	-	-	115.36	-
B7.4	**Consolidation**							
B7.4.1	Oedometer cell							
B7.4.1.01	Oedometer cell	Nr (per test)	-	-	-	-	124.23	-
B7.5	**Permeability**							
B7.5.1	Constant head							
B7.5.1.01	granular soils	Nr (per test)	-	-	-	-	133.11	-
B7.5.1.02	cohesive soils	Nr (per test)	-	-	-	-	177.48	-
B7.6	**Soil strength**							
B7.6.1	Quick undrained triaxial							
B7.6.1.01	Set of 3 nr, 38mm diameter specimens	Nr (per test)	-	-	-	-	79.86	-
B7.6.1.02	102mm diameter specimen	Nr (per test)	-	-	-	-	79.86	-
B7.6.2	Consolidated undrained triaxial, with pore water pressure mesurement							
B7.6.2.01	Multi-stage; 102mm diameter specimen	Nr (per test)	-	-	-	-	79.86	-
B7.6.2.02	Set of 3 nr, 38mm diameter samples: maximum 3 days	Nr (per test)	-	-	-	-	244.03	-
B7.6.2.03	Set of 3 nr, 38mm diameter samples: exceeding 3 days	Nr (per test)	-	-	-	-	244.03	-
B7.6.3	Consolidated drained triaxial, with volume chain measurement							
B7.6.3.01	Set of 3 nr, 38mm diameter samples: maximum 4 days	Nr (per test)	-	-	-	-	266.21	-
B7.6.3.02	Set of 3 nr, 38mm diameter samples: exceeding 4 days	Nr (per test)	-	-	-	-	266.21	-
B7.6.4	Shearbox: peak only							
B7.6.4.01	Quick undrained; 60 x 60mm	Nr (per test)	-	-	-	-	106.49	-
B7.6.4.02	Quick undrained; 100 x 100mm	Nr (per test)	-	-	-	-	133.11	-
B7.6.5	Shearbox: peak and residual							
B7.6.5.01	Consolidated drained: maximum 3 days	Nr (per test)	-	-	-	-	244.03	-
B7.6.6	Shearbox: residual only							
B7.6.6.01	Consolidated drained with measurement of residual strength: maximum 5 days	Nr (per test)	-	-	-	-	266.21	-
B7.6.6.02	Consolidated drained with measurement of residual strength: exceeding 5 days	Nr (per test)	-	-	-	-	266.21	-
B7.6.8	California bearing ratio							
B7.6.8.01	Remoulded at natural m/c and density	Nr (per test)	-	-	-	-	70.99	-

B7 Laboratory tests continued...

		Unit					Specialist Net £	CO_2 Kg
B7.6	**Soil strength**							
B7.6.8	California bearing ratio							
B7.6.8.02	Remoulded at specified m/c and density	Nr (per test)	-	-	-	-	70.99	-
B7.6.8.03	On undisturbed sample	Nr (per test)	-	-	-	-	62.12	-
B7.7	**Rock strength**							
B7.7.1	Unconfined compressive strength of core samples							
B7.7.1.01	100mm diameter samples: maximum 3 days	Nr (per test)	-	-	-	-	75.43	-
B7.7.1.02	100mm diameter samples: exceeding 3 days	Nr (per test)	-	-	-	-	75.43	-
B7.7.2	Consolidated drained triaxial, with volume change measurement							
B7.7.2.01	Set of 3nr, 38mm diameter samples: maximum 3 days	Nr (per test)	-	-	-	-	244.03	-
B7.7.2.02	Set of 3nr, 38mm diameter samples: exceeding 3 days	Nr (per test)	-	-	-	-	244.03	-
B7.7.3	Brazilian							
B7.7.3.01	100mm diameter samples	Nr (per test)	-	-	-	-	399.32	-
B7.7.5	Point load							
B7.7.5.01	Minimum dimensions of the samples 60mm	Nr (per test)	-	-	-	-	14.20	-

B8 Professional Services

Note(s): The following are rates for the various grades of technical staff who should be appropriately employed in the preparation of the report. Chargeable time shall include visiting sites to assess the soil, geological and topographical conditions, examination of samples and cores on site and in the laboratory, preparation of testing schedules, logs, sections, and analysis and writing of the report. Charges shall also be made in connection with site or office meetings investigated at the Client's / Engineer's request.

		Unit	Labour Hours	Labour Net £	Plant Net £	Materials Net £	Unit Net £	CO_2 Kg
B8.1	**Technician**							
B8.1.1	Technician							
B8.1.1.01	Technical assistant	Hr	1.00	30.00	-	-	30.00	-
B8.2	**Technician engineer**							
B8.2.1	Technician engineer							
B8.2.1.01	Assistant engineer	Hr	1.00	53.24	-	-	53.24	-
B8.3	**Engineer or geologist**							
B8.3.1	Graduate							
B8.3.1.01	Engineer or geologist	Hr	1.00	46.00	-	-	46.00	-
B8.3.2	Chartered							
B8.3.2.01	Senior engineer or geologist	Hr	1.00	88.74	-	-	88.74	-
B8.3.3	Principal or consultant							
B8.3.3.01	Chief engineer or geologist	Hr	1.00	85.50	-	-	85.50	-
B8.4	**Visits to the site**							
B8.4.1	Engineering grades							
B8.4.1.01	Assistant or engineer	Nr	-	-	-	-	35.50	-
B8.4.1.02	Senior or chief engineer	Nr	-	-	-	-	35.50	-
B8.5	**Overnight stays in connection with visits to the site**							
B8.5.1	Engineer							
B8.5.1.01	Assistant or engineer	Nr	-	-	-	-	106.49	-
B8.5.1.02	Senior or chief engineer	Nr	-	-	-	-	106.49	-

CLASS C:
GEOTECHNICAL AND OTHER SPECIALIST PROCESSES

Calculations used throughout Class C - Geotechnical and Other Specialist Processes

Labour

		Qty		Rate		Total
L A0150ICE	**Provision of concrete Labour Gang**					
	Labourer (Skill Rate 3)	1	x	14.34	=	£14.34
	Labourer (General Operative)	1	x	12.56	=	£12.56
	Banksman	0.5	x	13.53	=	£6.77
	Total hourly cost of gang				**=**	**£33.67**
L C0002ICE	**Bored Piling Labour Gang**					
	Ganger	2	x	16.99	=	£33.97
	Labourer (General Operative)	2	x	12.56	=	£25.12
	Craftsman WRA	2	x	16.68	=	£33.37
	Total hourly cost of gang				**=**	**£92.46**
L C0003ICE	**Diaphragam Wall Concreting Labour Gang**					
	Labourer (Skill Rate 3)	2	x	14.34	=	£28.68
	Labourer (General Operative)	2	x	12.56	=	£25.12
	Banksman	1	x	13.53	=	£13.53
	Total hourly cost of gang				**=**	**£67.33**
L C0004ICE	**Diaphragm Wall - Guide Wall Construction Labour Gang**					
	Ganger	2	x	16.99	=	£33.97
	Labourer (General Operative)	2	x	12.56	=	£25.12
	Banksman	2	x	13.53	=	£27.06
	Labourer (Skill Rate 3)	2	x	14.34	=	£28.68
	Labourer (General Operative)	2	x	12.56	=	£25.12
	Banksman	1	x	13.53	=	£13.53
	Craftsman WRA	2	x	16.68	=	£33.37
	Labourer (General Operative)	1	x	12.56	=	£12.56
	Total hourly cost of gang				**=**	**£199.41**
L C0005ICE	**Diaphragm Wall Excavation Labour Gang**					
	Ganger	2	x	16.99	=	£33.97
	Labourer (General Operative)	2	x	12.56	=	£25.12
	Banksman	2	x	13.53	=	£27.06
	Total hourly cost of gang				**=**	**£86.15**
L C0006ICE	**Diaphragm Wall Joints Labour Gang**					
	Craftsman WRA	2	x	16.68	=	£33.37
	Labourer (General Operative)	1	x	12.56	=	£12.56
	Total hourly cost of gang				**=**	**£45.93**
L C0007ICE	**Diaphragm Wall Steelfixing Labour Gang**					
	Craftsman WRA	2	x	16.68	=	£33.37
	Labourer (General Operative)	1	x	12.56	=	£12.56
	Total hourly cost of gang				**=**	**£45.93**
L C0008ICE	**Ground Anchorage Labour Gang**					
	Ganger	1	x	16.99	=	£16.99
	Labourer (General Operative)	1	x	12.56	=	£12.56
	Craftsman WRA	1	x	16.68	=	£16.68
	Total hourly cost of gang				**=**	**£46.23**
L C0009ICE	**Ground Anchorage Labour Gang (Mobilise / Demobilise / Move)**					
	Ganger	10	x	16.99	=	£169.86
	Labourer (General Operative)	10	x	12.56	=	£125.60
	Craftsman WRA	10	x	16.68	=	£166.84
	Total hourly cost of gang				**=**	**£462.30**

Plant

P C0002ICE — **Bored Piling (Medium Rig) Plant Gang**

Bored Piling Rig Medium	1	x	154.27	=	£154.27
Concrete Mixer - Schwing BP1000R					
Concrete Pumps	1	x	43.29	=	£43.29
Total hourly cost of gang				**=**	**£197.56**

P C0003ICE — **Bored Piling (Medium) Plant Gang (Mobilise / Demobilise / Move)**

Bored Piling Rig Medium	8	x	154.27	=	£1,234.19
Concrete Mixer - Schwing BP1000R					
Concrete Pumps	8	x	43.29	=	£346.31
Articulated Lorry	8	x	64.02	=	£512.14
Low Loader Trailer	8	x	13.05	=	£104.37
Bored Piling Rig Medium	10	x	154.27	=	£1,542.74
Concrete Mixer - Schwing BP1000R					
Concrete Pumps	10	x	43.29	=	£432.88
Total hourly cost of gang				**=**	**£4,172.63**

P C0006ICE — **Diaphragm Wall Hydrofraise Plant Gang**

Hydrofraise Set Up	1	x	495.87	=	£495.87
Bentonite Plant	1	x	107.94	=	£107.94
Total hourly cost of gang				**=**	**£603.81**

P C0008ICE — **Ground Anchorage (Mobilise / Demobilise / Move) Plant Gang**

Ground Anchor Drilling Rig	10	x	111.35	=	£1,113.47
Grouting Rig (Anchorage Items)	10	x	9.84	=	£98.38
Compressor - 480 cfm	10	x	18.85	=	£188.49
Concrete Mixer - Schwing BP1000R					
Concrete Pumps	10	x	43.29	=	£432.88
Bowsers (250 gallon water / fuel)	10	x	0.88	=	£8.79
Articulated Lorry	8	x	64.02	=	£512.14
Low Loader Trailer	8	x	13.05	=	£104.37
Total hourly cost of gang				**=**	**£2,458.52**

P C0009ICE — **Ground Anchorage Plant Gang**

Ground Anchor Drilling Rig	1	x	111.35	=	£111.35
Grouting Rig (Anchorage Items)	1	x	9.84	=	£9.84
Compressor - 480 cfm	1	x	18.85	=	£18.85
Concrete Mixer - Schwing BP1000R					
Concrete Pumps	1	x	43.29	=	£43.29
Bowsers (250 gallon water / fuel)	1	x	0.88	=	£0.88
Total hourly cost of gang				**=**	**£184.21**

P C0010ICE — **Grout Hole Plant Gang (Drilling rock or other artificial hard material)**

Anchor Drilling Rig (Rock)	1	x	79.67	=	£79.67
Compressor - 480 cfm	1	x	18.85	=	£18.85
Bowsers (250 gallon water / fuel)	1	x	0.88	=	£0.88
Total hourly cost of gang				**=**	**£99.40**

P C0011ICE — **Grout Hole Plant Gang (Drilling Soils)**

Anchor Drilling Rig (Soil)	1	x	73.74	=	£73.74
Compressor - 480 cfm	1	x	18.85	=	£18.85
Bowsers (250 gallon water / fuel)	1	x	0.88	=	£0.88
Total hourly cost of gang				**=**	**£93.47**

P C0012ICE — **Grout Hole Plant Gang (Grouting rock or other artificial hard material)**

Anchor Drilling Rig (Rock)	1	x	79.67	=	£79.67
Compressor - 480 cfm	1	x	18.85	=	£18.85
Bowsers (250 gallon water / fuel)	1	x	0.88	=	£0.88
Grouting Rig (Anchorage Items)	1	x	9.84	=	£9.84
Total hourly cost of gang				**=**	**£109.24**

Class C - Geotechnical and other Specialist Processes

Note(s): The rates in this section have been based on those supplied by a specialist sub-contractor and are supplied without prejudice as guide prices only.

C1 Drilling for Grout Holes through Materials other than Rock or Artificial Hard Material

Note(s): A sum of £1,750 for establishing on site all plant, equipment and staff and removing on completion is included in the rates for drilling, assuming a total of 50nr holes.

		Unit	Labour Hours	Labour Net £	Plant Net £	Materials Net £	Unit Net £	*CO_2 Kg*
C1.1	**Vertically downwards**							
C1.1.1	In holes of depth not exceeding 5m							
C1.1.1.01	Generally	m	0.18	8.32	16.82	-	25.14	*43.81*
C1.1.2	In holes of depth; 5 - 10m							
C1.1.2.01	Generally	m	0.20	9.25	18.69	-	27.94	*48.67*
C1.1.3	In holes of depth; 10 - 20m							
C1.1.3.01	Generally	m	0.22	10.17	20.56	-	30.73	*53.54*
C1.1.4	In holes of depth; 20 - 30m							
C1.1.4.01	Generally	m	0.25	11.56	23.36	-	34.92	*60.84*
C1.2	**Downwards at an angle 0 - 45 degrees to the vertical**							
C1.2.1	In holes of depth not exceeding 5m							
C1.2.1.01	Generally	m	0.18	8.32	16.82	-	25.14	*43.81*
C1.2.2	In holes of depth; 5 - 10m							
C1.2.2.01	Generally	m	0.20	9.25	18.69	-	27.94	*48.67*
C1.2.3	In holes of depth; 10 - 20m							
C1.2.3.01	Generally	m	0.22	10.17	20.56	-	30.73	*53.54*
C1.2.4	In holes of depth; 20 - 30m							
C1.2.4.01	Generally	m	0.25	11.56	23.36	-	34.92	*60.84*
C1.3	**Horizontally or downwards at an angle less than 45 degrees to the horizontal**							
C1.3.1	In holes of depth not exceeding 5m							
C1.3.1.01	Generally	m	0.18	8.32	16.82	-	25.14	*43.81*
C1.3.2	In holes of depth; 5 - 10m							
C1.3.2.01	Generally	m	0.20	9.25	18.69	-	27.94	*48.67*
C1.3.3	In holes of depth; 10 - 20m							
C1.3.3.01	Generally	m	0.22	10.17	20.56	-	30.73	*53.54*
C1.3.4	In holes of depth; 20 - 30m							
C1.3.4.01	Generally	m	0.25	11.56	23.36	-	34.92	*60.84*
C1.4	**Upwards at an angle of 0 - 45 degrees to the horizontal**							
C1.4.1	In holes of depth not exceeding 5m							
C1.4.1.01	Generally	m	0.30	13.87	28.04	-	41.91	*73.01*
C1.4.2	In holes of depth; 5 - 10m							
C1.4.2.01	Generally	m	0.35	16.18	32.71	-	48.89	*85.18*
C1.4.3	In holes of depth; 10 - 20m							
C1.4.3.01	Generally	m	0.40	18.49	37.38	-	55.87	*97.35*
C1.4.4	In holes of depth; 20 - 30m							
C1.4.4.01	Generally	m	0.50	23.11	46.73	-	69.84	*121.69*

C1 Drilling for Grout Holes through Materials other than Rock or Artificial Hard Material

		Unit	Labour Hours	Labour Net £	Plant Net £	Materials Net £	Unit Net £	CO_2 Kg
C1.5	**Upwards at an angle less than 45 degrees to the vertical**							
C1.5.1	In holes of depth not exceeding 5m							
C1.5.1.01	Generally	m	0.30	13.87	28.04	-	41.91	*73.01*
C1.5.2	In holes of depth; 5 - 10m							
C1.5.2.01	Generally	m	0.35	16.18	32.71	-	48.89	*85.18*
C1.5.3	In holes of depth; 10 - 20m							
C1.5.3.01	Generally	m	0.40	18.49	37.38	-	55.87	*97.35*
C1.5.4	In holes of depth; 20 - 30m							
C1.5.4.01	Generally	m	0.50	23.11	46.73	-	69.84	*121.69*

C2 Drilling for Grout Holes through Rock or Artificial Hard Material

Note(s): A sum of £1,750 for establishing on site all plant, equipment and staff and removing on completion is included in the rates for drilling, assuming a total of 50nr holes.

		Unit	Labour Hours	Labour Net £	Plant Net £	Materials Net £	Unit Net £	CO_2 Kg
C2.1	**Vertically downwards**							
C2.1.1	In holes of depth not exceeding 5m							
C2.1.1.01	Generally	m	0.16	7.40	15.90	-	23.30	*38.94*
C2.1.2	In holes of depth; 5 - 10m							
C2.1.2.01	Generally	m	0.20	9.25	19.88	-	29.13	*48.67*
C2.1.3	In holes of depth; 10 - 20m							
C2.1.3.01	Generally	m	0.24	11.10	23.85	-	34.95	*58.41*
C2.1.4	In holes of depth; 20 - 30m							
C2.1.4.01	Generally	m	0.30	13.87	29.82	-	43.69	*73.01*
C2.2	**Downwards at an angle 0 - 45 degrees to the vertical**							
C2.2.1	In holes of depth not exceeding 5m							
C2.2.1.01	Generally	m	0.16	7.40	15.90	-	23.30	*38.94*
C2.2.2	In holes of depth; 5 - 10m							
C2.2.2.01	Generally	m	0.20	9.25	19.88	-	29.13	*48.67*
C2.2.3	In holes of depth; 10 - 20m							
C2.2.3.01	Generally	m	0.24	11.10	23.85	-	34.95	*58.41*
C2.2.4	In holes of depth; 20 - 30m							
C2.2.4.01	Generally	m	0.30	13.87	29.82	-	43.69	*73.01*
C2.3	**Horizontally or downwards at an angle less than 45 degrees to the horizontal**							
C2.3.1	In holes of depth not exceeding 5m							
C2.3.1.01	Generally	m	0.16	7.40	15.90	-	23.30	*38.94*
C2.3.2	In holes of depth; 5 - 10m							
C2.3.2.01	Generally	m	0.20	9.25	19.88	-	29.13	*48.67*
C2.3.3	In holes of depth; 10 - 20m							
C2.3.3.01	Generally	m	0.24	11.10	23.85	-	34.95	*58.41*
C2.3.4	In holes of depth; 20 - 30m							
C2.3.4.01	Generally	m	0.30	13.87	29.82	-	43.69	*73.01*

C2 Drilling for Grout Holes through Rock or Artificial Hard Material continued...

		Unit	Labour Hours	Labour Net £	Plant Net £	Materials Net £	Unit Net £	CO_2 Kg
C2.4	**Upwards at an angle of 0 - 45 degrees to the horizontal**							
C2.4.1	In holes of depth not exceeding 5m							
C2.4.1.01	Generally	m	0.27	12.48	26.84	-	39.32	*65.71*
C2.4.2	In holes of depth; 5 - 10m							
C2.4.2.01	Generally	m	0.30	13.87	29.82	-	43.69	*73.01*
C2.4.3	In holes of depth; 10 - 20m							
C2.4.3.01	Generally	m	0.35	16.18	34.79	-	50.97	*85.18*
C2.4.4	In holes of depth; 20 - 30m							
C2.4.4.01	Generally	m	0.40	18.49	39.76	-	58.25	*97.35*
C2.5	**Upwards at an angle less than 45 degrees to the vertical**							
C2.5.1	In holes of depth not exceeding 5m							
C2.5.1.01	Generally	m	0.38	17.57	37.77	-	55.34	*92.48*
C2.5.2	In holes of depth; 5 - 10m							
C2.5.2.01	Generally	m	0.45	20.80	44.73	-	65.53	*109.52*
C2.5.3	In holes of depth; 10 - 20m							
C2.5.3.01	Generally	m	0.51	23.58	50.69	-	74.27	*124.12*
C2.5.4	In holes of depth; 20 - 30m							
C2.5.4.01	Generally	m	0.60	27.74	59.63	-	87.37	*146.02*

C4 Grout Holes

		Unit	Labour Hours	Labour Net £	Plant Net £	Materials Net £	Unit Net £	CO_2 Kg
C4.1	**Number of holes**							
C4.1.1	Generally							
C4.1.1.01	Number of holes	Nr	0.75	34.67	81.92	-	116.59	*182.53*
C4.2	**Number of stages**							
C4.2.1	Generally							
C4.2.1.01	Number of stages (4nr)	Nr	0.25	11.56	27.31	-	38.87	*60.84*
C4.3	**Single water pressure tests**							
C4.3.1	Generally							
C4.3.1.01	Single water pressure test	Nr	0.25	11.56	8.51	-	20.07	*27.50*
C4.4	**Multiple water pressure test**							
C4.4.1	Generally							
C4.4.1.01	Multiple water pressure test	Nr	0.50	23.11	17.01	-	40.12	*55.00*

C5 Grout Materials and Injections

Note(s): A sum of £3,000 for establishing on site all plant, equipment and staff and removing on completion is included in the rates for 'number of injections', assuming 50nr injections.

		Unit	Labour Hours	Labour Net £	Plant Net £	Materials Net £	Unit Net £	CO_2 Kg
C5.1	**Materials**							
C5.1.1	Cement							
C5.1.1.01	Generally	Tonne	-	-	-	150.12	150.12	*220.28*
C5.1.2	Pulverised fuel ash							
C5.1.2.01	Generally	Tonne	-	-	-	200.00	200.00	*420.00*

C5 Grout Materials and Injections continued...

		Unit	Labour Hours	Labour Net £	Plant Net £	Materials Net £	Unit Net £	CO_2 Kg
C5.1	**Materials**							
C5.1.3	Sand							
C5.1.3.01	Generally	Tonne	-	-	-	16.10	16.10	*5.00*
C5.1.4	Pea gravel							
C5.1.4.01	Generally	Tonne	-	-	-	24.03	24.03	*5.00*
C5.1.5	Bentonite							
C5.1.5.01	Generally	Tonne	-	-	-	300.00	300.00	*1,300.00*
C5.1.6	Chemicals							
C5.1.6.01	Colloidal Silica Chemical Grout	Tonne	-	-	-	3,155.00	3,155.00	*2,260.00*
C5.1.6.02	Sodium Silicate Chemical Grout	Tonne	-	-	-	1,780.00	1,780.00	*1,780.00*
C5.1.6.03	Acrylic Resin Chemical Grout	Tonne	-	-	-	4,040.00	4,040.00	*1,300.00*
C5.1.6.04	Polyurethane Resin Chemical Grout	Tonne	-	-	-	7,609.00	7,609.00	*2,000.00*
C5.2	**Injection**							
C5.2.1	Number of injections							
C5.2.1.01	Injection	Nr	0.02	14.33	165.33	-	179.66	*119.99*

C6 Diaphragm Walls

Note(s): A sum of £82,500 for establishing on site all plant, equipment and staff and removing on completion is included in the rates for excavation, assuming 1000m3 of excavation.

Diaphragm walls cannot comply with watertight structures codes and the degree of watertightness achievable must always be qualified.

		Unit	Labour Hours	Labour Net £	Plant Net £	Materials Net £	Unit Net £	CO_2 Kg
C6.1	**Excavation in material other than rock or artificial hard material**							
C6.1.1	Maximum depth; not exceeding 5m							
C6.1.1.01	Supply and disposal of bentonite slurry, walls 1m thick	m^3	0.33	28.69	71.80	60.00	160.49	*322.65*
C6.1.2	Maximum depth; 5m - 10m							
C6.1.2.01	Supply and disposal of bentonite slurry, walls 1m thick	m^3	0.33	28.69	71.80	60.00	160.49	*322.65*
C6.1.3	Maximum depth; 10m - 15m							
C6.1.3.01	Supply and disposal of bentonite slurry, walls 1m thick	m^3	0.33	28.69	71.80	60.00	160.49	*322.65*
C6.4	**Concrete**							
C6.4.1	Gade 25, 20mm aggregate							
C6.4.1.01	Walls; 1m thick	m^3	0.20	10.10	4.33	87.88	102.31	*286.51*
C6.5	**Plain round steel bar reinforcement to BS 4449**							
C6.5.3	Nominal size: 10mm							
C6.5.3.01	Cut, bent and fixed in place	Tonne	10.00	459.30	-	664.50	1,123.80	*1,710.00*
C6.5.5	Nominal size: 16mm							
C6.5.5.01	Cut, bent and fixed in place	Tonne	8.00	367.44	-	612.65	980.09	*1,710.00*

C6 Diaphragm Walls continued...

		Unit	Labour Hours	Labour Net £	Plant Net £	Materials Net £	Unit Net £	CO_2 Kg
C6.5	**Plain round steel bar reinforcement to BS 4449**							
C6.5.6	Nominal size: 20mm							
C6.5.6.01	Cut, bent and fixed in place	Tonne	8.00	367.44	-	612.65	**980.09**	*1,710.00*
C6.5.7	Nominal size: 25mm							
C6.5.7.01	Cut, bent and fixed in place	Tonne	8.00	367.44	-	612.23	**979.67**	*1,710.00*
C6.6	**Deformed high yield steel bar reinforcement to BS 4449**							
C6.6.3	Nominal size: 10mm							
C6.6.3.01	Cut, bent and fixed in place	Tonne	10.00	459.30	-	594.32	**1,053.62**	*1,710.00*
C6.6.5	Nominal size: 16mm							
C6.6.5.01	Cut, bent and fixed in place	Tonne	8.00	367.44	-	547.95	**915.39**	*1,710.00*
C6.6.6	Nominal size: 20mm							
C6.6.6.01	Cut, bent and fixed in place	Tonne	8.00	367.44	-	547.95	**915.39**	*1,710.00*
C6.6.7	Nominal size: 25mm							
C6.6.7.01	Cut, bent and fixed in place	Tonne	8.00	367.44	-	547.95	**915.39**	*1,710.00*
C6.7	**Waterproofed joints**							
C6.7.1	Waterproofed joints							
C6.7.1.01	Generally	Joint	2.00	87.17	3.55	15.07	**105.79**	*30.68*
C6.8	**Guided Walls**							
C6.8.1	Concrete grade 25; 20mm aggregate							
C6.8.1.01	Walls 1m wide x 1m deep, running each side of intended excavation	m	0.50	99.70	8.66	340.14	**448.50**	*1,086.02*

C7 Ground Anchorages

Note(s):

1) Ground anchors are commonly used to tie back steel sheet piling or other forms of support to the sides of major excavations or waterside structures in order to leave the front face of the support free from obstructions. The tendons which can be steel cable or bar are anchored into the ground behind the support wall by either attaching to a 'deadman' anchor or drilling a bore into the ground inserting the tendon with a suitable end plate and grouting the hole. The free end of the tendon is then joined to the support wall and tensioned to a stress exceeding that of the load to be carried. Anchors can be temporary or permanent.

2) In the following examples ready fabricated anchorage assemblies between 5m and 10m long, complete with corrosion protection are inserted into the previuosly bored holes and then ground into position.

3) A sum of £5,000 for establishing on site all plant, equipment and staff and removing on completion is included in the rates for 'number of ground anchorages', assuming a total of 50nr ground anchorages.

4) The rates for total length of tendons include drilling, temporary casing, supply of tendon and grouting in.

		Unit	Labour Hours	Labour Net £	Plant Net £	Materials Net £	Unit Net £	CO_2 Kg
C7.1	**Number in material other than rock or artificial hard material to a stated maximum depth**							
C7.1.1	Temporary							
C7.1.1.01	to a maximum depth of 15m	Nr	0.02	9.25	49.17	-	**58.42**	*55.74*
C7.1.2	Temporary with single corrosion protection							
C7.1.2.01	to a maximum depth of 15m	Nr	0.02	9.25	49.17	-	**58.42**	*55.74*
C7.1.3	Temporary with double corrosion protection							
C7.1.3.01	to a maximum depth of 15m	Nr	0.02	9.25	49.17	-	**58.42**	*55.74*

C7 Ground Anchorages continued...

		Unit	Labour Hours	Labour Net £	Plant Net £	Materials Net £	Unit Net £	CO_2 *Kg*
C7.1	**Number in material other than rock or artificial hard material to a stated maximum depth**							
C7.1.4	Permanent							
C7.1.4.01	to a maximum depth of 15m	Nr	0.02	9.25	49.17	-	**58.42**	*55.74*
C7.1.5	Permanent with single corrosion protection							
C7.1.5.01	to a maximum depth of 15m	Nr	0.02	9.25	49.17	-	**58.42**	*55.74*
C7.1.6	Permanent with double corrosion protection							
C7.1.6.01	to a maximum depth of 15m	Nr	0.02	9.25	49.17	-	**58.42**	*55.74*
C7.2	**Total length of tendons in material other than rock or artificial hard material**							
C7.2.1	Temporary							
C7.2.1.01	to a maximum depth of 15m	m	0.15	6.70	26.71	35.95	**69.36**	*64.60*
C7.2.2	Temporary with single corrosion protection							
C7.2.2.01	to a maximum depth of 15m	m	0.15	6.70	26.71	35.95	**69.36**	*64.60*
C7.2.3	Temporary with double corrosion protection							
C7.2.3.01	to a maximum depth of 15m	m	0.15	6.70	26.71	35.95	**69.36**	*64.60*
C7.2.4	Permanent							
C7.2.4.01	to a maximum depth of 15m	m	0.15	6.70	26.71	50.03	**83.44**	*69.51*
C7.2.5	Permanent with single corrosion protection							
C7.2.5.01	to a maximum depth of 15m	m	0.15	6.70	26.71	50.03	**83.44**	*69.51*
C7.2.6	Permanent with double corrosion protection							
C7.2.6.01	to a maximum depth of 15m	m	0.15	6.70	26.71	50.03	**83.44**	*69.51*
C7.3	**Number in material which includes rock or artificial hard material in a stated maximum**							
C7.3.1	Temporary							
C7.3.1.01	to a maximum depth of 15m	Nr	0.02	9.25	49.17	-	**58.42**	*55.74*
C7.3.2	Temporary with single corrosion protection							
C7.3.2.01	to a maximum depth of 15m	Nr	0.02	9.25	49.17	-	**58.42**	*55.74*
C7.3.3	Temporary with double corrosion protection							
C7.3.3.01	to a maximum depth of 15m	Nr	0.02	9.25	49.17	-	**58.42**	*55.74*
C7.3.4	Permanent							
C7.3.4.01	to a maximum depth of 15m	Nr	0.02	9.25	49.17	-	**58.42**	*55.74*
C7.3.5	Permanent with single corrosion protection							
C7.3.5.01	to a maximum depth of 15m	Nr	0.02	9.25	49.17	-	**58.42**	*55.74*
C7.3.6	Permanent with double corrosion protection							
C7.3.6.01	to a maximum depth of 15m	Nr	0.02	9.25	49.17	-	**58.42**	*55.74*
C7.4	**Total length of tendons in material which includes rock or artificial hard material**							
C7.4.1	Temporary							
C7.4.1.01	to a maximum depth of 15m	m	0.15	6.70	26.71	43.76	**77.17**	*64.60*
C7.4.2	Temporary with single corrosion protection							
C7.4.2.01	to a maximum depth of 15m	m	0.15	6.70	26.71	43.76	**77.17**	*64.60*
C7.4.3	Temporary with double corrosion protection							
C7.4.3.01	to a maximum depth of 15m	m	0.15	6.70	26.71	43.76	**77.17**	*64.60*
C7.4.4	Permanent							
C7.4.4.01	to a maximum depth of 15m	m	0.15	6.70	26.71	64.83	**98.24**	*69.51*

C7 Ground Anchorages continued...

		Unit	Labour Hours	Labour Net £	Plant Net £	Materials Net £	Unit Net £	*CO_2 Kg*
C7.4	**Total length of tendons in material which includes rock or artificial hard material**							
C7.4.5	Permanent with single corrosion protection							
C7.4.5.01	to a maximum depth of 15m	m	0.15	6.70	26.71	64.83	**98.24**	*69.51*
C7.4.6	Permanent with double corrosion protection							
C7.4.6.01	to a maximum depth of 15m	m	0.15	6.70	26.71	64.83	**98.24**	*69.51*

C8 Sand, Band and Wick Drains

Note(s): A sum of £10,000 for establishing on site all plant, equipment and staff and removing on completion is included in the rates for 'number of drains' assuming a total of 50nr sand drains.

		Unit	Labour Hours	Labour Net £	Plant Net £	Materials Net £	Unit Net £	*CO_2 Kg*
C8.1	**Number of drains**							
C8.1.3	Cross-sectional dimension: 200 - 300mm							
C8.1.3.01	Sand drains	Nr	0.02	11.46	83.45	-	**94.91**	*73.67*
C8.2	**Number of predrilled holes**							
C8.2.3	Cross-sectional dimension: 200 - 300mm							
C8.2.3.01	Sand drains	Nr	0.02	11.46	83.45	-	**94.91**	*73.67*
C8.4	**Depth of drains of maximum; not exceeding 10m**							
C8.4.2	Cross-sectional dimension; 100 - 200mm							
C8.4.2.01	Sand drains	m	0.02	1.57	3.36	0.27	**5.20**	*3.28*
C8.4.4	Cross-sectional dimension; 300 - 400mm							
C8.4.4.01	Sand drains	m	0.02	1.94	4.15	1.13	**7.22**	*4.29*
C8.5	**Depth of drains of maximum; 10 - 15m**							
C8.5.2	Cross-sectional dimension; 100 - 200mm							
C8.5.2.01	Sand drains	m	0.02	1.57	3.36	0.27	**5.20**	*3.28*
C8.5.4	Cross-sectional dimension; 300 - 400mm							
C8.5.4.01	Sand drains	m	0.03	2.31	4.94	1.13	**8.38**	*5.05*
C8.6	**Depth of drains of maximum; 15 - 20m**							
C8.6.2	Cross-sectional dimension; 100 - 200mm							
C8.6.2.01	Sand drains	m	0.03	3.05	6.52	0.27	**9.84**	*6.28*
C8.6.4	Cross-sectional dimension; 300 - 400mm							
C8.6.4.01	Sand drains	m	0.05	4.62	9.88	1.13	**15.63**	*9.74*

CLASS D:
DEMOLITION AND SITE CLEARANCE

Calculations used throughout Class D - Demolition and Site Clearance

Labour

		Qty		Rate		Total
L A0330ICE	**Clearance Labour Gang**					
	Ganger	1	x	16.99	=	£16.99
	Labourer (General Operative)	2	x	12.56	=	£25.12
	Total hourly cost of gang				**=**	**£42.11**

Plant

		Qty		Rate		Total
P A1330ICE	**Clearance Plant Gang**					
	Crawler Tractor / Dozer - Dresser 1004 48kW	1	x	28.68	=	£28.68
	Tipping Waggon - 16t 6-Wheel (24t Gr)	1	x	47.97	=	£47.97
	Compressor - 2-Tool (Complete)	1	x	4.86	=	£4.86
	Rock Drill	3	x	0.89	=	£2.66
	Total hourly cost of gang				**=**	**£84.17**
P A1331ICE	**Demolition Plant Gang**					
	Crawler Tractor / Dozer - Dresser 1004 48kW	1	x	28.68	=	£28.68
	Tipping Waggon - 16t 6-Wheel (24t Gr)	1	x	47.97	=	£47.97
	Compressor - 2-Tool (Complete)	1	x	4.86	=	£4.86
	Rock Drill	3	x	0.89	=	£2.66
	Cutting and Burning Gear	1	x	3.52	=	£3.52
	Hydraulic Excavator - Cat 320 96kW	1	x	33.98	=	£33.98
	Total hourly cost of gang				**=**	**£121.67**

Class D - Demolition and Site Clearance

D1 General Clearance

		Unit	Labour Hours	Labour Net £	Plant Net £	Materials Net £	Unit Net £	CO_2 *Kg*
D1.1	**Demolition and removal from site**							
D1.1.1	Articles, objects and obstructions over the total area of the site							
D1.1.1.01	Generally	ha	8.00	336.88	673.36	-	1,010.24	*439.00*
D1.1.1.02	Wooded areas including hedges and small trees	ha	24.00	1,010.64	2,020.08	-	3,030.72	*1,317.00*

D2 Trees

		Unit	Labour Hours	Labour Net £	Plant Net £	Materials Net £	Unit Net £	CO_2 *Kg*
D2.1	**Girth: 500mm - 1m**							
D2.1.1	Clearance of trees (girth measured 1m above ground); excluding stumps							
D2.1.1.01	Generally	Nr	0.39	16.42	32.83	-	49.25	*21.40*
D2.2	**Girth: 1 - 2m**							
D2.2.1	Clearance of trees (girth measured 1m above ground); excluding stumps							
D2.2.1.01	Generally	Nr	0.79	33.27	66.49	-	99.76	*43.35*
D2.3	**Girth: 2 - 3m**							
D2.3.1	Clearance of trees (girth measured 1m above ground); excluding stumps							
D2.3.1.01	Generally	Nr	3.00	126.33	252.51	-	378.84	*164.63*
D2.4	**Girth: 3 - 4m**							
D2.4.1	Clearance of trees (girth measured 1m above ground); excluding stumps							
D2.4.1.01	Generally	Nr	8.00	336.88	673.36	-	1,010.24	*439.00*
D2.5	**Girth: exceeding 5m**							
D2.5.1	Clearance of trees (girth measured 1m above ground); excluding stumps							
D2.5.1.01	Generally	Nr	12.50	526.38	1,052.13	-	1,578.51	*685.94*

D3 Stumps

		Unit	Labour Hours	Labour Net £	Plant Net £	Materials Net £	Unit Net £	CO_2 *Kg*
D3.1	**Diameter: 150 - 500mm**							
D3.1.1	Clearance of stumps							
D3.1.1.01	Holes backfilled with topsoil from site	Nr	0.50	21.06	42.09	-	63.15	*27.44*
D3.1.1.02	Holes backfilled with clean hardcore from site	Nr	0.60	25.27	50.50	-	75.77	*32.93*
D3.2	**Diameter: 500mm - 1m**							
D3.2.1	Clearance of stumps							
D3.2.1.01	Holes backfilled with topsoil from site	Nr	1.00	42.11	84.17	-	126.28	*54.88*
D3.2.1.02	Holes backfilled with clean hardcore from site	Nr	1.20	50.53	101.00	-	151.53	*65.85*

D3 Stumps continued...

		Unit	Labour Hours	Labour Net £	Plant Net £	Materials Net £	Unit Net £	CO_2 Kg
D3.3	**Diameter: exceeding 1m**							
D3.3.1	Clearance of stumps; diameter: 1.5m							
D3.3.1.01	Holes backfilled with topsoil from site	Nr	1.25	52.64	105.21	-	157.85	*68.59*
D3.3.1.02	Holes backfilled with clean hardcore from site	Nr	1.50	63.16	126.26	-	189.42	*82.31*

D4 Buildings

		Unit	Labour Hours	Labour Net £	Plant Net £	Materials Net £	Unit Net £	CO_2 Kg
D4.1	**Brickwork**							
D4.1.6	Volume: 1000 - 2500 m^3							
D4.1.6.01	Administration block; 2 storey height; 250mm thick traditional cavity wall with timber flat roof and bitumen felt finish; block partitions; 2nr timber staircases (work below Original Surface excluded); overall size 30 x 12m x 6m high	Nr	27.32	1,150.45	2,299.52	-	3,449.97	*1,499.19*

D5 Other Structures

		Unit	Labour Hours	Labour Net £	Plant Net £	Materials Net £	Unit Net £	CO_2 Kg
D5.2	**Concrete**							
D5.2.6	Volume: 1000 - 2500 m^3							
D5.2.6.01	Settlement tanks (work below Original Surface); 500mm thick reinforced concrete; 20m diameter at Original Surface tapered to 5m diameter at base; 10m height; including 300mm thick reinforced concrete inlet chamber 3 x 3 x 4m deep containing 300mm bore cast iron pipe and fitting together with 2nr valves and penstocks	Nr	159.00	6,695.49	13,383.03	-	20,078.52	*8,725.13*
D5.2.6.02	Sludge Tanks (work above Original Surface); 400mm thick reinforced concrete; 15 x 15 x 8m high; sloping reinforced concrete base 300mm thick suspended above Original Surface (work below Original Surface excluded).	Nr	175.00	7,369.25	14,729.75	-	22,099.00	*9,603.13*
D5.5	**Timber**							
D5.5.1	Volume: not exceeding 50m^3							
D5.5.1.01	Timber footbridge; above stream; 8 x 3m wide; timber rails 1.6m high	Nr	6.00	252.66	505.02	-	757.68	*329.25*

D6 Pipelines

		Unit	Labour Hours	Labour Net £	Plant Net £	Materials Net £	Unit Net £	CO_2 Kg
D6.1	**Nominal bore: 100 - 300mm**							
D6.1.1	Clay drains including concrete bed and surround 2m deep							
D6.1.1.01	Generally	m	0.08	3.28	9.49	-	12.77	*5.43*

D6 Pipelines continued...

		Unit	Labour Hours	Labour Net £	Plant Net £	Materials Net £	**Unit Net £**	*CO_2 Kg*
D6.1	**Nominal bore: 100 - 300mm**							
D6.1.2	Concrete pipelines including concrete bed and surround 2m deep							
D6.1.2.01	Generally	m	0.09	3.58	10.34	-	**13.92**	*5.91*
D6.1.3	Cast iron pipeline on metal supports at 2m centres suspended 1m above Final Surface.							
D6.1.3.01	Generally	m	0.08	3.28	9.49	-	**12.77**	*5.43*
D6.2	**Nominal bore: 300 - 500mm**							
D6.2.1	Concrete pipelines including concrete bed and surround 2m deep							
D6.2.1.01	Generally	m	0.09	3.83	11.07	-	**14.90**	*6.33*
D6.2.2	Cast iron pipeline on metal supports at 2m centres suspended 1m above Final Surface.							
D6.2.2.01	Generally	m	0.09	3.83	11.07	-	**14.90**	*6.33*
D6.3	**Nominal bore: exceeding 500mm**							
D6.3.1	Concrete pipelines including concrete bed and surround 2m deep							
D6.3.1.01	Nominal bore: 600mm	m	0.10	4.00	11.56	-	**15.56**	*6.61*
D6.3.2	Cast iron pipeline on metal supports at 2m centres suspended 1m above Final Surface.							
D6.3.2.01	Nominal bore: 600mm	m	0.10	4.00	11.56	-	**15.56**	*6.61*
D6.3.3	Ductile iron pipeline on concrete supports at 4m centres suspended 1m above Final Surface.							
D6.3.3.01	Nominal bore: 600mm	m	0.10	4.00	11.56	-	**15.56**	*6.61*
D6.3.3.02	Nominal bore: 800mm	m	0.12	5.05	14.60	-	**19.65**	*8.35*

CLASS E:
EARTHWORKS

Calculations used throughout Class E - Earthworks

Labour

		Qty		Rate		Total
L A0120ICE	**General Earthworks Labour Gang**					
	Ganger	1	x	16.99	=	£16.99
	Labourer (General Operative)	1	x	12.56	=	£12.56
	Banksman	1	x	13.53	=	£13.53
	Total hourly cost of gang				=	**£43.08**
L A0122ICE	**Drill and blast Labour Gang**					
	Driller	1	x	14.34	=	£14.34
	Shot firer	0.5	x	14.34	=	£7.17
	Total hourly cost of gang				=	**£21.51**
L A0123ICE	**Landscape Labour Gang**					
	Labourer (Skill Rate 3)	1	x	14.34	=	£14.34
	Labourer (General Operative)	1	x	12.56	=	£12.56
	Total hourly cost of gang				=	**£26.90**
L A0320ICE	**Waterproofing Labour Gang**					
	Ganger	1	x	16.99	=	£16.99
	Labourer (General Operative)	3	x	12.56	=	£37.68
	Total hourly cost of gang				=	**£54.67**

Plant

P A1120ICE	**Excavate, haul and deposit (Motorway)**					
	Crawler Tractor / Dozer - Terex TS24 C Scraper (Wheeled) 18.4m3	2	x	96.26	=	£192.53
	Crawler Tractor / Dozer - Cat 633E Scraper	2	x	90.12	=	£180.24
	Crawler Tractor / Dozer - Cat 302kW Pusher	1	x	84.26	=	£84.26
	Crawler Tractor / Dozer - Tractor D8 Blade	0.5	x	63.59	=	£31.79
	Crawler Tractor / Dozer - Cat 16H Grader	0.5	x	82.10	=	£41.05
	Total hourly cost of gang				=	**£529.87**
P A1121ICE	**Compaction (Motorway) Plant Gang**					
	Crawler Tractor / Dozer - Tractor D8 Blade	0.5	x	63.59	=	£31.79
	Crawler Tractor / Dozer - Cat 16H Grader	0.5	x	82.10	=	£41.05
	Roller - Case Vibromax W651	1	x	7.12	=	£7.12
	Total hourly cost of gang				=	**£79.96**
P A1122ICE	**Ripping Plant Gang**					
	Crawler Tractor / Dozer - Fiatallis FD145 93kW	1	x	51.51	=	£51.51
	Crawler Tractor / Dozer - Cat 302kW Pusher	1	x	84.26	=	£84.26
	Total hourly cost of gang				=	**£135.77**
P A1123ICE	**Breaking Plant Gang**					
	Hydraulic Excavator - Cat 320 96kW	1	x	33.98	=	£33.98
	Total hourly cost of gang				=	**£33.98**
P A1124ICE	**General excavation Plant Gang**					
	Hydraulic Excavator - Cat 166kW	1	x	41.41	=	£41.41
	Crawler Tractor / Dozer - Cat D6 LGP 160 Hp	0.5	x	48.61	=	£24.30
	Total hourly cost of gang				=	**£65.71**
P A1125ICE	**Trimming Plant Gang / preparation Plant Gang / spread and level Plant Gang**					
	Crawler Tractor / Dozer - Cat 16H Grader	0.34	x	82.10	=	£27.92
	Hydraulic Excavator - Cat 320 96kW	0.34	x	33.98	=	£11.55
	Crawler Tractor / Dozer - Cat D6 LGP 160 Hp	0.34	x	48.61	=	£16.53
	Total hourly cost of gang				=	**£56.00**

P A1126ICE	**General spoil haulage Plant Gang**					
	Dumper Truck - Volvo A25C 25t 6x6	3	x	56.35	=	£169.04
	Total hourly cost of gang				**=**	**£169.04**
P A1127ICE	**General compaction Plant Gang**					
	Roller - Bomag 90 900mm	1	x	3.27	=	£3.27
	Crawler Tractor / Dozer - Dresser 1004 48kW	1	x	28.68	=	£28.68
	Total hourly cost of gang				**=**	**£31.95**
P A1128ICE	**Drill and blast Plant Gang**					
	Waggon Drill with Steel & bits	1	x	4.58	=	£4.58
	Compressor - 375 cfm	1	x	14.95	=	£14.95
	Exploder with Circuit Tester	1	x	2.47	=	£2.47
	Total hourly cost of gang				**=**	**£22.00**

Class E - Earthworks

E2 Excavation for cuttings

Note(s): The following rates are for a typical Motorway cutting.

		Unit	Labour Hours	Labour Net £	Plant Net £	Materials Net £	Unit Net £	CO_2 Kg
E2.1	**Topsoil**							
E2.1.1	Typical for a motorway cutting							
E2.1.1.01	Generally	1000m^3	0.68	29.29	360.30	-	**389.59**	*300.46*
E2.2	**Materials other than topsoil, rock or artificial hard material**							
E2.2.1	Typical for a motorway cutting							
E2.2.1.01	Generally	1000m^3	0.68	29.29	360.30	-	**389.59**	*300.46*
E2.3	**Rock**							
E2.3.1	Typical for a motorway cutting							
E2.3.1.01	Rock (using D9 and towed ripper)	1000m^3	8.30	357.56	5,321.01	-	**5,678.57**	*4,307.21*
E2.4	**Stated artificial hard material exposed at the Commencing Surface**							
E2.4.1	Typical for a motorway cutting							
E2.4.1.01	Concrete pavement; 200mm thick	m^3	0.01	0.34	11.95	-	**12.29**	*9.78*
E2.4.1.02	Tarmacadam pavement; 200mm thick	m^3	0.00	0.17	2.39	-	**2.56**	*1.96*
E2.5	**Stated artificial hard material not exposed at the Commencing Surface**							
E2.5.1	Typical for a motorway cutting							
E2.5.1.01	Plain concrete pavement (using Hymac with breaker)	m^3	0.01	0.34	14.43	-	**14.77**	*7.94*
E2.5.1.02	Reinforced concrete pavement	m^3	0.02	0.69	24.11	-	**24.80**	*13.83*

E3 Excavation for Foundations

		Unit	Labour Hours	Labour Net £	Plant Net £	Materials Net £	Unit Net £	CO_2 Kg
E3.1	**Topsoil**							
E3.1.1	Maximum depth: not exceeding 0.25m							
E3.1.1.01	Generally	m^3	0.03	1.29	1.97	-	**3.26**	*1.10*
E3.2	**Material other than topsoil, rock or artificial hard material**							
E3.2.1	Maximum depth: not exceeding 0.25m							
E3.2.1.01	Generally	m^3	0.03	1.38	2.10	-	**3.48**	*1.17*
E3.2.2	Maximum depth: 0.25 - 0.5m							
E3.2.2.01	Generally	m^3	0.03	1.38	2.10	-	**3.48**	*1.17*
E3.2.3	Maximum depth: 0.5 - 1m							
E3.2.3.01	Generally	m^3	0.03	1.38	2.10	-	**3.48**	*1.17*
E3.2.4	Maximum depth: 1 - 2m							
E3.2.4.01	Generally	m^3	0.03	1.38	2.10	-	**3.48**	*1.17*
E3.2.5	Maximum depth: 2 - 5m							
E3.2.5.01	Generally	m^3	0.04	1.68	2.56	-	**4.24**	*1.43*

E3 Excavation for Foundations continued...

		Unit	Labour Hours	Labour Net £	Plant Net £	Materials Net £	Unit Net £	CO_2 Kg
E3.2	**Material other than topsoil, rock or artificial hard material**							
E3.2.6	Maximum depth: 5 - 10m							
E3.2.6.01	Generally	m^3	0.05	1.94	2.96	-	4.90	*1.65*
E3.2.7	Maximum depth: 10 - 15m							
E3.2.7.01	Generally	m^3	0.05	2.15	3.29	-	5.44	*1.83*
E3.3	**Rock**							
E3.3.1	Maximum depth: not exceeding 0.25m							
E3.3.1.01	Rock, well broken, (excavation by machines - using drill and blast ripper gangs)	m^3	0.14	4.52	6.14	-	10.66	*4.09*
E3.3.2	Maximum depth: 0.25 - 0.5m							
E3.3.2.01	Rock, well broken, (excavation by machines - using drill and blast ripper gangs)	m^3	0.14	4.52	6.14	-	10.66	*4.09*
E3.3.3	Maximum depth: 0.5 - 1m							
E3.3.3.01	Rock, well broken, (excavation by machines - using drill and blast ripper gangs)	m^3	0.15	4.84	6.58	-	11.42	*4.38*
E3.3.4	Maximum depth: 1 - 2m							
E3.3.4.01	Rock, well broken, (excavation by machines - using drill and blast ripper gangs)	m^3	0.17	5.49	7.46	-	12.95	*4.96*
E3.3.5	Maximum depth: 2 - 5m							
E3.3.5.01	Rock, well broken, (excavation by machines - using drill and blast ripper gangs)	m^3	0.21	6.78	9.21	-	15.99	*6.13*
E3.4	**Stated artificial hard material exposed at the Commencing Surface**							
E3.4.1	Plain concrete slab							
E3.4.1.01	Generally	m^3	0.34	14.65	11.55	-	26.20	*4.99*
E3.4.2	Tarmacadam pavement							
E3.4.2.01	Generally	m^3	0.17	7.32	5.78	-	13.10	*2.50*
E3.5	**Stated artificial hard material not exposed at the Commencing Surface**							
E3.5.1	Maximum depth: not exceeding 0.25m							
E3.5.1.01	Plain concrete (using breaking gang)	m^3	0.34	14.65	33.89	-	48.54	*17.44*
E3.5.1.02	Reinforced concrete	m^3	0.51	21.97	47.78	-	69.75	*24.84*
E3.5.2	Maximum depth: 0.25 - 0.5m							
E3.5.2.01	Plain concrete (using breaking gang)	m^3	0.34	14.65	33.89	-	48.54	*17.44*
E3.5.2.02	Reinforced concrete	m^3	0.51	21.97	47.78	-	69.75	*24.84*
E3.5.3	Maximum depth: 0.5 - 1m							
E3.5.3.01	Plain concrete (using breaking gang)	m^3	0.34	14.65	33.89	-	48.54	*17.44*
E3.5.3.02	Reinforced concrete	m^3	0.51	21.97	47.78	-	69.75	*24.84*
E3.5.4	Maximum depth: 1 - 2m							
E3.5.4.01	Plain concrete (using breaking gang)	m^3	0.39	16.80	38.88	-	55.68	*20.01*

E3 Excavation for Foundations continued...

		Unit	Labour Hours	Labour Net £	Plant Net £	Materials Net £	Unit Net £	CO_2 Kg
E3.5	**Stated artificial hard material not exposed at the Commencing Surface**							
E3.5.4	Maximum depth: 1 - 2m							
E3.5.4.02	Reinforced concrete	m^3	0.58	24.99	55.44	-	80.43	*28.72*

E4 General Excavation

Note(s): HARD ROCK

The following has been assumed for blasting of Hard Rock:-

1) Rock blasting in large open areas

2) The surface of the rock to be blasted has been cleaned of overburden and is suitable for access of wagon drills.

3) The rock is good hard rock not badly fissured.

4) Sufficient blasting agent has been used to ensure a high level of fragmentation, enabling straight forward excavation.

		Unit	Labour Hours	Labour Net £	Plant Net £	Materials Net £	Unit Net £	CO_2 Kg
E4.1	**Topsoil**							
E4.1.1	Maximum depth: not exceeding 0.25m							
E4.1.1.01	Generally	m^3	0.02	0.86	1.31	-	2.17	*0.73*
E4.2	**Material other than topsoil, rock or artificial hard material**							
E4.2.1	Maximum depth: not exceeding 0.25m							
E4.2.1.01	Loaded into wagons	m^3	0.02	0.99	1.51	-	2.50	*0.84*
E4.2.2	Maximum depth: 0.25 - 0.5m							
E4.2.2.01	Loaded into wagons	m^3	0.02	0.99	1.51	-	2.50	*0.84*
E4.2.3	Maximum depth: 0.5 - 1m							
E4.2.3.01	Loaded into wagons	m^3	0.02	0.99	1.51	-	2.50	*0.84*
E4.2.4	Maximum depth: 1 - 2m							
E4.2.4.01	Loaded into wagons	m^3	0.03	1.25	1.91	-	3.16	*1.06*
E4.2.5	Maximum depth: 2 - 5m							
E4.2.5.01	Loaded into wagons	m^3	0.03	1.25	1.91	-	3.16	*1.06*
E4.2.6	Maximum depth: 5 - 10m							
E4.2.6.01	Loaded into wagons	m^3	0.04	1.51	2.30	-	3.81	*1.28*
E4.2.7	Maximum depth: 10 - 15m							
E4.2.7.01	Loaded into wagons	m^3	0.04	1.59	2.43	-	4.02	*1.35*
E4.3	**Rock**							
E4.3.1	Maximum depth: not exceeding 0.25m							
E4.3.1.01	Rock; well broken (excavated by machine)	m^3	0.08	3.36	5.13	-	8.49	*2.86*
E4.3.1.02	Rock; hard (including drilling and blasting and ripping prior to excavation)	m^3	0.82	34.29	51.74	0.53	86.56	*29.61*
E4.3.1.03	For rail track; excavate ballast at formation level; Maximum depth: 150mm	m^3	0.06	22.40	19.61	-	42.01	*8.08*
E4.3.1.04	For rail track; excavate ballast at formation level; unsuitable material; Maximum depth: 150mm	m^3	0.06	20.62	18.06	-	38.68	*7.44*

E4 General Excavation continued...

		Unit	Labour Hours	Labour Net £	Plant Net £	Materials Net £	Unit Net £	CO_2 Kg
E4.3	**Rock**							
E4.3.1	Maximum depth: not exceeding 0.25m							
E4.3.1.05	as above; Maximum depth: 250mm	m^3	0.14	24.78	71.93	-	96.71	*43.41*
E4.3.2	Maximum depth: 0.25 - 0.5m							
E4.3.2.01	Rock; well broken (excavated by machine)	m^3	0.09	3.66	5.59	-	9.25	*3.11*
E4.3.2.02	Rock; hard (including drilling and blasting and ripping prior to excavation)	m^3	0.82	34.29	51.74	2.27	88.30	*29.79*
E4.3.2.03	For rail track; excavate ballast at formation level; Maximum depth: 300mm	m^3	0.07	24.53	21.48	-	46.01	*8.85*
E4.3.3	Maximum depth: 0.5 - 1m							
E4.3.3.01	Rock; well broken (excavated by machine)	m^3	0.09	3.66	5.59	-	9.25	*3.11*
E4.3.3.02	Rock; hard (including drilling and blasting and ripping prior to excavation)	m^3	0.84	35.19	53.10	2.27	90.56	*30.56*
E4.3.4	Maximum depth: 1 - 2m							
E4.3.4.01	Rock; well broken (excavated by machine)	m^3	0.09	3.96	6.05	-	10.01	*3.37*
E4.3.4.02	Rock; hard (including drilling and blasting and ripping prior to excavation)	m^3	0.87	36.10	54.46	2.27	92.83	*31.34*
E4.3.5	Maximum depth: 2 - 5m							
E4.3.5.01	Rock; well broken (excavated by machine)	m^3	0.11	4.65	7.10	-	11.75	*3.95*
E4.3.5.02	Rock; hard (including drilling and blasting and ripping prior to excavation)	m^3	0.89	37.00	55.82	2.27	95.09	*32.12*
E4.4	**Stated artificial hard material exposed at the Commencing Surface**							
E4.4.1	Maximum depth: not exceeding 0.25m							
E4.4.1.01	Plain concrete slab (using breaking gang)	m^3	0.30	12.92	10.19	-	23.11	*4.41*
E4.4.1.02	Tarmacadam pavement	m^3	0.15	6.46	5.10	-	11.56	*2.20*
E4.5	**Stated artificial hard material not exposed at the Commencing Surface**							
E4.5.1	Maximum depth: not exceeding 0.25m							
E4.5.1.01	Plain concrete (using breaking gang)	m^3	0.60	20.99	19.71	-	40.70	*10.98*
E4.5.1.02	Reinforced concrete	m^3	0.92	32.19	30.23	-	62.42	*16.84*
E4.5.2	Maximum depth: 0.25 - 0.5m							
E4.5.2.01	Plain concrete (using breaking gang)	m^3	0.60	20.99	19.71	-	40.70	*10.98*
E4.5.2.02	Reinforced concrete	m^3	0.92	32.19	30.23	-	62.42	*16.84*
E4.5.3	Maximum depth: 0.5 - 1m							
E4.5.3.01	Plain concrete (using breaking gang)	m^3	0.60	20.99	19.71	-	40.70	*10.98*
E4.5.3.02	Reinforced concrete	m^3	0.92	32.19	30.23	-	62.42	*16.84*

E4 General Excavation continued...

		Unit	Labour Hours	Labour Net £	Plant Net £	Materials Net £	Unit Net £	CO_2 Kg
E4.5	**Stated artificial hard material not exposed at the Commencing Surface**							
E4.5.4	Maximum depth: 1 - 2m							
E4.5.4.01	Plain concrete (using breaking gang)	m^3	0.78	27.29	25.63	-	52.92	*14.28*
E4.5.4.02	Reinforced concrete	m^3	1.02	35.69	33.51	-	69.20	*18.67*

E5 Excavation Ancillaries

		Unit	Labour Hours	Labour Net £	Plant Net £	Materials Net £	Unit Net £	CO_2 Kg
E5.1	**Trimming of excavated surfaces**							
E5.1.1	Topsoil							
E5.1.1.01	Horizontal	m^3	0.01	0.52	0.67	-	1.19	*0.51*
E5.1.1.02	Inclined at an angle of 10 - 45 degrees to the horizontal	m^3	0.01	0.52	0.67	-	1.19	*0.51*
E5.1.2	Material other than topsoil, rock or artificial hard material							
E5.1.2.01	Horizontal	m^3	0.01	0.52	0.67	-	1.19	*0.51*
E5.1.2.02	Inclined at an angle of 10 - 45 degrees to the horizontal	m^3	0.01	0.52	0.67	-	1.19	*0.51*
E5.1.2.03	Inclined at an angle of 45 - 90 degrees to the horizontal	m^3	0.02	0.65	0.84	-	1.49	*0.64*
E5.1.3	Rock							
E5.1.3.01	Horizontal	m^3	0.23	9.82	12.77	-	22.59	*9.77*
E5.1.3.02	Inclined at an angle of 10 - 45 degrees to the horizontal	m^3	0.23	9.82	12.77	-	22.59	*9.77*
E5.1.3.03	Inclined at an angle of 45 - 90 degrees to the horizontal	m^3	0.33	14.13	18.36	-	32.49	*14.06*
E5.1.3.04	Vertical	m^3	0.43	18.44	23.96	-	42.40	*18.35*
E5.2	**Preparation of excavated surfaces**							
E5.2.1	Topsoil							
E5.2.1.01	Horizontal	m^3	0.02	1.03	1.34	-	2.37	*1.03*
E5.2.1.02	Inclined at an angle of 10 - 45 degrees to the horizontal	m^3	0.02	1.03	1.34	-	2.37	*1.03*
E5.2.2	Material other than topsoil, rock or artificial hard material							
E5.2.2.01	Horizontal	m^3	0.02	1.03	1.34	-	2.37	*1.03*
E5.2.2.02	Inclined at an angle of 10 - 45 degrees to the horizontal	m^3	0.02	1.03	1.34	-	2.37	*1.03*
E5.2.2.03	Inclined at an angle of 45 - 90 degrees to the horizontal	m^3	0.03	1.21	1.57	-	2.78	*1.20*
E5.2.3	Rock							
E5.2.3.01	Horizontal	m^3	0.23	9.82	12.77	-	22.59	*9.77*
E5.2.3.02	Inclined at an angle of 10 - 45 degrees to the horizontal	m^3	0.23	9.82	12.77	-	22.59	*9.77*
E5.2.3.03	Inclined at an angle of 45 - 90 degrees to the horizontal	m^3	0.33	14.13	18.36	-	32.49	*14.06*
E5.2.3.04	Vertical	m^3	0.43	18.44	23.96	-	42.40	*18.35*
E5.3	**Disposal of excavated material**							
E5.3.1	Topsoil							
E5.3.1.01	Remove from site (transporting to tip distance 5km)	m^3	0.03	1.29	5.07	-	6.36	*3.40*
E5.3.1.02	Remove from site (transporting to tip distance 15km)	m^3	0.08	3.23	12.68	-	15.91	*8.50*

E5 Excavation Ancillaries continued...

		Unit	Labour Hours	Labour Net £	Plant Net £	Materials Net £	Unit Net £	CO_2 Kg
E5.3	**Disposal of excavated material**							
E5.3.1	Topsoil							
E5.3.1.03	Stored on site for re-use; stockpiled at sides of excavation	m^3	0.01	0.43	1.69	-	2.12	*1.13*
E5.3.1.04	Stored on site for re-use; stockpiled 100m from excavation	m^3	0.02	0.65	2.54	-	3.19	*1.70*
E5.3.2	Material other than topsoil, rock or artificial hard material							
E5.3.2.01	Remove from site (transporting to tip distance 5km)	m^3	0.03	1.29	5.07	-	6.36	*3.40*
E5.3.2.02	Remove from site (transporting to tip distance 15km)	m^3	0.08	3.23	12.68	-	15.91	*8.50*
E5.3.2.03	Stored on site for re-use; stockpiled at sides of excavation	m^3	0.01	0.43	1.69	-	2.12	*1.13*
E5.3.2.04	Stored on site for re-use; stockpiled 100m from excavation	m^3	0.02	0.65	2.54	-	3.19	*1.70*
E5.3.3	Rock							
E5.3.3.01	Remove from site (transporting to tip distance 5km)	m^3	0.04	1.51	5.92	-	7.43	*3.97*
E5.3.3.02	Remove from site (transporting to tip distance 15km)	m^3	0.08	3.45	13.52	-	16.97	*9.07*
E5.3.3.03	Stored on site for re-use; stockpiled at sides of excavation	m^3	0.02	0.65	2.54	-	3.19	*1.70*
E5.3.3.04	Stored on site for re-use; stockpiled 100m from excavation	m^3	0.02	0.86	3.38	-	4.24	*2.27*
E5.3.4	Stated artificial hard material							
E5.3.4.01	Remove from site (transporting to tip distance 5km)	m^3	0.04	1.51	5.92	-	7.43	*3.97*
E5.3.4.02	Remove from site (transporting to tip distance 15km)	m^3	0.08	3.45	13.52	-	16.97	*9.07*
E5.4	**Double handling of excavated material**							
E5.4.1	Topsoil							
E5.4.1.01	Removing from temporary stockpiles; distance to place of disposal (using general haulage gang) 30m	m^3	0.03	1.42	3.20	-	4.62	*1.98*
E5.4.1.02	as above; distance to place of disposal 100m	m^3	0.04	1.68	4.22	-	5.90	*2.66*
E5.4.1.03	as above; distance to place of disposal 500m	m^3	0.05	2.11	5.91	-	8.02	*3.79*
E5.4.1.04	as above; distance to place of disposal 500m	$1000m^3$	2.68	115.45	1,420.02	-	1,535.47	*1,184.16*
E5.4.1.05	as above; distance to place of disposal 750m	$1000m^3$	2.98	128.38	1,578.98	-	1,707.36	*1,316.72*
E5.4.1.06	as above; distance to place of disposal 1000m	$1000m^3$	3.38	145.61	1,790.93	-	1,936.54	*1,493.46*
E5.4.2	Material other than topsoil, rock or artificial hard material							
E5.4.2.01	Removing from temporary stockpiles; distance to place of disposal (using general haulage gang) 30m	m^3	0.03	1.42	3.20	-	4.62	*1.98*
E5.4.2.02	as above; distance to place of disposal 100m	m^3	0.04	1.68	4.22	-	5.90	*2.66*
E5.4.2.03	as above; distance to place of disposal 500m	m^3	0.05	2.11	5.91	-	8.02	*3.79*

E5 Excavation Ancillaries continued...

		Unit	Labour Hours	Labour Net £	Plant Net £	Materials Net £	Unit Net £	CO_2 *Kg*
E5.4	**Double handling of excavated material**							
E5.4.2	Material other than topsoil, rock or artificial hard material							
E5.4.2.04	as above; distance to place of disposal 500m	1000m^3	2.68	115.45	1,420.02	-	**1,535.47**	*1,184.16*
E5.4.2.05	as above; distance to place of disposal 750m	1000m^3	2.98	128.38	1,578.98	-	**1,707.36**	*1,316.72*
E5.4.2.06	as above; distance to place of disposal 1000m	1000m^3	3.38	145.61	1,790.93	-	**1,936.54**	*1,493.46*
E5.4.3	Rock							
E5.4.3.01	Removing from temporary stockpiles; distance to place of disposal (using general haulage gang) 30m	m^3	0.09	3.79	6.82	-	**10.61**	*3.99*
E5.4.3.02	as above; distance to place of disposal 100m	m^3	0.09	4.05	7.83	-	**11.88**	*4.67*
E5.4.3.03	as above; distance to place of disposal 500m	m^3	0.10	4.48	9.52	-	**14.00**	*5.80*
E5.4.3.04	as above; distance to place of disposal 500m	1000m^3	8.30	357.56	4,397.84	-	**4,755.40**	*3,667.36*
E5.4.3.05	as above; distance to place of disposal 750m	1000m^3	8.60	370.49	4,556.80	-	**4,927.29**	*3,799.92*
E5.4.3.06	as above; distance to place of disposal 1000m	1000m^3	9.60	413.57	5,086.66	-	**5,500.23**	*4,241.77*
E5.4.4	Stated artificial hard material							
E5.4.4.01	Removing from temporary stockpiles; distance to place of disposal (using general haulage gang) 30m	m^3	0.09	3.79	6.82	-	**10.61**	*3.99*
E5.4.4.02	as above; distance to place of disposal 100m	m^3	0.09	4.05	7.83	-	**11.88**	*4.67*
E5.4.4.03	as above; distance to place of disposal 500m	m^3	0.10	4.48	9.52	-	**14.00**	*5.80*
E5.4.4.04	as above; distance to place of disposal 500m	1000m^3	8.30	357.56	4,397.84	-	**4,755.40**	*3,667.36*
E5.4.4.05	as above; distance to place of disposal 750m	1000m^3	8.60	370.49	4,556.80	-	**4,927.29**	*3,799.92*
E5.4.4.06	as above; distance to place of disposal 1000m	1000m^3	9.60	413.57	5,086.66	-	**5,500.23**	*4,241.77*

E6 Filling

Note(s): Rates for filling include for spreading, levelling and compacting in layers where applicable (using spread and level and general haulage gangs)

		Unit	Labour Hours	Labour Net £	Plant Net £	Materials Net £	Unit Net £	CO_2 *Kg*
E6.1	**To structures**							
E6.1.1	Excavated topsoil							
E6.1.1.01	Generally	m^3	0.01	0.47	0.62	-	**1.09**	*0.47*
E6.1.1.02	Generally; taken from temporary stockpile distance 100m	m^3	0.01	0.47	3.20	-	**3.67**	*2.12*
E6.1.2	Imported topsoil							
E6.1.2.01	Generally	m^3	0.01	0.47	0.62	18.04	**19.13**	*34.05*
E6.1.3	Non-selected excavated material other than topsoil or rock							
E6.1.3.01	using spread, level, general haulage and compaction gangs	m^3	0.02	0.65	1.89	-	**2.54**	*1.00*

E6 Filling continued...

		Unit	Labour Hours	Labour Net £	Plant Net £	Materials Net £	Unit Net £	CO_2 Kg
E6.1	**To structures**							
E6.1.3	Non-selected excavated material other than topsoil or rock							
E6.1.3.02	including transporting directly from point of excavation distance 100m	m^3	0.03	1.42	3.92	-	**5.34**	*2.36*
E6.1.3.03	taken from temporary stockpile distance 100m	m^3	0.03	1.42	4.65	-	**6.07**	*2.76*
E6.1.4	Selected excavated material other than topsoil or rock							
E6.1.4.01	Generally	m^3	0.02	0.65	1.89	-	**2.54**	*1.00*
E6.1.4.02	including transporting directly from point of excavation distance 100m	m^3	0.03	1.42	3.92	-	**5.34**	*2.36*
E6.1.4.03	taken from temporary stockpile distance 100m	m^3	0.03	1.42	4.65	-	**6.07**	*2.76*
E6.1.5	Imported natural material other than topsoil or rock							
E6.1.5.01	Imported subsoil	m^3	0.01	0.47	1.89	23.09	**25.45**	*54.72*
E6.1.5.02	Imported granular material; DTp Spec. type 1	m^3	0.01	0.47	1.89	22.80	**25.16**	*9.00*
E6.1.5.03	Imported granular material; DTp Spec. type 2	m^3	0.01	0.47	1.89	24.40	**26.76**	*9.00*
E6.1.6	Excavated rock							
E6.1.6.01	Generally	m^3	0.02	0.95	1.23	-	**2.18**	*0.94*
E6.1.6.02	including transporting directly from point of excavation distance 100m	m^3	0.06	2.58	4.31	-	**6.89**	*2.66*
E6.1.6.03	taken from temporary stockpile distance 100m	m^3	0.06	2.58	8.26	-	**10.84**	*4.85*
E6.1.7	Imported rock							
E6.1.7.01	unscreened; maximum size 0.2m3	m^3	0.02	0.73	2.77	22.59	**26.09**	*8.96*
E6.1.8	Imported artificial material							
E6.1.8.01	Imported broken brick hardcore	m^3	0.01	0.47	1.89	18.68	**21.04**	*7.25*
E6.2	**Embankments**							
E6.2.1	Excavated topsoil							
E6.2.1.01	Generally	$1000m^3$	1.26	54.28	667.62	-	**721.90**	*556.73*
E6.2.1.02	taken from temporary stockpile distance 500m	$1000m^3$	2.21	95.21	1,191.78	-	**1,286.99**	*994.16*
E6.2.2	Imported topsoil							
E6.2.2.01	Generally	$1000m^3$	1.26	54.28	100.76	18,040.00	**18,195.04**	*33,665.64*
E6.2.3	Non-selected excavated material other than topsoil or rock							
E6.2.3.01	Generally	$1000m^3$	1.96	84.44	156.74	-	**241.18**	*133.21*
E6.2.3.02	including transporting directly from point of excavation distance 500m	$1000m^3$	1.96	84.44	1,195.27	-	**1,279.71**	*999.24*
E6.2.3.03	taken from temporary stockpile distance 500m	$1000m^3$	2.64	113.73	1,555.57	-	**1,669.30**	*1,299.70*
E6.2.4	Selected excavated material other than topsoil or rock							
E6.2.4.01	Generally	$1000m^3$	1.96	84.44	156.74	-	**241.18**	*133.21*

E6 Filling continued...

		Unit	Labour Hours	Labour Net £	Plant Net £	Materials Net £	Unit Net £	CO_2 Kg
E6.2	**Embankments**							
E6.2.4	Selected excavated material other than topsoil or rock							
E6.2.4.02	including transporting directly from point of excavation distance 500m	1000m^3	1.96	84.44	1,195.27	-	**1,279.71**	*999.24*
E6.2.4.03	taken from temporary stockpile distance 500m	1000m^3	2.64	113.73	1,555.57	-	**1,669.30**	*1,299.70*
E6.2.5	Imported natural material other than topsoil or rock							
E6.2.5.01	Imported subsoil	1000m^3	1.96	84.44	266.48	14,430.00	**14,780.92**	*33,797.22*
E6.2.5.02	Imported granular material; DTp Spec. type 1	1000m^3	1.96	84.44	266.48	22,800.00	**23,150.92**	*8,217.22*
E6.2.5.03	Imported granular material; DTp Spec. type 2	1000m^3	1.96	84.44	266.48	24,400.00	**24,750.92**	*8,217.22*
E6.2.6	Excavated rock							
E6.2.6.01	Generally	1000m^3	3.92	168.87	313.48	-	**482.35**	*266.42*
E6.2.6.02	including transporting directly from point of excavation distance 500m	1000m^3	1.96	84.44	2,390.53	-	**2,474.97**	*1,998.48*
E6.2.6.03	taken from temporary stockpile distance 500m	1000m^3	10.26	442.00	2,390.53	-	**2,832.53**	*1,998.48*
E6.2.7	Imported rock							
E6.2.7.01	unscreened; maximum size 0.2m3	1000m^3	2.94	126.66	399.72	22,590.00	**23,116.38**	*7,825.84*
E6.3	**General**							
E6.3.1	Excavated topsoil							
E6.3.1.01	Generally	m^3	0.01	0.47	0.62	-	**1.09**	*0.47*
E6.3.1.02	taken from temporary stockpile distance 100m (using spread and level gang and general haulage gang)	m^3	0.01	0.47	3.20	-	**3.67**	*2.12*
E6.3.2	Imported topsoil							
E6.3.2.01	Generally	m^3	0.01	0.47	0.62	28.86	**29.95**	*54.20*
E6.3.3	Non-selected excavated material other than topsoil or rock							
E6.3.3.01	Generally	m^3	0.03	1.42	1.67	-	**3.09**	*0.83*
E6.3.3.02	including transporting directly from point of excavation distance 100m	m^3	0.03	1.42	3.53	-	**4.95**	*2.07*
E6.3.3.03	taken from temporary stockpile distance 100m	m^3	0.03	1.42	4.25	-	**5.67**	*2.47*
E6.3.4	Selected excavated material other than topsoil or rock							
E6.3.4.01	Generally	m^3	0.03	1.42	1.67	-	**3.09**	*0.83*
E6.3.4.02	including transporting directly from point of excavation distance 100m	m^3	0.03	1.42	3.53	-	**4.95**	*2.07*
E6.3.4.03	taken from temporary stockpile distance 100m	m^3	0.03	1.42	4.25	-	**5.67**	*2.47*
E6.3.5	Imported natural material other than topsoil or rock							
E6.3.5.01	Imported subsoil	m^3	0.01	0.47	0.62	23.09	**24.18**	*54.20*

E6 Filling continued...

		Unit	Labour Hours	Labour Net £	Plant Net £	Materials Net £	Unit Net £	CO_2 Kg
E6.3	**General**							
E6.3.5	Imported natural material other than topsoil or rock							
E6.3.5.02	Imported granular material; DTp Spec. type 1 (using spread, level and general compaction gangs)	m^3	0.01	0.47	1.67	22.80	24.94	*8.83*
E6.3.5.03	Imported granular material; DTp Spec. type 2	m^3	0.01	0.47	1.67	24.40	26.54	*8.83*
E6.3.6	Excavated rock							
E6.3.6.01	Generally	m^3	0.03	1.42	2.96	-	4.38	*1.81*
E6.3.6.02	including transporting directly from point of excavation distance 100m	m^3	0.03	1.42	4.82	-	6.24	*3.06*
E6.3.6.03	taken from temporary stockpile distance 100m	m^3	0.03	1.46	7.05	-	8.51	*4.30*
E6.3.7	Imported rock							
E6.3.7.01	unscreened; maximum size 0.2m3	m^3	0.02	0.73	2.49	22.59	25.81	*8.74*
E6.4	**To stated depth or thickness**							
E6.4.1	Excavated topsoil							
E6.4.1.01	100mm depth; Generally	m^2	0.01	0.09	0.11	-	0.20	*0.09*
E6.4.1.02	100mm depth; taken from temporary stockpile distance 100m	m^2	0.01	0.09	0.52	-	0.61	*0.35*
E6.4.1.03	150mm depth; Generally	m^2	0.01	0.09	0.11	-	0.20	*0.09*
E6.4.1.04	150mm depth; taken from temporary stockpile distance 100m	m^2	0.01	0.09	0.58	-	0.67	*0.39*
E6.4.1.05	200mm depth; Generally	m^2	0.01	0.13	0.17	-	0.30	*0.13*
E6.4.1.06	200mm depth; taken from temporary stockpile distance 100m	m^2	0.01	0.13	0.87	-	1.00	*0.58*
E6.4.1.07	250mm depth; Generally	m^2	0.01	0.13	0.17	-	0.30	*0.13*
E6.4.1.08	250mm depth; taken from temporary stockpile distance 100m	m^2	0.01	0.13	0.87	-	1.00	*0.58*
E6.4.1.09	300mm depth; Generally	m^2	0.01	0.17	0.22	-	0.39	*0.17*
E6.4.1.10	300mm depth; taken from temporary stockpile distance 100m	m^2	0.01	0.17	1.16	-	1.33	*0.77*
E6.4.1.11	500mm depth; Generally	m^2	0.01	0.22	0.28	-	0.50	*0.21*
E6.4.1.12	500mm depth; taken from temporary stockpile distance 100m	m^2	0.01	0.22	1.45	-	1.67	*0.96*
E6.4.2	Imported topsoil							
E6.4.2.01	100mm depth; Imported topsoil	m^2	0.01	0.09	0.11	5.77	5.97	*10.83*
E6.4.2.02	150mm depth; Imported topsoil	m^2	0.01	0.09	0.11	5.77	5.97	*10.83*
E6.4.2.03	200mm depth; Imported topsoil	m^2	0.01	0.13	0.17	7.22	7.52	*13.56*
E6.4.2.04	250mm depth; Imported topsoil	m^2	0.01	0.13	0.17	8.08	8.38	*15.17*
E6.4.2.05	300mm depth; Imported topsoil	m^2	0.01	0.17	0.22	9.74	10.13	*18.30*
E6.4.2.06	500mm depth; Imported topsoil	m^2	0.01	0.22	0.28	14.43	14.93	*27.08*
E6.4.3	Non-selected excavated material other than topsoil or rock							
E6.4.3.01	100mm depth; Non-selected excavated material other than topsoil or rock	m^2	0.01	0.26	0.30	-	0.56	*0.15*

E6 Filling continued...

		Unit	Labour Hours	Labour Net £	Plant Net £	Materials Net £	Unit Net £	CO_2 Kg
E6.4	**To stated depth or thickness**							
E6.4.3	Non-selected excavated material other than topsoil or rock							
E6.4.3.02	100mm depth; Non-selected excavated material other than topsoil or rock; including transporting directly from point of excavation distance 100m	m^2	0.01	0.26	0.64	-	0.90	*0.38*
E6.4.3.03	100mm depth; Non-selected excavated material other than topsoil or rock; taken from temporary stockpile distance 100m	m^2	0.01	0.26	0.77	-	1.03	*0.45*
E6.4.3.04	150mm depth; Non-selected excavated material other than topsoil or rock	m^2	0.01	0.30	0.34	-	0.64	*0.16*
E6.4.3.05	150mm depth; Non-selected excavated material other than topsoil or rock; including transporting directly from point of excavation distance 100m	m^2	0.01	0.30	0.67	-	0.97	*0.39*
E6.4.3.06	150mm depth; Non-selected excavated material other than topsoil or rock; taken from temporary stockpile distance 100m	m^2	0.01	0.30	0.81	-	1.11	*0.46*
E6.4.3.07	200mm depth; Non-selected excavated material other than topsoil or rock	m^2	0.01	0.34	0.42	-	0.76	*0.21*
E6.4.3.08	200mm depth; Non-selected excavated material other than topsoil or rock; including transporting directly from point of excavation distance 100m	m^2	0.01	0.34	0.93	-	1.27	*0.55*
E6.4.3.09	200mm depth; Non-selected excavated material other than topsoil or rock; taken from temporary stockpile distance 100m	m^2	0.01	0.34	1.13	-	1.47	*0.66*
E6.4.3.10	250mm depth; Non-selected excavated material other than topsoil or rock	m^2	0.01	0.39	0.46	-	0.85	*0.23*
E6.4.3.11	250mm depth; Non-selected excavated material other than topsoil or rock; including transporting directly from point of excavation distance 100m	m^2	0.01	0.39	0.68	-	1.07	*0.47*
E6.4.3.12	250mm depth; Non-selected excavated material other than topsoil or rock; taken from temporary stockpile distance 100m	m^2	0.01	0.39	1.16	-	1.55	*0.67*
E6.4.3.13	300mm depth; Non-selected excavated material other than topsoil or rock	m^2	0.01	0.47	0.58	-	1.05	*0.29*
E6.4.3.14	300mm depth; Non-selected excavated material other than topsoil or rock; including transporting directly from point of excavation distance 100m	m^2	0.01	0.47	1.25	-	1.72	*0.74*

E6 Filling continued...

		Unit	Labour Hours	Labour Net £	Plant Net £	Materials Net £	Unit Net £	CO_2 Kg
E6.4	**To stated depth or thickness**							
E6.4.3	Non-selected excavated material other than topsoil or rock							
E6.4.3.15	300mm depth; Non-selected excavated material other than topsoil or rock; taken from temporary stockpile distance 100m	m^2	0.01	0.47	1.51	-	**1.98**	*0.89*
E6.4.3.16	500mm depth; Non-selected excavated material other than topsoil or rock	m^2	0.02	0.69	0.79	-	**1.48**	*0.39*
E6.4.3.17	500mm depth; Non-selected excavated material other than topsoil or rock; including transporting directly from point of excavation distance 100m	m^2	0.02	0.69	1.64	-	**2.33**	*0.95*
E6.4.3.18	500mm depth; Non-selected excavated material other than topsoil or rock; taken from temporary stockpile distance 100m	m^2	0.02	0.69	1.96	-	**2.65**	*1.14*
E6.4.4	Selected excavated material other than topsoil or rock							
E6.4.4.01	100mm depth; Selected excavated material other than topsoil or rock	m^2	0.01	0.26	0.30	-	**0.56**	*0.15*
E6.4.4.02	100mm depth; Selected excavated material other than topsoil or rock; including transporting directly from point of excavation distance 100m	m^2	0.01	0.26	0.64	-	**0.90**	*0.38*
E6.4.4.03	100mm depth; Selected excavated material other than topsoil or rock; taken from temporary stockpile distance 100m	m^2	0.01	0.26	0.77	-	**1.03**	*0.45*
E6.4.4.04	150mm depth; Selected excavated material other than topsoil or rock	m^2	0.01	0.30	0.34	-	**0.64**	*0.16*
E6.4.4.05	150mm depth; Selected excavated material other than topsoil or rock; including transporting directly from point of excavation distance 100m	m^2	0.01	0.30	0.67	-	**0.97**	*0.39*
E6.4.4.06	150mm depth; Selected excavated material other than topsoil or rock; taken from temporary stockpile distance 100m	m^2	0.01	0.30	0.81	-	**1.11**	*0.46*
E6.4.4.07	200mm depth; Selected excavated material other than topsoil or rock	m^2	0.01	0.34	0.42	-	**0.76**	*0.21*
E6.4.4.08	200mm depth; Selected excavated material other than topsoil or rock; including transporting directly from point of excavation distance 100m	m^2	0.01	0.34	0.93	-	**1.27**	*0.55*
E6.4.4.09	200mm depth; Selected excavated material other than topsoil or rock; taken from temporary stockpile distance 100m	m^2	0.01	0.34	1.13	-	**1.47**	*0.66*

E6 Filling continued...

		Unit	Labour Hours	Labour Net £	Plant Net £	Materials Net £	Unit Net £	CO_2 Kg
E6.4	**To stated depth or thickness**							
E6.4.4	Selected excavated material other than topsoil or rock							
E6.4.4.10	250mm depth; Selected excavated material other than topsoil or rock	m^2	0.01	0.39	0.46	-	**0.85**	*0.23*
E6.4.4.11	250mm depth; Selected excavated material other than topsoil or rock; including transporting directly from point of excavation distance 100m	m^2	0.01	0.39	0.96	-	**1.35**	*0.57*
E6.4.4.12	250mm depth; Selected excavated material other than topsoil or rock; taken from temporary stockpile distance 100m	m^2	0.01	0.39	1.16	-	**1.55**	*0.67*
E6.4.4.13	300mm depth; Selected excavated material other than topsoil or rock	m^2	0.01	0.47	0.58	-	**1.05**	*0.29*
E6.4.4.14	300mm depth; Selected excavated material other than topsoil or rock; including transporting directly from point of excavation distance 100m	m^2	0.01	0.47	1.25	-	**1.72**	*0.74*
E6.4.4.15	300mm depth; Selected excavated material other than topsoil or rock; taken from temporary stockpile distance 100m	m^2	0.01	0.47	1.51	-	**1.98**	*0.89*
E6.4.4.16	500mm depth; Selected excavated material other than topsoil or rock	m^2	0.02	0.69	0.79	-	**1.48**	*0.39*
E6.4.4.17	500mm depth; Selected excavated material other than topsoil or rock; including transporting directly from point of excavation distance 100m	m^2	0.02	0.69	1.64	-	**2.33**	*0.95*
E6.4.4.18	500mm depth; Selected excavated material other than topsoil or rock; taken from temporary stockpile distance 100m	m^2	0.02	0.69	1.96	-	**2.65**	*1.14*
E6.4.5	Imported natural material other than topsoil or rock							
E6.4.5.01	100mm depth; Imported subsoil	m^2	0.01	0.09	0.30	4.62	**5.01**	*10.90*
E6.4.5.02	100mm depth; Imported granular material; DTp Spec. type 1	m^2	0.01	0.09	0.30	4.56	**4.95**	*1.75*
E6.4.5.03	100mm depth; Imported granular material; DTp Spec. type 2	m^2	0.01	0.09	0.30	4.88	**5.27**	*1.75*
E6.4.5.04	150mm depth; Imported subsoil	m^2	0.01	0.09	0.34	4.62	**5.05**	*10.91*
E6.4.5.05	150mm depth; Imported granular material; DTp Spec. type 1	m^2	0.01	0.09	0.34	4.56	**4.99**	*1.76*
E6.4.5.06	150mm depth; Imported granular material; DTp Spec. type 2	m^2	0.01	0.09	0.34	4.88	**5.31**	*1.76*
E6.4.5.07	200mm depth; Imported subsoil	m^2	0.01	0.13	0.17	5.77	**6.07**	*13.56*
E6.4.5.08	200mm depth; Imported granular material; DTp Spec. type 1	m^2	0.01	0.13	0.42	5.70	**6.25**	*2.21*
E6.4.5.09	200mm depth; Imported granular material; DTp Spec. type 2	m^2	0.01	0.13	0.17	4.88	**5.28**	*1.76*
E6.4.5.10	250mm depth; Imported subsoil	m^2	0.01	0.13	0.46	6.49	**7.08**	*15.34*
E6.4.5.11	250mm depth; Imported granular material; DTp Spec. type 1	m^2	0.01	0.13	0.46	6.41	**7.00**	*2.48*

E6 Filling continued...

		Unit	Labour Hours	Labour Net £	Plant Net £	Materials Net £	Unit Net £	CO_2 Kg
E6.4	**To stated depth or thickness**							
E6.4.5	Imported natural material other than topsoil or rock							
E6.4.5.12	250mm depth; Imported granular material; DTp Spec. type 2	m^2	0.01	0.13	0.46	6.86	7.45	*2.48*
E6.4.5.13	300mm depth; Imported subsoil	m^2	0.01	0.17	0.58	7.79	8.54	*18.42*
E6.4.5.14	300mm depth; Imported granular material; DTp Spec. type 1	m^2	0.01	0.17	0.58	7.70	8.45	*2.99*
E6.4.5.15	300mm depth; Imported granular material; DTp Spec. type 2	m^2	0.01	0.17	0.58	8.24	8.99	*2.99*
E6.4.5.16	500mm depth; Imported subsoil	m^2	0.02	0.69	0.79	11.54	13.02	*27.25*
E6.4.5.17	500mm depth; Imported granular material; DTp Spec. type 1	m^2	0.02	0.69	0.79	11.40	12.88	*4.39*
E6.4.5.18	500mm depth; Imported granular material; DTp Spec. type 2	m^2	0.02	0.69	0.79	12.20	13.68	*4.39*
E6.4.6	Excavated rock							
E6.4.6.01	100mm depth; Excavated rock	m^2	0.01	0.13	0.53	-	0.66	*0.32*
E6.4.6.02	100mm depth; Excavated rock; including transporting directly from point of excavation distance 100m	m^2	0.01	0.26	0.87	-	1.13	*0.55*
E6.4.6.03	100mm depth; Excavated rock; taken from temporary stockpile distance 100m	m^2	0.01	0.26	1.26	-	1.52	*0.77*
E6.4.6.04	150mm depth; Excavated rock	m^2	0.01	0.30	0.62	-	0.92	*0.38*
E6.4.6.05	150mm depth; Excavated rock; including transporting directly from point of excavation distance 100m	m^2	0.01	0.30	0.95	-	1.25	*0.60*
E6.4.6.06	150mm depth; Excavated rock; taken from temporary stockpile distance 100m	m^2	0.01	0.30	1.41	-	1.71	*0.86*
E6.4.6.07	200mm depth; Excavated rock	m^2	0.01	0.34	0.76	-	1.10	*0.47*
E6.4.6.08	200mm depth; Excavated rock; including transporting directly from point of excavation distance 100m	m^2	0.01	0.34	1.27	-	1.61	*0.81*
E6.4.6.09	200mm depth; Excavated rock; taken from temporary stockpile distance 100m	m^2	0.01	0.34	1.86	-	2.20	*1.14*
E6.4.6.10	250mm depth; Excavated rock	m^2	0.01	0.39	0.56	-	0.95	*0.43*
E6.4.6.11	250mm depth; Excavated rock; including transporting directly from point of excavation distance 100m	m^2	0.01	0.39	1.35	-	1.74	*0.87*
E6.4.6.12	250mm depth; Excavated rock; taken from temporary stockpile distance 100m	m^2	0.01	0.39	2.01	-	2.40	*1.23*
E6.4.6.13	300mm depth; Excavated rock	m^2	0.01	0.47	0.97	-	1.44	*0.59*
E6.4.6.14	300mm depth; Excavated rock; including transporting directly from point of excavation distance 100m	m^2	0.01	0.47	0.68	-	1.15	*0.45*
E6.4.6.15	300mm depth; Excavated rock; taken from temporary stockpile distance 100m	m^2	0.01	0.47	2.37	-	2.84	*1.45*
E6.4.6.16	500mm depth; Excavated rock	m^2	0.02	0.69	1.46	-	2.15	*0.90*
E6.4.6.17	500mm depth; Excavated rock; including transporting directly from point of excavation distance 100m	m^2	0.02	0.69	2.48	-	4.33	*2.20*

E6 Filling continued...

Code	Description	Unit	Labour Hours	Labour Net £	Plant Net £	Materials Net £	Unit Net £	CO_2 Kg
E6.4	**To stated depth or thickness**							
E6.4.6	Excavated rock							
E6.4.6.18	500mm depth; Excavated rock; taken from temporary stockpile distance 100m	m²	0.02	0.73	3.59	-	4.32	*2.20*

E7 Filling Ancillaries

Code	Description	Unit	Labour Hours	Labour Net £	Plant Net £	Materials Net £	Unit Net £	CO_2 Kg
E7.1	**Trimming of filled surfaces**							
E7.1.1	Topsoil							
E7.1.1.01	Horizontal	m²	0.01	0.56	0.73	-	1.29	*0.56*
E7.1.1.02	Inclined at an angle of 10-45 degrees to the horizontal	m²	0.01	0.60	0.78	-	1.38	*0.60*
E7.1.1.03	Inclined at an angle of 45-90 degrees to the horizontal	m²	0.02	0.82	1.06	-	1.88	*0.81*
E7.1.2	Material other than topsoil, rock or artificial hard material							
E7.1.2.01	Horizontal	m²	0.01	0.56	0.73	-	1.29	*0.56*
E7.1.2.02	Inclined at an angle of 10-45 degrees to the horizontal	m²	0.01	0.60	0.78	-	1.38	*0.60*
E7.1.2.03	Inclined at an angle of 45-90 degrees to the horizontal	m²	0.02	0.82	1.06	-	1.88	*0.81*
E7.1.3	Rock							
E7.1.3.01	Horizontal	m²	0.23	9.91	12.88	-	22.79	*9.86*
E7.1.3.02	Inclined at an angle of 10-45 degrees to the horizontal	m²	0.25	10.90	14.17	-	25.07	*10.84*
E7.1.3.03	Inclined at an angle of 45-90 degrees to the horizontal	m²	0.37	16.07	20.88	-	36.95	*15.99*
E7.1.4	Stated artificial hard material							
E7.1.4.01	Plain concrete; Horizontal	m²	0.23	9.91	12.88	-	22.79	*9.86*
E7.1.4.02	Plain concrete; Inclined at an angle of 10-45 degrees to the horizontal	m²	0.25	10.90	14.17	-	25.07	*10.84*
E7.1.4.03	Plain concrete; Inclined at an angle of 45-90 degrees to the horizontal	m²	0.37	16.07	20.88	-	36.95	*15.99*
E7.2	**Preparation of filled surfaces**							
E7.2.1	Topsoil							
E7.2.1.01	Horizontal	m²	0.02	0.99	1.29	-	2.28	*0.99*
E7.2.1.02	Inclined at an angle of 10-45 degrees to the horizontal	m²	0.03	1.08	1.40	-	2.48	*1.07*
E7.2.1.03	Inclined at an angle of 45-90 degrees to the horizontal	m²	0.03	1.25	1.62	-	2.87	*1.24*
E7.2.2	Material other than topsoil, rock or artificial hard material							
E7.2.2.01	Horizontal	m²	0.02	0.99	1.29	-	2.28	*0.99*
E7.2.2.02	Inclined at an angle of 10-45 degrees to the horizontal	m²	0.03	1.08	1.40	-	2.48	*1.07*
E7.2.2.03	Inclined at an angle of 45-90 degrees to the horizontal	m²	0.03	1.25	1.62	-	2.87	*1.24*
E7.2.3	Rock							
E7.2.3.01	Horizontal	m²	0.14	6.03	7.84	-	13.87	*6.00*
E7.2.3.02	Inclined at an angle of 10-45 degrees to the horizontal	m²	0.15	6.55	8.51	-	15.06	*6.52*

E7 Filling continued...

		Unit	Labour Hours	Labour Net £	Plant Net £	Materials Net £	Unit Net £	CO_2 Kg
E7.2	**Preparation of filled surfaces**							
E7.2.3	Rock							
E7.2.3.03	Inclined at an angle of 45-90 degrees to the horizontal	m²	0.20	8.57	11.14	-	**19.71**	*8.53*
E7.2.4	Stated artificial hard material							
E7.2.4.01	Plain concrete; Horizontal	m²	0.14	6.03	7.84	-	**13.87**	*6.00*
E7.2.4.02	Plain concrete; Inclined at an angle of 10-45 degrees to the horizontal	m²	0.15	6.46	8.40	-	**14.86**	*6.43*
E7.2.4.03	Plain concrete; Inclined at an angle of 45-90 degrees to the horizontal	m²	0.20	8.62	11.20	-	**19.82**	*8.57*
E7.3	**Geotextiles**							
E7.3.1	Typar 136 ground stabilising matting; 150mm laps							
E7.3.1.01	Laid upon a surface inclined at an angle to the horizontal; not exceeding 10 degrees	m²	0.01	0.38	-	2.19	**2.57**	*1.10*
E7.3.1.02	as above; 10 - 45 degrees	m²	0.01	0.60	-	2.19	**2.79**	*1.10*
E7.3.1.03	as above; 45 - 90 degrees	m²	0.02	0.82	-	2.19	**3.01**	*1.10*
E7.3.1.04	Vertical	m²	0.02	1.04	-	2.19	**3.23**	*1.10*

E8 Landscaping

Note(s): Items for landscaping include fertilising, trimming and preparation of surfaces.

		Unit	Labour Hours	Labour Net £	Plant Net £	Materials Net £	Unit Net £	CO_2 Kg
E8.1	**Turfing**							
E8.1.1	Turfing with turf PC £2.50 per m²; laid with broken joints; rolling, watering, weeding, cutting, returfing until established							
E8.1.1.01	Laid upon a surface inclined at an angle to the horizontal; not exceeding 10 degrees	m²	0.12	3.34	-	2.50	**5.84**	-
E8.1.1.02	as above; 10 - 45 degrees	m²	0.14	3.66	-	2.50	**6.16**	-
E8.1.1.03	as above; 45 - 90 degrees	m²	0.24	6.35	-	2.50	**8.85**	-
E8.3	**Other grass seeding**							
E8.3.1	Seeding with grass seed PC £125 per 25 kg; sowing by hand at the rate of 0.05kg per m²; watering, weeding, raking, rolling, cutting, re-seeding until established							
E8.3.1.01	Laid upon a surface inclined at an angle to the horizontal; not exceeding 10 degrees	m²	0.01	0.11	-	2.50	**2.61**	-
E8.3.1.02	as above; 10 - 45 degrees	m²	0.01	0.11	-	2.50	**2.61**	-
E8.3.1.03	as above; 45 - 90 degrees	m²	0.01	0.13	-	2.50	**2.63**	-
E8.5	**Shrubs, stated species and size**							
E8.5.1	Providing and planting including excavating holes, backfilling etc							
E8.5.1.01	PC £2.90 Per Nr	Nr	0.13	3.50	-	2.90	**6.40**	-
E8.6	**Trees, stated species and size**							
E8.6.1	Trees including 50 x 50mm treated wrought softwood stakes and PVC ties							
E8.6.1.01	Medium; PC £25 Per Nr	Nr	0.18	4.84	-	25.00	**29.84**	-
E8.6.1.02	Large; PC £50 Per Nr	Nr	0.24	6.46	-	50.00	**56.46**	-

E8 Landscaping continued...

		Unit	Labour Hours	Labour Net £	Plant Net £	Materials Net £	Unit Net £	CO_2 Kg
E8.6	**Trees, stated species and size**							
E8.6.1	Trees including 50 x 50mm treated wrought softwood stakes and PVC ties							
E8.6.1.03	Mature trees 10m high; PC £170 Per Nr; 3 Nr 100mm diameter treated hardwood stakes; galvanised twisted wire ties and PVC collars	Nr	1.54	41.43	-	170.00	211.43	-
E8.7	**Hedges, stated species, size and spacing**							
E8.7.1	Single row							
E8.7.1.01	Hedges, privet; PC £0.85 Per Nr; 300mm centres	m	0.07	1.88	-	2.55	4.43	-
E8.7.1.02	as above; 450mm centres	m	0.05	1.35	-	1.91	3.26	-
E8.7.1.03	as above; 600mm centres	m	0.04	1.08	-	1.27	2.35	-
E8.7.2	Double row							
E8.7.2.01	Hedges, beech; staggered PC £0.85 Per Nr; 300mm centres	m	0.14	3.77	-	4.74	8.51	-
E8.7.2.02	as above; 450mm centres	m	0.09	2.42	-	3.56	5.98	-
E8.7.2.03	as above; 600mm centres	m	0.07	1.88	-	1.19	3.07	-

CLASS F:

IN SITU CONCRETE

Calculations used throughout Class F - In Situ Concrete

Labour

		Qty		Rate		Total
L A0150ICE	**Provision of concrete Labour Gang**					
	Labourer (Skill Rate 3)	1	x	14.34	=	£14.34
	Labourer (General Operative)	1	x	12.56	=	£12.56
	Banksman	0.5	x	13.53	=	£6.77
	Total hourly cost of gang				**=**	**£33.67**
L A0155ICE	**Placing of concrete Labour Gang**					
	Labourer (Skill Rate 3)	1	x	14.34	=	£14.34
	Labourer (General Operative)	4	x	12.56	=	£50.24
	Banksman	0.25	x	13.53	=	£3.38
	Ganger	1	x	16.99	=	£16.99
	Craftsman WRA	0.5	x	16.68	=	£8.34
	Total hourly cost of gang				=	**£93.29**

Plant

		Qty		Rate		Total
P A1150ICE	**Provision of concrete Plant Gang**					
	Concrete Mixer - Liner Rolpanit	1	x	37.36	=	£37.36
	Cement Silo 50t	1	x	2.47	=	£2.47
	Concrete Mixer - Schwing BP1000R					
	Concrete Pumps	1	x	43.29	=	£43.29
	Crawler Tractor / Dozer - Dresser 1004 48kW	1	x	28.68	=	£28.68
	Compressor - 250 cfm	1	x	10.81	=	£10.81
	Air Hose - 1 inch - 15m length	1	x	0.35	=	£0.35
	Total hourly cost of gang				**=**	**£122.96**
P A1155ICE	**Placing of concrete Plant Gang**					
	Air Vibrating Poker up to 75mm	3	x	1.25	=	£3.74
	Concrete Skip	2	x	0.71	=	£1.41
	Scabbler - Floor - 3 Headed	1	x	2.47	=	£2.47
	Scabbler - Floor - 5 Headed	1	x	3.52	=	£3.52
	Excavators Cable - NCK 305A 0.67m3	0.25	x	41.78	=	£10.45
	Compressor - 375 cfm	1	x	14.95	=	£14.95
	Total hourly cost of gang				**=**	**£36.54**

Class F - In Situ Concrete

Note(s): Provision of Concrete

1) The prices are based on site mixed concrete pumped from the batching plant to the point of placing.

2) The alternative means of transporting the concrete from the batching plant by dumpers or agitator trucks would be covered by the prices shown given similar conditions.

3) The rates quoted are for medium workability. If high workability is necessary becuase of high reinforcing stell and / or duct content than an addition of 5.5% to the rates will be an adequate indication of the cost.

4) Ground granulated blast furnance slag delivered to the site in bulk = £17.46 tonne.

5) It is usual practice to mix the blast furnance slag with OPC in the following proportions:

30% blast furnance 70% OPC
40% blast furnnace 60% OPC

F1 Provision of Concrete: Standard mix

		Unit	Labour Hours	Labour Net £	Plant Net £	Materials Net £	Unit Net £	CO_2 Kg
F1.1	**ST1**							
F1.1.3	Cement to BS EN 197; 20mm aggregate							
F1.1.3.01	Generally	m^3	0.20	6.73	24.59	59.35	90.67	*216.00*
F1.1.3.02	Rapid hardening cement	m^3	0.20	6.73	24.59	64.41	95.73	*241.55*
F1.1.4	Cement to BS EN 197; 40mm aggregate							
F1.1.4.01	Generally	m^3	0.20	6.73	24.59	61.02	92.34	*216.17*
F1.1.4.02	Rapid hardening cement	m^3	0.20	6.73	24.59	62.19	93.51	*216.00*
F1.2	**ST2**							
F1.2.3	Cement to BS EN 197; 20mm aggregate							
F1.2.3.01	Generally	m^3	0.20	6.73	24.59	65.72	97.04	*267.12*
F1.2.3.02	Rapid hardening cement	m^3	0.20	6.73	24.59	67.84	99.16	*267.12*
F1.2.4	Cement to BS EN 197; 40mm aggregate							
F1.2.4.01	Generally	m^3	0.20	6.73	24.59	63.70	95.02	*239.19*
F1.2.4.02	Rapid hardening cement	m^3	0.20	6.73	24.59	65.58	96.90	*239.19*
F1.3	**ST3**							
F1.3.3	Cement to BS EN 197; 20mm aggregate							
F1.3.3.01	Generally	m^3	0.20	6.73	24.59	68.98	100.30	*295.17*
F1.3.3.02	Rapid hardening cement	m^3	0.20	6.73	24.59	71.34	102.66	*295.17*
F1.3.4	Cement to BS EN 197; 40mm aggregate							
F1.3.4.01	Generally	m^3	0.20	6.73	24.59	67.53	98.85	*273.73*
F1.3.4.02	Rapid hardening cement	m^3	0.20	6.73	24.59	69.71	101.03	*273.73*
F1.4	**ST4**							
F1.4.1	Cement to BS EN 197; 10mm aggregate							
F1.4.1.01	Generally	m^3	0.20	6.73	24.59	79.97	111.29	*371.07*
F1.4.1.02	Rapid hardening cement	m^3	0.20	6.73	24.59	82.97	114.29	*371.07*
F1.4.2	Cement to BS EN 197; 14mm aggregate							
F1.4.2.01	Generally	m^3	0.20	6.73	24.59	76.35	107.67	*347.15*
F1.4.2.02	Rapid hardening cement	m^3	0.20	6.73	24.59	79.16	110.48	*347.15*

F1 Provision of Concrete: Standard mix continued...

		Unit	Labour Hours	Labour Net £	Plant Net £	Materials Net £	Unit Net £	CO_2 Kg
F1.4	**ST4**							
F1.4.3	Cement to BS EN 197; 20mm aggregate							
F1.4.3.01	Generally	m^3	0.20	6.73	24.59	74.20	105.52	*336.42*
F1.4.3.02	Rapid hardening cement	m^3	0.20	6.73	24.59	76.91	108.23	*336.42*
F1.4.4	Cement to BS EN 197; 40mm aggregate							
F1.4.4.01	Generally	m^3	0.20	6.73	24.59	72.40	103.72	*312.50*
F1.4.4.02	Rapid hardening cement	m^3	0.20	6.73	24.59	74.90	106.22	*312.50*
F1.4.7	Other stated cement; 20mm aggregate							
F1.4.7.01	Sulphate resisting cement to, BS 4027	m^3	0.20	6.73	24.59	74.44	105.76	*336.42*
F1.4.8	Other stated cement; 40mm aggregate							
F1.4.8.01	Sulphate resisting cement to, BS 4027	m^3	0.20	6.73	24.59	72.61	103.93	*312.50*
F1.5	**ST5**							
F1.5.1	Cement to BS EN 197; 10mm aggregate							
F1.5.1.01	Generally	m^3	0.20	6.73	24.59	86.70	118.02	*423.06*
F1.5.1.02	Rapid hardening cement	m^3	0.20	6.73	24.59	90.14	121.46	*423.06*
F1.5.2	Cement to BS EN 197; 14mm aggregate							
F1.5.2.01	Generally	m^3	0.20	6.73	24.59	83.68	115.00	*406.55*
F1.5.2.02	Rapid hardening cement	m^3	0.20	6.73	24.59	85.10	116.42	*394.10*
F1.5.3	Cement to BS EN 197; 20mm aggregate							
F1.5.3.01	Generally	m^3	0.20	6.73	24.59	77.86	109.18	*365.30*
F1.5.3.02	Rapid hardening cement	m^3	0.20	6.73	24.59	80.81	112.13	*365.30*
F1.5.4	Cement to BS EN 197; 40mm aggregate							
F1.5.4.01	Generally	m^3	0.20	6.73	24.59	74.80	106.12	*331.47*
F1.5.4.02	Rapid hardening cement	m^3	0.20	6.73	24.59	77.47	108.79	*331.47*
F1.5.7	Other stated cement; 20mm aggregate							
F1.5.7.01	Sulphate resisting cement to, BS 4027	m^3	0.20	6.73	24.59	78.11	109.43	*365.30*
F1.5.8	Other stated cement; 40mm aggregate							
F1.5.8.01	Sulphate resisting cement to, BS 4027	m^3	0.20	6.73	24.59	75.03	106.35	*331.47*

F2 Provision of Concrete: Designed mix

		Unit	Labour Hours	Labour Net £	Plant Net £	Materials Net £	Unit Net £	CO_2 Kg
F2.4	**Grade: C20**							
F2.4.1	Cement to BS EN 197; 10mm aggregate							
F2.4.1.01	Generally	m^3	0.20	6.73	24.59	91.25	122.57	*459.34*
F2.4.2	Cement to BS EN 197; 14mm aggregate							
F2.4.2.01	Generally	m^3	0.20	6.73	24.59	85.78	117.10	*422.22*
F2.4.3	Cement to BS EN 197; 20mm aggregate							
F2.4.3.01	Generally	m^3	0.20	6.73	24.59	80.33	111.65	*384.27*
F2.4.4	Cement to BS EN 197; 40mm aggregate							
F2.4.4.01	Generally	m^3	0.20	6.73	24.59	76.79	108.11	*347.14*

F2 Provision of Concrete: Designed mix continued...

		Unit	Labour Hours	Labour Net £	Plant Net £	Materials Net £	Unit Net £	CO_2 Kg
F2.4	**Grade: C20**							
F2.4.5	Other stated cement; 10mm aggregate							
F2.4.5.01	Sulphate resisting cement to, BS 4027	m^3	0.20	6.73	24.59	89.17	120.49	*442.84*
F2.4.6	Other stated cement; 14mm aggregate							
F2.4.6.01	Sulphate resisting cement to, BS 4027	m^3	0.20	6.73	24.59	86.21	117.53	*425.52*
F2.4.7	Other stated cement; 20mm aggregate							
F2.4.7.01	Sulphate resisting cement to, BS 4027	m^3	0.20	6.73	24.59	80.28	111.60	*382.62*
F2.4.8	Other stated cement; 40mm aggregate							
F2.4.8.01	Sulphate resisting cement to, BS 4027	m^3	0.20	6.73	24.59	77.10	108.42	*347.14*
F2.5	**Grade: C25**							
F2.5.1	Cement to BS EN 197; 10mm aggregate							
F2.5.1.01	Generally	m^3	0.20	6.73	24.59	101.47	132.79	*541.07*
F2.5.2	Cement to BS EN 197; 14mm aggregate							
F2.5.2.01	Generally	m^3	0.20	6.73	24.59	94.46	125.78	*491.51*
F2.5.3	Cement to BS EN 197; 20mm aggregate							
F2.5.3.01	Generally	m^3	0.20	6.73	24.59	85.34	116.66	*422.22*
F2.5.4	Cement to BS EN 197; 40mm aggregate							
F2.5.4.01	Generally	m^3	0.20	6.73	24.59	81.58	112.90	*384.27*
F2.6	**Grade: C30**							
F2.6.1	Cement to BS EN 197; 10mm aggregate							
F2.6.1.01	Generally	m^3	0.20	6.73	24.59	94.23	125.55	*485.74*
F2.6.2	Cement to BS EN 197; 14mm aggregate							
F2.6.2.01	Generally	m^3	0.20	6.73	24.59	91.11	122.43	*466.77*
F2.6.3	Cement to BS EN 197; 20mm aggregate							
F2.6.3.01	Generally	m^3	0.20	6.73	24.59	86.99	118.31	*437.89*
F2.6.4	Cement to BS EN 197; 40mm aggregate							
F2.6.4.01	Generally	m^3	0.20	6.73	24.59	80.89	112.21	*379.32*

F4 Provision of Concrete: Prescribed mix

		Unit	Labour Hours	Labour Net £	Plant Net £	Materials Net £	Unit Net £	CO_2 Kg
F4.1	**Provision of Concrete: Prescribed mix**							
F4.1.1	Cement to BS EN 197; 10mm aggregate							
F4.1.1.01	Grade 20	m^3	0.20	6.73	24.59	79.97	111.29	*371.07*
F4.1.1.02	Grade 25	m^3	0.20	6.73	24.59	86.70	118.02	*423.06*
F4.1.1.03	Grade 30	m^3	0.20	6.73	24.59	91.44	122.76	*463.47*
F4.1.1.04	Ordinary; Rapid Hardening Cement; Grade 20	m^3	0.20	6.73	24.59	82.97	114.29	*371.07*
F4.1.1.05	as above; Grade 25	m^3	0.20	6.73	24.59	90.14	121.46	*423.06*
F4.1.1.06	as above; Grade 30	m^3	0.20	6.73	24.59	95.23	126.55	*463.47*
F4.1.2	Cement to BS EN 197; 14mm aggregate							
F4.1.2.01	Grade 20	m^3	0.20	6.73	24.59	75.17	106.49	*338.85*

F4 Provision of Concrete: Prescribed mix continued...

		Unit	Labour Hours	Labour Net £	Plant Net £	Materials Net £	Unit Net £	CO_2 Kg
F4.1	**Provision of Concrete: Prescribed mix**							
F4.1.2	Cement to BS EN 197; 14mm aggregate							
F4.1.2.02	Grade 25	m^3	0.20	6.73	24.59	83.68	115.00	*406.55*
F4.1.2.03	Grade 30	m^3	0.20	6.73	24.59	88.40	119.72	*445.32*
F4.1.2.04	Ordinary; Rapid Hardening Cement; Grade 20	m^3	0.20	6.73	24.59	77.90	109.22	*338.85*
F4.1.2.05	as above; Grade 25	m^3	0.20	6.73	24.59	86.98	118.30	*406.55*
F4.1.2.06	as above; Grade 30	m^3	0.20	6.73	24.59	92.04	123.36	*445.32*
F4.1.3	Cement to BS EN 197; 20mm aggregate							
F4.1.3.01	Grade 7.5	m^3	0.20	6.73	24.59	59.35	90.67	*216.00*
F4.1.3.02	Grade 10	m^3	0.20	6.73	24.59	65.72	97.04	*267.12*
F4.1.3.03	Grade 15	m^3	0.20	6.73	24.59	68.98	100.30	*295.17*
F4.1.3.04	Grade 20	m^3	0.20	6.73	24.59	74.08	105.40	*335.59*
F4.1.3.05	Grade 25	m^3	0.20	6.73	24.59	77.86	109.18	*365.30*
F4.1.3.06	Grade 30	m^3	0.20	6.73	24.59	82.20	113.52	*399.94*
F4.1.3.07	Ordinary; Rapid Hardening Cement; Grade 7.5	m^3	0.20	6.73	24.59	61.03	92.35	*216.00*
F4.1.3.08	as above; Grade 10	m^3	0.20	6.73	24.59	67.84	99.16	*267.12*
F4.1.3.09	as above; Grade 15	m^3	0.20	6.73	24.59	71.34	102.66	*295.17*
F4.1.3.10	as above; Grade 20	m^3	0.20	6.73	24.59	76.79	108.11	*335.59*
F4.1.3.11	as above; Grade 25	m^3	0.20	6.73	24.59	80.81	112.13	*365.30*
F4.1.3.12	as above; Grade 30	m^3	0.20	6.73	24.59	85.45	116.77	*399.94*
F4.1.3.13	as above; Grade 40	m^3	0.20	6.73	24.59	88.03	119.35	*418.93*
F4.1.3.14	as above; Grade 50	m^3	0.20	6.73	24.59	89.34	120.66	*428.82*
F4.1.3.15	as above; Grade 60	m^3	0.20	6.73	24.59	91.89	123.21	*447.79*
F4.1.4	Cement to BS EN 197; 40mm aggregate							
F4.1.4.01	Grade 7.5	m^3	0.20	6.73	24.59	61.02	92.34	*216.17*
F4.1.4.02	Grade 10	m^3	0.20	6.73	24.59	63.70	95.02	*239.19*
F4.1.4.03	Grade 15	m^3	0.20	6.73	24.59	67.62	98.94	*273.76*
F4.1.4.04	Grade 20	m^3	0.20	6.73	24.59	72.40	103.72	*312.50*
F4.1.4.05	Grade 25	m^3	0.20	6.73	24.59	74.80	106.12	*331.47*
F4.1.4.06	Grade 30	m^3	0.20	6.73	24.59	78.72	110.04	*362.82*
F4.1.4.07	Ordinary; Rapid Hardening Cement; Grade 7.5	m^3	0.20	6.73	24.59	62.71	94.03	*216.17*
F4.1.4.08	as above; Grade 10	m^3	0.20	6.73	24.59	65.58	96.90	*239.19*
F4.1.4.09	as above; Grade 15	m^3	0.20	6.73	24.59	69.80	101.12	*273.76*
F4.1.4.10	as above; Grade 20	m^3	0.20	6.73	24.59	74.90	106.22	*312.50*
F4.1.4.11	as above; Grade 25	m^3	0.20	6.73	24.59	77.47	108.79	*331.47*
F4.1.4.12	as above; Grade 30	m^3	0.20	6.73	24.59	81.65	112.97	*362.82*
F4.1.4.13	as above; Grade 40	m^3	0.20	6.73	24.59	84.08	115.40	*380.14*
F4.1.4.14	as above; Grade 50	m^3	0.20	6.73	24.59	85.18	116.50	*388.39*
F4.1.4.15	as above; Grade 60	m^3	0.20	6.73	24.59	87.78	119.10	*405.81*
F4.1.5	Other stated cement; 10mm aggregate							
F4.1.5.01	Sulphate resisting cement to, BS 4027; Grade 20	m^3	0.20	6.73	24.59	80.23	111.55	*371.07*
F4.1.5.02	as above; Grade 25	m^3	0.20	6.73	24.59	87.00	118.32	*423.06*
F4.1.5.03	as above; Grade 30	m^3	0.20	6.73	24.59	91.77	123.09	*463.47*
F4.1.6	Other stated cement; 14mm aggregate							
F4.1.6.01	Sulphate resisting cement to, BS 4027; Grade 20	m^3	0.20	6.73	24.59	75.41	106.73	*338.85*
F4.1.6.02	as above; Grade 25	m^3	0.20	6.73	24.59	83.96	115.28	*406.55*
F4.1.6.03	as above; Grade 30	m^3	0.20	6.73	24.59	88.72	120.04	*445.32*

F4 Provision of Concrete: Prescribed mix continued...

		Unit	Labour Hours	Labour Net £	Plant Net £	Materials Net £	Unit Net £	CO_2 Kg
F4.1	**Provision of Concrete: Prescribed mix**							
F4.1.7	Other stated cement; 20mm aggregate							
F4.1.7.01	Sulphate resisting cement to, BS 4027; Grade 7.5	m^3	0.20	6.73	24.59	59.49	**90.81**	*216.00*
F4.1.7.02	as above; Grade 10	m^3	0.20	6.73	24.59	65.90	**97.22**	*267.12*
F4.1.7.03	as above; Grade 15	m^3	0.20	6.73	24.59	69.19	**100.51**	*295.17*
F4.1.7.04	as above; Grade 20	m^3	0.20	6.73	24.59	74.32	**105.64**	*335.59*
F4.1.7.05	as above; Grade 25	m^3	0.20	6.73	24.59	78.11	**109.43**	*365.30*
F4.1.7.06	as above; Grade 30	m^3	0.20	6.73	24.59	82.48	**113.80**	*399.94*
F4.1.7.07	as above; Grade 40	m^3	0.20	6.73	24.59	88.03	**119.35**	*418.93*
F4.1.7.08	as above; Grade 50	m^3	0.20	6.73	24.59	89.34	**120.66**	*428.82*
F4.1.7.09	as above; Grade 60	m^3	0.20	6.73	24.59	91.89	**123.21**	*447.79*
F4.1.8	Other stated cement; 40mm aggregate							
F4.1.8.01	Sulphate resisting cement to, BS 4027; Grade 7.5	m^3	0.20	6.73	24.59	61.17	**92.49**	*216.17*
F4.1.8.02	as above; Grade 10	m^3	0.20	6.73	24.59	63.86	**95.18**	*239.19*
F4.1.8.03	as above; Grade 15	m^3	0.20	6.73	24.59	67.81	**99.13**	*273.76*
F4.1.8.04	as above; Grade 20	m^3	0.20	6.73	24.59	72.61	**103.93**	*312.50*
F4.1.8.05	as above; Grade 25	m^3	0.20	6.73	24.59	75.03	**106.35**	*331.47*
F4.1.8.06	as above; Grade 30	m^3	0.20	6.73	24.59	78.97	**110.29**	*362.82*
F4.1.8.07	as above; Grade 40	m^3	0.20	6.73	24.59	84.08	**115.40**	*380.14*
F4.1.8.08	as above; Grade 50	m^3	0.20	6.73	24.59	85.18	**116.50**	*388.39*
F4.1.8.09	as above; Grade 60	m^3	0.20	6.73	24.59	87.78	**119.10**	*405.81*

F5 Placing of concrete: Mass

		Unit	Labour Hours	Labour Net £	Plant Net £	Materials Net £	Unit Net £	CO_2 Kg
F5.1	**Blinding**							
F5.1.1	Thickness: not exceeding 150mm							
F5.1.1.01	Generally	m^3	0.18	16.79	6.58	-	**23.37**	*5.06*
F5.1.1.02	Placed against excavated surface	m^3	0.21	19.59	7.67	-	**27.26**	*5.90*
F5.1.2	Thickness: 150 - 300mm							
F5.1.2.01	Generally	m^3	0.17	15.86	6.21	-	**22.07**	*4.77*
F5.1.2.02	Placed against excavated surface	m^3	0.20	18.66	7.31	-	**25.97**	*5.62*
F5.1.3	Thickness: 300 - 500mm							
F5.1.3.01	Generally	m^3	0.13	12.13	4.75	-	**16.88**	*3.65*
F5.1.3.02	Placed against excavated surface	m^3	0.14	13.06	5.12	-	**18.18**	*3.93*
F5.1.4	Thickness: exceeding 500mm							
F5.1.4.01	Generally	m^3	0.13	12.13	4.75	-	**16.88**	*3.65*
F5.1.4.02	Placed against excavated surface	m^3	0.14	13.06	5.12	-	**18.18**	*3.93*
F5.2	**Bases, footings, pile caps and ground slabs**							
F5.2.1	Thickness: not exceeding 150mm							
F5.2.1.01	Generally	m^3	0.19	17.73	6.94	-	**24.67**	*5.34*
F5.2.1.02	Placed against excavated surface	m^3	0.20	18.66	7.31	-	**25.97**	*5.62*
F5.2.2	Thickness: 150 - 300mm							
F5.2.2.01	Generally	m^3	0.18	16.79	6.58	-	**23.37**	*5.06*
F5.2.2.02	Placed against excavated surface	m^3	0.19	17.73	6.94	-	**24.67**	*5.34*
F5.2.3	Thickness: 300 - 500mm							
F5.2.3.01	Generally	m^3	0.14	13.06	5.12	-	**18.18**	*3.93*

F5 Placing of concrete: Mass continued...

		Unit	Labour Hours	Labour Net £	Plant Net £	Materials Net £	Unit Net £	CO_2 Kg
F5.2	**Bases, footings, pile caps and ground slabs**							
F5.2.3	Thickness: 300 - 500mm							
F5.2.3.02	Placed against excavated surface	m^3	0.15	13.99	5.48	-	19.47	*4.21*
F5.2.4	Thickness: exceeding 500mm							
F5.2.4.01	Generally	m^3	0.14	13.06	5.12	-	18.18	*3.93*
F5.2.4.02	Placed against excavated surface	m^3	0.15	13.99	5.48	-	19.47	*4.21*
F5.4	**Walls**							
F5.4.1	Thickness: not exceeding 150mm							
F5.4.1.01	Generally	m^3	0.22	20.52	8.04	-	28.56	*6.18*
F5.4.2	Thickness: 150 - 300mm							
F5.4.2.01	Generally	m^3	0.20	18.66	7.31	-	25.97	*5.62*
F5.4.3	Thickness: 300 - 500mm							
F5.4.3.01	Generally	m^3	0.16	14.93	5.85	-	20.78	*4.49*
F5.4.4	Thickness: exceeding 500mm							
F5.4.4.01	Generally	m^3	0.16	14.93	5.85	-	20.78	*4.49*
F5.8	**Other concrete forms**							
F5.8.1	Plinths							
F5.8.1.01	Size: 900 x 900 x 1200mm	m^3	0.40	37.32	14.62	-	51.94	*11.24*
F5.8.1.02	Size: 1000 x 1000 x 1200mm	m^3	0.40	37.32	14.62	-	51.94	*11.24*
F5.8.2	Thrust blocks							
F5.8.2.01	Size: 1200 x 1200 x 600mm	m^3	0.30	27.99	10.96	-	38.95	*8.43*
F5.8.3	Surround to precast concrete chambers							
F5.8.3.01	Wall thickness: 300mm	m^3	0.30	27.99	10.96	-	38.95	*8.43*
F5.8.4	Flling to removable duct covers							
F5.8.4.01	Thickness: 100mm	m^3	0.40	37.32	14.62	-	51.94	*11.24*

F6 Placing of concrete: Reinforced

		Unit	Labour Hours	Labour Net £	Plant Net £	Materials Net £	Unit Net £	CO_2 Kg
F6.2	**Bases, footings, pile caps and ground slabs**							
F6.2.1	Thickness: not exceeding 150mm							
F6.2.1.01	Generally	m^3	0.20	18.66	7.31	-	25.97	*5.62*
F6.2.2	Thickness: 150 - 300mm							
F6.2.2.01	Generally	m^3	0.19	17.73	6.94	-	24.67	*5.34*
F6.2.3	Thickness: 300 - 500mm							
F6.2.3.01	Generally	m^3	0.15	13.99	5.48	-	19.47	*4.21*
F6.2.4	Thickness: exceeding 500mm							
F6.2.4.01	Generally	m^3	0.15	13.99	5.48	-	19.47	*4.21*
F6.3	**Suspended slabs**							
F6.3.1	Thickness: not exceeding 150mm							
F6.3.1.01	Generally	m^3	0.24	22.39	8.77	-	31.16	*6.74*
F6.3.2	Thickness: 150 - 300mm							
F6.3.2.01	Generally	m^3	0.22	20.52	8.04	-	28.56	*6.18*

F6 Placing of concrete: Reinforced continued...

		Unit	Labour Hours	Labour Net £	Plant Net £	Materials Net £	Unit Net £	CO_2 Kg
F6.3	**Suspended slabs**							
F6.3.3	Thickness: 300 - 500mm							
F6.3.3.01	Generally	m^3	0.20	18.66	7.31	-	**25.97**	*5.62*
F6.3.4	Thickness: exceeding 500mm							
F6.3.4.01	Generally	m^3	0.20	18.66	7.31	-	**25.97**	*5.62*
F6.4	**Walls**							
F6.4.1	Thickness: not exceeding 150mm							
F6.4.1.01	Generally	m^3	0.24	22.39	8.77	-	**31.16**	*6.74*
F6.4.2	Thickness: 150 - 300mm							
F6.4.2.01	Generally	m^3	0.24	22.39	8.77	-	**31.16**	*6.74*
F6.4.3	Thickness: 300 - 500mm							
F6.4.3.01	Generally	m^3	0.20	18.66	7.31	-	**25.97**	*5.62*
F6.4.4	Thickness: exceeding 500mm							
F6.4.4.01	Generally	m^3	0.20	18.66	7.31	-	**25.97**	*5.62*
F6.5	**Columns and piers**							
F6.5.1	Cross sectional area: not exceeding $0.03m^2$							
F6.5.1.01	Generally	m^3	0.44	41.05	16.08	-	**57.13**	*12.36*
F6.5.2	Cross sectional area: 0.03 - $0.1m^2$							
F6.5.2.01	Generally	m^3	0.44	41.05	16.08	-	**57.13**	*12.36*
F6.5.3	Cross sectional area: 0.1 - $0.25m^2$							
F6.5.3.01	Generally	m^3	0.36	33.58	13.15	-	**46.73**	*10.11*
F6.5.4	Cross sectional area: 0.25 - $1m^2$							
F6.5.4.01	Generally	m^3	0.25	23.32	9.13	-	**32.45**	*7.02*
F6.5.5	Cross sectional area: exceeding $1m^2$							
F6.5.5.01	Generally	m^3	0.25	23.32	9.13	-	**32.45**	*7.02*
F6.6	**Beams**							
F6.6.1	Cross sectional area: not exceeding $0.03m^2$							
F6.6.1.01	Generally	m^3	0.44	41.05	16.08	-	**57.13**	*12.36*
F6.6.2	Cross sectional area: 0.03 - $0.1m^2$							
F6.6.2.01	Generally	m^3	0.44	41.05	16.08	-	**57.13**	*12.36*
F6.6.3	Cross sectional area: 0.1 - $0.25m^2$							
F6.6.3.01	Generally	m^3	0.36	33.58	13.15	-	**46.73**	*10.11*
F6.6.4	Cross sectional area: 0.25 - $1m^2$							
F6.6.4.01	Generally	m^3	0.25	23.32	9.13	-	**32.45**	*7.02*
F6.6.5	Cross sectional area: exceeding $1m^2$							
F6.6.5.01	Generally	m^3	0.25	23.32	9.13	-	**32.45**	*7.02*
F6.7	**Casing to metal sections**							
F6.7.1	Cross sectional area: not exceeding $0.03m^2$							
F6.7.1.01	Generally	m^3	0.50	46.65	18.27	-	**64.92**	*14.04*

F6 Placing of concrete: Reinforced continued...

		Unit	Labour Hours	Labour Net £	Plant Net £	Materials Net £	Unit Net £	CO_2 Kg
F6.7	**Casing to metal sections**							
F6.7.2	Cross sectional area: 0.03 - 0.1m²							
F6.7.2.01	Generally	m³	0.50	46.65	18.27	-	64.92	*14.04*
F6.7.3	Cross sectional area: 0.1- 0.25m²							
F6.7.3.01	Generally	m³	0.45	41.98	16.44	-	58.42	*12.64*
F6.7.4	Cross sectional area: 0.25 - 1m²							
F6.7.4.01	Generally	m³	0.40	37.32	14.62	-	51.94	*11.24*
F6.7.5	Cross sectional area: exceeding 1m²							
F6.7.5.01	Generally	m³	0.40	37.32	14.62	-	51.94	*11.24*
F6.8	**Other concrete forms**							
F6.8.1	Box culverts							
F6.8.1.01	Internal dimensions: 1200 x 800mm wall thickness 250mm	m³	0.23	21.46	8.40	-	29.86	*6.46*
F6.8.1.02	Internal dimensions: 1500 x 800mm wall thickness 250mm	m³	0.21	19.59	7.67	-	27.26	*5.90*
F6.8.2	Filling between precast concrete sections							
F6.8.2.01	Thickness: 200mm	m³	0.22	20.52	8.04	-	28.56	*6.18*
F6.8.3	Bollards							
F6.8.3.01	Diameter: 400mm	m³	0.40	37.32	14.62	-	51.94	*11.24*

F7 Placing of Concrete: Prestressed

		Unit	Labour Hours	Labour Net £	Plant Net £	Materials Net £	Unit Net £	CO_2 Kg
F7.3	**Suspended slabs**							
F7.3.1	Thickness: not exceeding 150mm							
F7.3.1.01	Generally	m³	0.29	27.05	10.60	-	37.65	*8.15*
F7.3.2	Thickness: 150 - 300mm							
F7.3.2.01	Generally	m³	0.29	27.05	10.60	-	37.65	*8.15*
F7.3.3	Thickness: 300 - 500mm							
F7.3.3.01	Generally	m³	0.20	18.66	7.31	-	25.97	*5.62*
F7.3.4	Thickness: exceeding 500mm							
F7.3.4.01	Generally	m³	0.20	18.66	7.31	-	25.97	*5.62*
F7.6	**Beams**							
F7.6.1	Cross sectional area: not exceeding 0.03m²							
F7.6.1.01	Generally	m³	0.50	46.65	18.27	-	64.92	*14.04*
F7.6.2	Cross sectional area: 0.03 - 0.1m²							
F7.6.2.01	Generally	m³	0.50	46.65	18.27	-	64.92	*14.04*
F7.6.3	Cross sectional area: 0.1 - 0.25m²							
F7.6.3.01	Generally	m³	0.50	46.65	18.27	-	64.92	*14.04*
F7.6.4	Cross sectional area: 0.25 - 1m²							
F7.6.4.01	Generally	m³	0.40	37.32	14.62	-	51.94	*11.24*
F7.6.5	Cross sectional area: exceeding 1m²							
F7.6.5.01	Generally	m³	0.40	37.32	14.62	-	51.94	*11.24*

CLASS G:
CONCRETE ANCILLARIES

Calculations used throughout Class G - Concrete Ancillaries

Labour

		Qty		Rate		Total
L A0130ICE	**Formwork (make, fix and strike) Labour Gang**					
	Craftsman WRA	1	x	16.68	=	£16.68
	Labourer (Skill Rate 3)	1	x	14.34	=	£14.34
	Carpenter (charge hand)	1	x	17.93	=	£17.93
	Total hourly cost of gang				**=**	**£48.95**
L A0140ICE	**Steel fixing Labour Gang**					
	Craftsman WRA	2	x	16.68	=	£33.37
	Labourer (General Operative)	1	x	12.56	=	£12.56
	Total hourly cost of gang				**=**	**£45.93**
L A0145ICE	**Welding Labour Gang**					
	Labourer (Skill Rate 3)	1	x	14.34	=	£14.34
	Fitters and Welders	2	x	16.68	=	£33.37
	Total hourly cost of gang				**=**	**£47.71**
L A0152ICE	**Concrete finish Labour Gang**					
	Labourer (Skill Rate 3)	1	x	14.34	=	£14.34
	Labourer (Skill Rate 4)	1	x	13.53	=	£13.53
	Total hourly cost of gang				**=**	**£27.87**

Plant

		Qty		Rate		Total
P A1040ICE	**Formwork (make) Plant Gang**					
	Saw Bench - 24 inch Diesel / Electric	1	x	1.89	=	£1.89
	Kango Type Tool - Electric Power Woodauger	1	x	0.57	=	£0.57
	Kango Type Tool - Electric Nut Runner	1	x	0.48	=	£0.48
	Total hourly cost of gang				**=**	**£2.94**
P A1035ICE	**Formwork (fix and strike) Plant Gang**					
	Kango Type Tool - Electric Power Woodauger	1	x	0.57	=	£0.57
	Kango Type Tool - Electric Nut Runner	1	x	0.48	=	£0.48
	Cranes Crawler - NCK 305B - 20t	0.25	x	45.36	=	£11.34
	Total hourly cost of gang				**=**	**£12.39**
P A1140ICE	**Steel fixing Plant Gang**					
	Cranes crawler - NCK 305C - 19t	0.25	x	43.26	=	£10.81
	Total hourly cost of gang				**=**	**£10.81**
P A1145ICE	**Welding Plant Gang**					
	Welding Set - 250 amp Diesel Electric Start Sil	1	x	3.52	=	£3.52
	Total hourly cost of gang				**=**	**£3.52**
P A1152ICE	**Concrete finish Plant Gang**					
	Compressor - 2-Tool (Complete)	1	x	4.86	=	£4.86
	Scabbler - Single Headed Hand	2	x	0.91	=	£1.83
	Scabbler - Floor - 3 Headed	1	x	2.47	=	£2.47
	Total hourly cost of gang				**=**	**£9.16**

Class G - Concrete Ancillaries

Note(s): Formwork

1) Beams - For Isolated Beams, prices include for formwork to three faces. For Attached Beams, prices include for formwork to two faces.

2) Columns - For Isolated Columns, prices include for formwork to four faces. For Attached Columns, prices inclde for formwork to three faces.

3) Walls - For Battered and Vertical Walls, material prices have been enhanced to cover extra propping and strutting.

4) Six uses of formwork have been assumed in the formwork section and thus the labour, plant and material prices bear one sixth of the 'make' element.

G1 Formwork: Rough Finish

		Unit	Labour Hours	Labour Net £	Plant Net £	Materials Net £	Unit Net £	CO_2 Kg
G1.1	**Plane horizontal**							
G1.1.1	Width: not exceeding 0.1m							
G1.1.1.01	Temporary	m	0.20	9.55	2.26	0.65	12.46	*0.60*
G1.1.1.02	Left in	m	0.33	16.35	3.71	3.96	24.02	*2.13*
G1.1.2	Width: 0.1 - 0.2m							
G1.1.2.01	Temporary	m	0.20	9.55	2.16	0.81	12.52	*0.65*
G1.1.2.02	Left in	m	0.33	16.35	4.15	4.95	25.45	*2.58*
G1.1.3	Width: 0.2 - 0.4m							
G1.1.3.01	Temporary	m^2	0.42	20.56	4.64	3.36	28.56	*2.04*
G1.1.3.02	Left in	m^2	1.00	48.96	8.75	19.78	77.49	*9.43*
G1.1.4	Width: 0.4 - 1.22m							
G1.1.4.01	Temporary	m^2	0.42	20.56	4.64	3.36	28.56	*2.04*
G1.1.4.02	Left in	m^2	0.78	38.19	8.75	19.78	66.72	*9.43*
G1.1.5	Width: exceeding 1.22m							
G1.1.5.01	Temporary	m^2	0.42	20.56	4.64	3.36	28.56	*2.04*
G1.1.5.02	Left in	m^2	0.72	35.25	8.75	19.78	63.78	*9.43*
G1.2	**Plane sloping**							
G1.2.1	Width: not exceeding 0.1m							
G1.2.1.01	Temporary	m	0.22	10.53	2.38	0.71	13.62	*0.64*
G1.2.1.02	Left in	m	0.37	18.02	4.08	3.96	26.06	*2.19*
G1.2.2	Width: 0.1 - 0.2m							
G1.2.2.01	Temporary	m	0.22	10.53	2.38	0.89	13.80	*0.71*
G1.2.2.02	Left in	m	0.37	18.02	4.08	7.91	30.01	*3.76*
G1.2.3	Width: 0.2 - 0.4m							
G1.2.3.01	Temporary	m^2	0.91	44.55	4.76	3.56	52.87	*2.13*
G1.2.3.02	Left in	m^2	1.04	50.92	8.90	19.78	79.60	*9.46*
G1.2.4	Width: 0.4 - 1.22m							
G1.2.4.01	Temporary	m^2	0.69	33.78	4.76	3.58	42.12	*2.14*
G1.2.4.01	Left in	m^2	0.80	39.17	19.78	8.90	67.85	*9.46*

G1 Formwork: Rough Finish continued...

		Unit	Labour Hours	Labour Net £	Plant Net £	Materials Net £	Unit Net £	CO_2 Kg
G1.2	**Plane sloping**							
G1.2.5	Width: exceeding 1.22m							
G1.2.5.01	Temporary	m^2	0.43	21.05	4.76	3.58	29.39	*2.14*
G1.2.5.02	Left in	m^2	0.74	36.08	8.90	19.78	64.76	*9.46*
G1.3	**Plane battered**							
G1.3.1	Width: not exceeding 0.1m							
G1.3.1.01	Temporary	m	0.23	11.46	2.60	0.77	14.83	*0.70*
G1.3.1.02	Left in	m	0.40	19.49	4.41	4.63	28.53	*2.50*
G1.3.2	Width: 0.1 - 0.2m							
G1.3.2.01	Temporary	m	0.23	11.46	2.60	0.97	15.03	*0.77*
G1.3.2.02	Left in	m	0.40	19.49	4.41	5.82	29.72	*2.97*
G1.3.3	Width: 0.2 - 0.4m							
G1.3.3.01	Temporary	m^2	0.94	46.02	5.20	3.92	55.14	*2.34*
G1.3.3.02	Left in	m^2	1.59	77.85	8.84	19.78	106.47	*9.20*
G1.3.4	Width: 0.4 - 1.22m							
G1.3.4.01	Temporary	m^2	0.70	34.42	7.79	4.69	46.90	*3.03*
G1.3.4.02	Left in	m^2	1.20	58.51	13.24	19.78	91.53	*9.86*
G1.3.5	Width: exceeding 1.22m							
G1.3.5.01	Temporary	m^2	0.47	23.01	10.39	7.83	41.23	*4.68*
G1.3.5.02	Left in	m^2	0.80	39.17	17.67	19.78	76.62	*10.52*
G1.4	**Plane vertical**							
G1.4.1	Width: not exceeding 0.1m							
G1.4.1.01	Temporary	m	0.25	12.39	2.81	0.77	15.97	*0.73*
G1.4.1.02	Left in	m	0.40	19.54	2.92	4.63	27.09	*2.31*
G1.4.2	Width: 0.1 - 0.2m							
G1.4.2.01	Temporary	m	0.25	12.39	2.81	0.97	16.17	*0.81*
G1.4.2.02	Left in	m	0.40	19.54	2.92	5.82	28.28	*2.79*
G1.4.3	Width: 0.2 - 0.4m							
G1.4.3.01	Temporary	m^2	1.02	49.94	5.63	3.92	59.49	*2.40*
G1.4.3.02	Left in	m^2	0.86	42.30	6.48	23.50	72.28	*10.60*
G1.4.4	Width: 0.4 - 1.22m							
G1.4.4.01	Temporary	m^2	0.77	37.90	8.58	4.69	51.17	*3.15*
G1.4.4.02	Left in	m^2	1.73	84.70	10.13	28.13	122.96	*13.24*
G1.4.5	Width: exceeding 1.22m							
G1.4.5.01	Temporary	m^2	0.52	25.46	11.26	7.83	44.55	*4.81*
G1.4.5.02	Left in	m^2	0.86	42.11	13.36	47.00	102.47	*21.39*

G1 Formwork: Rough Finish continued...

		Unit	Labour Hours	Labour Net £	Plant Net £	Materials Net £	Unit Net £	CO_2 Kg
G1.5	**Curved to one radius in one plane**							
G1.5.1	Width: not exceeding 0.1m							
G1.5.1.01	1m radius; Temporary	m	0.31	14.98	3.37	0.77	19.12	*0.81*
G1.5.1.02	1m radius; Left in	m	0.48	23.40	3.50	4.63	31.53	*2.41*
G1.5.1.03	2m radius; Temporary	m	0.29	14.25	3.21	0.87	18.33	*0.83*
G1.5.1.04	2m radius; Left in	m	0.46	22.42	3.34	4.63	30.39	*2.38*
G1.5.2	Width: 0.1 - 0.2m							
G1.5.2.01	1m radius; Temporary	m	0.31	14.98	3.37	0.97	19.32	*0.89*
G1.5.2.02	1m radius; Left in	m	0.48	23.40	3.50	5.82	32.72	*2.88*
G1.5.2.03	2m radius; Temporary	m	0.29	14.25	3.21	1.11	18.57	*0.92*
G1.5.2.04	2m radius; Left in	m	0.46	22.42	3.34	5.82	31.58	*2.86*
G1.5.3	Width: 0.2 - 0.4m							
G1.5.3.01	1m radius; Temporary	m^2	0.94	46.02	6.26	3.92	56.20	*3.02*
G1.5.3.02	1m radius; Left in	m^2	1.04	50.72	7.81	23.50	82.03	*10.85*
G1.5.3.03	2m radius; Temporary	m^2	1.17	57.28	6.47	4.49	68.24	*2.76*
G1.5.3.04	2m radius; Left in	m^2	1.98	96.94	7.45	23.50	127.89	*10.79*
G1.5.4	Width: 0.4 - 1.22m							
G1.5.4.01	1m radius; Temporary	m^2	0.94	45.92	10.36	4.69	60.97	*3.42*
G1.5.4.02	1m radius; Left in	m^2	1.98	96.94	12.27	28.13	137.34	*13.65*
G1.5.4.03	2m radius; Temporary	m^2	0.89	43.57	9.83	5.38	58.78	*3.61*
G1.5.4.04	2m radius; Left in	m^2	1.51	73.78	11.62	28.13	113.53	*13.53*
G1.5.5	Width: exceeding 1.22m							
G1.5.5.01	1m radius; Temporary	m^2	0.62	30.36	13.59	7.83	51.78	*5.16*
G1.5.5.02	1m radius; Left in	m^2	2.07	101.35	16.09	47.00	164.44	*21.93*
G1.5.5.03	2m radius; Temporary	m^2	0.58	28.40	12.94	9.00	50.34	*5.52*
G1.5.5.04	2m radius; Left in	m^2	0.99	48.47	15.36	47.00	110.83	*21.79*
G1.6	**Other curved**							
G1.6.1	Width: not exceeding 0.1m							
G1.6.1.01	Temporary; Curved to conical shaped surfaces; 1m minimum radius; 2m maximum radius	m	0.41	20.07	3.84	0.89	24.80	*1.13*
G1.6.1.02	Left in; Curved to conical shaped surfaces; 1m minimum radius; 2m maximum radius	m	0.80	39.17	4.45	4.63	48.25	*2.74*
G1.6.2	Width: 0.1 - 0.2m							
G1.6.2.01	Temporary; Curved to conical shaped surfaces; 1m minimum radius; 2m maximum radius	m	0.51	24.97	3.84	1.11	29.92	*1.22*

G1 Formwork: Rough Finish continued...

		Unit	Labour Hours	Labour Net £	Plant Net £	Materials Net £	Unit Net £	CO_2 Kg
G1.6	**Other curved**							
G1.6.2	Width: 0.1 - 0.2m							
G1.6.2.02	Left in; Curved to conical shaped surfaces; 1m minimum radius; 2m maximum radius	m	0.80	39.17	4.45	5.80	**49.42**	*3.21*
G1.6.3	Width: 0.2 - 0.4m							
G1.6.3.01	Temporary; Curved to conical shaped surfaces; 1m minimum radius; 2m maximum radius	m^2	1.02	49.94	8.44	4.47	**62.85**	*3.48*
G1.6.3.02	Left in; Curved to conical shaped surfaces; 1m minimum radius; 2m maximum radius	m^2	3.55	173.81	12.20	23.48	**209.49**	*11.81*
G1.6.4	Width: 0.4 - 1.22m							
G1.6.4.01	Temporary; Curved to conical shaped surfaces; 1m minimum radius; 2m maximum radius	m^2	1.55	75.89	11.82	5.38	**93.09**	*4.53*
G1.6.4.02	Left in; Curved to conical shaped surfaces; 1m minimum radius; 2m maximum radius	m^2	2.62	128.28	20.19	28.13	**176.60**	*15.27*
G1.6.5	Width: Exceeding 1.22m							
G1.6.5.01	Temporary; Curved to conical shaped surfaces; 1m minimum radius; 2m maximum radius	m^2	1.02	49.94	15.58	9.00	**74.52**	*6.73*
G1.6.5.02	Left in; Curved to conical shaped surfaces; 1m minimum radius; 2m maximum radius	m^2	1.73	84.70	26.48	47.00	**158.18**	*24.05*
G1.7	**For voids**							
G1.7.1	Small void depth: not exceeding 0.5m							
G1.7.1.01	Temporary; formwork left in; Cross-sectional area not exceeding 0.1m^2	Nr	0.95	46.51	7.12	25.91	**79.54**	*11.68*
G1.7.1.02	Temporary; For voids; polystyrene void former; Cross-sectional area not exceeding 0.1m^2	Nr	0.70	34.27	-	3.67	**37.94**	*3.00*
G1.7.2	Small void depth: 0.5 - 1m							
G1.7.2.01	Temporary; formwork left in; Cross-sectional area not exceeding 0.1m^2	Nr	1.29	63.16	9.71	51.63	**124.50**	*22.44*
G1.7.2.02	Temporary; For voids; polystyrene void former; Cross-sectional area not exceeding 0.1m^2	Nr	0.70	34.27	-	7.34	**41.61**	*6.00*
G1.7.3	Small void depth: 1 - 2m							
G1.7.3.01	Temporary; formwork left in; Cross-sectional area not exceeding 0.1m^2	Nr	1.72	84.21	12.91	104.24	**201.36**	*43.98*
G1.7.3.02	Temporary; For voids; polystyrene void former; Cross-sectional area not exceeding 0.1m^2	Nr	1.00	48.96	-	14.67	**63.63**	*12.00*
G1.7.4	Small void depth: Stated exceeding 2m							
G1.7.4.01	Temporary; formwork left in; Cross-sectional area not exceeding 0.1m^2	Nr	2.58	126.32	19.25	140.83	**286.40**	*59.71*
G1.7.4.02	Temporary; For voids; polystyrene void former; Cross-sectional area not exceeding 0.1m^2	Nr	1.00	48.96	-	22.01	**70.94**	*18.00*

G1 Formwork: Rough Finish continued...

		Unit	Labour Hours	Labour Net £	Plant Net £	Materials Net £	Unit Net £	CO_2 Kg
G1.7	**For voids**							
G1.7.5	Large void depth: not exceeding 0.5m							
G1.7.5.01	Temporary; formwork left in; Cross-sectional area not exceeding 0.1m²	Nr	1.29	63.16	9.71	51.63	**124.50**	*22.42*
G1.7.5.02	Temporary; For voids; polystyrene void former; Cross-sectional area not exceeding 0.1m²	Nr	0.70	34.27	-	18.34	**52.61**	*15.00*
G1.7.6	Large void depth: 0.5 - 1m							
G1.7.6.01	Temporary; formwork left in; Cross-sectional area not exceeding 0.1m²	Nr	1.72	84.21	12.91	104.24	**201.36**	*43.98*
G1.7.6.02	Temporary; For voids; polystyrene void former; Cross-sectional area not exceeding 0.1m²	Nr	1.00	48.96	-	36.68	**85.64**	*30.00*
G1.7.7	Large void depth: 1 - 2m							
G1.7.7.01	Temporary; formwork left in; Cross-sectional area not exceeding 0.1m²	Nr	2.58	126.32	19.25	140.83	**286.40**	*59.71*
G1.7.7.02	Temporary; For voids; polystyrene void former; Cross-sectional area not exceeding 0.1m²	Nr	1.00	48.96	-	73.36	**122.32**	*60.00*
G1.7.8	Large void depth: Stated exceeding 2m							
G1.7.8.01	Temporary; formwork left in; Cross-sectional area not exceeding 0.1m²	Nr	4.80	235.01	42.42	195.82	**473.25**	*85.56*
G1.7.8.02	Temporary; For voids; polystyrene void former; Cross-sectional area not exceeding 0.1m²	Nr	1.50	73.44	-	110.04	**183.48**	*90.00*
G1.8	**For concrete components of constant cross-section**							
G1.8.1	Beams							
G1.8.1.01	For concrete components of constant cross-section; Isolated; 100 x 200mm	m	0.34	16.65	3.93	1.68	**22.26**	*1.24*
G1.8.1.02	as above; Isolated; 100 x 300mm	m	0.48	23.26	5.54	2.31	**31.11**	*1.72*
G1.8.1.03	as above; Isolated; 200 x 200mm	m	0.41	20.17	4.72	2.02	**26.91**	*1.49*
G1.8.1.04	as above; Isolated; 200 x 300mm	m	0.57	28.01	6.29	2.69	**36.99**	*1.98*
G1.8.1.05	as above; Isolated; 400 x 400mm	m	0.86	42.30	9.44	4.04	**55.78**	*2.97*
G1.8.1.06	as above; Isolated; 400 x 600mm	m	1.15	56.40	12.58	5.38	**74.36**	*3.97*
G1.8.1.07	as above; Isolated; 500 x 800mm	m	1.43	69.91	16.52	7.06	**93.49**	*5.21*
G1.8.1.08	as above; Attached; 100 x 200mm	m	0.34	16.65	3.93	1.35	**21.93**	*1.11*
G1.8.1.09	as above; Attached; 100 x 300mm	m	0.48	23.26	5.54	1.86	**30.66**	*1.54*
G1.8.1.10	as above; Attached; 200 x 200mm	m	0.41	20.17	4.72	1.62	**26.51**	*1.33*
G1.8.1.11	as above; Attached; 200 x 300mm	m	0.57	28.01	6.29	2.16	**36.46**	*1.77*
G1.8.1.12	as above; Attached; 400 x 400mm	m	0.86	42.30	9.44	3.22	**54.96**	*2.65*

G1 Formwork: Rough Finish continued...

		Unit	Labour Hours	Labour Net £	Plant Net £	Materials Net £	Unit Net £	CO_2 Kg
G1.8	**For concrete components of constant cross-section**							
G1.8.1	Beams							
G1.8.1.13	as above; Attached; 400 x 600mm	m	1.15	56.40	12.58	4.31	73.29	*3.54*
G1.8.1.14	as above; Attached; 500 x 800mm	m	1.43	69.91	16.52	5.66	92.09	*4.65*
G1.8.2	Columns							
G1.8.2.01	For concrete components of constant cross-section; Isolated; 100 x 200mm	m	0.40	19.39	4.58	2.02	25.99	*1.47*
G1.8.2.02	as above; Isolated; 100 x 300mm	m	0.53	26.00	6.10	2.69	34.79	*1.96*
G1.8.2.03	as above; Isolated; 200 x 200mm	m	0.53	26.00	6.10	2.69	34.79	*1.96*
G1.8.2.04	as above; Isolated; 200 x 300mm	m	0.55	26.93	6.36	3.36	36.65	*2.27*
G1.8.2.05	as above; Isolated; 400 x 400mm	m	0.77	37.70	9.75	5.38	52.83	*3.55*
G1.8.2.06	as above; Isolated; 400 x 600mm	m	0.88	43.04	9.83	6.73	59.60	*4.14*
G1.8.2.07	as above; Isolated; 500 x 800mm	m	1.15	56.30	12.81	8.74	77.85	*5.39*
G1.8.2.08	as above; Attached; 100 x 200mm	m	0.26	12.93	2.95	1.68	17.56	*1.11*
G1.8.2.09	as above; Attached; 100 x 300mm	m	0.35	17.33	3.98	2.35	23.66	*1.53*
G1.8.2.10	as above; Attached; 200 x 200mm	m	0.35	17.33	3.98	2.02	23.33	*1.39*
G1.8.2.11	as above; Attached; 200 x 300mm	m	0.44	21.59	4.88	2.69	29.16	*1.80*
G1.8.2.12	as above; Attached; 400 x 400mm	m	0.70	34.47	7.83	4.04	46.34	*2.77*
G1.8.2.13	as above; Attached; 400 x 600mm	m	0.88	43.04	9.83	5.38	58.25	*3.60*
G1.8.2.14	as above; Attached; 500 x 800mm	m	1.15	56.30	12.81	7.06	76.17	*4.72*
G1.8.3	Walls							
G1.8.3.01	250mm thick x 750mm high	m	0.76	37.21	8.57	5.04	50.82	*3.27*
G1.8.3.02	250mm thick x 1000mm high	m	1.12	54.84	12.75	6.73	74.32	*4.55*
G1.8.3.03	400mm thick x 1000mm high	m	1.12	54.84	12.75	6.73	74.32	*4.55*
G1.8.4	Other members							
G1.8.4.01	Box culverts; Internal dimensions 1 x 1m; wall thickness 250mm	m	4.25	208.18	37.99	27.30	273.47	*16.67*
G1.8.4.02	Box culverts; Internal dimensions 2 x 2m; wall thickness 250mm	m	9.83	481.18	106.40	81.85	669.43	*48.56*
G1.8.4.03	Box culverts; Internal dimensions 2 x 2m; wall thickness 400mm	m	10.34	506.34	76.06	85.61	668.01	*49.43*
G1.8.5	Projections							
G1.8.5.01	Nibs; 50 x 50mm deep	m	0.36	17.63	4.18	1.98	23.79	*1.39*
G1.8.5.02	Nibs; 100 x 100mm deep	m	0.36	17.63	4.18	3.96	25.77	*2.18*
G1.8.6	Intrusions							
G1.8.6.01	Rebates 50 x 50mm deep	m	0.18	8.81	2.03	1.27	12.11	*0.98*
G1.8.6.02	Rebates 100 x 100mm deep	m	0.18	8.81	2.03	4.25	15.09	*2.59*

G2 Formwork: Fair Finish

		Unit	Labour Hours	Labour Net £	Plant Net £	Materials Net £	Unit Net £	CO_2 Kg
G2.1	**Plane horizontal**							
G2.1.1	Width: not exceeding 0.1m							
G2.1.1.01	Generally	m	0.20	9.55	2.16	0.67	12.38	*0.58*
G2.1.2	Width: 0.1 - 0.2m							
G2.1.2.01	Generally	m	0.20	9.55	2.16	0.83	12.54	*0.65*
G2.1.3	Width: 0.2 - 0.4m							
G2.1.3.01	Generally	m^2	0.91	44.55	4.64	3.43	52.62	*2.04*
G2.1.4	Width: 0.4 - 1.22m							
G2.1.4.01	Generally	m^2	0.69	33.78	4.64	3.43	41.85	*2.04*
G2.1.5	Width: exceeding 1.22m							
G2.1.5.01	Generally	m^2	0.42	20.56	4.64	3.43	28.63	*2.04*
G2.2	**Plane sloping**							
G2.2.1	Width: not exceeding 0.1m							
G2.2.1.01	Generally	m	0.22	10.53	1.69	0.73	12.95	*0.62*
G2.2.2	Width: 0.1 - 0.2m							
G2.2.2.01	Generally	m	0.22	10.53	2.38	0.91	13.82	*0.71*
G2.2.3	Width: 0.2 - 0.4m							
G2.2.3.01	Generally	m^2	0.69	33.78	4.76	3.65	42.19	*2.14*
G2.2.4	Width: 0.4 - 1.22m							
G2.2.4.01	Generally	m^2	0.43	21.05	4.76	3.65	29.46	*2.14*
G2.2.5	Width: exceeding 1.22m							
G2.2.5.01	Generally	m^2	0.47	23.01	4.76	3.65	31.42	*2.14*
G2.3	**Plane battered**							
G2.3.1	Width: not exceeding 0.1m							
G2.3.1.01	Generally	m	0.23	11.46	2.60	0.79	14.85	*0.70*
G2.3.2	Width: 0.1 - 0.2m							
G2.3.2.01	Generally	m	0.23	11.46	2.60	0.99	15.05	*0.77*
G2.3.3	Width: 0.2 - 0.4m							
G2.3.3.01	Generally	m^2	0.94	46.02	5.20	4.00	55.22	*2.34*
G2.3.4	Width: 0.4 - 1.22m							
G2.3.4.01	Generally	m^2	0.70	34.42	7.79	4.78	46.99	*3.03*
G2.3.5	Width: exceeding 1.22m							
G2.3.5.01	Generally	m^2	0.47	23.01	10.39	7.99	41.39	*4.68*
G2.4	**Plane vertical**							
G2.4.1	Width: not exceeding 0.1m							
G2.4.1.01	Generally	m	0.25	12.39	2.81	0.79	15.99	*0.73*
G2.4.2	Width: 0.1 - 0.2m							
G2.4.2.01	Generally	m	0.25	12.39	2.77	0.97	16.13	*0.79*
G2.4.3	Width: 0.2 - 0.4m							
G2.4.3.01	Generally	m^2	1.02	49.94	5.63	4.00	59.57	*2.40*

G2 Formwork: Fair Finish continued...

		Unit	Labour Hours	Labour Net £	Plant Net £	Materials Net £	Unit Net £	CO_2 Kg
G2.4	**Plane vertical**							
G2.4.4	Width: 0.4 - 1.22m							
G2.4.4.01	Generally	m^2	0.77	37.90	8.58	4.78	51.26	*3.15*
G2.4.5	Width: exceeding 1.22m							
G2.4.5.01	Generally	m^2	0.52	25.46	11.26	7.99	44.71	*4.81*
G2.5	**Curved to one radius in one plane**							
G2.5.1	Width: not exceeding 0.1m							
G2.5.1.01	1m radius	m	0.31	14.98	3.37	0.79	19.14	*0.81*
G2.5.1.02	2m radius	m	0.29	14.25	3.21	0.89	18.35	*0.83*
G2.5.2	Width: 0.1 - 0.2m							
G2.5.2.01	1m radius	m	0.31	14.98	3.37	0.99	19.34	*0.89*
G2.5.2.02	2m radius	m	0.29	14.25	3.21	1.13	18.59	*0.92*
G2.5.3	Width: 0.2 - 0.4m							
G2.5.3.01	1m radius	m^2	1.23	60.22	6.79	4.00	71.01	*2.58*
G2.5.3.02	2m radius	m^2	0.58	28.59	6.47	4.58	39.64	*2.76*
G2.5.4	Width: 0.4 - 1.22m							
G2.5.4.01	1m radius	m^2	0.94	45.92	10.36	4.78	61.06	*3.42*
G2.5.4.02	2m radius	m^2	0.89	43.57	9.83	5.49	58.89	*3.61*
G2.5.5	Width: exceeding 1.22m							
G2.5.5.01	1m radius	m^2	0.62	30.36	13.59	7.99	51.94	*5.16*
G2.5.5.02	2m radius	m^2	1.17	57.19	12.94	9.18	79.31	*5.52*
G2.6	**Other curved**							
G2.6.1	Curved to conical shaped surfaces; 1m minimum radius; 2m maximum radius							
G2.6.1.01	Width: not exceeding 0.1m	m	0.51	24.77	3.84	0.89	29.50	*1.12*
G2.6.1.02	Width: 0.1 - 0.2m	m	0.51	24.77	3.84	1.13	29.74	*1.22*
G2.6.1.03	Width: 0.2 - 0.4m	m^2	2.03	99.39	7.75	4.58	111.72	*3.35*
G2.6.1.04	Width: 0.4 - 1.22m	m^2	1.55	75.89	11.82	5.49	93.20	*4.53*
G2.6.1.05	Width: exceeding 1.22m	m^2	1.02	49.94	15.58	9.18	74.70	*6.73*
G2.8	**For concrete components of constant cross-section**							
G2.8.1	Beams							
G2.8.1.01	Isolated; 100 x 200mm	m	0.34	16.65	3.93	1.72	22.30	*1.24*
G2.8.1.02	Isolated; 100 x 300mm	m	0.48	23.26	5.54	2.36	31.16	*1.72*
G2.8.1.03	Isolated; 200 x 200mm	m	0.41	20.17	4.72	2.06	26.95	*1.49*
G2.8.1.04	Isolated; 200 x 300mm	m	0.57	28.01	6.29	2.74	37.04	*1.98*
G2.8.1.05	Isolated; 400 x 400mm	m	0.86	42.30	9.44	4.12	55.86	*2.97*
G2.8.1.06	Isolated; 400 x 600mm	m	1.15	56.40	12.58	5.49	74.47	*3.97*

G2 Formwork: Fair Finish continued...

		Unit	Labour Hours	Labour Net £	Plant Net £	Materials Net £	Unit Net £	CO_2 Kg
G2.8	**For concrete components of constant cross-section**							
G2.8.1	Beams							
G2.8.1.07	Isolated; 500 x 800mm	m	1.43	69.91	16.52	7.20	**93.63**	*5.21*
G2.8.1.08	Attached; 100 x 200mm	m	0.34	16.65	3.93	1.37	**21.95**	*1.11*
G2.8.1.09	Attached; 100 x 300mm	m	0.48	23.26	5.54	1.90	**30.70**	*1.54*
G2.8.1.10	Attached; 200 x 200mm	m	0.41	20.17	4.72	1.65	**26.54**	*1.33*
G2.8.1.11	Attached; 200 x 300mm	m	0.57	28.01	6.29	2.20	**36.50**	*1.77*
G2.8.1.12	Attached; 400 x 400mm	m	0.86	42.30	9.44	3.29	**55.03**	*2.65*
G2.8.1.13	Attached; 400 x 600mm	m	1.15	56.40	12.58	4.40	**73.38**	*3.54*
G2.8.1.14	Attached; 500 x 800mm	m	1.43	69.91	16.52	5.77	**92.20**	*4.65*
G2.8.2	Columns							
G2.8.2.01	Isolated; 100 x 200mm	m	0.40	19.39	4.59	2.06	**26.04**	*1.48*
G2.8.2.02	Isolated; 100 x 300mm	m	0.53	26.00	4.07	2.74	**32.81**	*1.89*
G2.8.2.03	Isolated; 200 x 200mm	m	0.53	26.00	6.10	2.74	**34.84**	*1.96*
G2.8.2.04	Isolated; 200 x 300mm	m	0.55	26.93	6.36	3.43	**36.72**	*2.27*
G2.8.2.05	Isolated; 400 x 400mm	m	0.77	37.70	9.75	5.49	**52.94**	*3.55*
G2.8.2.06	Isolated; 400 x 600mm	m	0.88	43.04	9.83	6.86	**59.73**	*4.14*
G2.8.2.07	Isolated; 500 x 800mm	m	1.15	56.30	12.81	8.92	**78.03**	*5.39*
G2.8.2.08	Attached; 100 x 200mm	m	0.26	12.93	2.95	1.72	**17.60**	*1.11*
G2.8.2.09	Attached; 100 x 300mm	m	0.35	17.33	3.98	2.40	**23.71**	*1.53*
G2.8.2.10	Attached; 200 x 200mm	m	0.35	17.33	3.98	2.06	**23.37**	*1.39*
G2.8.2.11	Attached; 200 x 300mm	m	0.44	21.59	4.88	2.74	**29.21**	*1.80*
G2.8.2.12	Attached; 400 x 400mm	m	0.70	34.47	7.83	4.12	**46.42**	*2.77*
G2.8.2.13	Attached; 400 x 600mm	m	0.88	43.04	9.84	5.49	**58.37**	*3.61*
G2.8.2.14	Attached; 500 x 800mm	m	1.15	56.30	12.81	7.20	**76.31**	*4.72*
G2.8.3	Walls							
G2.8.3.01	250mm thick x 750mm high	m	0.76	37.21	8.57	5.15	**50.93**	*3.27*
G2.8.3.02	250mm thick x 1000mm high	m	1.12	54.84	12.75	6.86	**74.45**	*4.55*
G2.8.3.03	400mm thick x 1000mm high	m	1.12	54.84	12.75	6.86	**74.45**	*4.55*
G2.8.4	Other Members							
G2.8.4.01	Box culverts; Internal dimensions 1 x 1m; wall thickness 250mm	m	4.25	208.18	37.99	27.85	**274.02**	*16.67*
G2.8.4.02	Box culverts; Internal dimensions 2 x 2m; wall thickness 250mm	m	9.83	481.18	106.40	83.50	**671.08**	*48.56*
G2.8.4.03	Box culverts; Internal dimensions 2 x 2m; wall thickness 400mm	m	10.34	506.34	109.21	87.36	**702.91**	*50.52*

G2 Formwork: Fair Finish continued...

		Unit	Labour Hours	Labour Net £	Plant Net £	Materials Net £	Unit Net £	CO_2 Kg
G2.8	**For concrete components of constant cross-section**							
G2.8.5	Projections							
G2.8.5.01	Nibs; 50 x 50mm deep	m	0.36	17.63	4.18	2.02	23.83	*1.39*
G2.8.5.02	Nibs; 100 x 100mm deep	m	0.36	17.63	4.18	4.04	25.85	*2.18*
G2.8.6	Intrusions							
G2.8.6.01	Rebates 50 x 50mm deep	m	0.18	8.81	2.03	1.27	12.11	*0.98*
G2.8.6.02	Rebates 100 x 100mm deep	m	0.18	8.81	2.03	6.74	17.58	*2.92*

G3 Formwork: Other stated finish

		Unit	Labour Hours	Labour Net £	Plant Net £	Materials Net £	Unit Net £	CO_2 Kg
G3.1	**Plane horizontal**							
G3.1.1	Width: not exceeding 0.1m							
G3.1.1.01	Rough Board Finish	m	0.21	10.28	2.34	0.78	13.40	*0.72*
G3.1.1.02	Extra Smooth Finish	m	0.21	10.28	2.34	0.87	13.49	*0.62*
G3.1.2	Width: 0.1 - 0.2m							
G3.1.2.01	Rough Board Finish	m	0.21	10.28	2.34	0.96	13.58	*0.80*
G3.1.2.02	Extra Smooth Finish	m	0.21	10.28	2.34	1.08	13.70	*0.68*
G3.1.3	Width: 0.2 - 0.4m							
G3.1.3.01	Rough Board Finish	m^2	0.91	44.55	4.67	4.00	53.22	*2.57*
G3.1.3.02	Extra Smooth Finish	m^2	0.91	44.55	4.67	4.47	53.69	*2.05*
G3.1.4	Width: 0.4 - 1.22m							
G3.1.4.01	Rough Board Finish	m^2	0.69	33.78	4.67	4.00	42.45	*2.57*
G3.1.4.02	Extra Smooth Finish	m^2	0.69	33.78	4.67	4.47	42.92	*2.05*
G3.1.5	Width: exceeding 1.22m							
G3.1.5.01	Rough Board Finish	m^2	0.43	21.05	4.67	4.00	29.72	*2.57*
G3.1.5.02	Extra Smooth Finish	m^2	0.43	21.05	4.67	4.47	30.19	*2.05*
G3.2	**Plane sloping**							
G3.2.1	Width: not exceeding 0.1m							
G3.2.1.01	Rough Board Finish	m	0.23	11.31	2.55	0.85	14.71	*0.78*
G3.2.1.02	Extra Smooth Finish	m	0.23	11.31	2.55	0.95	14.81	*0.67*
G3.2.2	Width: 0.1 - 0.2m							
G3.2.2.01	Rough Board Finish	m	0.23	11.31	2.55	1.06	14.92	*0.88*
G3.2.2.02	Extra Smooth Finish	m	0.23	11.31	2.55	1.18	15.04	*0.74*
G3.2.3	Width: 0.2 - 0.4m							
G3.2.3.01	Rough Board Finish	m^2	0.94	46.02	5.14	4.00	55.16	*2.64*
G3.2.3.02	Extra Smooth Finish	m^2	0.94	46.02	5.14	4.76	55.92	*2.21*
G3.2.4	Width: 0.4 - 1.22m							
G3.2.4.01	Rough Board Finish	m^2	0.70	34.27	5.14	4.00	43.41	*2.64*
G3.2.4.02	Extra Smooth Finish	m^2	0.70	34.27	5.14	4.76	44.17	*2.21*

G3 Formwork: Other stated finish continued...

		Unit	Labour Hours	Labour Net £	Plant Net £	Materials Net £	Unit Net £	CO_2 Kg
G3.2	**Plane sloping**							
G3.2.5	Width: exceeding 1.22m							
G3.2.5.01	Rough Board Finish	m^2	0.47	23.16	5.14	4.00	**32.30**	*2.64*
G3.2.5.02	Extra Smooth Finish	m^2	0.47	23.16	5.14	4.76	**33.06**	*2.21*
G3.3	**Plane battered**							
G3.3.1	Width: not exceeding 0.1m							
G3.3.1.01	Rough Board Finish	m	0.25	12.34	2.81	0.85	**16.00**	*0.81*
G3.3.1.02	Extra Smooth Finish	m	0.25	12.34	2.81	1.03	**16.18**	*0.73*
G3.3.2	Width: 0.1 - 0.2m							
G3.3.2.01	Rough Board Finish	m	0.25	12.34	2.81	1.06	**16.21**	*0.91*
G3.3.2.02	Extra Smooth Finish	m	0.25	12.34	2.81	1.29	**16.44**	*0.81*
G3.3.3	Width: 0.2 - 0.4m							
G3.3.3.01	Rough Board Finish	m^2	0.52	25.26	6.41	4.66	**36.33**	*3.11*
G3.3.3.02	Extra Smooth Finish	m^2	0.52	25.26	6.41	5.21	**36.88**	*2.51*
G3.3.4	Width: 0.4 - 1.22m							
G3.3.4.01	Rough Board Finish	m^2	0.57	27.91	8.58	5.58	**42.07**	*3.88*
G3.3.4.02	Extra Smooth Finish	m^2	0.70	34.42	7.79	6.24	**48.45**	*3.03*
G3.3.5	Width: exceeding 1.22m							
G3.3.5.01	Rough Board Finish	m^2	1.03	50.43	8.60	9.32	**68.35**	*5.65*
G3.3.5.02	Extra Smooth Finish	m^2	1.03	50.43	8.60	10.42	**69.45**	*4.44*
G3.4	**Plane vertical**							
G3.4.1	Width: not exceeding 0.1m							
G3.4.1.01	Rough Board Finish	m	0.29	13.95	2.81	0.92	**17.68**	*0.85*
G3.4.1.02	Extra Smooth Finish	m	0.29	13.95	2.81	1.03	**17.79**	*0.73*
G3.4.2	Width: 0.1 - 0.2m							
G3.4.2.01	Rough Board Finish	m	0.29	13.95	1.92	1.15	**17.02**	*0.92*
G3.4.2.02	Extra Smooth Finish	m	0.29	13.95	1.92	1.29	**17.16**	*0.77*
G3.4.3	Width: 0.2 - 0.4m							
G3.4.3.01	Rough Board Finish	m^2	1.14	55.81	6.41	4.66	**66.88**	*3.11*
G3.4.3.02	Extra Smooth Finish	m^2	1.14	55.81	6.41	5.21	**67.43**	*2.51*
G3.4.4	Width: 0.4 - 1.22m							
G3.4.4.01	Rough Board Finish	m^2	0.94	46.02	10.36	5.58	**61.96**	*4.14*
G3.4.4.02	Extra Smooth Finish	m^2	0.94	46.02	10.36	6.24	**62.62**	*3.42*
G3.4.5	Width: exceeding 1.22m							
G3.4.5.01	Rough Board Finish	m^2	1.23	60.22	13.59	9.32	**83.13**	*6.37*
G3.4.5.02	Extra Smooth Finish	m^2	1.23	60.22	13.59	10.42	**84.23**	*5.16*

G3 Formwork: Other stated finish continued...

		Unit	Labour Hours	Labour Net £	Plant Net £	Materials Net £	Unit Net £	CO_2 Kg
G3.5	**Curved to one radius in one plane**							
G3.5.1	Width: not exceeding 0.1m							
G3.5.1.01	Rough Board Finish; 1m radius	m	0.34	16.74	3.36	0.92	21.02	*0.93*
G3.5.1.02	Extra Smooth Finish; 1m radius	m	0.34	16.74	3.36	1.03	21.13	*0.81*
G3.5.1.03	Rough Board Finish; 2m radius	m	0.33	16.01	3.23	0.92	20.16	*0.91*
G3.5.1.04	Extra Smooth Finish; 2m radius	m	0.33	16.01	3.23	1.03	20.27	*0.79*
G3.5.2	Width: 0.1 - 0.2m							
G3.5.2.01	Rough Board Finish; 1m radius	m	0.34	16.74	3.36	1.15	21.25	*1.04*
G3.5.2.02	Extra Smooth Finish; 1m radius	m	0.34	16.74	3.36	1.29	21.39	*0.89*
G3.5.2.03	Rough Board Finish; 2m radius	m	0.33	16.01	3.23	1.15	20.39	*1.02*
G3.5.2.04	Extra Smooth Finish; 2m radius	m	0.33	16.01	3.23	1.47	20.71	*0.92*
G3.5.3	Width: 0.2 - 0.4m							
G3.5.3.01	Rough Board Finish; 1m radius	m^2	1.37	67.08	7.69	4.66	79.43	*3.30*
G3.5.3.02	Extra Smooth Finish; 1m radius	m^2	1.37	67.08	7.69	5.21	79.98	*2.70*
G3.5.3.03	Rough Board Finish; 2m radius	m^2	1.31	64.14	7.38	4.66	76.18	*3.26*
G3.5.3.04	Extra Smooth Finish; 2m radius	m^2	1.31	64.14	7.38	5.21	76.73	*2.66*
G3.5.4	Width: 0.4 - 1.22m							
G3.5.4.01	Rough Board Finish; 1m radius	m^2	0.68	33.29	11.26	5.58	50.13	*4.28*
G3.5.4.02	Extra Smooth Finish; 1m radius	m^2	0.94	45.92	10.36	6.24	62.52	*3.42*
G3.5.4.03	Rough Board Finish; 2m radius	m^2	0.65	31.82	8.19	5.58	45.59	*3.84*
G3.5.4.04	Extra Smooth Finish; 2m radius	m^2	0.89	43.57	9.83	7.16	60.56	*3.61*
G3.5.5	Width: exceeding 1.22m							
G3.5.5.01	Rough Board Finish; 1m radius	m^2	1.37	66.98	15.36	9.32	91.66	*6.61*
G3.5.5.02	Extra Smooth Finish; 1m radius	m^2	1.37	66.98	15.36	10.42	92.76	*5.40*
G3.5.5.03	Rough Board Finish; 2m radius	m^2	1.31	64.19	14.72	9.32	88.23	*6.51*
G3.5.5.04	Extra Smooth Finish; 2m radius	m^2	1.31	64.19	14.72	11.98	90.89	*5.77*
G3.6	**Other curved**							
G3.6.1	Width: not exceeding 0.1m							
G3.6.1.01	Rough Board Finish	m	0.59	28.89	3.91	1.29	34.09	*1.30*
G3.6.1.02	Extra Smooth Finish	m	0.59	28.89	3.91	1.71	34.51	*1.30*
G3.6.2	Width: 0.1 - 0.2m							
G3.6.2.01	Rough Board Finish	m	0.59	28.89	3.91	1.60	34.40	*1.43*
G3.6.2.02	Extra Smooth Finish	m	0.59	28.89	3.91	2.13	34.93	*1.43*
G3.6.3	Width: 0.2 - 0.4m							
G3.6.3.01	Rough Board Finish	m^2	2.28	111.63	8.75	6.47	126.85	*4.34*
G3.6.3.02	Extra Smooth Finish	m^2	2.28	111.63	8.75	8.61	128.98	*4.34*

G3 Formwork: Other stated finish continued...

		Unit	Labour Hours	Labour Net £	Plant Net £	Materials Net £	Unit Net £	CO_2 Kg
G3.6	**Other curved**							
G3.6.4	Width: 0.4 - 1.22m							
G3.6.4.01	Rough Board Finish	m^2	1.71	83.72	13.12	7.73	**104.57**	*5.73*
G3.6.4.02	Extra Smooth Finish	m^2	1.71	83.72	13.12	10.29	**107.13**	*5.73*
G3.6.5	Width: exceeding 1.22m							
G3.6.5.01	Rough Board Finish	m^2	1.40	68.54	17.50	12.92	**98.96**	*8.68*
G3.6.5.02	Extra Smooth Finish	m^2	1.40	68.54	17.50	17.19	**103.23**	*8.68*
G3.8	**For concrete components of constant cross-section**							
G3.8.1	Beams							
G3.8.1.01	Rough Board Finish; Isolated; 100 x 200mm	m	0.35	16.89	3.95	2.00	**22.84**	*1.51*
G3.8.1.02	Extra Smooth Finish; Isolated; 100 x 200mm	m	0.35	16.89	3.95	2.24	**23.08**	*1.25*
G3.8.1.03	Rough Board Finish; Isolated; 100 x 300mm	m	0.48	23.65	5.53	2.80	**31.98**	*2.11*
G3.8.1.04	Extra Smooth Finish; Isolated; 100 x 300mm	m	0.48	23.65	5.53	3.13	**32.31**	*1.74*
G3.8.1.05	Rough Board Finish; Isolated; 200 x 200mm	m	0.41	20.27	4.74	2.40	**27.41**	*1.81*
G3.8.1.06	Extra Smooth Finish; Isolated; 200 x 200mm	m	0.41	20.27	4.74	2.68	**27.69**	*1.50*
G3.8.1.07	Rough Board Finish; Isolated; 200 x 300mm	m	0.55	27.03	6.32	3.20	**36.55**	*2.41*
G3.8.1.08	Extra Smooth Finish; Isolated; 200 x 300mm	m	0.55	27.03	6.32	3.58	**36.93**	*1.99*
G3.8.1.09	Rough Board Finish; Isolated; 400 x 400mm	m	0.83	40.54	9.47	4.80	**54.81**	*3.62*
G3.8.1.10	Extra Smooth Finish; Isolated; 400 x 400mm	m	0.83	40.54	9.47	5.37	**55.38**	*2.99*
G3.8.1.11	Rough Board Finish; Isolated; 400 x 600mm	m	1.10	54.05	12.63	6.40	**73.08**	*4.82*
G3.8.1.12	Extra Smooth Finish; Isolated; 400 x 600mm	m	1.10	54.05	12.63	7.16	**73.84**	*3.99*
G3.8.1.13	Rough Board Finish; Isolated; 500 x 800mm	m	1.45	70.94	16.58	8.40	**95.92**	*6.33*
G3.8.1.14	Extra Smooth Finish; Isolated; 500 x 800mm	m	1.45	70.94	16.58	9.40	**96.92**	*5.23*
G3.8.1.15	Rough Board Finish; Attached; 100 x 200mm	m	0.35	16.89	2.61	1.60	**21.10**	*1.27*
G3.8.1.16	Extra Smooth Finish; Attached; 100 x 200mm	m	0.35	16.89	2.61	1.79	**21.29**	*1.06*
G3.8.1.17	Rough Board Finish; Attached; 100 x 300mm	m	0.48	23.65	5.53	2.14	**31.32**	*1.80*
G3.8.1.18	Extra Smooth Finish; Attached; 100 x 300mm	m	0.48	23.65	5.53	2.47	**31.65**	*1.55*
G3.8.1.19	Rough Board Finish; Attached; 200 x 200mm	m	0.41	20.27	4.74	1.93	**26.94**	*1.59*
G3.8.1.20	Extra Smooth Finish; Attached; 200 x 200mm	m	0.41	20.27	4.74	2.16	**27.17**	*1.34*
G3.8.1.21	Rough Board Finish; Attached; 200 x 300mm	m	0.55	27.03	6.32	2.56	**35.91**	*2.12*
G3.8.1.22	Extra Smooth Finish; Attached; 200 x 300mm	m	0.57	28.01	6.29	2.87	**37.17**	*1.77*
G3.8.1.23	Rough Board Finish; Attached; 400 x 400mm	m	0.83	40.54	9.47	3.84	**53.85**	*3.17*

G3 Formwork: Other stated finish continued...

		Unit	Labour Hours	Labour Net £	Plant Net £	Materials Net £	Unit Net £	CO_2 *Kg*
G3.8	**For concrete components of constant cross-section**							
G3.8.1	Beams							
G3.8.1.24	Extra Smooth Finish; Attached; 400 x 400mm	m	0.86	42.30	9.44	4.29	**56.03**	*2.65*
G3.8.1.25	Rough Board Finish; Attached; 400 x 600mm	m	1.10	54.05	12.63	5.13	**71.81**	*4.23*
G3.8.1.26	Extra Smooth Finish; Attached; 400 x 600mm	m	1.15	56.40	12.58	5.74	**74.72**	*3.54*
G3.8.1.27	Rough Board Finish; Attached; 500 x 800mm	m	1.45	70.94	16.58	6.73	**94.25**	*5.55*
G3.8.1.28	Extra Smooth Finish; Attached; 500 x 800mm	m	1.45	70.94	16.58	7.53	**95.05**	*4.68*
G3.8.2	Columns							
G3.8.2.01	Rough Board Finish; Isolated; 100 x 200mm	m	0.41	20.27	3.08	2.52	**25.87**	*1.63*
G3.8.2.02	Extra Smooth Finish; Isolated; 100 x 200mm	m	0.41	20.27	3.08	2.82	**26.17**	*1.30*
G3.8.2.03	Rough Board Finish; Isolated; 100 x 300mm	m	0.56	27.17	4.16	3.36	**34.69**	*2.18*
G3.8.2.04	Extra Smooth Finish; Isolated; 100 x 300mm	m	0.56	27.17	4.16	3.76	**35.09**	*1.74*
G3.8.2.05	Rough Board Finish; Isolated; 200 x 200mm	m	0.56	27.17	4.16	3.36	**34.69**	*2.18*
G3.8.2.06	Extra Smooth Finish; Isolated; 200 x 200mm	m	0.56	27.17	4.16	3.76	**35.09**	*1.74*
G3.8.2.07	Rough Board Finish; Isolated; 200 x 300mm	m	0.58	28.20	5.10	4.21	**37.51**	*2.72*
G3.8.2.08	Extra Smooth Finish; Isolated; 200 x 300mm	m	0.58	28.20	5.10	4.71	**38.01**	*2.17*
G3.8.2.09	Rough Board Finish; Isolated; 400 x 400mm	m	0.81	39.66	8.19	6.71	**54.56**	*4.34*
G3.8.2.10	Extra Smooth Finish; Isolated; 400 x 400mm	m	0.81	39.66	8.19	7.50	**55.35**	*3.46*
G3.8.2.11	Rough Board Finish; Isolated; 400 x 600mm	m	0.92	44.99	10.27	8.40	**63.66**	*5.43*
G3.8.2.12	Extra Smooth Finish; Isolated; 400 x 600mm	m	0.92	44.99	10.27	9.40	**64.66**	*4.34*
G3.8.2.13	Rough Board Finish; Isolated; 500 x 800mm	m	1.20	58.85	13.39	10.92	**83.16**	*7.07*
G3.8.2.14	Extra Smooth Finish; Isolated; 500 x 800mm	m	1.20	58.85	13.39	12.21	**84.45**	*5.65*
G3.8.2.15	Rough Board Finish; Attached; 100 x 200mm	m	0.28	13.51	3.08	20.94	**37.53**	*10.19*
G3.8.2.16	Extra Smooth Finish; Attached; 100 x 200mm	m	0.28	13.51	3.08	23.42	**40.01**	*7.47*
G3.8.2.17	Rough Board Finish; Attached; 100 x 300mm	m	0.37	18.12	4.16	2.94	**25.22**	*1.98*
G3.8.2.18	Extra Smooth Finish; Attached; 100 x 300mm	m	0.37	18.12	4.16	3.29	**25.57**	*1.60*
G3.8.2.19	Rough Board Finish; Attached; 200 x 200mm	m	0.37	18.12	4.16	2.52	**24.80**	*1.79*
G3.8.2.20	Extra Smooth Finish; Attached; 200 x 200mm	m	0.37	18.12	4.16	2.82	**25.10**	*1.46*
G3.8.2.21	Rough Board Finish; Attached; 200 x 300mm	m	0.46	22.57	5.10	3.36	**31.03**	*2.32*
G3.8.2.22	Extra Smooth Finish; Attached; 200 x 300mm	m	0.46	22.57	5.10	3.76	**31.43**	*1.88*
G3.8.2.23	Rough Board Finish; Attached; 400 x 400mm	m	0.74	36.03	8.19	5.04	**49.26**	*3.56*

G3 Formwork: Other stated finish continued...

		Unit	Labour Hours	Labour Net £	Plant Net £	Materials Net £	Unit Net £	CO_2 Kg
G3.8	**For concrete components of constant cross-section**							
G3.8.2	Columns							
G3.8.2.24	Extra Smooth Finish; Attached; 400 x 400mm	m	0.74	36.03	8.19	5.63	**49.85**	*2.90*
G3.8.2.25	Rough Board Finish; Attached; 400 x 600mm	m	0.92	44.99	10.27	6.73	**61.99**	*4.66*
G3.8.2.26	Extra Smooth Finish; Attached; 400 x 600mm	m	0.92	44.99	10.27	7.53	**62.79**	*3.78*
G3.8.2.27	Rough Board Finish; Attached; 500 x 800mm	m	1.20	58.85	13.39	8.82	**81.06**	*6.09*
G3.8.2.28	Extra Smooth Finish; Attached; 500 x 800mm	m	1.20	58.85	13.39	9.87	**82.11**	*4.94*
G3.8.3	Walls							
G3.8.3.01	Rough Board Finish; 250mm thick x 750mm high	m	0.86	41.86	9.24	6.00	**57.10**	*4.16*
G3.8.3.02	Extra Smooth Finish; 250mm thick x 750mm high	m	0.86	41.86	9.24	6.71	**57.81**	*3.38*
G3.8.3.03	Rough Board Finish; 250mm thick x 1000mm high	m	1.10	53.86	12.32	8.00	**74.18**	*5.55*
G3.8.3.04	Extra Smooth Finish; 250mm thick x 1000mm high	m	1.12	54.84	12.75	8.95	**76.54**	*4.55*
G3.8.3.05	Rough Board Finish; 400mm thick x 1000mm high	m	1.10	53.86	12.32	8.00	**74.18**	*5.55*
G3.8.3.06	Extra Smooth Finish; 400mm thick x 1000mm high	m	1.10	53.86	12.32	8.95	**75.13**	*4.51*
G3.8.4	Other Members							
G3.8.4.01	Rough Board Finish; Box culverts; Internal dimensions 1 x 1m; wall thickness 250mm	m	4.46	218.56	39.88	34.09	**292.53**	*21.94*
G3.8.4.02	Extra Smooth Finish; Box culverts; Internal dimensions 1 x 1m; wall thickness 250mm	m	4.46	218.56	39.88	38.14	**296.58**	*17.51*
G3.8.4.03	Rough Board Finish; Box culverts; Internal dimensions 2 x 2m; wall thickness 250mm	m	10.32	505.22	111.72	102.24	**719.18**	*64.30*
G3.8.4.04	Extra Smooth Finish; Box culverts; Internal dimensions 2 x 2m; wall thickness 250mm	m	10.32	505.22	111.72	114.36	**731.30**	*50.99*
G3.8.4.05	Rough Board Finish; Box culverts; Internal dimensions 2 x 2m; wall thickness 400mm	m	10.86	531.66	114.67	108.52	**754.85**	*67.69*
G3.8.4.06	Extra Smooth Finish; Box culverts; Internal dimensions 2 x 2m; wall thickness 400mm	m	10.86	531.66	114.67	121.39	**767.72**	*53.57*
G3.8.5	Projections							
G3.8.5.01	Extra Smooth Finish; Nibs; 50 x 50mm deep	m	0.36	17.63	2.76	2.63	**23.02**	*1.35*
G3.8.5.02	Extra Smooth Finish; Nibs; 100 x 100mm deep	m	0.36	17.63	2.76	4.87	**25.26**	*2.01*
G3.8.6	Intrusions							
G3.8.6.01	Extra Smooth Finish; Rebates 50 x 50mm deep	m	0.36	17.63	1.30	2.63	**21.56**	*1.05*
G3.8.6.02	Extra Smooth Finish; Rebates 100 x 100mm deep	m	0.36	17.63	1.30	2.63	**21.56**	*1.05*

G5 Reinforcement

		Unit	Labour Hours	Labour Net £	Plant Net £	Materials Net £	Unit Net £	*CO_2 Kg*
G5.1	**Plain round steel bars, BS 4449**							
G5.1.1	Nominal size: 6mm							
G5.1.1.01	Standard lengths	Tonne	16.96	778.97	183.43	636.68	1,599.08	*1,743.19*
G5.1.1.02	Bent and cut to length	Tonne	16.96	778.97	183.43	711.71	1,674.11	*1,743.19*
G5.1.2	Nominal size: 8mm							
G5.1.2.01	Standard lengths	Tonne	16.96	778.97	183.34	619.19	1,581.50	*1,743.17*
G5.1.2.02	Bent and cut to length	Tonne	16.96	778.97	183.34	692.11	1,654.42	*1,743.17*
G5.1.3	Nominal size: 10mm							
G5.1.3.01	Standard lengths	Tonne	13.65	626.94	147.56	594.32	1,368.82	*1,736.70*
G5.1.3.02	Bent and cut to length	Tonne	13.65	626.94	147.56	664.50	1,439.00	*1,736.70*
G5.1.4	Nominal size: 12mm							
G5.1.4.01	Standard lengths	Tonne	11.82	542.89	127.77	579.78	1,250.44	*1,733.12*
G5.1.4.02	Bent and cut to length	Tonne	11.82	542.89	127.77	648.27	1,318.93	*1,733.12*
G5.1.5	Nominal size: 16mm							
G5.1.5.01	Standard lengths	Tonne	10.28	472.16	111.13	547.95	1,131.24	*1,730.11*
G5.1.5.02	Bent and cut to length	Tonne	10.28	472.16	111.13	612.65	1,195.94	*1,730.11*
G5.1.6	Nominal size: 20mm							
G5.1.6.01	Standard lengths	Tonne	9.59	440.47	103.67	547.95	1,092.09	*1,728.76*
G5.1.6.02	Bent and cut to length	Tonne	9.59	440.47	103.67	612.65	1,156.79	*1,728.76*
G5.1.7	Nominal size: 25mm							
G5.1.7.01	Standard lengths	Tonne	8.79	403.72	95.02	547.95	1,046.69	*1,727.19*
G5.1.7.02	Bent and cut to length	Tonne	8.79	403.72	95.02	612.23	1,110.97	*1,727.19*
G5.1.8	Nominal size: exceeding 32mm							
G5.1.8.01	32mm; Standard lengths	Tonne	8.35	383.52	90.26	550.90	1,024.68	*1,726.33*
G5.1.8.02	32mm; Bent and cut to length	Tonne	8.35	383.52	90.26	615.81	1,089.59	*1,726.33*
G5.1.8.03	40mm; Standard lengths	Tonne	7.85	360.55	84.86	554.91	1,000.32	*1,725.35*
G5.1.8.04	40mm; Bent and cut to length	Tonne	7.85	360.55	84.86	622.98	1,068.39	*1,725.35*
G5.2	**Deformed high yield steel bars, BS 4449**							
G5.2.1	Nominal size: 6mm							
G5.2.1.01	Standard lengths	Tonne	16.96	778.97	183.34	636.68	1,598.99	*1,743.17*
G5.2.1.02	Bent and cut to length	Tonne	16.96	778.97	183.34	711.71	1,674.02	*1,743.17*
G5.2.2	Nominal size: 8mm							
G5.2.2.01	Standard lengths	Tonne	16.96	778.97	183.34	619.19	1,581.50	*1,743.17*
G5.2.2.02	Bent and cut to length	Tonne	16.96	778.97	183.34	692.11	1,654.42	*1,743.17*
G5.2.3	Nominal size: 10mm							
G5.2.3.01	Standard lengths	Tonne	13.65	626.94	147.56	594.32	1,368.82	*1,736.70*
G5.2.3.02	Bent and cut to length	Tonne	13.65	626.94	147.56	664.50	1,439.00	*1,736.70*

G5 Reinforcement continued...

		Unit	Labour Hours	Labour Net £	Plant Net £	Materials Net £	Unit Net £	CO_2 Kg
G5.2	**Deformed high yield steel bars, BS 4449**							
G5.2.4	Nominal size: 12mm							
G5.2.4.01	Standard lengths	Tonne	11.82	542.89	127.77	579.78	1,250.44	*1,733.12*
G5.2.4.02	Bent and cut to length	Tonne	11.82	542.89	127.77	648.27	1,318.93	*1,733.12*
G5.2.5	Nominal size: 16mm							
G5.2.5.01	Standard lengths	Tonne	10.28	472.16	111.13	547.95	1,131.24	*1,730.11*
G5.2.5.02	Bent and cut to length	Tonne	10.28	472.16	111.13	612.65	1,195.94	*1,730.11*
G5.2.6	Nominal size: 20mm							
G5.2.6.01	Standard lengths	Tonne	9.59	440.47	103.67	547.95	1,092.09	*1,728.76*
G5.2.6.02	Bent and cut to length	Tonne	9.59	440.47	103.67	612.65	1,156.79	*1,728.76*
G5.2.7	Nominal size: 25mm							
G5.2.7.01	Standard lengths	Tonne	8.79	403.72	95.02	547.95	1,046.69	*1,727.19*
G5.2.7.02	Bent and cut to length	Tonne	8.79	403.72	95.02	612.65	1,111.39	*1,727.19*
G5.2.8	Nominal size: exceeding 32mm							
G5.2.8.01	32mm; Standard lengths	Tonne	8.35	383.52	90.26	550.90	1,024.68	*1,726.33*
G5.2.8.02	32mm; Bent and cut to length	Tonne	8.35	383.52	90.26	615.81	1,089.59	*1,726.33*
G5.2.8.03	40mm; Standard lengths	Tonne	7.85	360.55	84.86	554.91	1,000.32	*1,725.35*
G5.2.8.04	40mm; Bent and cut to length	Tonne	7.85	360.55	84.86	622.98	1,068.39	*1,725.35*
G5.3	**Stainless steel bars of stated quality**							
G5.3.3	Nominal size: 10mm							
G5.3.3.01	Stainless steel bars; type 316 S66 stainless steel and warm worked; standard lengths	Tonne	13.65	626.94	147.56	4,690.00	5,464.50	*6,176.70*
G5.3.3.02	as above; bent and cut to length	Tonne	13.65	626.94	147.56	4,880.00	5,654.50	*6,176.70*
G5.3.4	Nominal size: 12mm							
G5.3.4.01	Stainless steel bars; type 316 S66 stainless steel and warm worked; standard lengths	Tonne	11.82	542.89	127.77	4,070.00	4,740.66	*6,173.12*
G5.3.4.02	as above; bent and cut to length	Tonne	11.82	542.89	127.77	4,240.50	4,911.16	*6,173.12*
G5.3.5	Nominal size: 16mm							
G5.3.5.01	Stainless steel bars; type 316 S66 stainless steel and warm worked; standard lengths	Tonne	10.28	472.16	111.13	4,207.00	4,790.29	*6,170.11*
G5.3.5.02	as above; bent and cut to length	Tonne	10.28	472.16	111.13	4,335.00	4,918.29	*6,170.11*
G5.3.6	Nominal size: 20mm							
G5.3.6.01	Stainless steel bars; type 316 S66 stainless steel and warm worked; standard lengths	Tonne	9.59	440.47	103.67	5,300.00	5,844.14	*6,168.76*
G5.3.6.02	as above; bent and cut to length	Tonne	9.59	440.47	103.67	5,445.50	5,989.64	*6,168.76*
G5.3.7	Nominal size: 25mm							
G5.3.7.01	Stainless steel bars; type 316 S66 stainless steel and warm worked; standard lengths	Tonne	8.79	403.72	95.02	5,715.00	6,213.74	*6,167.19*
G5.3.7.02	as above; bent and cut to length	Tonne	8.79	403.72	95.02	5,844.00	6,342.74	*6,167.19*

G5 Reinforcement continued...

		Unit	Labour Hours	Labour Net £	Plant Net £	Materials Net £	Unit Net £	CO_2 Kg
G5.3	**Stainless steel bars of stated quality**							
G5.3.8	Nominal size: exceeding 32mm							
G5.3.8.01	Stainless steel bars; type 316 S66 stainless steel and warm worked; standard lengths	Tonne	8.35	383.52	90.26	5,567.00	**6,040.78**	*6,166.33*
G5.3.8.02	as above; bent and cut to length	Tonne	8.35	383.52	90.26	5,696.50	**6,170.28**	*6,166.33*
G5.5	**Special joints**							
G5.5.1	Plain round steel bars, BS 4449 welded to mild steel; including wire brush cleaning and preparing surfaces. (Cost of bars not included).							
G5.5.1.01	Nominal size: 6mm	Nr	0.70	33.40	2.46	0.04	**35.90**	*1.54*
G5.5.1.02	Nominal size: 8mm	Nr	0.70	33.40	2.46	0.04	**35.90**	*1.54*
G5.5.1.03	Nominal size: 20mm	Nr	1.50	71.56	5.28	0.11	**76.95**	*3.34*
G5.5.2	Deformed high yield bars, BS 4449 welded to mild steel; including wire brush cleaning and preparing surfaces. (Cost of bars not included).							
G5.5.2.01	Nominal size: 6mm	Nr	0.70	33.40	2.46	0.04	**35.90**	*1.54*
G5.5.2.02	Nominal size: 8mm	Nr	0.70	33.40	2.46	0.04	**35.90**	*1.54*
G5.5.2.03	Nominal size: 20mm	Nr	1.50	71.56	5.28	0.11	**76.95**	*3.34*
G5.5.3	Stainless steel bars type 316, S66 welded to mild steel; including wire brush cleaning and preparing surfaces. (Cost of bars not included).							
G5.5.3.01	Nominal size: 6mm	Nr	0.80	38.17	2.82	0.13	**41.12**	*1.87*
G5.5.3.02	Nominal size: 8mm	Nr	0.80	38.17	2.82	0.13	**41.12**	*1.87*
G5.5.3.03	Nominal size: 20mm	Nr	1.60	76.34	5.63	0.38	**82.35**	*3.89*
G5.6	**Steel fabric, BS 4483**							
G5.6.1	Nominal mass: not exceeding 2kg/m^2							
G5.6.1.01	0.77kg/m2; D49	m^2	0.06	2.76	-	1.35	**4.11**	*1.93*
G5.6.1.02	1.54kg/m2; A98	m^2	0.06	2.76	-	1.48	**4.24**	*3.87*
G5.6.2	Nominal mass: 2 - 3kg/m^2							
G5.6.2.01	2.22kg/m2; A142	m^2	0.06	2.76	-	1.43	**4.19**	*5.57*
G5.6.2.02	2.61kg/m2; C283	m^2	0.06	2.76	-	1.85	**4.61**	*6.55*
G5.6.3	Nominal mass: 3 - 4kg/m^2							
G5.6.3.01	3.02kg/m2; A193	m^2	0.06	2.76	-	1.98	**4.74**	*7.58*
G5.6.3.02	3.05kg/m2; B196	m^2	0.07	3.22	-	3.62	**6.84**	*7.66*
G5.6.3.03	3.41kg/m2; C385	m^2	0.07	3.22	-	2.23	**5.45**	*8.56*
G5.6.3.04	3.73kg/m2; B283	m^2	0.07	3.22	-	2.42	**5.64**	*9.36*
G5.6.3.05	3.95kg/m2; A252	m^2	0.09	4.13	-	2.61	**6.74**	*9.92*
G5.6.4	Nominal mass: 4 - 5kg/m^2							
G5.6.4.01	4.34kg/m2; C503	m^2	0.09	4.13	-	2.87	**7.00**	*10.89*
G5.6.4.02	4.53kg/m2; B385	m^2	0.10	4.59	-	2.94	**7.53**	*11.37*

G5 Reinforcement continued...

		Unit	Labour Hours	Labour Net £	Plant Net £	Materials Net £	Unit Net £	CO_2 Kg
G5.6	**Steel fabric, BS 4483**							
G5.6.5	Nominal mass: 5 - 6kg/m²							
G5.6.5.01	5.55kg/m2; C636	m²	0.10	4.59	-	3.67	**8.26**	*13.93*
G5.6.5.02	5.93kg/m2; B503	m²	0.10	4.59	-	3.85	**8.44**	*14.88*
G5.6.6	Nominal mass: 6 - 7kg/m²							
G5.6.6.01	6.16kg/m2; A393	m²	0.13	5.97	1.41	4.00	**11.38**	*15.72*
G5.6.6.02	6.72kg/m2; C785	m²	0.13	5.97	1.41	4.02	**11.40**	*17.12*
G5.6.8	Nominal mass: stated exceeding 8kg/m²							
G5.6.8.01	8.14kg/m2; B785	m²	0.13	5.97	1.41	5.24	**12.62**	*20.69*
G5.6.8.02	10.90kg/m2; B1131	m²	0.14	6.43	1.51	7.04	**14.98**	*27.71*

G6 Joints

		Unit	Labour Hours	Labour Net £	Plant Net £	Materials Net £	Unit Net £	CO_2 Kg
G6.1	**Open surface plain**							
G6.1.1	Average width: stated exceeding 0.5m							
G6.1.1.01	Generally	m²	0.10	2.79	0.92	-	**3.71**	*0.66*
G6.1.2	Average width : 0.5 - 1m							
G6.1.2.01	Generally	m²	0.09	2.51	0.82	-	**3.33**	*0.59*
G6.1.3	Average width : 1.5m							
G6.1.3.01	Generally	m²	0.08	2.23	0.73	-	**2.96**	*0.53*
G6.2	**Open surface with filler**							
G6.2.1	Average width : stated exceeding 0.5m							
G6.2.1.01	13mm Korkpak joint filler	m²	0.23	11.26	-	7.07	**18.33**	*1.65*
G6.2.1.02	19mm Korkpak joint filler	m²	0.23	11.26	-	10.85	**22.11**	*2.38*
G6.2.1.03	25mm Korkpak joint filler	m²	0.23	11.26	-	12.79	**24.05**	*3.30*
G6.2.2	Average width : 0.5 - 1m							
G6.2.2.01	13mm Korkpak joint filler	m²	0.20	9.79	-	7.07	**16.86**	*1.65*
G6.2.2.02	19mm Korkpak joint filler	m²	0.20	9.79	-	10.85	**20.64**	*2.38*
G6.2.2.03	25mm Korkpak joint filler	m²	0.20	9.79	-	12.79	**22.58**	*3.30*
G6.2.3	Average width : 1.5m							
G6.2.3.01	13mm Korkpak joint filler	m²	0.17	8.32	-	7.07	**15.39**	*1.65*
G6.2.3.02	19mm Korkpak joint filler	m²	0.17	8.32	-	10.85	**19.17**	*2.38*
G6.2.3.03	25mm Korkpak joint filler	m²	0.17	8.32	-	12.79	**21.11**	*3.30*
G6.3	**Formed surface plain**							
G6.3.1	Average width : stated exceeding 0.5m							
G6.3.1.01	Generally; including formwork	m²	0.51	24.87	5.63	5.04	**35.54**	*2.81*

G6 Joints continued...

		Unit	Labour Hours	Labour Net £	Plant Net £	Materials Net £	Unit Net £	CO_2 Kg
G6.3	**Formed surface plain**							
G6.3.2	Average width : 0.5 - 1m							
G6.3.2.01	Generally; including formwork	m^2	0.69	33.78	7.54	5.04	**46.36**	*3.11*
G6.3.3	Average width : 1.5m							
G6.3.3.01	Generally; including formwork	m^2	0.75	36.62	7.93	5.04	**49.59**	*3.20*
G6.4	**Formed surface with filler**							
G6.4.1	Average width : stated exceeding 0.5m							
G6.4.1.01	13mm Korkpak joint filler	m^2	0.63	30.75	3.91	12.12	**46.78**	*4.41*
G6.4.1.02	19mm Korkpak joint filler	m^2	0.63	30.75	5.63	15.90	**52.28**	*5.19*
G6.4.1.03	25mm Korkpak joint filler	m^2	0.63	30.75	5.63	17.84	**54.22**	*6.11*
G6.4.2	Average width : 0.5 - 1m							
G6.4.2.01	13mm Korkpak joint filler	m^2	0.69	33.78	4.30	12.12	**50.20**	*4.49*
G6.4.2.02	19mm Korkpak joint filler	m^2	0.69	33.98	6.19	15.90	**56.07**	*5.27*
G6.4.2.03	25mm Korkpak joint filler	m^2	0.69	33.98	6.19	17.84	**58.01**	*6.20*
G6.4.3	Average width : 1.5m							
G6.4.3.01	13mm Korkpak joint filler	m^2	0.75	36.72	4.68	12.12	**53.52**	*4.56*
G6.4.3.02	19mm Korkpak joint filler	m^2	0.75	36.62	6.81	15.90	**59.33**	*5.36*
G6.4.3.03	25mm Korkpak joint filler	m^2	0.75	36.62	6.81	17.84	**61.27**	*6.29*
G6.5	**Plastics or rubber waterstops**							
G6.5.1	Average width : not exceeding 150mm							
G6.5.1.01	PVC Flat 'X' dumbell junction pieces; width 100mm	Nr	0.55	26.93	-	25.33	**52.26**	*9.19*
G6.5.1.02	Rubber flat dumbell; width 150mm	Nr	0.21	10.28	-	35.44	**45.72**	*7.16*
G6.5.1.03	Rubber flat 'L' dumbell junction piece; width 150mm	Nr	0.31	15.18	-	84.99	**100.17**	*13.17*
G6.5.1.04	Rubber vertical 'L' dumbell junction piece; width 150mm	Nr	0.50	24.48	-	84.99	**109.47**	*13.17*
G6.5.1.05	Heavy duty PVC flat 'T' dumbell junction piece; width 150mm	Nr	0.50	24.48	-	84.77	**109.25**	*10.28*
G6.5.1.06	Heavy duty PVC vertical 'T' dumbell junction piece; width 150mm	Nr	0.55	26.93	-	84.77	**111.70**	*10.28*
G6.5.1.07	Heavy duty PVC flat 'X' dumbell junction piece; width 150mm	Nr	0.60	29.38	-	102.38	**131.76**	*10.48*
G6.5.2	Average width : 150 - 200mm							
G6.5.2.01	PVC Flat centre bulb; width 150mm	Nr	0.55	26.93	-	25.33	**52.26**	*9.19*
G6.5.2.02	PVC Flat 'L' centre bulb junction (2 way); width 150mm	Nr	0.31	15.18	-	12.14	**27.32**	*9.98*
G6.5.2.03	PVC Vertical 'L' centre bulb junction (2 way); width 150mm	Nr	0.50	24.48	-	10.93	**35.41**	*9.98*
G6.5.2.04	PVC Flat 'T' centre bulb junction (3 way); width 150mm	Nr	0.50	24.48	-	23.71	**48.19**	*10.28*

G6 Joints continued...

		Unit	Labour Hours	Labour Net £	Plant Net £	Materials Net £	Unit Net £	CO_2 Kg
G6.5	**Plastics or rubber waterstops**							
G6.5.2	Average width : 150 - 200mm							
G6.5.2.05	PVC Vertical 'T' centre bulb junction (3 way); width 150mm	Nr	0.55	26.93	-	25.04	**51.97**	*10.28*
G6.5.2.06	PVC Flat 'X' dumbell junction pieces; width 170mm	Nr	0.60	29.38	-	28.88	**58.26**	*10.48*
G6.5.3	Average width : 200 - 300mm							
G6.5.3.01	PVC Flat centre bulb; width 200mm	Nr	0.26	12.73	-	9.74	**22.47**	*4.99*
G6.5.3.02	PVC Flat centre bulb; width 250mm	Nr	0.31	15.18	-	12.45	**27.63**	*6.24*
G6.5.3.03	PVC Flat 'L' centre bulb junction (2 way); width 200mm	Nr	0.36	17.63	-	17.87	**35.50**	*10.19*
G6.5.3.04	PVC Flat 'L' centre bulb junction (2 way); width 250mm	Nr	0.36	17.63	-	22.85	**40.48**	*10.39*
G6.5.3.05	PVC Vertical 'L' centre bulb junction (2 way); width 200mm	Nr	0.55	26.93	-	19.08	**46.01**	*10.19*
G6.5.3.06	PVC Vertical 'L' centre bulb junction (2 way); width 250mm	Nr	0.60	29.38	-	20.93	**50.31**	*10.39*
G6.5.3.07	PVC Flat 'T' centre bulb junction (3 way); width 200mm	Nr	0.55	26.93	-	28.12	**55.05**	*10.49*
G6.5.3.08	PVC Flat 'T' centre bulb junction (3 way); width 250mm	Nr	0.60	29.38	-	34.31	**63.69**	*10.71*
G6.5.3.09	PVC Vertical 'T' centre bulb junction (3 way); width 200mm	Nr	0.60	29.38	-	28.88	**58.26**	*10.49*
G6.5.3.10	PVC Vertical 'T' centre bulb junction (3 way); width 250mm	Nr	0.60	29.38	-	35.12	**64.50**	*10.71*
G6.5.3.11	PVC Flat 'X' dumbell junction pieces; width 210mm	Nr	0.65	31.82	-	34.77	**66.59**	*10.68*
G6.5.3.12	PVC Flat 'X' dumbell junction pieces; width 250mm	Nr	0.70	34.27	-	42.20	**76.47**	*10.92*
G6.5.3.13	Rubber flat dumbell; width 230mm	m	0.26	12.73	-	51.38	**64.11**	*10.97*
G6.5.3.14	Rubber flat 'L' dumbell junction piece; width 230mm	Nr	0.36	17.63	-	98.70	**116.33**	*13.71*
G6.5.3.15	Rubber vertical 'L' dumbell junction piece; width 230mm	Nr	0.60	29.38	-	98.70	**128.08**	*13.71*
G6.5.3.16	Heavy duty PVC flat 'T' dumbell junction piece; width 230mm	Nr	0.60	29.38	-	106.29	**135.67**	*10.71*
G6.5.3.17	Heavy duty PVC vertical 'T' dumbell junction piece; width 230mm	Nr	0.65	31.82	-	106.28	**138.10**	*10.71*
G6.5.3.18	Heavy duty PVC flat 'X' dumbell junction piece; width 230mm	Nr	0.70	34.27	-	119.37	**153.64**	*10.92*
G6.7	**Sealed rebates or grooves**							
G6.7.1	Cold poured Expandite Colpor 200 joint sealing compound; forming groove							
G6.7.1.01	5 x 15mm	m	0.15	4.18	-	0.27	**4.45**	*0.01*
G6.7.1.02	10 x 10mm	m	0.15	4.18	-	0.45	**4.63**	*0.01*
G6.7.1.03	10 x 15mm	m	0.15	4.18	-	0.53	**4.71**	*0.01*
G6.7.1.04	10 x 20mm	m	0.15	4.18	-	0.71	**4.89**	*0.02*
G6.7.1.05	10 x 25mm	m	0.15	4.18	-	1.07	**5.25**	*0.03*
G6.7.1.06	15 x 20mm	m	0.15	4.18	-	1.16	**5.34**	*0.03*

G6 Joints continued...

		Unit	Labour Hours	Labour Net £	Plant Net £	Materials Net £	Unit Net £	CO_2 Kg
G6.7	**Sealed rebates or grooves**							
G6.7.1	Cold poured Expandite Colpor 200 joint sealing compound; forming groove							
G6.7.1.07	15 x 25mm	m	0.15	4.18	-	1.25	5.43	*0.03*
G6.7.1.08	15 x 40mm	m	0.25	6.97	-	2.67	9.64	*0.07*
G6.7.1.09	20 x 25mm	m	0.25	6.97	-	2.23	9.20	*0.06*
G6.7.1.10	20 x 40mm	m	0.25	6.97	-	3.56	10.53	*0.10*
G6.7.1.11	20 x 50mm	m	0.25	6.97	-	4.45	11.42	*0.12*
G6.7.1.12	25 x 30mm	m	0.25	6.97	-	3.20	10.17	*0.09*
G6.7.1.13	25 x 40mm	m	0.25	6.97	-	4.45	11.42	*0.12*
G6.7.1.14	25 x 50mm	m	0.35	9.75	-	4.98	14.73	*0.13*
G6.7.1.15	30 x 40mm	m	0.35	9.75	-	5.34	15.09	*0.14*
G6.7.1.16	30 x 50mm	m	0.35	9.75	-	6.76	16.51	*0.18*
G6.7.1.17	50 x 50mm	m	0.45	12.54	-	10.68	23.22	*0.29*
G6.8	**Dowels**							
G6.8.1	Plain or greased							
G6.8.1.01	Plain mild steel dowel bars with cages 0.5m long; cast into one side of joint; 12mm diameter	Nr	0.10	4.59	-	0.14	4.73	*1.51*
G6.8.1.02	as above; 16mm diameter	Nr	0.10	4.59	-	0.25	4.84	*2.68*
G6.8.1.03	as above; 20mm diameter	Nr	0.13	5.74	-	0.38	6.12	*4.19*
G6.8.1.04	as above; 25mm diameter	Nr	0.13	5.74	-	0.54	6.28	*6.54*
G6.8.1.05	Plain mild steel dowel bars with cages 1m long; cast into one side of joint; 12mm diameter	Nr	0.13	5.74	-	0.26	6.00	*1.51*
G6.8.1.06	as above; 16mm diameter	Nr	0.13	5.74	-	0.46	6.20	*2.68*
G6.8.1.07	as above; 20mm diameter	Nr	0.15	6.89	-	0.68	7.57	*4.19*
G6.8.1.08	as above; 25mm diameter	Nr	0.15	6.89	-	0.96	7.85	*6.54*
G6.8.1.09	Plain mild steel dowel bars with cages 1m long; cast into one side of joint and debonding for a length of 500mm; 12mm diameter	Nr	0.15	6.89	-	0.26	7.15	*1.51*
G6.8.1.10	as above; 16mm diameter	Nr	0.15	6.89	-	0.46	7.35	*2.68*
G6.8.1.11	as above; 20mm diameter	Nr	0.17	7.58	-	0.68	8.26	*4.19*
G6.8.1.12	as above; 25mm diameter	Nr	0.17	7.58	-	0.96	8.54	*6.54*
G6.8.2	Sleeved or capped							
G6.8.2.02	16mm diameter	Nr	0.17	7.58	-	0.46	8.04	*2.68*
G6.8.2.03	20mm diameter	Nr	0.18	8.27	-	0.68	8.95	*4.19*
G6.8.2.04	25mm diameter	Nr	0.18	8.27	-	0.96	9.23	*6.54*

G7 Post-tensioned Prestressing

Note(s): The following prices are guide prices only for the use in preliminary approximate estimating.

Prestressing tendons vary greatly in size, for example the K-Range system provides tendons with capacities in the range of 1060 KN to 10230 KN depending on the number of prestressing strands incorporated in the tendon. The most reasonable method of assessing prestressing costs is probably that based on the tonnage of prestressing steel required, although prices, even on the basis, vary considerably depending on the individual tendon capacity, tendon lengths, total quantities and the type of structure. Tonnage can be assessed on the basis of 4.5kg of steel per metre per 1000kN of Tendon characteristic strenght (Tendon working loads specified are normally around 70% of this value). Current prices are around £2750 + 30% per tonne of prestressing steel. Small works containing less than 15 tonnes of steel would fall at the top end of this price range with the average around 40-50 tonnes. Unit prices bottom out at 100 tonnes and over. Tendons less than 15m long are rarely formed from prestressing steel as for these lengths bar tendons are usually cheaper. EXAMPLE: 12nr. Tendons on each 3 structures, tendons 32mm long with specified force of 3535 KN at 70% characteristic strength.

100% characteristic strength = 3525 / 0.7 = 5036kN

Tonnage = 12 x 3 x 32 x 5036 x 4.5 / 1000 = 26.1 tonnes.

This is a relatively small job so price will be above the median, say £2750 + 15% = £3162.50/tonne x 26.1 tonnes = £82541 and the unit tendon rice / 3 / 12 = £2293 per tendon. The rates include supplying and threading the prestressing cable, the supply and fixing of steel ducts and anchorages and the stressing and grouting of the tendons.

*It is usual for the main contractor to fix in position in their shutter the load distribution trumpet component of the anchorage assembly.

		Unit	Labour Hours	Labour Net £	Plant Net £	Materials Net £	Unit Net £	*CO_2 Kg*
G7.1	**Horizontal internal tendons in in situ concrete**							
G7.1.6	Length: 20 - 25m							
G7.1.6.01	Length: 20 - 25m	Nr	6.00	355.14	337.62	1,650.00	**2,342.76**	*371.68*
G7.1.8	Length: stated exceeding 30m							
G7.1.8.01	Length; 32m	Nr	6.00	355.14	337.62	1,692.00	**2,384.76**	*395.62*
G7.2	**Inclined or vertical internal tendons in in situ concrete**							
G7.2.6	Length: 20 - 25m							
G7.2.6.01	Length: 20 - 25m	Nr	8.00	473.52	450.16	1,650.00	**2,573.68**	*459.90*
G7.2.8	Length: stated exceeding 30m							
G7.2.8.01	Length; 32m	Nr	8.00	473.52	450.16	1,692.00	**2,615.68**	*483.84*

G8 Concrete Accessories

		Unit	Labour Hours	Labour Net £	Plant Net £	Materials Net £	Unit Net £	CO_2 Kg
G8.1	**Finishing of top surfaces**							
G8.1.1	Wood Float							
G8.1.1.01	level	m^2	0.05	1.39	-	-	1.39	-
G8.1.1.02	to crossfalls	m^2	0.07	1.95	-	-	1.95	-
G8.1.2	Steel trowel							
G8.1.2.01	level	m^2	0.05	1.39	-	-	1.39	-
G8.1.2.02	to crossfalls	m^2	0.07	1.95	-	-	1.95	-
G8.2	**Finishing of formed surfaces**							
G8.2.2	Bush hammering							
G8.2.2.01	walls	m^2	0.70	19.51	6.41	-	25.92	*4.62*
G8.2.2.02	beams	m^2	1.00	27.87	9.15	-	37.02	*6.59*
G8.2.2.03	columns	m^2	0.83	23.13	7.59	-	30.72	*5.47*
G8.2.3	Other stated surface treatment carried out after striking formwork							
G8.2.3.01	Rubbing down concrete surfaces after striking formwork; walls	m^2	0.17	4.74	-	-	4.74	-
G8.2.3.02	as above; beams	m^2	0.20	5.57	-	-	5.57	-
G8.2.3.03	as above; columns	m^2	0.20	5.57	-	-	5.57	-
G8.3	**Inserts**							
G8.3.1	Linear inserts							
G8.3.1.01	Building in pipes (supply excluded); 250mm thick reinforced concrete; 100mm nominal bore	m	0.34	16.65	-	-	16.65	-
G8.3.1.02	as above; 150mm nominal bore	m	0.34	16.65	-	-	16.65	-
G8.3.1.03	as above; 300mm nominal bore	m	0.45	22.03	-	-	22.03	-
G8.3.2	Other inserts							
G8.3.2.01	Grouting in foundation bolts (supply excluded); 250mm thick reinforced concrete; 20 x 20 x 100mm deep	Nr	0.25	12.24	-	0.10	12.34	*0.35*
G8.3.2.02	as above; 25 x 25 x 175mm deep	Nr	0.25	12.24	-	0.10	12.34	*0.35*
G8.3.2.03	as above; 200 x 200 x 500mm deep	Nr	0.25	12.24	-	0.19	12.43	*0.70*
G8.3.2.04	as above; 300 x 200 x 500mm deep	Nr	0.25	12.24	-	0.29	12.53	*1.05*
G8.4	**Grouting under plates**							
G8.4.1	Area: not exceeding $0.1m^2$							
G8.4.1.01	Grouting in cement mortar (1:3); 25mm thick, Area:	Nr	0.34	16.65	-	0.29	16.94	*1.05*
G8.4.1.02	Grouting in cement mortar (1:3); 50mm thick, Area:	Nr	0.45	22.03	-	0.58	22.61	*2.11*
G8.4.2	Area: 0.1 - $0.5m^2$							
G8.4.2.01	Grouting in cement mortar (1:3); 25mm thick, Area:	Nr	0.34	16.65	-	0.58	17.23	*2.11*

G8 Concrete Accessories continued...

		Unit	Labour Hours	Labour Net £	Plant Net £	Materials Net £	Unit Net £	CO_2 *Kg*
G8.4	**Grouting under plates**							
G8.4.2	Area: 0.1 - 0.5m²							
G8.4.2.02	Grouting in cement mortar (1:3); 50mm thick, Area:	Nr	0.45	22.03	-	1.15	**23.18**	*4.22*
G8.4.3	Area: 0.5 - 1m²							
G8.4.3.01	Grouting in cement mortar (1:3); 25mm thick, Area:	Nr	0.45	22.03	-	0.96	**22.99**	*3.51*
G8.4.3.02	Grouting in cement mortar (1:3); 50mm thick, Area:	Nr	0.60	29.38	-	0.96	**30.34**	*3.51*
G8.4.4	Area: Stated exceeding 1m²							
G8.4.4.01	Grouting in cement mortar (1:3); 25mm thick, Area:	Nr	0.50	24.48	-	4.80	**29.28**	*17.57*
G8.4.4.02	Grouting in cement mortar (1:3); 50mm thick, Area:	Nr	0.60	29.38	-	4.80	**34.18**	*17.57*

CLASS H:
PRECAST CONCRETE

Calculations used throughout Class H - Precast Concrete

Labour

		Qty		Rate		Total
L G0001ICE	**Precast Concrete Install Labour Gang**					
	Labourer (Skill Rate 3)	2	x	14.34	=	£28.68
	Ganger	1	x	16.99	=	£16.99
	Banksman	1	x	13.53	=	£13.53
	Total hourly cost of gang				**=**	**£59.20**

Plant

		Qty		Rate		Total
P G0001ICE	**Precast Concrete Install Plant Gang**					
	Cranes Transit - 25t	1	x	56.27	=	£56.27
	Total hourly cost of gang				**=**	**£56.27**

Class H - Precast Concrete

H2 Prestressed Pre-tensioned Beams

Note(s): The following prices regarding bridge beams has been derived from a specialist sub-contractor and are guide prices for approximate estimating purpose only. The prices are for supply and deliver only.

		Unit	Labour Hours	Labour Net £	Plant Net £	Materials Net £	**Unit Net £**	*CO_2 Kg*
H2.3	**Length: 7 - 10m**							
H2.3.4	Mass: 1 - 2 t							
H2.3.4.01	Bridge Beams; Inverted 'T' Beams; Length 8m; top flange width 205mm; bottom flange width 495mm; Section T1; depth 380mm; cross-sectional area 98000mm^2; mass 1.88 t	Nr	-	-	-	700.00	**700.00**	*404.20*
H2.3.5	Mass: 2 - 5 t							
H2.3.5.01	Bridge Beams; Inverted 'T' Beams; Length 8m; top flange width 205mm; bottom flange width 495mm; Section T2; depth 420mm; cross-sectional area 106200mm^2; mass 2.04t	Nr	-	-	-	800.00	**800.00**	*438.60*
H2.3.5.02	as above; Section T3; depth 535mm; cross-sectional area 114275mm^2; mass 2.19 t	Nr	-	-	-	900.00	**900.00**	*470.85*
H2.4	**Length: 10 - 15m**							
2.4.5	Mass: 2 - 5t							
H2.4.5.01	Bridge Beams; Inverted 'T' Beams; Length 12m; top flange width 205mm; bottom flange width 495mm; Section T4; depth 575mm; cross-sectional area 122475mm^2; mass 3.54 t	Nr	-	-	-	1,000.00	**1,000.00**	*761.10*
H2.4.5.02	as above; Section T5; depth 615mm; cross-sectional area 130675mm^2; mass 3.76 t	Nr	-	-	-	1,200.00	**1,200.00**	*808.40*
H2.4.5.03	as above; Section T6; depth 655mm; cross-sectional area 138875mm^2; mass 4 t	Nr	-	-	-	1,300.00	**1,300.00**	*860.00*
H2.4.5.04	as above; Section T7; depth 695mm; cross-sectional area 147075mm^2; mass 4.25 t	Nr	-	-	-	1,500.00	**1,500.00**	*913.75*
H2.4.5.05	as above; Section T8; depth 735mm; cross-sectional area 155160mm^2; mass 4.48 t	Nr	-	-	-	1,700.00	**1,700.00**	*963.20*
H2.5	**Length: 15 - 20m**							
2.5.6	Mass: 5 - 10t							
H2.5.6.01 H	Bridge Beams; Inverted 'T' Beams; Length 18m; top flange width 400mm; bottom flange width 970mm; Section T9; depth 775mm; cross-sectional area 163 360mm^2; mass 7.06 t	Nr	-	-	-	1,800.00	**1,800.00**	*1,517.90*
H2.5.6.02	as above; Section T10; depth 815mm; cross-sectional area 171560mm^2; mass 7.43 t	Nr	-	-	-	2,000.00	**2,000.00**	*1,597.45*

H2 Prestressed Pre-tensioned Beams continued...

		Unit	Labour Hours	Labour Net £	Plant Net £	Materials Net £	Unit Net £	CO_2 Kg
H2.5	**Length: 15 - 20m**							
H2.5.7	Mass: 10 - 20 t							
H2.5.7.01	Bridge Beams; 'M' Beams; Length 18m; base width 970mm; leg thickness 165mm; Section M2; depth 720mm; cross-sectional area 316650mm^2; mass 13.7 t	Nr	-	-	-	4,600.00	4,600.00	*2,945.50*
H2.5.7.02	as above; Section M3; depth 800mm; cross-sectional area 348650mm^2; mass 15.1 t	Nr	-	-	-	5,200.00	5,200.00	*3,246.50*
H2.5.7.03	as above; Section M4; depth 880mm; cross-sectional area 355050mm^2; mass 15.37 t	Nr	-	-	-	6,200.00	6,200.00	*3,304.55*
H2.5.7.04	Bridge Beams; 'Y' Beams; Length 16m; base width 750mm; Section Y1; depth 700mm; cross sectional area 309202mm^2; mass 12.4 t	Nr	-	-	-	4,600.00	4,600.00	*2,666.00*
H2.5.7.05	as above; Section Y2; depth 800mm; cross sectional area 339882mm^2; mass 13.6 t	Nr	-	-	-	5,400.00	5,400.00	*2,924.00*
H2.5.8	Mass: stated exceeding 20 t							
H2.5.8.01	Bridge Beams; 'U' Beams; Length 18m; base width 970mm; leg thickness 165mm; Section U1; depth 800mm; cross-sectional area 466450mm^2; mass 20.2 t	Nr	-	-	-	8,100.00	8,100.00	*4,343.00*
H2.5.8.02	as above; Section U3; depth 900mm; cross-sectional area 499450mm^2; mass 21.64 t	Nr	-	-	-	9,600.00	9,600.00	*4,652.60*
H2.5.8.03	as above; Section U5; depth 1000mm; cross-sectional area; 532450mm^2; mass 23.06 t	Nr	-	-	-	11,200.00	11,200.00	*4,957.90*
H2.5.8.04	as above; Section U7; depth 1100mm; cross-sectional area; 565450mm^2; mass 24.48 t	Nr	-	-	-	13,400.00	13,400.00	*5,263.20*
H2.6	**Length: 20 - 30m**							
H2.6.7	Mass: 10 - 20 t							
H2.6.7.01	Section Y3; depth 900mm; cross sectional area 373444mm^2; mass 19.6 t	Nr	-	-	-	6,600.00	6,600.00	*4,214.00*
H2.6.7.02	as above; Section Y4; depth 1000mm; cross sectional area 409890mm^2; mass 21.5 t	Nr	-	-	-	7,600.00	7,600.00	*4,622.50*
H2.6.8	Mass: exceeding 20 t							
H2.6.8.01	Bridge Beams; 'M' Beams; Length 22m; top flange width 400mm; bottom flange width 970mm; Section M5; depth 960mm; cross-sectional area 380650mm^2; mass 20.13 t	Nr	-	-	-	6,400.00	6,400.00	*4,403.20*
H2.6.8.02	as above; Section M6; depth 1040mm; cross-sectional area 387050mm^2; mass 20.48 t	Nr	-	-	-	7,200.00	7,200.00	*4,403.20*
H2.6.8.03	as above; Section M7; depth 1120mm; cross-sectional area 393450mm^2; mass 20.83 t	Nr	-	-	-	8,400.00	8,400.00	*4,478.45*

H2 Prestressed Pre-tensioned Beams continued...

		Unit	Labour Hours	Labour Net £	Plant Net £	Materials Net £	Unit Net £	CO_2 Kg
H2.6	**Length: 20 - 30m**							
H2.6.8	Mass: exceeding 20t							
H2.6.8.04	Bridge Beams; 'M' Beams; Length 26m; top flange width 400mm; bottom flange width 970mm; Section M8; depth 1200mm; cross-sectional area 419050mm²; mass 26.21 t	Nr	-	-	-	8,100.00	**8,100.00**	*5,635.15*
H2.6.8.05	as above; Section M9; depth 1280mm; cross-sectional area 425450mm²; mass 26.60 t	Nr	-	-	-	9,200.00	**9,200.00**	*5,719.00*
H2.6.8.06	as above; Section M10; depth 1360mm; cross-sectional area 457450mm²; mass 28.63 t	Nr	-	-	-	10,100.00	**10,100.00**	*6,155.45*
H2.6.8.07	Bridge Beams; 'U' Beams; Length 22m; base width 970mm; leg thickness 165mm; Section U8; depth 1200mm; cross-sectional area 598450mm²; mass 31.66 t	Nr	-	-	-	15,300.00	**15,300.00**	*6,806.90*
H2.6.8.08	as above; Section U9; depth 1300mm; cross-sectional area 631450mm²; mass 33.42 t	Nr	-	-	-	17,300.00	**17,300.00**	*7,185.30*
H2.6.8.09	Bridge Beams; 'U' Beams; Length 30m; base width 970mm; leg thickness 165mm; Section U10; depth 1400mm; cross-sectional area 664450mm²; mass 47.94 t	Nr	-	-	-	19,500.00	**19,500.00**	*10,298.50*
H2.6.8.10	as above; Section U11; depth 1500mm; cross-sectional area 697450mm²; mass 50.34 t	Nr	-	-	-	21,100.00	**21,100.00**	*10,823.10*
H2.6.8.11	as above; Section U12; depth 1600mm; cross-sectional area 730450mm²; mass 52.71 t	Nr	-	-	-	23,400.00	**23,400.00**	*11,332.65*
H2.6.8.12	Bridge Beams; 'Y' Beams; Length 25m; base width 750mm; Section Y5; depth 1100mm; cross sectional area 449220mm²; mass 28.1t	Nr	-	-	-	8,700.00	**8,700.00**	*6,041.50*
H2.6.8.13	as above; Section Y6; depth 1200mm; cross sectional area 491433mm²; mass 30.7t	Nr	-	-	-	9,800.00	**9,800.00**	*6,600.50*
H2.6.8.14	Bridge Beams; 'Y' Beams; Length 30m; base width 750mm; Section Y7; depth 1300mm; cross sectional area 536530mm²; mass 40.2t	Nr	-	-	-	11,100.00	**11,100.00**	*8,643.00*
H2.6.8.15	as above; Section Y8; depth 1400mm; cross sectional area 584708mm²; mass 43.9t	Nr	-	-	-	12,000.00	**12,000.00**	*9,438.50*

H5 Slabs

Note(s): Prestressed precast concrete floors or roofs; hoisting and fixing on prepared bearings; grouting joints; designed to allow 1.5kN/m2 for screeds.

		Unit	Labour Hours	Labour Net £	Plant Net £	Materials Net £	Unit Net £	CO_2 Kg
H5.3	**Area: 4 - 15m2**							
H5.3.5	Mass: 2 - 5 t							
H5.3.5.01	Prestressed precast concrete floors or roofs; hoisting and fixing on prepared bearings; grouting joints; designed to allow 1.5kN/m^2 for screeds; Superimposed loads maximum 5kN/m^2; 6m x 1.2m x 250mm deep; mass 4.25 t	Nr	1.00	59.19	56.27	288.00	**403.46**	*957.86*
H5.3.6	Mass: 5 - 10 t							
H5.3.6.01	Prestressed precast concrete floors or roofs; hoisting and fixing on prepared bearings; grouting joints; designed to allow 1.5kN/m^2 for screeds; Superimposed loads maximum 5kN/m^2; 9m x 1.2m x 250mm deep; mass 6.4 t	Nr	1.00	59.19	56.27	432.00	**547.46**	*1,420.11*
H5.3.6.02	as above; 12m x 1.2m x 250mm deep; mass 8.5 t	Nr	1.00	59.19	56.27	648.00	**763.46**	*1,871.61*
H5.3.7	Mass: 10 - 20 t							
H5.3.7.01	Prestressed precast concrete floors or roofs; hoisting and fixing on prepared bearings; grouting joints; designed to allow 1.5kN/m^2 for screeds; Superimposed loads maximum 10kN/m^2; 6m x 2.4m x 300mm deep; mass 10.2 t	Nr	1.00	59.19	56.27	576.00	**691.46**	*2,237.11*
H5.4	**Area: 15 - 50m2**							
H5.4.8	Mass: stated exceeding 20 t							
H5.4.8.01	Prestressed precast concrete floors or roofs; hoisting and fixing on prepared bearings; grouting joints; designed to allow 1.5kN/m^2 for screeds; Superimposed loads maximum 10kN/m^2; 9m x 2.4m x 400mm deep; mass 20.4 t	Nr	1.00	59.19	56.27	1,080.00	**1,195.46**	*4,430.11*
H5.4.8.02	as above; 12m x 2.4m x 600mm deep; mass 40.8 t	Nr	1.00	59.19	56.27	1,728.00	**1,843.46**	*8,816.11*

H7 Units for Subways, Culverts and Ducts

Note(s): Culverts

The prices are specialist sub-contractor guide prices for approximate estimating only. The prices are for supply and delivery only and are applicable to sites within 100 miles of the point of supply for minimum quantities of 30 linear metres which are not subjected to deep fill conditions. Conditions of exposure assumed to be severe. Standard cross-sections are available in many sizes and firm prices can only be quoted against full loading information and design specification.

		Unit	Labour Hours	Labour Net £	Plant Net £	Materials Net £	**Unit Net £**	*CO_2 Kg*
H7.1	**Standard Box Culvert Units**							
H7.1.1	Precast concrete; internal cross-sectional dimensions:							
H7.1.1.01	1200mm width x 600mm height	m	-	-	-	220.50	**220.50**	*285.95*
H7.1.1.02	1800mm width x 1200mm height	m	-	-	-	585.75	**585.75**	*520.30*
H7.1.1.03	2400mm width x 1800mm height	m	-	-	-	823.50	**823.50**	*1,092.20*
H7.1.1.04	3000mm width x 1800mm height	m	-	-	-	1,119.00	**1,119.00**	*1,391.05*

CLASS I:
PIPEWORK - PIPES

Calculations used throughout Class I - Pipework - Pipes

Labour

Code	Description	Qty		Rate		Total
L A0184ICE	Small bore pipes in shallow trenches Labour Gang					
	Banksman	1	x	13.53	=	£13.53
	Ganger	1	x	16.99	=	£16.99
	Pipelayer (standard rate)	1	x	14.34	=	£14.34
	Labourer (General Operative)	5	x	12.56	=	£62.80
	Total hourly cost of gang				=	£107.66
L A0185ICE	Small bore pipes in deep trenches Labour Gang					
	Banksman	2	x	13.53	=	£27.06
	Ganger	1	x	16.99	=	£16.99
	Pipelayer (standard rate)	1	x	14.34	=	£14.34
	Labourer (General Operative)	8	x	12.56	=	£100.48
	Timberman	1	x	14.34	=	£14.34
	Total hourly cost of gang				=	£173.21
L A0186ICE	Large bore pipes in shallow trench Labour Gang					
	Ganger	1	x	16.99	=	£16.99
	Pipelayer (large pipes)	1	x	15.91	=	£15.91
	Labourer (General Operative)	5	x	12.56	=	£62.80
	Banksman	1	x	13.53	=	£13.53
	Total hourly cost of gang				=	£109.23
L A0187ICE	Large bore pipes in deep trench Labour Gang					
	Ganger	1	x	16.99	=	£16.99
	Pipelayer (large pipes)	1	x	15.91	=	£15.91
	Labourer (General Operative)	8	x	12.56	=	£100.48
	Banksman	2	x	13.53	=	£27.06
	Timberman	1	x	14.34	=	£14.34
	Total hourly cost of gang				=	£174.78
L A0188ICE	Small bore steel pipes in shallow trench Labour Gang					
	Ganger	1	x	16.99	=	£16.99
	Fitters and Welders	1	x	16.68	=	£16.68
	Labourer (Skill Rate 3)	3	x	14.34	=	£43.02
	Banksman	1	x	13.53	=	£13.53
	Labourer (General Operative)	5	x	12.56	=	£62.80
	Total hourly cost of gang				=	£153.02
L A0189ICE	Small bore steel pipes in deep trench Labour Gang					
	Ganger	1	x	16.99	=	£16.99
	Labourer (General Operative)	8	x	12.56	=	£100.48
	Labourer (Skill Rate 3)	3	x	14.34	=	£43.02
	Fitters and Welders	1	x	16.68	=	£16.68
	Banksman	1	x	13.53	=	£13.53
	Timberman	1	x	14.34	=	£14.34
	Total hourly cost of gang				=	£205.04
L A0190ICE	Large bore steel pipes in shallow trench Labour Gang					
	Fitters and Welders	2	x	16.68	=	£33.37
	Labourer (Skill Rate 3)	4	x	14.34	=	£57.36
	Labourer (General Operative)	5	x	12.56	=	£62.80
	Ganger	1	x	16.99	=	£16.99
	Banksman	1	x	13.53	=	£13.53
	Total hourly cost of gang				=	£184.05

L A0191ICE	**Large bore steel pipes in deep trench Labour Gang**					
	Ganger	1	x	16.99	=	£16.99
	Banksman	1	x	13.53	=	£13.53
	Fitters and Welders	2	x	16.68	=	£33.37
	Timberman	1	x	14.34	=	£14.34
	Labourer (Skill Rate 3)	4	x	14.34	=	£57.36
	Labourer (General Operative)	8	x	12.56	=	£100.48
	Total hourly cost of gang				**=**	**£236.07**
L A0192ICE	**Small bore pipes in shallow trench in french drain Labour Gang**					
	Banksman	1	x	13.53	=	£13.53
	Ganger	1	x	16.99	=	£16.99
	Pipelayer (standard rate)	1	x	14.34	=	£14.34
	Labourer (General Operative)	4	x	12.56	=	£50.24
	Total hourly cost of gang				**=**	**£95.10**
L A0193ICE	**Small bore iron pipes not in trenches Labour Gang**					
	Ganger	1	x	16.99	=	£16.99
	Pipelayer (standard rate)	1	x	14.34	=	£14.34
	Labourer (General Operative)	2	x	12.56	=	£25.12
	Banksman	1	x	13.53	=	£13.53
	Total hourly cost of gang				**=**	**£69.98**
L A0194ICE	**Large bore iron pipes not in trenches Labour Gang**					
	Ganger	1	x	16.99	=	£16.99
	Pipelayer (large pipes)	1	x	15.91	=	£15.91
	Labourer (General Operative)	2	x	12.56	=	£25.12
	Banksman	1	x	13.53	=	£13.53
	Total hourly cost of gang				**=**	**£71.55**
L A0195ICE	**Small bore steel pipes not in trenches Labour Gang**					
	Fitters and Welders	1	x	16.68	=	£16.68
	Labourer (Skill Rate 3)	2	x	14.34	=	£28.68
	Labourer (General Operative)	2	x	12.56	=	£25.12
	Banksman	1	x	13.53	=	£13.53
	Ganger	1	x	16.99	=	£16.99
	Total hourly cost of gang				**=**	**£101.00**
L A0196ICE	**Large bore steel pipes not in trenches Labour Gang**					
	Fitters and Welders	1	x	16.68	=	£16.68
	Labourer (Skill Rate 3)	2	x	14.34	=	£28.68
	Labourer (General Operative)	5	x	12.56	=	£62.80
	Banksman	1	x	13.53	=	£13.53
	Ganger	1	x	16.99	=	£16.99
	Total hourly cost of gang				**=**	**£138.68**

Plant

P A1184ICE	**Small bore pipes in shallow trench Plant Gang**					
	Hydraulic Excavator - Cat 320 96kW	1	x	33.98	=	£33.98
	Pump - Godwin ET50 23m3/h 4 inches	1	x	2.74	=	£2.74
	Vibrating Plate Diesel 24kN	1	x	2.36	=	£2.36
	Trench Sheets	90	x	0.08	=	£7.15
	Acrow Props	70	x	0.08	=	£5.56
	Landrover 4WD	1	x	15.10	=	£15.10
	Total hourly cost of gang				**=**	**£66.89**
P A1185ICE	**Small bore pipes in deep trench Plant Gang**					
	Hydraulic Excavator - Cat 166kW	1	x	41.41	=	£41.41
	Pump - Godwin ET75 74m3/h 4 inches	2	x	4.12	=	£8.23
	Vibrating Plate Diesel 33.5kN	1	x	2.76	=	£2.76
	Trench Sheets	150	x	0.08	=	£11.92
	Acrow Props	100	x	0.08	=	£7.95
	Timber Baulks	3	x	0.61	=	£1.83
	Landrover 4WD	1	x	15.10	=	£15.10
	Total hourly cost of gang				**=**	**£89.20**

P A1186ICE	**Large bore in shallow trench Plant Gang**					
	Hydraulic Excavator - Cat 166kW	1	x	41.41	=	£41.41
	Pump - Godwin ET50 23m3/h 4 inches	1	x	2.74	=	£2.74
	Vibrating Plate Diesel 24kN	1	x	2.36	=	£2.36
	Trench Sheets	90	x	0.08	=	£7.15
	Acrow Props	70	x	0.08	=	£5.56
	Cranes Crawler - 22RB - 15t	1	x	38.37	=	£38.37
	Landrover 4WD	1	x	15.10	=	£15.10
	Total hourly cost of gang				=	**£112.69**
P A1187ICE	**Large bore pipes in deep trench Plant Gang**					
	Hydraulic Excavator - Cat 166kW	1	x	41.41	=	£41.41
	Pump - Godwin ET75 74m3/h 4 inches	2	x	4.12	=	£8.23
	Vibrating Plate Diesel 33.5kN	1	x	2.76	=	£2.76
	Trench Sheets	150	x	0.08	=	£11.92
	Acrow Props	100	x	0.08	=	£7.95
	Timber Baulks	3	x	0.61	=	£1.83
	Cranes Crawler - 22RB - 15t	1	x	38.37	=	£38.37
	Landrover 4WD	1	x	15.10	=	£15.10
	Total hourly cost of gang				=	**£127.57**
P A1188ICE	**Small bore steel pipes in shallow trench Plant Gang**					
	Hydraulic Excavator - Cat 320 96kW	1	x	33.98	=	£33.98
	Pump - Godwin ET50 23m3/h 4 inches	1	x	2.74	=	£2.74
	Vibrating Plate Diesel 24kN	1	x	2.36	=	£2.36
	Trench Sheets	90	x	0.08	=	£7.15
	Acrow Props	70	x	0.08	=	£5.56
	Landrover 4WD	1	x	15.10	=	£15.10
	Welding Set - 300 amp Diesel Electric Start Sil	1	x	4.18	=	£4.18
	Crawler Tractor / Dozer - Cat 561 Sideboom	1	x	41.44	=	£41.44
	Total hourly cost of gang				=	**£112.51**
P A1189ICE	**Small bore steel pipes in deep trench Plant Gang**					
	Hydraulic Excavator - Cat 166kW	1	x	41.41	=	£41.41
	Pump - Godwin ET75 74m3/h 4 inches	2	x	4.12	=	£8.23
	Vibrating Plate Diesel 33.5kN	1	x	2.76	=	£2.76
	Trench Sheets	150	x	0.08	=	£11.92
	Acrow Props	100	x	0.08	=	£7.95
	Timber Baulks	3	x	0.61	=	£1.83
	Landrover 4WD	1	x	15.10	=	£15.10
	Welding Set - 300 amp Diesel Electric Start Sil	1	x	4.18	=	£4.18
	Cranes Crawler - 22RB - 15t	1	x	38.37	=	£38.37
	Total hourly cost of gang				=	**£131.75**
P A1190ICE	**Large bore steel pipes in shallow trench Plant Gang**					
	Hydraulic Excavator - Cat 166kW	1	x	41.41	=	£41.41
	Pump - Godwin ET50 23m3/h 4 inches	1	x	2.74	=	£2.74
	Vibrating Plate Diesel 24kN	1	x	2.36	=	£2.36
	Trench Sheets	90	x	0.08	=	£7.15
	Acrow Props	70	x	0.08	=	£5.56
	Landrover 4WD	1	x	15.10	=	£15.10
	Welding Set - 300 amp Diesel Electric Start Sil	1	x	4.18	=	£4.18
	Cranes Crawler - 22RB - 15t	1	x	38.37	=	£38.37
	Total hourly cost of gang				=	**£116.87**
P A1191ICE	**Large bore steel pipes in deep trench Plant Gang**					
	Hydraulic Excavator - Cat 166kW	1	x	41.41	=	£41.41
	Pump - Godwin ET75 74m3/h 4 inches	2	x	4.12	=	£8.23
	Vibrating Plate Diesel 33.5kN	1	x	2.76	=	£2.76
	Trench Sheets	150	x	0.08	=	£11.92
	Acrow Props	100	x	0.08	=	£7.95
	Timber Baulks	3	x	0.61	=	£1.83
	Landrover 4WD	1	x	15.10	=	£15.10
	Welding Set - 300 amp Diesel Electric Start Sil	2	x	4.18	=	£8.37
	Cranes Crawler - NCK 406C - 30t	1	x	48.55	=	£48.55
	Total hourly cost of gang				=	**£146.12**

P A1194ICE	**Placing materials in bed, haunches and surrounds Plant Gang**					
	Vibrating Plate Diesel 33.5kN	1	x	2.76	=	£2.76
	Crawler Tractor / Dozer - Cat 941	0.5	x	35.36	=	£17.68
	Total hourly cost of gang				=	**£20.44**
P A1195ICE	**Large bore iron pipes not in trenches Plant Gang**					
	Cranes Crawler - 22RB - 15t	1	x	38.37	=	£38.37
	Total hourly cost of gang				=	**£38.37**
P A1196ICE	**Steel pipes not in trenches Plant Gang**					
	Welding Set - 300 amp Diesel Electric Start Sil	2	x	4.18	=	£8.37
	Crawler Tractor / Dozer - Cat 561 Sideboom	1	x	41.44	=	£41.44
	Total hourly cost of gang				=	**£49.81**
P A1197ICE	**Small bore MDPE in shallow trench Plant Gang**					
	Hydraulic Excavator - Cat 320 96kW	2	x	33.98	=	£67.96
	Pump - Godwin ET50 23m3/h 4 inches	1	x	2.74	=	£2.74
	Vibrating Plate Diesel 24kN	1	x	2.36	=	£2.36
	Trench Sheets	90	x	0.08	=	£7.15
	Acrow Props	70	x	0.08	=	£5.56
	Landrover 4WD	1	x	15.10	=	£15.10
	Welding Set - Plastic Pipe Welding (Small)	2	x	6.39	=	£12.78
	Total hourly cost of gang				=	**£113.65**

Class I - Pipework - Pipes

Note(s): Unit prices for this section are based upon the following assumptions:

1) Excavations require a minimum of pumping.

2) No allowance has been made for testing pipework.

3) Prices include for backfilling trenches with excavated material and spreading surplus at sides of trench.

4) No allowance has been made for Double Handling of pipes along an easement.

5) Back-fill hard rammed around small sizes up to 150mm above crown then in layers compacted with plate vibrator.

6) Deep dig prices allow for some support but exclude close sheeting or driven piling. Prices also assume adequate working space to batter sides and store excavated material.

7) No allowance has been made for encountering cross services.

8) Steel pipe items are shown with and without linings.

9) Backfill excluded from prices for pipes in French Drains.

10) Gang build ups assume 'Deep Trench' = 3 - 3.5m deep or over and 'Large bore' = 600mm diameter or over.

I1 Clay Pipes

		Unit	Labour Hours	Labour Net £	Plant Net £	Materials Net £	Unit Net £	CO_2 *Kg*
I1.1	**Nominal bore: not exceeding 200mm**							
I1.1.2	In trenches, depth: not exceeding 1.5m							
I1.1.2.01	Vitrified clay pipes, BS 65, 'Extra Strength' spigot & socket flexible joints; Nominal bore 100mm	m	0.06	6.46	4.01	15.77	**26.24**	*11.29*
I1.1.2.02	as above; Nominal bore 150mm	m	0.08	8.18	5.09	18.99	**32.26**	*16.57*
I1.1.2.03	Vitrified clay pipes, BS 65, 'Extra Strength': plain end with sleeve joints; Nominal bore 100mm	m	0.06	6.46	4.01	4.58	**15.05**	*6.03*
I1.1.2.04	as above; Nominal bore 150mm	m	0.08	8.18	5.09	14.29	**27.56**	*9.84*
I1.1.2.05	as above; Nominal bore 200mm	m	0.09	9.58	5.95	29.36	**44.89**	*13.57*
I1.1.2.06	Vitrified clay pipes, BS 65, 'Surface Water' quality: spigot & socket cement joints; Nominal bore 100mm	m	0.06	6.46	4.01	7.30	**17.77**	*11.29*
I1.1.2.07	as above; Nominal bore 150mm	m	0.08	8.18	5.09	18.09	**31.36**	*16.57*
I1.1.2.08	Vitrified clay pipes, BS 65, British Standard 'Normal' quality: spigot & socket cement joints; Nominal bore 100mm	m	0.06	6.46	4.01	15.95	**26.42**	*11.29*
I1.1.2.09	as above; Nominal bore 150mm	m	0.08	8.18	5.09	20.97	**34.24**	*16.57*
I1.1.2.10	Vitrified clay pipes, BS 65, 'Perforated' plain end with sleeve joints; Nominal bore 100mm	m	0.06	6.46	4.01	12.16	**22.63**	*6.03*
I1.1.2.11	as above; Nominal bore 150mm	m	0.08	8.18	5.09	16.62	**29.89**	*9.84*
I1.1.2.12	Clay land drains; BS 1196; plain butt joints; Nominal bore 75mm	m	0.04	4.31	2.68	4.37	**11.36**	*4.71*
I1.1.2.13	as above; in french drains	m	0.04	3.80	2.68	4.37	**10.85**	*4.71*
I1.1.2.14	Clay land drains; BS 1196; plain butt joints; Nominal bore 100mm	m	0.05	4.84	3.01	6.75	**14.60**	*6.13*
I1.1.2.15	as above; in french drains	m	0.05	4.28	3.01	6.75	**14.04**	*6.13*
I1.1.2.16	Clay land drains; BS 1196; plain butt joints; Nominal bore 150mm	m	0.05	5.38	3.35	13.66	**22.39**	*10.96*
I1.1.2.17	as above; in french drains	m	0.05	4.75	3.35	13.66	**21.76**	*10.96*

I1 Clay Pipes continued...

		Unit	Labour Hours	Labour Net £	Plant Net £	Materials Net £	Unit Net £	CO_2 Kg
I1.1	**Nominal bore: not exceeding 200mm**							
I1.1.3	In trenches, depth: 1.5 - 2m							
I1.1.3.01	Vitrified clay pipes, BS 65, 'Extra Strength' spigot & socket flexible joints; Nominal bore 100mm	m	0.08	8.18	5.09	15.77	**29.04**	*11.72*
I1.1.3.02	as above; Nominal bore 150mm	m	0.09	9.37	5.82	18.99	**34.18**	*16.86*
I1.1.3.03	Vitrified clay pipes, BS 65, 'Extra Strength': plain end with sleeve joints; Nominal bore 100mm	m	0.08	8.18	5.09	4.58	**17.85**	*6.45*
I1.1.3.04	as above; Nominal bore 150mm	m	0.09	9.37	5.82	14.29	**29.48**	*10.13*
I1.1.3.05	as above; Nominal bore 200mm	m	0.10	10.44	6.49	29.36	**46.29**	*13.78*
I1.1.3.06	Vitrified clay pipes, BS 65, 'Surface Water' quality: spigot & socket cement joints; Nominal bore 100mm	m	0.08	8.18	5.09	7.30	**20.57**	*11.72*
I1.1.3.07	as above; Nominal bore 150mm	m	0.09	9.37	5.82	18.09	**33.28**	*16.86*
I1.1.3.08	Vitrified clay pipes, BS 65, British Standard 'Normal' quality: spigot & socket cement joints; Nominal bore 100mm	m	0.08	8.18	5.09	15.95	**29.22**	*11.72*
I1.1.3.09	as above; Nominal bore 150mm	m	0.09	9.37	5.82	20.97	**36.16**	*16.86*
I1.1.3.10	Vitrified clay pipes, BS 65, 'Perforated' plain end with sleeve joints; Nominal bore 100mm	m	0.08	8.18	5.09	12.16	**25.43**	*6.45*
I1.1.3.11	as above; Nominal bore 150mm	m	0.09	9.37	5.82	16.62	**31.81**	*10.13*
I1.1.3.12	Clay land drains; BS 1196; plain butt joints; Nominal bore 75mm	m	0.06	6.46	4.01	4.37	**14.84**	*5.23*
I1.1.3.13	as above; in french drains	m	0.06	5.71	4.01	4.37	**14.09**	*5.23*
I1.1.3.14	Clay land drains; BS 1196; plain butt joints; Nominal bore 100mm	m	0.07	7.00	4.35	6.75	**18.10**	*6.65*
I1.1.3.15	as above; in french drains	m	0.07	6.18	4.35	6.75	**17.28**	*6.65*
I1.1.3.16	Clay land drains; BS 1196; plain butt joints; Nominal bore 150mm	m	0.07	7.54	4.68	13.66	**25.88**	*11.49*
I1.1.3.17	as above; in french drains	m	0.07	6.66	4.68	13.66	**25.00**	*11.49*
I1.1.4	In trenches, depth: 2 - 2.5m							
I1.1.4.01	Vitrified clay pipes, BS 65, 'Extra Strength' spigot & socket flexible joints; Nominal bore 100mm	m	0.11	11.52	7.16	15.77	**34.45**	*12.53*
I1.1.4.02	as above; Nominal bore 150mm	m	0.12	12.81	7.96	18.99	**39.76**	*17.70*
I1.1.4.03	Vitrified clay pipes, BS 65, 'Extra Strength': plain end with sleeve joints; Nominal bore 100mm	m	0.11	11.52	7.16	4.58	**23.26**	*7.27*
I1.1.4.04	as above; Nominal bore 150mm	m	0.12	12.81	7.96	14.29	**35.06**	*10.97*
I1.1.4.05	as above; Nominal bore 200mm	m	0.13	14.10	8.77	29.36	**52.23**	*14.68*
I1.1.4.06	Vitrified clay pipes, BS 65, 'Surface Water' quality: spigot & socket cement joints; Nominal bore 100mm	m	0.11	11.52	7.16	7.30	**25.98**	*12.53*
I1.1.4.07	as above; Nominal bore 150mm	m	0.12	12.81	7.96	18.09	**38.86**	*17.70*
I1.1.4.08	Vitrified clay pipes, BS 65, British Standard 'Normal' quality: spigot & socket cement joints; Nominal bore 100mm	m	0.11	11.52	7.16	15.95	**34.63**	*12.53*
I1.1.4.09	as above; Nominal bore 150mm	m	0.12	12.81	7.96	20.97	**41.74**	*17.70*
I1.1.4.10	Vitrified clay pipes, BS 65, 'Perforated' plain end with sleeve joints; Nominal bore 100mm	m	0.11	11.52	7.16	12.16	**30.84**	*7.27*

I1 Clay Pipes continued...

		Unit	Labour Hours	Labour Net £	Plant Net £	Materials Net £	Unit Net £	CO_2 Kg
I1.1	**Nominal bore: not exceeding 200mm**							
I1.1.4	In trenches, depth: 2 - 2.5m							
I1.1.4.11	as previous item; Nominal bore 150mm	m	0.12	12.81	7.96	16.62	**37.39**	*10.97*
I1.1.4.12	Clay land drains; BS 1196; plain butt joints; Nominal bore 150mm	m	0.10	10.77	6.69	13.66	**31.12**	*12.28*
I1.1.4.13	as above; in french drains	m	0.10	9.51	6.69	13.66	**29.86**	*12.28*
I1.1.5	In trenches, depth: 2.5 - 3m							
I1.1.5.01	Vitrified clay pipes, BS 65, 'Extra Strength' spigot & socket flexible joints; Nominal bore 100mm	m	0.13	14.32	8.90	15.77	**38.99**	*13.22*
I1.1.5.02	as above; Nominal bore 150mm	m	0.15	15.93	9.90	18.99	**44.82**	*18.47*
I1.1.5.03	Vitrified clay pipes, BS 65, 'Extra Strength': plain end with sleeve joints; Nominal bore 100mm	m	0.13	14.32	8.90	4.58	**27.80**	*7.95*
I1.1.5.04	as above; Nominal bore 150mm	m	0.15	15.93	9.90	14.29	**40.12**	*11.73*
I1.1.5.05	as above; Nominal bore 200mm	m	0.16	17.23	10.71	29.36	**57.30**	*15.44*
I1.1.5.06	Vitrified clay pipes, BS 65, 'Surface Water' quality: spigot & socket cement joints; Nominal bore 100mm	m	0.13	14.32	8.90	7.30	**30.52**	*13.22*
I1.1.5.07	as above; Nominal bore 150mm	m	0.15	15.93	9.90	18.09	**43.92**	*18.47*
I1.1.5.08	Vitrified clay pipes, BS 65, British Standard 'Normal' quality: spigot & socket cement joints; Nominal bore 100mm	m	0.13	14.32	8.90	15.95	**39.17**	*13.22*
I1.1.5.09	as above; Nominal bore 150mm	m	0.15	15.93	9.90	20.97	**46.80**	*18.47*
I1.1.5.10	Vitrified clay pipes, BS 65, 'Perforated' plain end with sleeve joints; Nominal bore 100mm	m	0.13	14.00	8.70	12.16	**34.86**	*7.87*
I1.1.5.11	as above; Nominal bore 150mm	m	0.15	15.93	9.90	16.62	**42.45**	*11.73*
I1.1.6	In trenches, depth: 3 - 3.5m							
I1.1.6.01	Vitrified clay pipes, BS 65, 'Extra Strength' spigot & socket flexible joints; Nominal bore 100mm	m	0.18	30.83	15.88	15.77	**62.48**	*16.07*
I1.1.6.02	as above; Nominal bore 150mm	m	0.20	33.78	17.39	18.99	**70.16**	*21.54*
I1.1.6.03	Vitrified clay pipes, BS 65, 'Extra Strength': plain end with sleeve joints; Nominal bore 100mm	m	0.18	30.83	15.88	4.58	**51.29**	*10.81*
I1.1.6.04	as above; Nominal bore 150mm	m	0.20	33.78	17.39	14.29	**65.46**	*14.81*
I1.1.6.05	as above; Nominal bore 200mm	m	0.20	34.64	17.84	29.36	**81.84**	*18.37*
I1.1.6.06	Vitrified clay pipes, BS 65, 'Surface Water' quality: spigot & socket cement joints; Nominal bore 100mm	m	0.18	30.83	15.88	7.30	**54.01**	*16.07*
I1.1.6.07	as above; Nominal bore 150mm	m	0.20	33.78	17.39	18.09	**69.26**	*21.54*
I1.1.6.08	Vitrified clay pipes, BS 65, British Standard 'Normal' quality: spigot & socket cement joints; Nominal bore 100mm	m	0.18	30.83	15.88	15.95	**62.66**	*16.07*
I1.1.6.09	as above; Nominal bore 150mm	m	0.20	33.78	17.39	20.97	**72.14**	*21.54*
I1.1.6.10	Vitrified clay pipes, BS 65, 'Perforated' plain end with sleeve joints; Nominal bore 100mm	m	0.18	30.83	15.88	12.16	**58.87**	*10.81*
I1.1.6.11	as above; Nominal bore 150mm	m	0.20	33.78	17.39	16.62	**67.79**	*14.81*

I1 Clay Pipes continued...

		Unit	Labour Hours	Labour Net £	Plant Net £	Materials Net £	Unit Net £	*CO_2 Kg*
I1.1	**Nominal bore: not exceeding 200mm**							
I1.1.7	In trenches, depth: 3.5 - 4m							
I1.1.7.01	Vitrified clay pipes, BS 65, 'Extra Strength': spigot & socket flexible joint; Nominal bore 100mm	m	0.21	37.41	15.77	19.27	**72.45**	*17.43*
I1.1.7.02	as above; Nominal bore 150mm	m	0.24	40.70	20.96	18.99	**80.65**	*22.97*
I1.1.7.03	Vitrified clay pipes, BS 65, 'Extra Strength': plain end with sleeve joints; Nominal bore 100mm	m	0.22	37.41	19.27	4.58	**61.26**	*12.17*
I1.1.7.04	as above; Nominal bore 150mm	m	0.24	40.70	20.96	14.29	**75.95**	*16.23*
I1.1.7.05	as above; Nominal bore 200mm	m	0.25	43.30	22.30	29.36	**94.96**	*20.16*
I1.1.7.06	Vitrified clay pipes, BS 65, 'Surface Water' quality: spigot & socket cement joints; Nominal bore 100mm	m	0.22	37.41	19.27	7.30	**63.98**	*17.43*
I1.1.7.07	as above; Nominal bore 150mm	m	0.24	40.70	20.96	18.09	**79.75**	*22.97*
I1.1.7.08	Vitrified clay pipes, BS 65, British Standard 'Normal' quality: spigot & socket cement joints; Nominal bore 100mm	m	0.22	37.41	19.27	15.95	**72.63**	*17.43*
I1.1.7.09	as above; Nominal bore 150mm	m	0.24	40.70	20.96	20.97	**82.63**	*22.97*
I1.1.7.10	Vitrified clay pipes, BS 65, 'Perforated' plain end with sleeve joints; Nominal bore 100mm	m	0.22	37.41	19.27	12.16	**68.84**	*12.17*
I1.1.7.11	as above; Nominal bore 150mm	m	0.24	40.70	20.96	16.62	**78.28**	*16.23*
I1.1.8	In trenches, depth: exceeding 4m							
I1.1.8.01	Vitrified clay pipes, BS 65, 'Extra Strength' spigot & socket flexible joints; Nominal bore 100mm; depth: 4 - 4.5m	m	0.40	69.28	35.68	15.77	**120.73**	*24.01*
I1.1.8.02	as above; depth: 4.5 - 5m	m	0.53	92.32	47.54	15.77	**155.63**	*28.76*
I1.1.8.03	as above; Nominal bore 150mm; depth: 4 - 4.5m	m	0.42	72.92	37.55	18.99	**129.46**	*29.61*
I1.1.8.04	as above; depth: 4.5 - 5m	m	0.57	98.90	50.93	18.99	**168.82**	*34.97*
I1.1.8.05	Vitrified clay pipes, BS 65, 'Extra Strength': plain end with sleeve joints; Nominal bore 100mm; depth: 4 - 4.5m	m	0.40	69.28	35.68	4.58	**109.54**	*18.74*
I1.1.8.06	as above; depth: 4.5 - 5m	m	0.53	92.32	47.54	4.58	**144.44**	*23.49*
I1.1.8.07	as above; Nominal bore 150mm; depth: 4 - 4.5m	m	0.42	72.92	37.55	14.29	**124.76**	*22.88*
I1.1.8.08	as above; depth: 4.5 - 5m	m	0.57	98.90	50.93	14.29	**164.12**	*28.24*
I1.1.8.09	Vitrified clay pipes, BS 65, 'Extra Strength': plain end with sleeve joints; Nominal bore 200mm; depth: 4 - 4.5m	m	0.44	76.91	39.60	29.36	**145.87**	*27.09*
I1.1.8.10	as above; depth: 4.5 - 5m	m	0.62	106.52	54.86	29.36	**190.74**	*33.20*
I1.1.8.11	Vitrified clay pipes, BS 65, 'Surface Water' quality: spigot & socket cement joints; Nominal bore 100mm; depth: 4 - 4.5m	m	0.40	69.28	35.68	7.30	**112.26**	*24.01*
I1.1.8.12	as above; depth: 4.5 - 5m	m	0.53	92.32	47.54	7.30	**147.16**	*28.76*
I1.1.8.13	as above; Nominal bore 150mm; depth: 4 - 4.5m	m	0.42	72.92	37.55	18.09	**128.56**	*29.61*
I1.1.8.14	as above; depth: 4.5 - 5m	m	0.57	98.90	50.93	18.09	**167.92**	*34.97*
I1.1.8.15	Vitrified clay pipes, BS 65, British Standard 'Normal' quality: spigot & socket cement joints; Nominal bore 100mm; depth: 4 - 4.5m	m	0.40	69.28	35.68	15.95	**120.91**	*24.01*
I1.1.8.16	as above; depth: 4.5 - 5m	m	0.53	92.32	47.54	15.95	**155.81**	*28.76*
I1.1.8.17	Vitrified clay pipes, BS 65, British Standard 'Normal' quality: spigot & socket cement joints; Nominal bore 150mm; depth: 4 - 4.5m	m	0.42	72.92	37.55	20.97	**131.44**	*29.61*

I1 Clay Pipes continued...

		Unit	Labour Hours	Labour Net £	Plant Net £	Materials Net £	Unit Net £	CO_2 Kg
I1.1	**Nominal bore: not exceeding 200mm**							
I1.1.8	In trenches, depth: exceeding 4m							
I1.1.8.18	as previous item; depth: 4.5 - 5m	m	0.57	98.90	50.93	20.97	**170.80**	*34.97*
I1.1.8.19	Vitrified clay pipes, BS 65, 'Perforated' plain end with sleeve joints; Nominal bore 100mm; depth: 4 - 4.5m	m	0.40	69.28	35.68	12.16	**117.12**	*18.74*
I1.1.8.20	as above; depth: 4.5 - 5m	m	0.53	92.32	47.54	12.16	**152.02**	*23.49*
I1.1.8.21	Vitrified clay pipes, BS 65, 'Perforated' plain end with sleeve joints; Nominal bore 150mm; depth: 4 - 4.5m	m	0.42	72.92	37.55	16.62	**127.09**	*22.88*
I1.1.8.22	as above; depth: 4.5 - 5m	m	0.57	98.90	50.93	16.62	**166.45**	*28.24*
I1.2	**Nominal bore: 200 - 300mm**							
I1 2.2	In trenches, depth: not exceeding 1.5m							
I1.2.2.01	Vitrified clay pipes, BS 65, 'Extra Strength' spigot & socket flexible joints; Nominal bore 225mm	m	0.09	10.12	6.29	36.65	**53.06**	*22.83*
I1.2.2.02	as above; Nominal bore 300mm	m	0.11	12.27	7.63	57.29	**77.19**	*38.29*
I1.2.2.03	Vitrified clay pipes, BS 65, 'Extra Strength': plain end with sleeve joints; Nominal bore 225mm	m	0.09	10.12	6.29	35.90	**52.31**	*21.12*
I1.2.2.04	Vitrified clay pipes, BS 65, 'Surface Water' quality: spigot & socket cement joints; Nominal bore 225mm	m	0.09	10.12	6.29	42.36	**58.77**	*22.83*
I1.2.2.05	as above; Nominal bore 300mm	m	0.11	11.84	7.36	66.18	**85.38**	*38.19*
I1.2.2.06	Vitrified clay pipes, BS 65, British Standard 'Normal' quality: spigot & socket cement joints; Nominal bore 225mm	m	0.09	10.12	6.29	40.55	**56.96**	*22.83*
I1.2.2.07	as above; Nominal bore 300mm	m	0.11	12.27	7.63	63.91	**83.81**	*38.29*
I1.2.2.08	Vitrified clay pipes, BS 65, 'Perforated' plain end with sleeve joints; Nominal bore 225mm	m	0.09	10.12	6.29	32.46	**48.87**	*21.12*
I1.2.2.09	as above; Nominal bore 300mm	m	0.11	11.84	7.36	58.27	**77.47**	*32.34*
I1.2.2.10	Clay land drains; BS 1196; plain butt joints; Nominal bore 225mm	m	0.07	7.54	4.68	34.57	**46.79**	*17.08*
I1 2.3	In trenches, depth: 1.5 - 2m							
I1.2.3.01	Vitrified clay pipes, BS 65, 'Extra Strength' spigot & socket flexible joints; Nominal bore 225mm	m	0.10	10.87	6.76	36.65	**54.28**	*23.02*
I1.2.3.02	as above; Nominal bore 300mm	m	0.12	13.24	8.23	57.29	**78.76**	*38.53*
I1.2.3.03	Vitrified clay pipes, BS 65, 'Extra Strength': plain end with sleeve joints; Nominal bore 225mm	m	0.10	10.87	6.76	35.90	**53.53**	*21.30*
I1.2.3.04	Vitrified clay pipes, BS 65, 'Surface Water' quality: spigot & socket cement joints; Nominal bore 225mm	m	0.10	10.87	6.76	42.36	**59.99**	*23.02*
I1.2.3.05	as above; Nominal bore 300mm	m	0.12	13.24	8.23	66.18	**87.65**	*38.53*
I1.2.3.06	Vitrified clay pipes, BS 65, British Standard 'Normal' quality: spigot & socket cement joints; Nominal bore 225mm	m	0.10	10.87	6.76	40.55	**58.18**	*23.02*
I1.2.3.07	as above; Nominal bore 300mm	m	0.12	13.24	8.23	63.91	**85.38**	*38.53*
I1.2.3.08	Vitrified clay pipes, BS 65, 'Perforated' plain end with sleeve joints; Nominal bore 225mm	m	0.10	10.87	6.76	32.46	**50.09**	*21.30*

I1 Clay Pipes continued...

		Unit	Labour Hours	Labour Net £	Plant Net £	Materials Net £	Unit Net £	CO_2 Kg
I1.2	**Nominal bore: 200 - 300mm**							
I1.2.3	In trenches, depth: 1.5 - 2m							
I1.2.3.09	as above; Nominal bore 300mm	m	0.12	13.24	8.23	58.27	**79.74**	*32.68*
I1.2.3.10	Clay land drains; BS 1196; plain butt joints; Nominal bore 225mm	m	0.09	9.69	6.02	34.57	**50.28**	*17.61*
I1.2.4	In trenches, depth: 2 - 2.5m							
I1.2.4.01	Vitrified clay pipes, BS 65, 'Extra Strength' spigot & socket flexible joints; Nominal bore 225mm	m	0.14	14.64	9.10	36.65	**60.39**	*23.94*
I1.2.4.02	as above; Nominal bore 300mm	m	0.15	15.61	9.70	57.29	**82.60**	*39.11*
I1.2.4.03	Vitrified clay pipes, BS 65, 'Extra Strength': plain end with sleeve joints; Nominal bore 225mm	m	0.14	14.64	9.10	35.90	**59.64**	*22.22*
I1.2.4.04	Vitrified clay pipes, BS 65, 'Surface Water' quality: spigot & socket cement joints; Nominal bore 225mm	m	0.14	14.64	9.10	42.36	**66.10**	*23.94*
I1.2.4.05	as above; Nominal bore 300mm	m	0.15	15.61	9.70	66.18	**91.49**	*39.11*
I1.2.4.06	Vitrified clay pipes, BS 65, British Standard 'Normal' quality: spigot & socket cement joints; Nominal bore 225mm	m	0.14	14.64	9.10	40.55	**64.29**	*23.94*
I1.2.4.07	as above; Nominal bore 300mm	m	0.15	15.61	9.70	63.91	**89.22**	*39.11*
I1.2.4.08	Vitrified clay pipes, BS 65, 'Perforated' plain end with sleeve joints; Nominal bore 225mm	m	0.14	14.64	9.10	32.46	**56.20**	*22.22*
I1.2.4.09	as above; Nominal bore 300mm	m	0.15	15.61	9.70	58.27	**83.58**	*33.26*
I1.2.4.10	Clay land drains; BS 1196; plain butt joints; Nominal bore 225mm	m	0.13	13.46	8.36	34.57	**56.39**	*18.53*
I1.2.5	In trenches, depth: 2.5 - 3m							
I1.2.5.01	Vitrified clay pipes, BS 65, 'Extra Strength' spigot & socket flexible joints; Nominal bore 225mm	m	0.17	17.98	11.17	36.65	**65.80**	*24.75*
I1.2.5.02	as above; Nominal bore 300mm	m	0.19	20.56	12.78	57.29	**90.63**	*40.32*
I1.2.5.03	Vitrified clay pipes, BS 65, 'Extra Strength': plain end with sleeve joints; Nominal bore 225mm	m	0.17	17.98	11.17	35.90	**65.05**	*23.04*
I1.2.5.04	Vitrified clay pipes, BS 65, 'Surface Water' quality: spigot & socket cement joints; Nominal bore 225mm	m	0.17	17.98	11.17	42.36	**71.51**	*24.75*
I1.2.5.05	as above; Nominal bore 300mm	m	0.19	20.56	12.78	66.18	**99.52**	*40.32*
I1.2.5.06	Vitrified clay pipes, BS 65, British Standard 'Normal' quality: spigot & socket cement joints; Nominal bore 225mm	m	0.17	17.98	11.17	40.55	**69.70**	*24.75*
I1.2.5.07	as above; Nominal bore 300mm	m	0.19	20.56	12.78	63.91	**97.25**	*40.32*
I1.2.5.08	Vitrified clay pipes, BS 65, 'Perforated' plain end with sleeve joints; Nominal bore 225mm	m	0.17	17.98	11.17	32.46	**61.61**	*23.04*
I1.2.5.09	as above; Nominal bore 300mm	m	0.19	20.56	12.78	66.18	**99.52**	*40.32*
I1.2.6	In trenches, depth: 3 - 3.5m							
I1.2.6.01	Vitrified clay pipes, BS 65, 'Extra Strength' spigot & socket flexible joints; Nominal bore 225mm	m	0.22	37.41	19.27	36.65	**93.33**	*28.07*
I1.2.6.02	as above; Nominal bore 300mm	m	0.24	41.92	21.59	57.29	**120.80**	*43.94*
I1.2.6.03	Vitrified clay pipes, BS 65, 'Extra Strength': plain end with sleeve joints; Nominal bore 225mm	m	0.22	37.41	19.27	35.90	**92.58**	*26.36*

I1 Clay Pipes continued...

		Unit	Labour Hours	Labour Net £	Plant Net £	Materials Net £	Unit Net £	CO_2 Kg
I1.2	**Nominal bore: 200 - 300mm**							
I1.2.6	In trenches, depth: 3 - 3.5m							
I1.2.6.04	Vitrified clay pipes, BS 65, 'Surface Water' quality: spigot & socket cement joints; Nominal bore 225mm	m	0.22	37.41	19.27	42.36	99.04	*28.07*
I1.2.6.05	as above; Nominal bore 300mm	m	0.24	41.92	21.59	66.18	129.69	*43.94*
I1.2.6.06	Vitrified clay pipes, BS 65, British Standard 'Normal' quality: spigot & socket cement joints; Nominal bore 225mm	m	0.22	37.41	19.27	40.55	97.23	*28.07*
I1.2.6.07	as above; Nominal bore 300mm	m	0.24	41.92	21.59	63.91	127.42	*43.94*
I1.2.6.08	Vitrified clay pipes, BS 65, 'Perforated' plain end with sleeve joints; Nominal bore 225mm	m	0.22	37.41	19.27	32.46	89.14	*26.36*
I1.2.6.09	as above; Nominal bore 300mm	m	0.24	41.92	21.59	58.27	121.78	*38.09*
I1.2.7	In trenches, depth: 3.5 - 4m							
I1.2.7.01	Vitrified clay pipes, BS 65, 'Extra Strength' spigot & socket flexible joints; Nominal bore 225mm	m	0.27	46.25	23.82	36.65	106.72	*29.90*
I1.2.7.02	as above; Nominal bore 300mm	m	0.31	53.35	27.47	57.29	138.11	*46.30*
I1.2.7.03	Vitrified clay pipes, BS 65, 'Extra Strength': plain end with sleeve joints; Nominal bore 225mm	m	0.28	47.81	24.62	35.90	108.33	*28.50*
I1.2.7.04	Vitrified clay pipes, BS 65, 'Surface Water' quality: spigot & socket cement joints; Nominal bore 225mm	m	0.27	46.25	23.82	42.36	112.43	*29.90*
I1.2.7.05	as above; Nominal bore 300mm	m	0.31	53.35	27.47	66.18	147.00	*46.30*
I1.2.7.06	Vitrified clay pipes, BS 65, British Standard 'Normal' quality: spigot & socket cement joints; Nominal bore 225mm	m	0.27	46.25	23.82	40.55	110.62	*29.90*
I1.2.7.07	as above; Nominal bore 300mm	m	0.31	53.35	27.47	63.91	144.73	*46.30*
I1.2.7.08	Vitrified clay pipes, BS 65, 'Perforated' plain end with sleeve joints; Nominal bore 225mm	m	0.27	46.25	23.82	32.46	102.53	*28.18*
I1.2.7.09	as above; Nominal bore 300mm	m	0.31	53.35	27.47	58.27	139.09	*40.45*
I1.2.8	In trenches, depth: exceeding 4m							
I1.2.8.01	Vitrified clay pipes, BS 65, 'Extra Strength' spigot & socket flexible joints; Nominal bore 225mm; depth: 4 - 4.5m	m	0.47	81.58	42.01	36.65	160.24	*37.18*
I1.2.8.02	as above; depth: 4.5 - 5m	m	0.62	106.52	54.86	36.65	198.03	*42.33*
I1.2.8.03	as above; Nominal bore 300mm; depth: 4 - 4.5m	m	0.50	86.61	44.60	57.29	188.50	*53.16*
I1.2.8.04	as above; depth: 4.5 - 5m	m	0.67	116.05	59.76	57.29	233.10	*59.23*
I1.2.8.05	Vitrified clay pipes, BS 65, 'Extra Strength': plain end with sleeve joints; Nominal bore 225mm; depth: 4 - 4.5m	m	0.47	81.58	42.01	35.90	159.49	*35.47*
I1.2.8.06	as above; depth: 4.5 - 5m	m	0.62	106.52	54.86	35.90	197.28	*40.61*
I1.2.8.07	Vitrified clay pipes, BS 65, 'Surface Water' quality: spigot & socket cement joints; Nominal bore 225mm; depth: 4 - 4.5m 4 - 4.5m	m	0.47	81.58	42.01	42.36	165.95	*37.18*
I1.2.8.08	as above; depth: 4.5 - 5m	m	0.62	106.52	54.86	42.36	203.74	*42.33*
I1.2.8.09	as above; Nominal bore 300mm; depth: 4 - 4.5m	m	0.50	86.61	44.60	66.18	197.39	*53.16*

I1 Clay Pipes continued...

		Unit	Labour Hours	Labour Net £	Plant Net £	Materials Net £	Unit Net £	CO_2 Kg
I1.2	**Nominal bore: 200 - 300mm**							
I1.2.8	In trenches, depth: exceeding 4m							
I1.2.8.10	as above; depth: 4.5 - 5m	m	0.67	116.05	59.76	66.18	**241.99**	*59.23*
I1.2.8.11	Vitrified clay pipes, BS 65, British Standard 'Normal' quality: spigot & socket cement joints; Nominal bore 225mm; depth: 4 - 4.5m	m	0.47	81.58	42.01	40.55	**164.14**	*37.18*
I1.2.8.12	as above; depth: 4.5 - 5m	m	0.62	106.52	54.86	40.55	**201.93**	*42.33*
I1.2.8.13	as above; Nominal bore 300mm; depth: 4 - 4.5m	m	0.50	86.61	44.60	63.91	**195.12**	*53.16*
I1.2.8.14	as above; depth: 4.5 - 5m	m	0.67	116.05	59.76	63.91	**239.72**	*59.23*
I1.2.8.15	Vitrified clay pipes, BS 65, 'Perforated' plain end with sleeve joints; Nominal bore 225mm; depth: 4 - 4.5m	m	0.47	81.58	42.01	32.46	**156.05**	*35.47*
I1.2.8.16	as above; depth: 4.5 - 5m	m	0.62	106.52	54.86	32.46	**193.84**	*40.61*
I1.2.8.17	as above; Nominal bore 300mm; depth: 4 - 4.5m	m	0.50	86.61	44.60	58.27	**189.48**	*47.31*
I1.2.8.18	as above; depth: 4.5 - 5m	m	0.67	116.05	59.76	58.27	**234.08**	*53.38*
I1.3	**Nominal bore: 300 - 600mm**							
I1.3.2	In trenches, depth: not exceeding 1.5m							
I1.3.2.01	Vitrified clay pipes, BS 65, 'Extra Strength' spigot & socket flexible joints; Nominal bore 375mm	m	0.12	13.24	8.23	138.79	**160.26**	*54.67*
I1.3.2.02	as above; Nominal bore 450mm	m	0.16	17.23	10.71	183.61	**211.55**	*79.21*
I1.3.2.03	Vitrified clay pipes, BS 65, 'Surface Water' quality: spigot & socket cement joints; Nominal bore 375mm	m	0.12	13.24	8.23	154.01	**175.48**	*54.67*
I1.3.2.04	as above; Nominal bore 450mm	m	0.16	17.23	10.71	196.16	**224.10**	*79.21*
I1.3.2.05	Vitrified clay pipes, BS 65, British Standard 'Normal' quality: spigot & socket cement joints; Nominal bore 375mm	m	0.12	13.24	8.23	102.50	**123.97**	*54.67*
I1.3.2.06	as above; Nominal bore 450mm	m	0.16	17.23	10.71	168.88	**196.82**	*79.21*
I1.3.3	In trenches, depth: 1.5 - 2m							
I1.3.3.01	Vitrified clay pipes, BS 65, 'Extra Strength' spigot & socket flexible joints; Nominal bore 375mm	m	0.13	14.32	8.90	138.79	**162.01**	*54.93*
I1.3.3.02	as above; Nominal bore 450mm	m	0.20	21.53	13.38	183.61	**218.52**	*80.27*
I1.3.3.03	Vitrified clay pipes, BS 65, 'Surface Water' quality: spigot & socket cement joints; Nominal bore 375mm	m	0.13	14.32	8.90	154.01	**177.23**	*54.93*
I1.3.3.04	as above; Nominal bore 450mm	m	0.20	21.53	13.38	196.16	**231.07**	*80.27*
I1.3.3.05	Vitrified clay pipes, BS 65, British Standard 'Normal' quality: spigot & socket cement joints; Nominal bore 375mm	m	0.13	14.32	8.90	102.50	**125.72**	*54.93*
I1.3.3.06	as above; Nominal bore 450mm	m	0.20	21.53	13.38	168.88	**203.79**	*80.27*
I1.3.4	In trenches, depth: 2 - 2.5m							
I1.3.4.01	Vitrified clay pipes, BS 65, 'Extra Strength' spigot & socket flexible joints; Nominal bore 375mm	m	0.19	20.02	12.45	138.79	**171.26**	*56.33*
I1.3.4.02	as above; Nominal bore 450mm	m	0.23	24.65	15.32	183.61	**223.58**	*81.03*

I1 Clay Pipes continued...

		Unit	Labour Hours	Labour Net £	Plant Net £	Materials Net £	Unit Net £	*CO_2 Kg*
I1.3	**Nominal bore: 300 - 600mm**							
I1.3.4	In trenches, depth: 2 - 2.5m							
I1.3.4.03	Vitrified clay pipes, BS 65, 'Surface Water' quality: spigot & socket cement joints; Nominal bore 375mm	m	0.19	20.02	12.45	154.01	186.48	*56.33*
I1.3.4.04	as above; Nominal bore 450mm	m	0.23	24.65	15.32	196.16	236.13	*81.03*
I1.3.4.05	Vitrified clay pipes, BS 65, British Standard 'Normal' quality: spigot & socket cement joints; Nominal bore 375mm	m	0.19	20.02	12.45	102.50	134.97	*56.33*
I1.3.4.06	as above; Nominal bore 450mm	m	0.23	24.65	15.32	168.88	208.85	*81.03*
I1.3.5	In trenches, depth: 2.5 - 3m							
I1.3.5.01	Vitrified clay pipes, BS 65, 'Extra Strength' spigot & socket flexible joints; Nominal bore 375mm	m	0.22	23.90	14.85	138.79	177.54	*57.27*
I1.3.5.02	as above; Nominal bore 450mm	m	0.27	28.75	17.86	183.61	230.22	*82.03*
I1.3.5.03	Vitrified clay pipes, BS 65, 'Surface Water' quality: spigot & socket cement joints; Nominal bore 375mm	m	0.22	23.90	14.85	154.01	192.76	*57.27*
I1.3.5.04	as above; Nominal bore 450mm	m	0.27	28.75	17.86	196.16	242.77	*82.03*
I1.3.5.05	Vitrified clay pipes, BS 65, British Standard 'Normal' quality: spigot & socket cement joints; Nominal bore 375mm	m	0.22	23.90	14.85	102.50	141.25	*57.27*
I1.3.5.06	as above; Nominal bore 450mm	m	0.27	28.75	17.86	168.88	215.49	*82.03*
I1.3.6	In trenches, depth: 3 - 3.5m							
I1.3.6.01	Vitrified clay pipes, BS 65, 'Extra Strength' spigot & socket flexible joints; Nominal bore 375mm	m	0.28	47.81	24.62	138.79	211.22	*61.29*
I1.3.6.02	as above; Nominal bore 450mm	m	0.32	55.43	28.54	183.61	267.58	*86.43*
I1.3.6.03	Vitrified clay pipes, BS 65, 'Surface Water' quality: spigot & socket cement joints; Nominal bore 375mm	m	0.28	47.81	24.62	154.01	226.44	*61.29*
I1.3.6.04	as above; Nominal bore 450mm	m	0.32	55.43	28.54	196.16	280.13	*86.43*
I1.3.6.05	Vitrified clay pipes, BS 65, British Standard 'Normal' quality: spigot & socket cement joints; Nominal bore 375mm	m	0.28	47.81	24.62	102.50	174.93	*61.29*
I1.3.6.06	as above; Nominal bore 450mm	m	0.32	55.43	28.54	168.88	252.85	*86.43*
I1.3.7	In trenches, depth: 3.5 - 4m							
I1.3.7.01	Vitrified clay pipes, BS 65, 'Extra Strength' spigot & socket flexible joints; Nominal bore 375mm	m	0.36	63.05	32.47	138.79	234.31	*64.43*
I1.3.7.02	as above; Nominal bore 450mm	m	0.44	76.91	39.60	183.61	300.12	*90.86*
I1.3.7.03	Vitrified clay pipes, BS 65, 'Surface Water' quality: spigot & socket cement joints; Nominal bore 375mm	m	0.36	63.05	32.47	154.01	249.53	*64.43*
I1.3.7.04	as above; Nominal bore 450mm	m	0.44	76.91	39.60	196.16	312.67	*90.86*
I1.3.7.05	Vitrified clay pipes, BS 65, British Standard 'Normal' quality: spigot & socket cement joints; Nominal bore 375mm	m	0.36	63.05	32.47	102.50	198.02	*64.43*
I1.3.7.06	as above; Nominal bore 450mm	m	0.44	76.91	39.60	168.88	285.39	*90.86*

I1 Clay Pipes continued...

		Unit	Labour Hours	Labour Net £	Plant Net £	Materials Net £	Unit Net £	CO_2 Kg
I1.3	**Nominal bore: 300 - 600mm**							
I1.3.8	In trenches, depth: exceeding 4m							
I1.3.8.01	Vitrified clay pipes, BS 65, 'Extra Strength' spigot & socket flexible joints; Nominal bore 375mm; depth: 4 - 4.5m	m	0.57	98.90	50.93	138.79	**288.62**	*71.83*
I1.3.8.02	as above; depth: 4.5 - 5m	m	0.73	125.92	64.85	138.79	**329.56**	*77.40*
I1.3.8.03	as above; Nominal bore 450mm; In trenches; depth: 4 - 4.5m	m	0.62	106.52	54.86	183.61	**344.99**	*96.97*
I1.3.8.04	as above; depth: 4.5 - 5m	m	0.80	138.57	71.36	183.61	**393.54**	*103.58*
I1.3.8.05	Vitrified clay pipes, BS 65, 'Surface Water' quality: spigot & socket cement joints; Nominal bore 375mm; depth: 4 - 4.5m	m	0.57	98.90	50.93	154.01	**303.84**	*71.83*
I1.3.8.06	as above; depth: 4.5 - 5m	m	0.73	125.92	64.85	154.01	**344.78**	*77.40*
I1.3.8.07	as above; Nominal bore 450mm; depth: 4 - 4.5m	m	0.62	106.52	54.86	196.16	**357.54**	*96.97*
I1.3.8.08	as above; depth: 4.5 - 5m	m	0.80	138.57	71.36	196.16	**406.09**	*103.58*
I1.3.8.09	Vitrified clay pipes, BS 65, British Standard 'Normal' quality: spigot & socket cement joints; Nominal bore 375mm; depth: 4 - 4.5m	m	0.57	98.90	50.93	102.50	**252.33**	*71.83*
I1.3.8.10	as above; depth: 4.5 - 5m	m	0.73	125.92	64.85	102.50	**293.27**	*77.40*
I1.3.8.11	as above; Nominal bore 450mm; depth: 4 - 4.5m	m	0.62	106.52	54.86	168.88	**330.26**	*96.97*
I1.3.8.12	as above; depth: 4.5 - 5m	m	0.80	138.57	71.36	168.88	**378.81**	*103.58*

I2 Concrete pipes

		Unit	Labour Hours	Labour Net £	Plant Net £	Materials Net £	Unit Net £	CO_2 Kg
I2.1	**Nominal bore: not exceeding 200mm**							
I2.1.2	In trenches, depth: not exceeding 1.5m							
I2.1.2.01	Concrete porous pipes, BS 5911, Ogee joints; Nominal bore 150mm	m	0.08	8.61	5.35	4.40	**18.36**	*10.71*
I2.1.3	In trenches, depth: 1.5 - 2m							
I2.1.3.01	Concrete porous pipes, BS 5911, Ogee joints; Nominal bore 150mm	m	0.09	9.69	6.02	4.40	**20.11**	*10.97*
I2.1.4	In trenches, depth: 2 - 2.5m							
I2.1.4.01	Concrete porous pipes, BS 5911, Ogee joints; Nominal bore 150mm	m	0.11	11.84	7.36	4.40	**23.60**	*11.49*
I2.1.5	In trenches, depth: 2.5 - 3m							
I2.1.5.01	Concrete porous pipes, BS 5911, Ogee joints; Nominal bore 150mm	m	0.15	16.15	10.04	4.40	**30.59**	*12.55*
I2.1.6	In trenches, depth: 3 - 3.5m							
I2.1.6.01	Concrete porous pipes, BS 5911, Ogee joints; Nominal bore 150mm	m	0.18	31.18	16.06	4.40	**51.64**	*15.03*
I2.1.7	In trenches, depth: 3.5 - 4m							
I2.1.7.01	Concrete porous pipes, BS 5911, Ogee joints; Nominal bore 150mm	m	0.20	34.64	17.84	4.40	**56.88**	*15.74*

I2 Concrete pipes continued...

		Unit	Labour Hours	Labour Net £	Plant Net £	Materials Net £	Unit Net £	CO_2 Kg
I2.1	**Nominal bore: not exceeding 200mm**							
I2.1.8	In trenches, depth: exceeding 4m							
I2.1.8.01	Concrete porous pipes, BS 5911, Ogee joints; Nominal bore 150mm; depth: 4 - 4.5m	m	0.27	46.77	24.08	4.40	75.25	*18.25*
I2.1.8.02	as above; depth: 4.5 - 5m	m	0.40	69.28	35.68	4.40	109.36	*22.89*
I2.2	**Nominal bore: 200 - 300mm**							
I2.2.2	In trenches, depth: not exceeding 1.5m							
I2.2.2.01	Concrete pipes, BS 5911, Class '120'; rebated flexible joints with mastic sealant to internal faces; Nominal bore 300mm	m	0.14	14.96	9.30	14.11	38.37	*40.21*
I2.2.2.02	Concrete porous pipes, BS 5911, Ogee joints; Nominal bore 225mm	m	0.09	9.69	6.02	5.72	21.43	*15.27*
I2.2.2.03	as above; Nominal bore 300mm	m	0.11	11.84	7.36	8.74	27.94	*22.24*
I2.2.3	In trenches, depth: 1.5 - 2m							
I2.2.3.01	Concrete pipes, BS 5911, Class '120'; rebated flexible joints with mastic sealant to internal faces; Nominal bore 300mm	m	0.16	17.23	10.71	14.11	42.05	*40.76*
I2.2.3.02	Concrete porous pipes, BS 5911, Ogee joints; Nominal bore 225mm	m	0.11	11.84	7.36	5.72	24.92	*15.79*
I2.2.3.03	as above; Nominal bore 300mm	m	0.13	14.00	8.70	8.74	31.44	*22.77*
I2.2.4	In trenches, depth: 2 - 2.5m							
I2.2.4.01	Concrete pipes, BS 5911, Class '120'; rebated flexible joints with mastic sealant to internal faces; Nominal bore 300mm	m	0.18	19.16	11.91	14.11	45.18	*41.23*
I2.2.4.02	Concrete porous pipes, BS 5911, Ogee joints; Nominal bore 225mm	m	0.12	12.92	8.03	5.72	26.67	*16.06*
I2.2.4.03	as above; Nominal bore 300mm	m	0.14	15.07	9.37	8.74	33.18	*23.03*
I2.2.5	In trenches, depth: 2.5 - 3m							
I2.2.5.01	Concrete pipes, BS 5911, Class '120'; rebated flexible joints with mastic sealant to internal faces; Nominal bore 300mm	m	0.20	21.53	13.38	14.11	49.02	*41.81*
I2.2.5.02	Concrete porous pipes, BS 5911, Ogee joints; Nominal bore 225mm	m	0.16	17.23	10.71	5.72	33.66	*17.11*
I2.2.5.03	as above; Nominal bore 300mm	m	0.17	18.30	11.37	8.74	38.41	*23.82*
I2.2.6	In trenches, depth: 3 - 3.5m							
I2.2.6.01	Concrete pipes, BS 5911, Class '120'; rebated flexible joints with mastic sealant to internal faces; Nominal bore 300mm	m	0.20	34.64	17.84	14.11	66.59	*43.69*
I2.2.6.02	Concrete porous pipes, BS 5911, Ogee joints; Nominal bore 225mm	m	0.20	34.64	17.84	5.72	58.20	*20.04*
I2.2.6.03	as above; Nominal bore 300mm	m	0.22	38.11	19.62	8.74	66.47	*27.21*

I2 Concrete pipes continued...

		Unit	Labour Hours	Labour Net £	Plant Net £	Materials Net £	Unit Net £	CO_2 Kg
I2.2	**Nominal bore: 200 - 300mm**							
I2.2.7	In trenches, depth: 3.5 - 4m							
I2.2.7.01	Concrete pipes, BS 5911, Class '120'; rebated flexible joints with mastic sealant to internal faces; Nominal bore 300mm	m	0.23	39.67	20.43	14.11	74.21	*44.73*
I2.2.7.02	Concrete porous pipes, BS 5911, Ogee joints; Nominal bore 225mm	m	0.23	39.84	20.52	5.72	66.08	*21.12*
I2.2.7.03	as above; Nominal bore 300mm	m	0.26	45.03	23.19	8.74	76.96	*28.64*
I2.2.8	In trenches, depth: exceeding 4m							
I2.2.8.01	Concrete pipes, BS 5911, Class '120'; rebated flexible joints with mastic sealant to internal faces; Nominal bore 300mm; depth: 4 - 4.5m	m	0.29	50.40	25.96	14.11	90.47	*46.95*
I2.2.8.02	as above; depth: 4.5 - 5m	m	0.36	61.66	31.76	14.11	107.53	*49.27*
I2.2.8.03	as above; depth: 5 - 5.5m	m	0.40	69.28	35.68	14.11	119.07	*50.84*
I2.2.8.04	as above; depth: 5.5 - 6m	m	0.53	92.32	47.54	14.11	153.97	*55.59*
I2.2.8.05	Concrete porous pipes, BS 5911, Ogee joints; Nominal bore 225mm; depth: 4 - 4.5m	m	0.30	51.96	26.76	5.72	84.44	*23.62*
I2.2.8.06	as above; depth: 4.5 - 5m	m	0.44	76.21	39.25	5.72	121.18	*28.62*
I2.2.8.07	as above; Nominal bore 300mm; depth: 4 - 4.5m	m	0.32	55.43	28.54	8.74	92.71	*30.78*
I2.2.8.08	as above; depth: 4.5 - 5m	m	0.47	50.60	31.45	8.74	90.79	*31.72*
I2.3	**Nominal bore: 300 - 600mm**							
I2.3.2	In trenches, depth: not exceeding 1.5m							
I2.3.2.01	Concrete pipes, BS 5911, Class '120'; rebated flexible joints with mastic sealant to internal faces; Nominal bore 375mm	m	0.15	15.61	9.70	17.54	42.85	*47.25*
I2.3.2.02	as above; Nominal bore 450mm	m	0.16	17.23	10.71	20.34	48.28	*65.27*
I2.3.2.03	Concrete porous pipes, BS 5911, Ogee joints; Nominal bore 375mm	m	0.13	14.00	8.70	14.18	36.88	*29.22*
I2.3.2.04	as above; Nominal bore 450mm	m	0.16	17.23	10.71	15.88	43.82	*41.84*
I2.3.2.05	as above; Nominal bore 525mm	m	0.16	17.48	18.03	18.36	53.87	*44.68*
I2.3.2.06	as above; Nominal bore 600mm	m	0.18	19.66	20.29	27.65	67.60	*58.32*
I2.3.3	In trenches, depth: 1.5 - 2m							
I2.3.3.01	Concrete pipes, BS 5911, Class '120'; rebated flexible joints with mastic sealant to internal faces; Nominal bore 375mm	m	0.17	18.09	11.24	17.54	46.87	*47.85*
I2.3.3.02	as above; Nominal bore 450mm	m	0.19	20.24	12.58	20.34	53.16	*66.01*
I2.3.3.03	as above; Nominal bore 600mm	m	0.18	19.66	20.29	28.89	68.84	*111.21*
I2.3.3.04	Concrete porous pipes, BS 5911, Ogee joints; Nominal bore 375mm	m	0.16	17.23	10.71	14.18	42.12	*30.01*
I2.3.3.05	as above; Nominal bore 450mm	m	0.18	19.38	12.04	15.88	47.30	*42.36*
I2.3.3.06	as above; Nominal bore 525mm	m	0.18	19.66	20.29	18.36	58.31	*45.42*
I2.3.3.07	as above; Nominal bore 600mm	m	0.20	21.85	22.54	27.65	72.04	*59.07*

I2 Concrete pipes continued...

		Unit	Labour Hours	Labour Net £	Plant Net £	Materials Net £	Unit Net £	CO_2 Kg
I2.3	**Nominal bore: 300 - 600mm**							
I2.3.4	In trenches, depth: 2 - 2.5m							
I2.3.4.01	Concrete pipes, BS 5911, Class '120'; rebated flexible joints with mastic sealant to internal faces; Nominal bore 375mm	m	0.19	20.24	12.58	17.54	**50.36**	*48.38*
I2.3.4.02	as above; Nominal bore 450mm	m	0.21	22.93	14.25	20.34	**57.52**	*66.67*
I2.3.4.03	as above; Nominal bore 600mm	m	0.20	21.85	22.54	28.89	**73.28**	*111.96*
I2.3.4.04	Concrete porous pipes, BS 5911, Ogee joints; Nominal bore 375mm	m	0.18	19.38	12.04	14.18	**45.60**	*30.54*
I2.3.4.05	as above; Nominal bore 450mm	m	0.20	21.53	13.38	15.88	**50.79**	*42.89*
I2.3.4.06	as above; Nominal bore 525mm	m	0.20	21.85	22.54	18.36	**62.75**	*46.17*
I2.3.4.07	as above; Nominal bore 600mm	m	0.22	24.03	24.79	27.65	**76.47**	*59.82*
I2.3.5	In trenches, depth: 2.5 - 3m							
I2.3.5.01	Concrete pipes, BS 5911, Class '120'; rebated flexible joints with mastic sealant to internal faces; Nominal bore 375mm	m	0.21	22.93	14.25	17.54	**54.72**	*49.04*
I2.3.5.02	as above; Nominal bore 450mm	m	0.25	26.48	16.46	20.34	**63.28**	*67.53*
I2.3.5.03	as above; Nominal bore 600mm	m	0.23	25.12	25.92	28.89	**79.93**	*113.08*
I2.3.5.04	Concrete porous pipes, BS 5911, Ogee joints; Nominal bore 375mm	m	0.20	21.53	13.38	14.18	**49.09**	*31.06*
I2.3.5.05	as above; Nominal bore 450mm	m	0.23	24.76	15.39	15.88	**56.03**	*43.68*
I2.3.5.06	as above; Nominal bore 525mm	m	0.23	25.12	25.92	18.36	**69.40**	*47.29*
I2.3.5.07	as above; Nominal bore 600mm	m	0.24	26.22	27.05	27.65	**80.92**	*60.57*
I2.3.6	In trenches, depth: 3 - 3.5m							
I2.3.6.01	Concrete pipes, BS 5911, Class '120'; rebated flexible joints with mastic sealant to internal faces; Nominal bore 375mm	m	0.21	36.89	19.00	17.54	**73.43**	*51.04*
I2.3.6.02	as above; Nominal bore 450mm	m	0.25	42.61	21.94	20.34	**84.89**	*69.85*
I2.3.6.03	as above; Nominal bore 600mm	m	0.23	40.20	29.34	28.89	**98.43**	*113.57*
I2.3.6.04	Concrete porous pipes, BS 5911, Ogee joints; Nominal bore 375mm	m	0.25	43.30	22.30	14.18	**79.78**	*34.73*
I2.3.6.05	as above; Nominal bore 450mm	m	0.27	46.77	24.08	15.88	**86.73**	*47.27*
I2.3.6.06	as above; Nominal bore 525mm	m	0.27	47.19	34.44	18.36	**99.99**	*49.36*
I2.3.6.07	as above; Nominal bore 600mm	m	0.29	50.69	37.00	27.65	**115.34**	*63.05*
I2.3.7	In trenches, depth: 3.5 - 4m							
I2.3.7.01	Concrete pipes, BS 5911, Class '120'; rebated flexible joints with mastic sealant to internal faces; Nominal bore 375mm	m	0.25	42.61	21.94	17.54	**82.09**	*52.22*
I2.3.7.02	as above; Nominal bore 450mm	m	0.29	50.40	25.96	20.34	**96.70**	*71.46*
I2.3.7.03	as above; Nominal bore 600mm	m	0.29	50.69	37.00	28.89	**116.58**	*115.94*
I2.3.7.04	Concrete porous pipes, BS 5911, Ogee joints; Nominal bore 375mm	m	0.29	50.23	25.87	14.18	**90.28**	*36.16*
I2.3.7.05	as above; Nominal bore 450mm	m	0.32	55.43	28.54	15.88	**99.85**	*49.06*
I2.3.7.06	as above; Nominal bore 525mm	m	0.32	55.93	40.82	18.36	**115.11**	*51.33*
I2.3.7.07	as above; Nominal bore 600mm	m	0.35	61.17	44.65	27.65	**133.47**	*65.42*
I2.3.8	In trenches, depth: exceeding 4m							
I2.3.8.01	Concrete pipes, BS 5911, Class '120'; rebated flexible joints with mastic sealant to internal faces; Nominal bore 375mm; depth: 4 - 4.5m	m	0.32	55.43	28.54	17.54	**101.51**	*54.86*
I2.3.8.02	as above; depth: 4.5 - 5m	m	0.40	69.28	35.68	17.54	**122.50**	*57.72*

I2 Concrete pipes continued...

		Unit	Labour Hours	Labour Net £	Plant Net £	Materials Net £	Unit Net £	CO_2 Kg
I2.3	**Nominal bore: 300 - 600mm**							
I2.3.8	In trenches, depth: exceeding 4m							
I2.3.8.03	as previous item; depth: 5 - 5.5m	m	0.43	73.96	38.09	17.54	**129.59**	*58.68*
I2.3.8.04	as above; depth: 5.5 - 6m	m	0.56	97.17	50.04	17.54	**164.75**	*63.47*
I2.3.8.05	as above; Nominal bore 450mm; depth: 4 - 4.5m	m	0.34	58.37	30.06	20.34	**108.77**	*73.10*
I2.3.8.06	as above; depth: 4.5 - 5m	m	0.43	73.96	38.09	20.34	**132.39**	*76.31*
I2.3.8.07	as above; depth: 5 - 5.5m	m	0.46	79.16	40.76	20.34	**140.26**	*77.39*
I2.3.8.08	as above; depth: 5.5 - 6m	m	0.58	100.81	51.91	20.34	**173.06**	*81.85*
I2.3.8.09	as above; Nominal bore 600mm; depth: 4 - 4.5m	m	0.34	59.43	43.37	28.89	**131.69**	*117.91*
I2.3.8.10	as above; depth: 4.5 - 5m	m	0.43	75.16	54.86	28.89	**158.91**	*121.46*
I2.3.8.11	as above; depth: 5 - 5.5m	m	0.46	80.40	58.68	28.89	**167.97**	*122.65*
I2.3.8.12	as above; depth: 5.5 - 6m	m	0.58	101.37	73.99	28.89	**204.25**	*127.39*
I2.3.8.13	Concrete porous pipes, BS 5911, Ogee joints; Nominal bore 375mm; depth: 4 - 4.5m	m	0.35	60.62	31.22	14.18	**106.02**	*38.30*
I2.3.8.14	as above; depth: 4.5 - 5m	m	0.50	86.61	44.60	14.18	**145.39**	*43.66*
I2.3.8.15	as above; Nominal bore 450mm; depth: 4 - 4.5m	m	0.40	69.28	35.68	15.88	**120.84**	*51.91*
I2.3.8.16	as above; depth: 4.5 - 5m	m	0.53	91.80	47.28	15.88	**154.96**	*56.56*
I2.3.8.17	as above; Nominal bore 525mm; depth: 4 - 4.5m	m	0.40	69.91	51.03	18.36	**139.30**	*54.49*
I2.3.8.18	as above; depth: 4.5 - 5m	m	0.53	92.63	67.61	18.36	**178.60**	*59.62*
I2.3.8.19	as above; depth: 5 - 5.5m	m	0.67	117.10	85.47	18.36	**220.93**	*65.15*
I2.3.8.20	as above; depth: 5.5 - 6m	m	0.80	139.82	102.06	18.36	**260.24**	*70.28*
I2.3.8.21	as above; Nominal bore 600mm; depth: 4 - 4.5m	m	0.42	73.41	53.58	27.65	**154.64**	*68.18*
I2.3.8.22	as above; depth: 4.5 - 5m	m	0.57	99.62	72.71	27.65	**199.98**	*74.10*
I2.3.8.23	as above; depth: 5 - 5.5m	m	0.73	127.59	93.13	27.65	**248.37**	*80.42*
I2.3.8.24	as above; depth: 5.5 - 6m	m	0.89	155.55	113.54	27.65	**296.74**	*86.73*
I2.4	**Nominal bore: 600 - 900mm**							
I2.4.3	In trenches, depth: 1.5 - 2m							
I2.4.3.01	Concrete pipes, BS 5911, Class '120'; rebated flexible joints with mastic sealant to internal faces; Nominal bore 750mm	m	0.23	25.12	25.92	49.40	**100.44**	*137.59*
I2.4.3.02	as above; Nominal bore 900mm	m	0.27	29.49	30.43	68.16	**128.08**	*184.24*
I2.4.4	In trenches, depth: 2 - 2.5m							
I2.4.4.01	Concrete pipes, BS 5911, Class '120'; rebated flexible joints with mastic sealant to internal faces; Nominal bore 750mm	m	0.25	27.31	28.18	49.40	**104.89**	*138.34*
I2.4.4.02	as above; Nominal bore 900mm	m	0.29	31.68	32.68	68.16	**132.52**	*184.98*
I2.4.5	In trenches, depth: 2.5 - 3m							
I2.4.5.01	Concrete pipes, BS 5911, Class '120'; rebated flexible joints with mastic sealant to internal faces; Nominal bore 750mm	m	0.27	29.49	30.43	49.40	**109.32**	*139.09*
I2.4.5.02	as above; Nominal bore 900mm	m	0.32	34.95	36.06	68.16	**139.17**	*186.10*
I2.4.6	In trenches, depth: 3 - 3.5m							
I2.4.6.01	Concrete pipes, BS 5911, Class '120'; rebated flexible joints with mastic sealant to internal faces; Nominal bore 750mm	m	0.27	47.19	34.44	49.40	**131.03**	*139.66*
I2.4.6.02	as above; Nominal bore 900mm	m	0.32	55.93	40.82	68.16	**164.91**	*186.78*

I2 Concrete pipes continued...

		Unit	Labour Hours	Labour Net £	Plant Net £	Materials Net £	Unit Net £	CO_2 Kg
I2.4	**Nominal bore: 600 - 900mm**							
I2.4.7	In trenches, depth: 3.5 - 4m							
I2.4.7.01	Concrete pipes, BS 5911, Class '120'; rebated flexible joints with mastic sealant to internal faces; Nominal bore 750mm	m	0.32	55.93	40.82	49.40	146.15	*141.63*
I2.4.7.02	as above; Nominal bore 900mm	m	0.36	62.92	45.93	68.16	177.01	*188.36*
I2.4.8	In trenches, depth: exceeding 4m							
I2.4.8.01	Concrete pipes, BS 5911, Class '120'; rebated flexible joints with mastic sealant to internal faces; Nominal bore 750mm; depth: 4 - 4.5m	m	0.36	62.92	45.93	49.40	158.25	*143.21*
I2.4.8.02	as above; depth: 4.5 - 5m	m	0.46	80.40	58.68	49.40	188.48	*147.16*
I2.4.8.03	as above; depth: 5 - 5.5m	m	0.53	92.63	67.61	49.40	209.64	*149.92*
I2.4.8.04	as above; depth: 5.5 - 6m	m	0.64	111.86	81.64	49.40	242.90	*154.26*
I2.4.8.05	as above; Nominal bore 900mm; depth: 4 - 4.5m	m	0.40	69.91	51.03	68.16	189.10	*189.94*
I2.4.8.06	as above; depth: 4.5 - 5m	m	0.53	92.63	67.61	68.16	228.40	*195.07*
I2.4.8.07	as above; depth: 5 - 5.5m	m	0.58	101.37	73.99	68.16	243.52	*197.05*
I2.4.8.08	as above; depth: 5.5 - 6m	m	0.71	124.09	90.57	68.16	282.82	*202.18*
I2.5	**Nominal bore: 900 - 1200mm**							
I2.5.3	In trenches, depth: 1.5 - 2m							
I2.5.3.01	Concrete pipes, BS 5911, Class '120'; rebated flexible joints with mastic sealant to internal faces; Nominal bore 1200mm	m	0.32	34.95	36.06	96.50	167.51	*312.95*
I2.5.4	In trenches, depth: 2 - 2.5m							
I2.5.4.01	Concrete pipes, BS 5911, Class '120'; rebated flexible joints with mastic sealant to internal faces; Nominal bore 1200mm	m	0.36	39.32	40.57	96.50	176.39	*314.45*
I2.5.5	In trenches, depth: 2.5 - 3m							
I2.5.5.01	Concrete pipes, BS 5911, Class '120'; rebated flexible joints with mastic sealant to internal faces; Nominal bore 1200mm	m	0.40	43.69	45.08	96.50	185.27	*315.94*
I2.5.6	In trenches, depth: 3 - 3.5m							
I2.5.6.01	Concrete pipes, BS 5911, Class '120'; rebated flexible joints with mastic sealant to internal faces; Nominal bore 1200mm	m	0.40	69.91	51.03	96.50	217.44	*316.79*
I2.5.7	In trenches, depth: 3.5 - 4m							
I2.5.7.01	Concrete pipes, BS 5911, Class '120'; rebated flexible joints with mastic sealant to internal faces; Nominal bore 1200mm	m	0.46	80.40	58.68	96.50	235.58	*319.16*
I2.5.8	In trenches, depth: exceeding 4m							
I2.5.8.01	Concrete pipes, BS 5911, Class '120'; rebated flexible joints with mastic sealant to internal faces; Nominal bore 1200mm; depth: 4 - 4.5m	m	0.53	92.63	67.61	96.50	256.74	*321.92*

I2 Concrete pipes continued...

		Unit	Labour Hours	Labour Net £	Plant Net £	Materials Net £	Unit Net £	CO_2 Kg
I2.5	**Nominal bore: 900 - 1200mm**							
I2.5.8	In trenches, depth: exceeding 4m							
I2.5.8.02	as above; depth: 4.5 - 5m	m	0.64	111.86	81.64	96.50	290.00	*326.26*
I2.5.8.03	as above; depth: 5 - 5.5m	m	0.71	124.09	90.57	96.50	311.16	*329.03*
I2.5.8.04	as above; depth: 5.5 - 6m	m	0.80	139.82	102.06	96.50	338.38	*332.58*
I2.6	**Nominal bore: 1200 - 1500mm**							
I2.6.3	In trenches, depth: 1.5 - 2m							
I2.6.3.01	Concrete pipes, BS 5911, Class '120'; rebated flexible joints with mastic sealant to internal faces; Nominal bore 1500mm	m	0.40	43.69	45.08	188.33	277.10	*470.74*
I2.6.4	In trenches, depth: 2 - 2.5m							
I2.6.4.01	Concrete pipes, BS 5911, Class '120'; rebated flexible joints with mastic sealant to internal faces; Nominal bore 1500mm	m	0.46	50.25	51.84	188.33	290.42	*472.98*
I2.6.5	In trenches, depth: 2.5 - 3m							
I2.6.5.01	Concrete pipes, BS 5911, Class '120'; rebated flexible joints with mastic sealant to internal faces; Nominal bore 1500mm	m	0.53	57.89	59.73	188.33	305.95	*475.60*
I2.6.6	In trenches, depth: 3 - 3.5m							
I2.6.6.01	Concrete pipes, BS 5911, Class '120'; rebated flexible joints with mastic sealant to internal faces; Nominal bore 1500mm	m	0.53	92.63	67.61	188.33	348.57	*476.72*
I2.6.7	In trenches, depth: 3.5 - 4m							
I2.6.7.01	Concrete pipes, BS 5911, Class '120'; rebated flexible joints with mastic sealant to internal faces; Nominal bore 1500mm	m	0.58	101.37	73.99	188.33	363.69	*478.70*
I2.6.8	In trenches, depth: exceeding 4m							
I2.6.8.01	Concrete pipes, BS 5911, Class '120'; rebated flexible joints with mastic sealant to internal faces; Nominal bore 1500mm; depth: 4 - 4.5m	m	0.64	111.86	81.64	188.33	381.83	*481.06*
I2.6.8.02	as above; depth: 4.5 - 5m	m	0.71	124.09	90.57	188.33	402.99	*483.83*
I2.6.8.03	as above; depth: 5 - 5.5m	m	0.80	139.82	102.06	188.33	430.21	*487.38*
I2.6.8.04	as above; depth: 5.5 - 6m	m	1.07	187.01	136.50	188.33	511.84	*498.04*
I2.7	**Nominal bore: 1500 - 1800mm**							
I2.7.3	In trenches, depth: 1.5 - 2m							
I2.7.3.01	Concrete pipes, BS 5911, Class '120'; rebated flexible joints with mastic sealant to internal faces; Nominal bore 1800mm	m	0.53	57.89	59.73	274.54	392.16	*630.40*
I2.7.4	In trenches, depth: 2 - 2.5m							
I2.7.4.01	Concrete pipes, BS 5911, Class '120'; rebated flexible joints with mastic sealant to internal faces; Nominal bore 1800mm	m	0.58	63.35	65.37	274.54	403.26	*632.27*

I2 Concrete pipes continued...

		Unit	Labour Hours	Labour Net £	Plant Net £	Materials Net £	Unit Net £	CO_2 Kg
I2.7	**Nominal bore: 1500 - 1800mm**							
I2.7.5	In trenches, depth: 2.5 - 3m							
I2.7.5.01	Concrete pipes, BS 5911, Class '120'; rebated flexible joints with mastic sealant to internal faces; Nominal bore 1800mm	m	0.64	69.91	72.13	274.54	**416.58**	*634.51*
I2.7.6	In trenches, depth: 3 - 3.5m							
I2.7.6.01	Concrete pipes, BS 5911, Class '120'; rebated flexible joints with mastic sealant to internal faces; Nominal bore 1800mm	m	0.64	111.86	81.64	274.54	**468.04**	*635.86*
I2.7.7	In trenches, depth: 3.5 - 4m							
I2.7.7.01	Concrete pipes, BS 5911, Class '120'; rebated flexible joints with mastic sealant to internal faces; Nominal bore 1800mm	m	0.71	124.09	90.57	274.54	**489.20**	*638.63*
I2.7.8	In trenches, depth: exceeding 4m							
I2.7.8.01	Concrete pipes, BS 5911, Class '120'; rebated flexible joints with mastic sealant to internal faces; Nominal bore 1800mm; depth: 4 - 4.5m	m	0.80	139.82	102.06	274.54	**516.42**	*642.18*
I2.7.8.02	as above; depth: 4.5 - 5m	m	1.07	187.01	136.50	274.54	**598.05**	*652.84*
I2.7.8.03	as above; depth: 5 - 5.5m	m	1.25	218.47	159.46	274.54	**652.47**	*659.95*
I2.7.8.04	as above; depth: 5.5 - 6m	m	1.60	279.65	204.11	274.54	**758.30**	*673.76*

I3 Iron pipes

		Unit	Labour Hours	Labour Net £	Plant Net £	Materials Net £	Unit Net £	CO_2 Kg
I3.1	**Nominal bore: not exceeding 200mm**							
I3.1.1	Not in trenches							
I3.1.1.01	Ductile spun iron pipes; concrete lined, BS EN 598, spigot & socket Tyton joints; Nominal bore 100mm; above ground on pipe supports (supports priced elsewhere)	m	0.08	5.60	-	27.55	**33.15**	*41.03*
I3.1.1.02	as above; Nominal bore 150mm; above ground on pipe supports (supports priced elsewhere)	m	0.10	7.00	-	36.50	**43.50**	*65.79*
I3.1.2	In trenches, depth: not exceeding 1.5m							
I3.1.2.01	Ductile spun iron pipes; concrete lined, BS EN 598, spigot & socket Tyton joints; Nominal bore 100mm	m	0.08	8.61	5.35	27.55	**41.51**	*43.14*
I3.1.2.02	as above; Nominal bore 150mm	m	0.08	7.61	5.35	36.50	**49.46**	*67.89*
I3.1.3	In trenches, depth: 1.5 - 2m							
I3.1.3.01	Ductile spun iron pipes; concrete lined, BS EN 598, spigot & socket Tyton joints; Nominal bore 100mm	m	0.08	9.04	5.62	27.55	**42.21**	*43.24*
I3.1.3.02	as above; Nominal bore 150mm	m	0.09	8.56	6.02	36.50	**51.08**	*68.16*

I3 Iron pipes continued...

		Unit	Labour Hours	Labour Net £	Plant Net £	Materials Net £	Unit Net £	CO_2 Kg
I3.1	**Nominal bore: not exceeding 200mm**							
I3.1.4	In trenches, depth: 2 - 2.5m							
I3.1.4.01	Ductile spun iron pipes; concrete lined, BS EN 598, spigot & socket Tyton joints; Nominal bore 100mm	m	0.09	10.12	6.29	27.55	**43.96**	*43.50*
I3.1.4.02	as above; Nominal bore 150mm	m	0.11	10.46	7.36	36.50	**54.32**	*68.68*
I3.1.5	In trenches, depth: 2.5 - 3m							
I3.1.5.01	Ductile spun iron pipes; concrete lined, BS EN 598, spigot & socket Tyton joints; Nominal bore 100mm	m	0.11	12.27	7.63	27.55	**47.45**	*44.03*
I3.1.5.02	as above; Nominal bore 150mm	m	0.14	15.07	9.37	36.50	**60.94**	*69.47*
I3.1.6	In trenches, depth: 3 - 3.5m							
I3.1.6.01	Ductile spun iron pipes; concrete lined, BS EN 598, spigot & socket Tyton joints; Nominal bore 100mm	m	0.11	19.75	10.17	27.55	**57.47**	*45.10*
I3.1.6.02	as above; Nominal bore 150mm	m	0.14	24.25	12.49	36.50	**73.24**	*70.79*
I3.1.7	In trenches, depth: 3.5 - 4m							
I3.1.7.01	Ductile spun iron pipes; concrete lined, BS EN 598, spigot & socket Tyton joints; Nominal bore 100mm	m	0.13	23.04	11.86	27.55	**62.45**	*45.78*
I3.1.7.02	as above; Nominal bore 150mm	m	0.17	29.45	15.16	36.50	**81.11**	*71.86*
I3.1.8	In trenches, depth: exceeding 4m							
I3.1.8.01	Ductile spun iron pipes; concrete lined, BS EN 598, spigot & socket Tyton joints; Nominal bore 100mm; depth: 4 - 4.5m	m	0.17	29.10	14.99	27.55	**71.64**	*47.03*
I3.1.8.02	as above; depth: 4.5 - 5m	m	0.20	34.64	17.84	27.55	**80.03**	*48.17*
I3.1.8.03	as above; depth: 5 - 5.5m	m	0.27	46.25	23.82	27.55	**97.62**	*50.57*
I3.1.8.04	as above; depth: 5.5 - 6m	m	0.36	63.05	32.47	27.55	**123.07**	*54.03*
I3.1.8.05	as above; Nominal bore 150mm; depth: 4 - 4.5m	m	0.20	34.64	17.84	36.50	**88.98**	*72.93*
I3.1.8.06	as above; depth: 4.5 - 5m	m	0.25	43.30	22.30	36.50	**102.10**	*74.72*
I3.1.8.07	as above; depth: 5 - 5.5m	m	0.29	50.23	25.87	36.50	**112.60**	*76.15*
I3.1.8.08	as above; depth: 5.5 - 6m	m	0.40	69.28	35.68	36.50	**141.46**	*80.08*
I3.2	**Nominal bore: 200 - 300mm**							
I3.2.1	Not in trenches							
I3.2.1.01	Ductile spun iron pipes; concrete lined, BS EN 598, spigot & socket Tyton joints; Nominal bore 300mm; above ground on pipe supports (supports priced elsewhere)	m	0.13	9.10	4.99	82.26	**96.35**	*175.22*
I3.2.2	In trenches, depth: not exceeding 1.5m							
I3.2.2.01	Ductile spun iron pipes; concrete lined, BS EN 598, spigot & socket Tyton joints; Nominal bore 300mm	m	0.13	14.00	8.70	82.26	**104.96**	*178.15*

I3 Iron pipes continued...

		Unit	Labour Hours	Labour Net £	Plant Net £	Materials Net £	Unit Net £	CO_2 Kg
I3.2	**Nominal bore: 200 - 300mm**							
I3.2.3	In trenches, depth: 1.5 - 2m							
I3.2.3.01	Ductile spun iron pipes; concrete lined, BS EN 598, spigot & socket Tyton joints; Nominal bore 300mm	m	0.14	15.07	9.37	82.26	**106.70**	*178.41*
I3.2.4	In trenches, depth: 2 - 2.5m							
I3.2.4.01	Ductile spun iron pipes; concrete lined, BS EN 598, spigot & socket Tyton joints; Nominal bore 300mm	m	0.16	17.23	10.71	82.26	**110.20**	*178.94*
I3.2.5	In trenches, depth: 2.5 - 3m							
I3.2.5.01	Ductile spun iron pipes; concrete lined, BS EN 598, spigot & socket Tyton joints; Nominal bore 300mm	m	0.19	20.46	12.71	82.26	**115.43**	*179.73*
I3.2.6	In trenches, depth: 3 - 3.5m							
I3.2.6.01	Ductile spun iron pipes; concrete lined, BS EN 598, spigot & socket Tyton joints; Nominal bore 300mm	m	0.19	32.91	16.95	82.26	**132.12**	*181.52*
I3.2.7	In trenches, depth: 3.5 - 4m							
I3.2.7.01	Ductile spun iron pipes; concrete lined, BS EN 598, spigot & socket Tyton joints; Nominal bore 300mm	m	0.21	36.37	18.73	82.26	**137.36**	*182.23*
I3.2.8	In trenches, depth: exceeding 4m							
I3.2.8.01	Ductile spun iron pipes; concrete lined, BS EN 598, spigot & socket Tyton joints; Nominal bore 300mm; depth: 4 - 4.5m	m	0.29	50.40	25.96	82.26	**158.62**	*185.13*
I3.2.8.02	as above; depth: 4.5 - 5m	m	0.36	61.66	31.76	82.26	**175.68**	*187.45*
I3.2.8.03	as above; depth: 5 - 5.5m	m	0.40	69.28	35.68	82.26	**187.22**	*189.02*
I3.2.8.04	as above; depth: 5.5 - 6m	m	0.53	92.32	47.54	82.26	**222.12**	*193.77*
I3.3	**Nominal bore: 300 - 600mm**							
I3.3.1	Not in trenches							
I3.3.1.01	Ductile spun iron pipes; concrete lined, BS EN 598, spigot & socket Tyton joints; Nominal bore 600mm; above ground on pipe supports (supports priced elsewhere)	m	0.18	12.88	-	222.03	**234.91**	*451.68*
I3.3.1.02	as above; Nominal bore 450mm; above ground on pipe supports (supports priced elsewhere)	m	0.16	11.20	-	144.69	**155.89**	*294.28*
I3.3.2	In trenches, depth: not exceeding 1.5m							
I3.3.2.01	Ductile spun iron pipes; concrete lined, BS EN 598, spigot & socket Tyton joints; Nominal bore 600mm	m	0.16	17.55	10.91	222.03	**250.49**	*455.97*
I3.3.2.02	as above; Nominal bore 450mm	m	0.15	15.61	9.70	144.69	**170.00**	*298.10*

I3 Iron pipes continued...

		Unit	Labour Hours	Labour Net £	Plant Net £	Materials Net £	Unit Net £	CO_2 Kg
I3.3	**Nominal bore: 300 - 600mm**							
I3.3.3	In trenches, depth: 1.5 - 2m							
I3.3.3.01	Ductile spun iron pipes; concrete lined, BS EN 598, spigot & socket Tyton joints; Nominal bore 600mm	m	0.19	20.24	12.58	222.03	**254.85**	*456.63*
I3.3.3.02	as above; Nominal bore 450mm	m	0.17	18.09	11.24	144.69	**174.02**	*298.70*
I3.3.4	In trenches, depth: 2 - 2.5m							
I3.3.4.01	Ductile spun iron pipes; concrete lined, BS EN 598, spigot & socket Tyton joints; Nominal bore 600mm	m	0.21	22.93	14.25	222.03	**259.21**	*457.29*
I3.3.4.02	as above; Nominal bore 450mm	m	0.19	20.24	12.58	144.69	**177.51**	*299.23*
I3.3.5	In trenches, depth: 2.5 - 3m							
I3.3.5.01	Ductile spun iron pipes; concrete lined, BS EN 598, spigot & socket Tyton joints; Nominal bore 600mm	m	0.25	26.48	16.46	222.03	**264.97**	*458.15*
I3.3.5.02	as above; Nominal bore 450mm	m	0.21	22.93	14.25	144.69	**181.87**	*299.89*
I3.3.6	In trenches, depth: 3 - 3.5m							
I3.3.6.01	Ductile spun iron pipes; concrete lined, BS EN 598, spigot & socket Tyton joints; Nominal bore 600mm	m	0.25	42.61	21.94	222.03	**286.58**	*460.47*
I3.3.6.02	as above; Nominal bore 450mm	m	0.21	36.89	19.00	144.69	**200.58**	*301.89*
I3.3.7	In trenches, depth: 3.5 - 4m							
I3.3.7.01	Ductile spun iron pipes; concrete lined, BS EN 598, spigot & socket Tyton joints; Nominal bore 600mm	m	0.29	50.40	25.96	222.03	**298.39**	*462.08*
I3.3.7.02	as above; Nominal bore 450mm	m	0.25	42.61	21.94	144.69	**209.24**	*303.07*
I3.3.8	In trenches, depth: exceeding 4m							
I3.3.8.01	Ductile spun iron pipes; concrete lined, BS EN 598, spigot & socket Tyton joints; Nominal bore 450mm; depth: 4 - 4.5m	m	0.32	55.43	28.54	144.69	**228.66**	*305.71*
I3.3.8.02	as above; depth: 4.5 - 5m	m	0.40	69.28	35.68	144.69	**249.65**	*308.57*
I3.3.8.03	as above; depth: 5 - 5.5m	m	0.43	73.96	38.09	144.69	**256.74**	*309.54*
I3.3.8.04	as above; depth: 5.5 - 6m	m	0.56	97.17	50.04	144.69	**291.90**	*314.32*
I3.3.8.05	as above; Nominal bore 600mm; depth: 4 - 4.5m	m	0.34	58.37	30.06	222.03	**310.46**	*463.72*
I3.3.8.06	as above; depth: 4.5 - 5m	m	0.43	73.96	38.09	222.03	**334.08**	*466.93*
I3.3.8.07	as above; depth: 5 - 5.5m	m	0.46	79.16	40.76	222.03	**341.95**	*468.01*
I3.3.8.08	as above; depth: 5.5 - 6m	m	0.58	100.81	51.91	222.03	**374.75**	*472.47*
I3.4	**Nominal bore: 600 - 900mm**							
I3.4.1	Not in trenches							
I3.4.1.01	Ductile spun iron pipes; concrete lined, BS EN 598, Stantyte joints with rubber gasket; Nominal bore 800mm; above ground on pipe supports (supports priced elsewhere)	m	0.23	16.45	-	365.92	**382.37**	*576.18*
I3.4.1.02	as above; Nominal bore 900mm; above ground on pipe supports (supports priced elsewhere)	m	0.27	19.32	-	436.37	**455.69**	*662.58*

I3 Iron pipes continued...

		Unit	Labour Hours	Labour Net £	Plant Net £	Materials Net £	Unit Net £	CO_2 Kg
I3.4	**Nominal bore: 600 - 900mm**							
I3.4.3	In trenches, depth: 1.5 - 2m							
I3.4.3.01	Ductile spun iron pipes; concrete lined, BS EN 598, Stantyte joints with rubber gasket; Nominal bore 800mm	m	0.23	25.01	25.81	365.92	**416.74**	*584.74*
I3.4.3.02	as above; Nominal bore 900mm	m	0.27	29.16	30.09	436.37	**495.62**	*672.56*
I3.4.4	In trenches, depth: 2 - 2.5m							
I3.4.4.01	Ductile spun iron pipes; concrete lined, BS EN 598, Stantyte joints with rubber gasket; Nominal bore 800mm	m	0.25	26.87	27.72	365.92	**420.51**	*585.37*
I3.4.4.02	as above; Nominal bore 900mm	m	0.29	31.79	32.80	436.37	**500.96**	*673.45*
I3.4.5	In trenches, depth: 2.5 - 3m							
I3.4.5.01	Ductile spun iron pipes; concrete lined, BS EN 598, Stantyte joints with rubber gasket; Nominal bore 800mm	m	0.27	29.16	30.09	365.92	**425.17**	*586.16*
I3.4.5.02	as above; Nominal bore 900mm	m	0.32	34.95	36.06	436.37	**507.38**	*674.54*
I3.4.6	In trenches, depth: 3 - 3.5m							
I3.4.6.01	Ductile spun iron pipes; concrete lined, BS EN 598, Stantyte joints with rubber gasket; Nominal bore 800mm	m	0.27	46.67	34.06	365.92	**446.65**	*586.72*
I3.4.6.02	as above; Nominal bore 900mm	m	0.32	55.93	40.82	436.37	**533.12**	*675.21*
I3.4.7	In trenches, depth: 3.5 - 4m							
I3.4.7.01	Ductile spun iron pipes; concrete lined, BS EN 598, Stantyte joints with rubber gasket; Nominal bore 800mm	m	0.32	55.93	40.82	365.92	**462.67**	*588.82*
I3.4.7.02	as above; Nominal bore 900mm	m	0.36	62.22	45.41	436.37	**544.00**	*676.63*
I3.4.8	In trenches, depth: exceeding 4m							
I3.4.8.01	Ductile spun iron pipes; concrete lined, BS EN 598, Stantyte joints with rubber gasket; Nominal bore 800mm; depth: 4 - 4.5m	m	0.36	62.22	45.41	365.92	**473.55**	*590.24*
I3.4.8.02	as above; depth: 4.5 - 5m	m	0.46	79.87	58.30	365.92	**504.09**	*594.22*
I3.4.8.03	as above; depth: 5 - 5.5m	m	0.53	93.16	67.99	365.92	**527.07**	*597.22*
I3.4.8.04	as above; depth: 5.5 - 6m	m	0.64	111.86	81.64	365.92	**559.42**	*601.45*
I3.4.8.05	as above; Nominal bore 900mm; depth: 4 - 4.5m	m	0.40	69.91	51.03	436.37	**557.31**	*678.37*
I3.4.8.06	as above; depth: 4.5 - 5m	m	0.53	93.16	67.99	436.37	**597.52**	*683.62*
I3.4.8.07	as above; depth: 5 - 5.5m	m	0.58	101.72	74.25	436.37	**612.34**	*685.56*
I3.4.8.08	as above; depth: 5.5 - 6m	m	0.71	124.27	90.70	436.37	**651.34**	*690.65*
I3.5	**Nominal bore: 900 - 1200mm**							
I3.5.1	Not in trenches							
I3.5.1.01	Ductile spun iron pipes; concrete lined, BS EN 598, Stantyte joints with rubber gasket; Nominal bore 1000mm; above ground on pipe supports (supports priced elsewhere)	m	0.29	20.75	-	556.29	**577.04**	*775.52*

I3 Iron pipes continued...

		Unit	Labour Hours	Labour Net £	Plant Net £	Materials Net £	Unit Net £	CO_2 Kg
I3.5	**Nominal bore: 900 - 1200mm**							
I3.5.1	Not in trenches							
I3.5.1.02	as above; Nominal bore 1200mm; above ground on pipe supports (supports priced elsewhere)	m	0.36	25.75	-	761.29	**787.04**	*888.47*
I3.5.3	In trenches, depth: 1.5 - 2m							
I3.5.3.01	Ductile spun iron pipes; concrete lined, BS EN 598, Stantyte joints with rubber gasket; Nominal bore 1000mm	m	0.32	34.95	36.06	556.29	**627.30**	*787.48*
I3.5.3.02	as above; Nominal bore 1200mm	m	0.32	34.95	36.06	761.29	**832.30**	*900.42*
I3.5.4	In trenches, depth: 2 - 2.5m							
I3.5.4.01	Ductile spun iron pipes; concrete lined, BS EN 598, Stantyte joints with rubber gasket; Nominal bore 1000mm	m	0.36	39.00	40.23	556.29	**635.52**	*788.86*
I3.5.4.02	as above; Nominal bore 1200mm	m	0.36	39.00	40.23	761.29	**840.52**	*901.80*
I3.5.5	In trenches, depth: 2.5 - 3m							
I3.5.5.01	Ductile spun iron pipes; concrete lined, BS EN 598, Stantyte joints with rubber gasket; Nominal bore 1000mm	m	0.40	43.69	45.08	556.29	**645.06**	*790.47*
I3.5.5.02	as above; Nominal bore 1200mm	m	0.40	43.69	45.08	761.29	**850.06**	*903.41*
I3.5.6	In trenches, depth: 3 - 3.5m							
I3.5.6.01	Ductile spun iron pipes; concrete lined, BS EN 598, Stantyte joints with rubber gasket; Nominal bore 1000mm	m	0.40	69.91	51.03	556.29	**677.23**	*791.31*
I3.5.6.02	as above; Nominal bore 1200mm	m	0.40	69.91	51.03	761.29	**882.23**	*904.26*
I3.5.7	In trenches, depth: 3.5 - 4m							
I3.5.7.01	Ductile spun iron pipes; concrete lined, BS EN 598, Stantyte joints with rubber gasket; Nominal bore 1000mm	m	0.46	79.87	58.30	556.29	**694.46**	*793.56*
I3.5.7.02	as above; Nominal bore 1200mm	m	0.46	79.87	58.30	761.29	**899.46**	*906.51*
I3.5.8	In trenches, depth: exceeding 4m							
I3.5.8.01	Ductile spun iron pipes; concrete lined, BS EN 598, Stantyte joints with rubber gasket; Nominal bore 1000mm; depth: 4 - 4.5m	m	0.53	93.16	67.99	556.29	**717.44**	*796.56*
I3.5.8.02	as above; depth: 4.5 - 5m	m	0.64	111.86	81.64	556.29	**749.79**	*800.79*
I3.5.8.03	as above; depth: 5 - 5.5m	m	0.71	124.27	90.70	556.29	**771.26**	*803.59*
I3.5.8.04	as above; depth: 5.5 - 6m	m	0.80	139.82	102.06	556.29	**798.17**	*807.10*
I3.5.8.05	as above; Nominal bore 1200mm; depth: 4 - 4.5m	m	0.53	93.16	67.99	761.29	**922.44**	*909.51*
I3.5.8.06	as above; depth: 4.5 - 5m	m	0.64	111.86	81.64	761.29	**954.79**	*913.73*
I3.5.8.07	as above; depth: 5 - 5.5m	m	0.71	124.27	90.70	761.29	**976.26**	*916.53*
I3.5.8.08	as above; depth: 5.5 - 6m	m	0.80	139.82	102.06	761.29	**1,003.17**	*920.05*

13 Iron pipes continued...

		Unit	Labour Hours	Labour Net £	Plant Net £	Materials Net £	Unit Net £	CO_2 Kg
13.7	**Nominal bore: 1500 - 1800mm**							
13.7.1	Not in trenches							
13.7.1.01	Ductile spun iron pipes; concrete lined, BS EN 598, Stantyte joints with rubber gasket; Nominal bore 1600mm; above ground on pipe supports (supports priced elsewhere)	m	0.49	35.05	-	1,485.44	**1,520.49**	*1,001.41*
13.7.2	In trenches, depth: not exceeding 1.5m							
13.7.2.01	Ductile spun iron pipes; concrete lined, BS EN 598, Stantyte joints with rubber gasket; Nominal bore 1600mm	m	0.42	46.20	47.67	1,485.44	**1,579.31**	*1,017.21*
13.7.3	In trenches, depth: 1.5 - 2m							
13.7.3.01	Ductile spun iron pipes; concrete lined, BS EN 598, Stantyte joints with rubber gasket; Nominal bore 1600mm	m	0.49	53.52	55.22	1,485.44	**1,594.18**	*1,019.71*
13.7.4	In trenches, depth: 2 - 2.5m							
13.7.4.01	Ductile spun iron pipes; concrete lined, BS EN 598, Stantyte joints with rubber gasket; Nominal bore 1600mm	m	0.58	63.35	65.37	1,485.44	**1,614.16**	*1,023.08*
13.7.5	In trenches, depth: 2.5 - 3m							
13.7.5.01	Ductile spun iron pipes; concrete lined, BS EN 598, Stantyte joints with rubber gasket; Nominal bore 1600mm	m	0.73	79.74	82.27	1,485.44	**1,647.45**	*1,028.68*
13.7.6	In trenches, depth: 3 - 3.5m							
13.7.6.01	Ductile spun iron pipes; concrete lined, BS EN 598, Stantyte joints with rubber gasket; Nominal bore 1600mm	m	0.73	127.59	93.13	1,485.44	**1,706.16**	*1,030.23*
13.7.7	In trenches, depth: 3.5 - 4m							
13.7.7.01	Ductile spun iron pipes; concrete lined, BS EN 598, Stantyte joints with rubber gasket; Nominal bore 1600mm	m	0.80	139.82	102.06	1,485.44	**1,727.32**	*1,032.99*
13.7.8	In trenches, depth: exceeding 4m							
13.7.8.01	Ductile spun iron pipes; concrete lined, BS EN 598, Stantyte joints with rubber gasket; Nominal bore 1600mm; depth: 4 - 4.5m	m	0.80	139.82	102.06	1,485.44	**1,727.32**	*1,032.99*
13.7.8.02	as above; depth: 4.5 - 5m	m	1.07	186.49	136.12	1,485.44	**1,808.05**	*1,043.53*
13.7.8.03	as above; depth: 5 - 5.5m	m	1.25	218.47	159.46	1,485.44	**1,863.37**	*1,050.75*
13.7.8.04	as above; depth: 5.5 - 6m	m	1.60	279.65	204.11	1,485.44	**1,969.20**	*1,064.57*

I4 Steel pipes

		Unit	Labour Hours	Labour Net £	Plant Net £	Materials Net £	Unit Net £	CO_2 Kg
I4.1	**Nominal bore: not exceeding 200mm**							
I4.1.1	Not in trenches							
I4.1.1.01	Steel pipes, BS EN 10216, ends bevelled; 9 m average length; welded joints, internal and external grit blasting; external coating on one coat bituminous primer; three coats bituminous enamel; inner wrap of fibreglass; outer wrap of bitumen impregnated fibreglass to BS 534, one coat of solar reflecting Vynamatt SP; internal lining of one coat bituminous primer, spun lining of bituminous enamel to BS 534, cold applied bitumen base tape on PVC carrier and primer to joint; 55% overlap; Nominal bore 101.7mm; above ground on pipe supports (supports priced elsewhere)	m	0.09	9.09	5.48	46.53	**61.10**	*57.35*
I4.1.1.02	as above; Nominal bore 154.1mm; above ground on pipe supports (supports priced elsewhere)	m	0.09	9.09	4.48	49.75	**63.32**	*82.80*
I4.1.2	In trenches, depth: not exceeding 1.5m							
I4.1.2.01	Steel pipes, BS EN 10216, ends bevelled; 9 m average length; welded joints, internal and external grit blasting; external coating on one coat bituminous primer; three coats bituminous enamel; inner wrap of fibreglass; outer wrap of bitumen impregnated fibreglass to BS 534, one coat of solar reflecting Vynamatt SP; internal lining of one coat bituminous primer, spun lining of bituminous enamel to BS 534, cold applied bitumen base tape on PVC carrier and primer to joint; 55% overlap; Nominal bore 101.7mm	m	0.09	13.77	10.13	43.78	**67.68**	*59.03*
I4.1.2.02	as above; Nominal bore 154.1mm	m	0.09	13.77	10.13	49.75	**73.65**	*84.95*
I4.1.3	In trenches, depth: 1.5 - 2m							
I4.1.3.01	Steel pipes, BS EN 10216, ends bevelled; 9 m average length; welded joints, internal and external grit blasting; external coating on one coat bituminous primer; three coats bituminous enamel; inner wrap of fibreglass; outer wrap of bitumen impregnated fibreglass to BS 534, one coat of solar reflecting Vynamatt SP; internal lining of one coat bituminous primer, spun lining of bituminous enamel to BS 534, cold applied bitumen base tape on PVC carrier and primer to joint; 55% overlap; Nominal bore 101.7mm	m	0.09	13.77	10.13	43.78	**67.68**	*59.03*
I4.1.3.02	as above; Nominal bore 154.1mm	m	0.10	15.30	11.25	49.75	**76.30**	*85.42*

I4 Steel pipes continued...

		Unit	Labour Hours	Labour Net £	Plant Net £	Materials Net £	Unit Net £	CO_2 Kg
I4.1	**Nominal bore: not exceeding 200mm**							
I4.1.4	In trenches, depth: 2 - 2.5m							
I4.1.4.01	Steel pipes, BS EN 10216, ends bevelled; 9 m average length; welded joints, internal and external grit blasting; external coating on one coat bituminous primer; three coats bituminous enamel; inner wrap of fibreglass; outer wrap of bitumen impregnated fibreglass to BS 534, one coat of solar reflecting Vynamatt SP; internal lining of one coat bituminous primer, spun lining of bituminous enamel to BS 534, cold applied bitumen base tape on PVC carrier and primer to joint; 55% overlap; Nominal bore 101.7mm	m	0.09	13.77	10.13	43.78	67.68	*59.03*
I4.1.4.02	as above; Nominal bore 154.1mm	m	0.11	16.83	12.38	49.75	78.96	*85.88*
I4.1.5	In trenches, depth: 2.5 - 3m							
I4.1.5.01	Steel pipes, BS EN 10216, ends bevelled; 9 m average length; welded joints, internal and external grit blasting; external coating on one coat bituminous primer; three coats bituminous enamel; inner wrap of fibreglass; outer wrap of bitumen impregnated fibreglass to BS 534, one coat of solar reflecting Vynamatt SP; internal lining of one coat bituminous primer, spun lining of bituminous enamel to BS 534, cold applied bitumen base tape on PVC carrier and primer to joint; 55% overlap; Nominal bore 101.7mm	m	0.09	13.77	10.13	43.78	67.68	*59.03*
I4.1.5.02	as above; Nominal bore 154.1mm	m	0.13	19.13	14.07	49.75	82.95	*86.58*
I4.1.6	In trenches, depth: 3 - 3.5m							
I4.1.6.01	Steel pipes, BS EN 10216, ends bevelled; 9 m average length; welded joints, internal and external grit blasting; external coating on one coat bituminous primer; three coats bituminous enamel; inner wrap of fibreglass; outer wrap of bitumen impregnated fibreglass to BS 534, one coat of solar reflecting Vynamatt SP; internal lining of one coat bituminous primer, spun lining of bituminous enamel to BS 534, cold applied bitumen base tape on PVC carrier and primer to joint; 55% overlap; Nominal bore 101.7mm	m	0.13	27.48	17.65	43.78	88.91	*60.46*
I4.1.6.02	as above; Nominal bore 154.1mm	m	0.13	27.48	17.65	49.75	94.88	*86.38*

I4 Steel pipes continued...

		Unit	Labour Hours	Labour Net £	Plant Net £	Materials Net £	Unit Net £	CO_2 Kg
I4.1	**Nominal bore: not exceeding 200mm**							
I4.1.7	In trenches, depth: 3.5 - 4m							
I4.1.7.01	Steel pipes, BS EN 10216, ends bevelled; 9 m average length; welded joints, internal and external grit blasting; external coating on one coat bituminous primer; three coats bituminous enamel; inner wrap of fibreglass; outer wrap of bitumen impregnated fibreglass to BS 534, one coat of solar reflecting Vynamatt SP; internal lining of one coat bituminous primer, spun lining of bituminous enamel to BS 534, cold applied bitumen base tape on PVC carrier and primer to joint; 55% overlap; Nominal bore 101.7mm	m	0.16	32.81	21.08	43.78	97.67	*61.55*
I4.1.7.02	as above; Nominal bore 154.1mm	m	0.16	32.81	21.08	49.75	103.64	*87.47*
I4.1.8	In trenches, depth: exceeding 4m							
I4.1.8.01	Steel pipes, BS EN 10216, ends bevelled; 9 m average length; welded joints, internal and external grit blasting; external coating on one coat bituminous primer; three coats bituminous enamel; inner wrap of fibreglass; outer wrap of bitumen impregnated fibreglass to BS 534, one coat of solar reflecting Vynamatt SP; internal lining of one coat bituminous primer, spun lining of bituminous enamel to BS 534, cold applied bitumen base tape on PVC carrier and primer to joint; 55% overlap; Nominal bore 101.7mm; depth 4-4.5m	m	0.30	62.33	40.05	43.78	146.16	*67.59*
I4.1.8.02	as above; depth: 4.5 - 5m	m	0.25	51.26	32.94	43.78	127.98	*65.32*
I4.1.8.03	as above; depth: 5 - 5.5m	m	0.36	73.81	47.43	43.78	165.02	*69.94*
I4.1.8.04	as above; Nominal bore 154.1mm; depth: 4 - 4.5m	m	0.21	42.03	27.01	49.75	118.79	*89.36*
I4.1.8.05	as above; depth: 4.5 - 5m	m	0.25	51.26	32.94	49.75	133.95	*91.24*
I4.1.8.06	as above; depth: 5 - 5.5m	m	0.36	73.81	47.43	49.75	170.99	*95.86*

I4 Steel pipes continued...

		Unit	Labour Hours	Labour Net £	Plant Net £	Materials Net £	Unit Net £	CO_2 Kg
I4.3	**Nominal bore: 300 - 600mm**							
I4.3.1	Not in trenches							
I4.3.1.01	Steel pipes, BS EN 10216, ends bevelled; 9 m average length; welded joints, internal and external grit blasting; external coating on one coat bituminous primer; three coats bituminous enamel; inner wrap of fibreglass; outer wrap of bitumen impregnated fibreglass to BS 534, one coat of solar reflecting Vynamatt SP; internal lining of one coat bituminous primer, spun lining of bituminous enamel to BS 534, cold applied bitumen base tape on PVC carrier and primer to joint; 55% overlap; Nominal bore 304.9mm; above ground on pipe supports (supports priced elsewhere)	m	0.16	16.16	7.97	101.37	**125.50**	*253.55*
I4.3.1.02	as above; Nominal bore 438.2mm; above ground on pipe supports (supports priced elsewhere)	m	0.18	18.18	8.96	211.64	**238.78**	*364.33*
I4.3.2	In trenches, depth: not exceeding 1.5m							
I4.3.2.01	Steel pipes, BS EN 10216, ends bevelled; 9 m average length; welded joints, internal and external grit blasting; external coating on one coat bituminous primer; three coats bituminous enamel; inner wrap of fibreglass; outer wrap of bitumen impregnated fibreglass to BS 534, one coat of solar reflecting Vynamatt SP; internal lining of one coat bituminous primer, spun lining of bituminous enamel to BS 534, cold applied bitumen base tape on PVC carrier and primer to joint; 55% overlap; Nominal bore 304.9mm	m	0.13	19.89	14.63	101.38	**135.90**	*255.96*
I4.3.2.02	as above; Nominal bore 438.2mm	m	0.13	19.89	14.63	211.65	**246.17**	*366.29*
I4.3.3	In trenches, depth: 1.5 - 2m							
I4.3.3.01	Steel pipes, BS EN 10216, ends bevelled; 9 m average length; welded joints, internal and external grit blasting; external coating on one coat bituminous primer; three coats bituminous enamel; inner wrap of fibreglass; outer wrap of bitumen impregnated fibreglass to BS 534, one coat of solar reflecting Vynamatt SP; internal lining of one coat bituminous primer, spun lining of bituminous enamel to BS 534, cold applied bitumen base tape on PVC carrier and primer to joint; 55% overlap; Nominal bore 304.9mm	m	0.15	22.95	16.88	101.38	**141.21**	*256.90*
I4.3.3.02	as above; Nominal bore 438.2mm	m	0.15	22.95	16.88	211.65	**251.48**	*367.22*

I4 Steel pipes continued...

		Unit	Labour Hours	Labour Net £	Plant Net £	Materials Net £	Unit Net £	*CO_2 Kg*
I4.3	**Nominal bore: 300 - 600mm**							
I4.3.4	In trenches, depth: 2 - 2.5m							
I4.3.4.01	Steel pipes, BS EN 10216, ends bevelled; 9 m average length; welded joints, internal and external grit blasting; external coating on one coat bituminous primer; three coats bituminous enamel; inner wrap of fibreglass; outer wrap of bitumen impregnated fibreglass to BS 534, one coat of solar reflecting Vynamatt SP; internal lining of one coat bituminous primer, spun lining of bituminous enamel to BS 534, cold applied bitumen base tape on PVC carrier and primer to joint; 55% overlap; Nominal bore 304.9mm	m	0.18	27.54	20.26	101.38	**149.18**	*258.29*
I4.3.4.02	as above; Nominal bore 438.2mm	m	0.18	27.54	20.26	211.65	**259.45**	*368.62*
I4.3.5	In trenches, depth: 2.5 - 3m							
I4.3.5.01	Steel pipes, BS EN 10216, ends bevelled; 9 m average length; welded joints, internal and external grit blasting; external coating on one coat bituminous primer; three coats bituminous enamel; inner wrap of fibreglass; outer wrap of bitumen impregnated fibreglass to BS 534, one coat of solar reflecting Vynamatt SP; internal lining of one coat bituminous primer, spun lining of bituminous enamel to BS 534, cold applied bitumen base tape on PVC carrier and primer to joint; 55% overlap; Nominal bore 304.9mm	m	0.22	32.90	24.19	101.38	**158.47**	*259.92*
I4.3.5.02	as above; Nominal bore 438.2mm	m	0.22	32.90	24.19	211.65	**268.74**	*370.25*
I4.3.6	In trenches, depth: 3 - 3.5m							
I4.3.6.01	Steel pipes, BS EN 10216, ends bevelled; 9 m average length; welded joints, internal and external grit blasting; external coating on one coat bituminous primer; three coats bituminous enamel; inner wrap of fibreglass; outer wrap of bitumen impregnated fibreglass to BS 534, one coat of solar reflecting Vynamatt SP; internal lining of one coat bituminous primer, spun lining of bituminous enamel to BS 534, cold applied bitumen base tape on PVC carrier and primer to joint; 55% overlap; Nominal bore 304.9mm	m	0.22	45.93	29.51	101.38	**176.82**	*259.30*
I4.3.6.02	as above; Nominal bore 438.2mm	m	0.22	45.93	29.51	211.65	**287.09**	*369.63*

I4 Steel pipes continued...

		Unit	Labour Hours	Labour Net £	Plant Net £	Materials Net £	Unit Net £	CO_2 Kg
I4.3	**Nominal bore: 300 - 600mm**							
I4.3.7	In trenches, depth: 3.5 - 4m							
I4.3.7.01	Steel pipes, BS EN 10216, ends bevelled; 9 m average length; welded joints, internal and external grit blasting; external coating on one coat bituminous primer; three coats bituminous enamel; inner wrap of fibreglass; outer wrap of bitumen impregnated fibreglass to BS 534, one coat of solar reflecting Vynamatt SP; internal lining of one coat bituminous primer, spun lining of bituminous enamel to BS 534, cold applied bitumen base tape on PVC carrier and primer to joint; 55% overlap; Nominal bore 304.9mm	m	0.25	52.08	33.46	101.38	**186.92**	*260.56*
I4.3.7.02	as above; Nominal bore 438.2mm	m	0.25	52.08	33.46	211.65	**297.19**	*370.89*
I4.3.8	In trenches, depth: exceeding 4m							
I4.3.8.01	Steel pipes, BS EN 10216, ends bevelled; 9 m average length; welded joints, internal and external grit blasting; external coating on one coat bituminous primer; three coats bituminous enamel; inner wrap of fibreglass; outer wrap of bitumen impregnated fibreglass to BS 534, one coat of solar reflecting Vynamatt SP; internal lining of one coat bituminous primer, spun lining of bituminous enamel to BS 534, cold applied bitumen base tape on PVC carrier and primer to joint; 55% overlap; Nominal bore 304.9mm; depth 4-4.5m	m	0.30	62.33	40.05	101.38	**203.76**	*262.66*
I4.3.8.02	as above; depth: 4.5 - 5m	m	0.36	73.81	47.43	101.38	**222.62**	*265.01*
I4.3.8.03	as above; depth: 5 - 5.5m	m	0.44	90.22	57.97	101.38	**249.57**	*268.36*
I4.3.8.04	as above; Nominal bore 438.2mm; depth: 4 - 4.5m	m	0.30	62.33	40.05	211.65	**314.03**	*372.99*
I4.3.8.05	as above; depth: 4.5 - 5m	m	0.36	73.81	47.43	211.65	**332.89**	*375.34*
I4.3.8.06	as above; depth: 5 - 5.5m	m	0.44	90.22	57.97	211.65	**359.84**	*378.69*

I4 Steel pipes continued...

		Unit	Labour Hours	Labour Net £	Plant Net £	Materials Net £	Unit Net £	CO_2 Kg
I4.4	**Nominal bore: 600 - 900mm**							
I4.4.1	Not in trenches							
I4.4.1.01	Steel pipes, BS EN 10216, ends bevelled; 9 m average length; welded joints, internal and external grit blasting; external coating on one coat bituminous primer; three coats bituminous enamel; inner wrap of fibreglass; outer wrap of bitumen impregnated fibreglass to BS 534, one coat of solar reflecting Vynamatt SP; internal lining of one coat bituminous primer, spun lining of bituminous enamel to BS 534, cold applied bitumen base tape on PVC carrier and primer to joint; 55% overlap; Nominal bore 641mm; above ground on pipe supports (supports priced elsewhere)	m	0.23	31.90	11.45	293.55	**336.90**	*530.96*
I4.4.1.02	as above; Nominal bore 692mm	m	0.27	37.44	13.45	306.10	**356.99**	*587.04*
I4.4.1.03	as above; Nominal bore 794mm	m	0.29	40.22	14.44	350.25	**404.91**	*671.90*
I4.4.1.04	as above; Nominal bore 895mm	m	0.22	30.51	10.96	405.46	**446.93**	*751.40*
I4.4.3	In trenches, depth: 1.5 - 2m							
I4.4.3.01	Steel pipes, BS EN 10216, ends bevelled; 9 m average length; welded joints, internal and external grit blasting; external coating on one coat bituminous primer; three coats bituminous enamel; inner wrap of fibreglass; outer wrap of bitumen impregnated fibreglass to BS 534, one coat of solar reflecting Vynamatt SP; internal lining of one coat bituminous primer, spun lining of bituminous enamel to BS 534, cold applied bitumen base tape on PVC carrier and primer to joint; 55% overlap; Nominal bore 641mm	m	0.16	29.45	18.70	293.57	**341.72**	*532.11*
I4.4.3.02	as above; Nominal bore 692mm	m	0.17	31.29	19.87	306.12	**357.28**	*587.67*
I4.4.3.03	as above; Nominal bore 794mm	m	0.17	31.29	19.87	350.28	**401.44**	*672.08*
I4.4.3.04	as above; Nominal bore 895mm	m	0.22	40.49	25.72	405.49	**471.70**	*755.16*
I4.4.4	In trenches, depth: 2 - 2.5m							
I4.4.4.01	Steel pipes, BS EN 10216, ends bevelled; 9 m average length; welded joints, internal and external grit blasting; external coating on one coat bituminous primer; three coats bituminous enamel; inner wrap of fibreglass; outer wrap of bitumen impregnated fibreglass to BS 534, one coat of solar reflecting Vynamatt SP; internal lining of one coat bituminous primer, spun lining of bituminous enamel to BS 534, cold applied bitumen base tape on PVC carrier and primer to joint; 55% overlap; Nominal bore 641mm	m	0.20	36.81	23.38	293.57	**353.76**	*533.70*
I4.4.4.02	as above; Nominal bore 692mm	m	0.21	38.65	24.55	306.12	**369.32**	*589.26*

I4 Steel pipes continued...

		Unit	Labour Hours	Labour Net £	Plant Net £	Materials Net £	Unit Net £	CO_2 *Kg*
I4.4	**Nominal bore: 600 - 900mm**							
I4.4.4	In trenches, depth: 2 - 2.5m							
I4.4.4.03	as previous item; Nominal bore 794mm	m	0.21	38.65	24.55	350.28	**413.48**	*673.67*
I4.4.4.04	as above; Nominal bore 895mm	m	0.26	47.85	30.39	405.49	**483.73**	*756.75*
I4.4.5	In trenches, depth: 2.5 - 3m							
I4.4.5.01	Steel pipes, BS EN 10216, ends bevelled; 9 m average length; welded joints, internal and external grit blasting; external coating on one coat bituminous primer; three coats bituminous enamel; inner wrap of fibreglass; outer wrap of bitumen impregnated fibreglass to BS 534, one coat of solar reflecting Vynamatt SP; internal lining of one coat bituminous primer, spun lining of bituminous enamel to BS 534, cold applied bitumen base tape on PVC carrier and primer to joint; 55% overlap; Nominal bore 641mm	m	0.27	48.77	30.98	293.57	**373.32**	*536.29*
I4.4.5.02	as above; Nominal bore 692mm	m	0.28	50.61	32.14	306.12	**388.87**	*591.85*
I4.4.5.03	as above; Nominal bore 794mm	m	0.28	50.61	32.14	350.28	**433.03**	*676.26*
I4.4.5.04	as above; Nominal bore 895mm	m	0.30	54.29	34.48	405.49	**494.26**	*758.14*
I4.4.6	In trenches, depth: 3 - 3.5m							
I4.4.6.01	Steel pipes, BS EN 10216, ends bevelled; 9 m average length; welded joints, internal and external grit blasting; external coating on one coat bituminous primer; three coats bituminous enamel; inner wrap of fibreglass; outer wrap of bitumen impregnated fibreglass to BS 534, one coat of solar reflecting Vynamatt SP; internal lining of one coat bituminous primer, spun lining of bituminous enamel to BS 534, cold applied bitumen base tape on PVC carrier and primer to joint; 55% overlap; Nominal bore 641mm	m	0.27	64.68	40.04	293.57	**398.29**	*537.94*
I4.4.6.02	as above; Nominal bore 692mm	m	0.28	67.04	41.50	306.12	**414.66**	*593.55*
I4.4.6.03	as above; Nominal bore 794mm	m	0.28	67.04	41.50	350.28	**458.82**	*677.96*
I4.4.6.04	as above; Nominal bore 895mm	m	0.30	71.76	44.42	405.49	**521.67**	*759.94*

I4 Steel pipes continued...

		Unit	Labour Hours	Labour Net £	Plant Net £	Materials Net £	Unit Net £	CO_2 Kg
I4.4	**Nominal bore: 600 - 900mm**							
I4.4.7	In trenches, depth: 3.5 - 4m							
I4.4.7.01	Steel pipes, BS EN 10216, ends bevelled; 9 m average length; welded joints, internal and external grit blasting; external coating on one coat bituminous primer; three coats bituminous enamel; inner wrap of fibreglass; outer wrap of bitumen impregnated fibreglass to BS 534, one coat of solar reflecting Vynamatt SP; internal lining of one coat bituminous primer, spun lining of bituminous enamel to BS 534, cold applied bitumen base tape on PVC carrier and primer to joint; 55% overlap; Nominal bore 641mm	m	0.28	66.80	41.35	293.57	**401.72**	*538.34*
I4.4.7.02	as above; Nominal bore 692mm	m	0.30	70.82	43.84	306.12	**420.78**	*594.26*
I4.4.7.03	as above; Nominal bore 794mm	m	0.30	70.82	43.84	350.28	**464.94**	*678.67*
I4.4.7.04	as above; Nominal bore 895mm	m	0.35	82.62	51.14	405.49	**539.25**	*761.99*
I4.4.8	In trenches, depth: exceeding 4m							
I4.4.8.01	Steel pipes, BS EN 10216, ends bevelled; 9 m average length; welded joints, internal and external grit blasting; external coating on one coat bituminous primer; three coats bituminous enamel; inner wrap of fibreglass; outer wrap of bitumen impregnated fibreglass to BS 534, one coat of solar reflecting Vynamatt SP; internal lining of one coat bituminous primer, spun lining of bituminous enamel to BS 534, cold applied bitumen base tape on PVC carrier and primer to joint; 55% overlap; Nominal bore 641mm; depth 4-4.5m	m	0.31	73.18	45.30	293.57	**412.05**	*539.54*
I4.4.8.02	as above; depth: 4.5 - 5m	m	0.37	87.34	54.06	293.57	**434.97**	*542.21*
I4.4.8.03	as above; depth: 5 - 5.5m	m	0.50	118.03	73.06	293.57	**484.66**	*548.01*
I4.4.8.04	as above; depth: 5.5 - 6m	m	0.57	134.55	83.29	293.57	**511.41**	*551.12*
I4.4.8.05	as above; Nominal bore 692mm; depth: 4 - 4.5m	m	0.33	77.90	48.22	306.12	**432.24**	*595.60*
I4.4.8.06	as above; depth: 4.5 - 5m	m	0.40	94.42	58.45	306.12	**458.99**	*598.72*
I4.4.8.07	as above; depth: 5 - 5.5m	m	0.53	125.11	77.44	306.12	**508.67**	*604.51*
I4.4.8.08	as above; depth: 5.5 - 6m	m	0.62	146.36	90.59	306.12	**543.07**	*608.52*
I4.4.8.09	as above; Nominal bore 794mm; depth: 4 - 4.5m	m	0.33	77.90	48.22	350.28	**476.40**	*680.01*
I4.4.8.10	as above; depth: 4.5 - 5m	m	0.40	94.42	58.45	350.28	**503.15**	*683.13*
I4.4.8.11	as above; depth: 5 - 5.5m	m	0.53	125.11	77.44	350.28	**552.83**	*688.92*
I4.4.8.12	as above; depth: 5.5 - 6m	m	0.62	146.36	90.59	350.28	**587.23**	*692.93*
I4.4.8.13	as above; Nominal bore 895mm; depth: 4 - 4.5m	m	0.40	94.42	58.45	405.49	**558.36**	*764.21*
I4.4.8.14	as above; depth: 4.5 - 5m	m	0.47	110.95	68.68	405.49	**585.12**	*767.33*
I4.4.8.15	as above; depth: 5 - 5.5m	m	0.62	146.36	90.59	405.49	**642.44**	*774.01*
I4.4.8.16	as above; depth: 5.5 - 6m	m	0.73	172.32	106.67	405.49	**684.48**	*778.91*

I4 Steel pipes continued...

		Unit	Labour Hours	Labour Net £	Plant Net £	Materials Net £	Unit Net £	CO_2 Kg
I4.5	**Nominal bore: 900 - 1200mm**							
I4.5.1	Not in trenches							
I4.5.1.01	Steel pipes, BS EN 10216, ends bevelled; 9 m average length; welded joints, internal and external grit blasting; external coating on one coat bituminous primer; three coats bituminous enamel; inner wrap of fibreglass; outer wrap of bitumen impregnated fibreglass to BS 534, one coat of solar reflecting Vynamatt SP; internal lining of one coat bituminous primer, spun lining of bituminous enamel to BS 534, cold applied bitumen base tape on PVC carrier and primer to joint; 55% overlap; Nominal bore 997mm; above ground on pipe supports (supports priced elsewhere)	m	0.24	33.28	11.95	464.26	**509.49**	*839.59*
I4.5.1.02	as above; Nominal bore 1195mm; above ground on pipe supports (supports priced elsewhere)	m	0.27	37.44	13.45	551.51	**602.40**	*1,287.55*
I4.5.3	In trenches, depth: 1.5 - 2m							
I4.5.3.01	Steel pipes, BS EN 10216, ends bevelled; 9 m average length; welded joints, internal and external grit blasting; external coating on one coat bituminous primer; three coats bituminous enamel; inner wrap of fibreglass; outer wrap of bitumen impregnated fibreglass to BS 534, one coat of solar reflecting Vynamatt SP; internal lining of one coat bituminous primer, spun lining of bituminous enamel to BS 534, cold applied bitumen base tape on PVC carrier and primer to joint; 55% overlap; Nominal bore 997mm	m	0.24	44.17	28.05	464.29	**536.51**	*843.69*
I4.5.3.02	as above; Nominal bore 1195mm	m	0.27	49.69	31.56	551.55	**632.80**	*1,292.17*
I4.5.4	In trenches, depth: 2 - 2.5m							
I4.5.4.01	Steel pipes, BS EN 10216, ends bevelled; 9 m average length; welded joints, internal and external grit blasting; external coating on one coat bituminous primer; three coats bituminous enamel; inner wrap of fibreglass; outer wrap of bitumen impregnated fibreglass to BS 534, one coat of solar reflecting Vynamatt SP; internal lining of one coat bituminous primer, spun lining of bituminous enamel to BS 534, cold applied bitumen base tape on PVC carrier and primer to joint; 55% overlap; Nominal bore 997mm	m	0.28	50.61	32.14	464.29	**547.04**	*845.08*
I4.5.4.02	as above; Nominal bore 1195mm	m	0.30	55.21	35.07	551.55	**641.83**	*1,293.36*

I4 Steel pipes continued...

		Unit	Labour Hours	Labour Net £	Plant Net £	Materials Net £	Unit Net £	CO_2 Kg
I4.5	**Nominal bore: 900 - 1200mm**							
I4.5.5	In trenches, depth: 2.5 - 3m							
I4.5.5.01	Steel pipes, BS EN 10216, ends bevelled; 9 m average length; welded joints, internal and external grit blasting; external coating on one coat bituminous primer; three coats bituminous enamel; inner wrap of fibreglass; outer wrap of bitumen impregnated fibreglass to BS 534, one coat of solar reflecting Vynamatt SP; internal lining of one coat bituminous primer, spun lining of bituminous enamel to BS 534, cold applied bitumen base tape on PVC carrier and primer to joint; 55% overlap; Nominal bore 997mm	m	0.31	56.13	35.65	464.29	**556.07**	*846.28*
I4.5.5.02	as above; Nominal bore 1195mm	m	0.33	59.81	37.99	551.55	**649.35**	*1,294.36*
I4.5.6	In trenches, depth: 3 - 3.5m							
I4.5.6.01	Steel pipes, BS EN 10216, ends bevelled; 9 m average length; welded joints, internal and external grit blasting; external coating on one coat bituminous primer; three coats bituminous enamel; inner wrap of fibreglass; outer wrap of bitumen impregnated fibreglass to BS 534, one coat of solar reflecting Vynamatt SP; internal lining of one coat bituminous primer, spun lining of bituminous enamel to BS 534, cold applied bitumen base tape on PVC carrier and primer to joint; 55% overlap; Nominal bore 997mm	m	0.31	74.12	45.88	464.29	**584.29**	*848.12*
I4.5.6.02	as above; Nominal bore 1195mm	m	0.33	78.84	48.80	551.55	**679.19**	*1,296.29*
I4.5.7	In trenches, depth: 3.5 - 4m							
I4.5.7.01	Steel pipes, BS EN 10216, ends bevelled; 9 m average length; welded joints, internal and external grit blasting; external coating on one coat bituminous primer; three coats bituminous enamel; inner wrap of fibreglass; outer wrap of bitumen impregnated fibreglass to BS 534, one coat of solar reflecting Vynamatt SP; internal lining of one coat bituminous primer, spun lining of bituminous enamel to BS 534, cold applied bitumen base tape on PVC carrier and primer to joint; 55% overlap; Nominal bore 997mm	m	0.38	89.70	55.53	464.29	**609.52**	*851.06*
I4.5.7.02	as above; Nominal bore 1195mm	m	0.44	103.87	64.29	551.55	**719.71**	*1,301.01*

I4 Steel pipes continued...

		Unit	Labour Hours	Labour Net £	Plant Net £	Materials Net £	Unit Net £	CO_2 Kg
I4.5	**Nominal bore: 900 - 1200mm**							
I4.5.8	In trenches, depth: exceeding 4m							
I4.5.8.01	Steel pipes, BS EN 10216, ends bevelled; 9 m average length; welded joints, internal and external grit blasting; external coating on one coat bituminous primer; three coats bituminous enamel; inner wrap of fibreglass; outer wrap of bitumen impregnated fibreglass to BS 534, one coat of solar reflecting Vynamatt SP; internal lining of one coat bituminous primer, spun lining of bituminous enamel to BS 534, cold applied bitumen base tape on PVC carrier and primer to joint; 55% overlap; Nominal bore 997mm; depth 4-4.5m	m	0.44	103.87	64.29	464.29	**632.45**	*853.73*
I4.5.8.02	as above; depth: 4.5 - 5m	m	0.53	125.11	77.44	464.29	**666.84**	*857.74*
I4.5.8.03	as above; depth: 5 - 5.5m	m	0.67	158.16	97.90	464.29	**720.35**	*863.98*
I4.5.8.04	as above; depth: 5.5 - 6m	m	0.80	188.85	116.90	464.29	**770.04**	*869.77*
I4.5.8.05	as above; Nominal bore 1195mm; depth: 4 - 4.5m	m	0.53	125.11	77.44	551.55	**754.10**	*1,305.02*
I4.5.8.06	as above; depth: 4.5 - 5m	m	0.67	158.16	97.90	551.55	**807.61**	*1,311.26*
I4.5.8.07	as above; depth: 5 - 5.5m	m	0.89	210.09	130.05	551.55	**891.69**	*1,321.06*
I4.5.8.08	as above; depth: 5.5 - 6m	m	1.00	236.06	146.12	551.55	**933.73**	*1,325.96*
I4.7	**Nominal bore: 1500 - 1800mm**							
I4.7.1	Not in trenches							
I4.7.1.01	Steel pipes, BS EN 10216, ends bevelled; 9 m average length; welded joints, internal and external grit blasting; external coating on one coat bituminous primer; three coats bituminous enamel; inner wrap of fibreglass; outer wrap of bitumen impregnated fibreglass to BS 534, one coat of solar reflecting Vynamatt SP; internal lining of one coat bituminous primer, spun lining of bituminous enamel to BS 534, cold applied bitumen base tape on PVC carrier and primer to joint; 55% overlap; Nominal bore 1595mm; above ground on pipe supports (supports priced elsewhere)	m	0.36	49.92	17.93	1,164.83	**1,232.68**	*1,724.27*
I4.7.2	In trenches, depth: not exceeding 1.5m							
I4.7.2.01	Steel pipes, BS EN 10216, ends bevelled; 9 m average length; welded joints, internal and external grit blasting; external coating on one coat bituminous primer; three coats bituminous enamel; inner wrap of fibreglass; outer wrap of bitumen impregnated fibreglass to BS 534, one coat of solar reflecting Vynamatt SP; internal lining of one coat bituminous primer, spun lining of bituminous enamel to BS 534, cold applied bitumen base tape on PVC carrier and primer to joint; 55% overlap; Nominal bore 1595mm	m	0.21	38.65	24.55	1,164.87	**1,228.07**	*1,724.45*

I4 Steel pipes continued...

		Unit	Labour Hours	Labour Net £	Plant Net £	Materials Net £	Unit Net £	*CO_2 Kg*
I4.7	**Nominal bore: 1500 - 1800mm**							
I4.7.3	In trenches, depth: 1.5 - 2m							
I4.7.3.01	Steel pipes, BS EN 10216, ends bevelled; 9 m average length; welded joints, internal and external grit blasting; external coating on one coat bituminous primer; three coats bituminous enamel; inner wrap of fibreglass; outer wrap of bitumen impregnated fibreglass to BS 534, one coat of solar reflecting Vynamatt SP; internal lining of one coat bituminous primer, spun lining of bituminous enamel to BS 534, cold applied bitumen base tape on PVC carrier and primer to joint; 55% overlap; Nominal bore 1595mm	m	0.28	51.53	32.73	1,164.87	**1,249.13**	*1,727.24*
I4.7.4	In trenches, depth: 2 - 2.5m							
I4.7.4.01	Steel pipes, BS EN 10216, ends bevelled; 9 m average length; welded joints, internal and external grit blasting; external coating on one coat bituminous primer; three coats bituminous enamel; inner wrap of fibreglass; outer wrap of bitumen impregnated fibreglass to BS 534, one coat of solar reflecting Vynamatt SP; internal lining of one coat bituminous primer, spun lining of bituminous enamel to BS 534, cold applied bitumen base tape on PVC carrier and primer to joint; 55% overlap; Nominal bore 1595mm	m	0.36	66.25	42.08	1,164.87	**1,273.20**	*1,730.42*
I4.7.5	In trenches, depth: 2.5 - 3m							
I4.7.5.01	Steel pipes, BS EN 10216, ends bevelled; 9 m average length; welded joints, internal and external grit blasting; external coating on one coat bituminous primer; three coats bituminous enamel; inner wrap of fibreglass; outer wrap of bitumen impregnated fibreglass to BS 534, one coat of solar reflecting Vynamatt SP; internal lining of one coat bituminous primer, spun lining of bituminous enamel to BS 534, cold applied bitumen base tape on PVC carrier and primer to joint; 55% overlap; Nominal bore 1595mm	m	0.44	80.06	50.85	1,164.87	**1,295.78**	*1,733.41*

I4 Steel pipes continued...

		Unit	Labour Hours	Labour Net £	Plant Net £	Materials Net £	Unit Net £	CO_2 Kg
I4.7	**Nominal bore: 1500 - 1800mm**							
I4.7.6	In trenches, depth: 3 - 3.5m							
I4.7.6.01	Steel pipes, BS EN 10216, ends bevelled; 9 m average length; welded joints, internal and external grit blasting; external coating on one coat bituminous primer; three coats bituminous enamel; inner wrap of fibreglass; outer wrap of bitumen impregnated fibreglass to BS 534, one coat of solar reflecting Vynamatt SP; internal lining of one coat bituminous primer, spun lining of bituminous enamel to BS 534, cold applied bitumen base tape on PVC carrier and primer to joint; 55% overlap; Nominal bore 1595mm	m	0.44	104.81	64.88	1,164.87	**1,334.56**	*1,735.86*
I4.7.7	In trenches, depth: 3.5 - 4m							
I4.7.7.01	Steel pipes, BS EN 10216, ends bevelled; 9 m average length; welded joints, internal and external grit blasting; external coating on one coat bituminous primer; three coats bituminous enamel; inner wrap of fibreglass; outer wrap of bitumen impregnated fibreglass to BS 534, one coat of solar reflecting Vynamatt SP; internal lining of one coat bituminous primer, spun lining of bituminous enamel to BS 534, cold applied bitumen base tape on PVC carrier and primer to joint; 55% overlap; Nominal bore 1595mm	m	0.53	125.11	77.44	1,164.87	**1,367.42**	*1,739.69*
I4.7.8	In trenches, depth: exceeding 4m							
I4.7.8.01	Steel pipes, BS EN 10216, ends bevelled; 9 m average length; welded joints, internal and external grit blasting; external coating on one coat bituminous primer; three coats bituminous enamel; inner wrap of fibreglass; outer wrap of bitumen impregnated fibreglass to BS 534, one coat of solar reflecting Vynamatt SP; internal lining of one coat bituminous primer, spun lining of bituminous enamel to BS 534, cold applied bitumen base tape on PVC carrier and primer to joint; 55% overlap; Nominal bore 1595mm; depth 4-4.5m	m	0.67	158.16	97.90	1,164.87	**1,420.93**	*1,745.93*
I4.7.8.02	as above; depth: 4.5 - 5m	m	0.89	210.09	130.05	1,164.87	**1,505.01**	*1,755.73*
I4.7.8.03	as above; depth: 5 - 5.5m	m	1.33	313.96	194.34	1,164.87	**1,673.17**	*1,775.33*
I4.7.8.04	as above; depth: 5.5 - 6m	m	1.60	377.70	233.79	1,164.87	**1,776.36**	*1,787.35*

I5 Polyvinyl Chloride pipes

		Unit	Labour Hours	Labour Net £	Plant Net £	Materials Net £	Unit Net £	CO_2 Kg
I5.1	**Nominal bore: not exceeding 200mm**							
I5.1.2	In trenches, depth: not exceeding 1.5m							
I5.1.2.01	Unplasticised PVC pipes, BS EN 1452 and BS 3506, Class 'C'; 6m lengths; compression joints with rubber ring; Nominal bore 50mm	m	0.08	8.61	5.35	6.28	**20.24**	*5.20*
I5.1.2.02	as above; Nominal bore 100mm	m	0.09	9.69	6.02	17.20	**32.91**	*6.54*
I5.1.2.03	as above; Nominal bore 150mm	m	0.08	8.61	5.35	37.38	**51.34**	*7.95*
I5.1.3	In trenches, depth: 1.5 - 2m							
I5.1.3.01	Unplasticised PVC pipes, BS EN 1452 and BS 3506, Class 'C'; 6m lengths; compression joints with rubber ring; Nominal bore 50mm	m	0.09	9.69	6.02	6.28	**21.99**	*5.46*
I5.1.3.02	as above; Nominal bore 100mm	m	0.10	10.77	6.69	17.20	**34.66**	*6.80*
I5.1.3.03	as above; Nominal bore 150mm	m	0.11	11.84	7.36	37.38	**56.58**	*8.73*
I5.1.4	In trenches, depth: 2 - 2.5m							
I5.1.4.01	Unplasticised PVC pipes, BS EN 1452 and BS 3506, Class 'C'; 6m lengths; compression joints with rubber ring; Nominal bore 50mm	m	0.10	15.30	6.69	6.28	**28.27**	*5.73*
I5.1.4.02	as above; Nominal bore 100mm	m	0.11	11.84	7.36	17.20	**36.40**	*7.07*
I5.1.4.03	as above; Nominal bore 150mm	m	0.13	14.00	8.70	37.38	**60.08**	*9.26*
I5.1.5	In trenches, depth: 2.5 - 3m							
I5.1.5.01	Unplasticised PVC pipes, BS EN 1452 and BS 3506, Class 'C'; 6m lengths; compression joints with rubber ring; Nominal bore 50mm	m	0.11	11.84	7.36	6.28	**25.48**	*5.99*
I5.1.5.02	as above; Nominal bore 100mm	m	0.13	14.00	8.70	17.20	**39.90**	*7.59*
I5.1.5.03	as above; Nominal bore 150mm	m	0.15	16.15	10.04	37.38	**63.57**	*9.79*
I5.1.6	In trenches, depth: 3 - 3.5m							
I5.1.6.01	Unplasticised PVC pipes, BS EN 1452 and BS 3506, Class 'C'; 6m lengths; compression joints with rubber ring; Nominal bore 50mm	m	0.12	12.92	10.70	6.28	**29.90**	*7.38*
I5.1.6.02	as above; Nominal bore 100mm	m	0.15	25.98	13.38	17.20	**56.56**	*9.53*
I5.1.6.03	as above; Nominal bore 150mm	m	0.15	25.98	13.38	37.38	**76.74**	*11.20*
I5.1.7	In trenches, depth: 3.5 - 4m							
I5.1.7.01	Unplasticised PVC pipes, BS EN 1452 and BS 3506, Class 'C'; 6m lengths; compression joints with rubber ring; Nominal bore 50mm	m	0.14	15.07	12.49	6.28	**33.84**	*8.10*
I5.1.7.02	as above; Nominal bore 100mm;	m	0.18	31.18	16.06	17.20	**64.44**	*10.60*
I5.1.7.03	as above; Nominal bore 150mm	m	0.18	31.18	16.06	37.38	**84.62**	*12.27*

I5 Polyvinyl Chloride pipes continued...

		Unit	Labour Hours	Labour Net £	Plant Net £	Materials Net £	Unit Net £	CO_2 Kg
I5.1	**Nominal bore: not exceeding 200mm**							
I5.1.8	In trenches, depth: exceeding 4m							
I5.1.8.01	Unplasticised PVC pipes, BS EN 1452 and BS 3506, Class 'C'; 6m lengths; compression joints with rubber ring; Nominal bore 50mm; depth 4-4.5m	m	0.18	19.38	16.06	6.28	41.71	*9.53*
I5.1.8.02	as above; Bore 50mm; depth: 5 - 5.5m	m	0.22	23.69	19.62	6.28	49.59	*10.96*
I5.1.8.03	as above; Bore 100mm; depth: 4.5 - 5m	m	0.22	38.11	19.62	17.20	74.93	*12.03*
I5.1.8.04	as above; Bore 100mm; depth: 5 - 5.5m	m	0.25	43.30	22.30	17.20	82.80	*13.10*
I5.1.8.05	as above; Bore 150mm; depth: 4 - 4.5m	m	0.22	38.11	19.62	37.38	95.11	*13.70*
I5.1.8.06	as above; Bore 150mm; depth: 4.5 - 5m	m	0.30	51.96	26.76	37.38	116.10	*16.56*
I5.2	**Nominal bore: 200 - 300mm**							
I5.2.2	In trenches, depth: not exceeding 1.5m							
I5.2.2.01	Unplasticised PVC pipes, BS EN 1452 and BS 3506, Class 'C'; 6m lengths; compression joints with rubber ring; Nominal bore 300mm	m	0.11	11.84	7.36	128.72	147.92	*21.07*
I5.2.3	In trenches, depth: 1.5 - 2m							
I5.2.3.01	Unplasticised PVC pipes, BS EN 1452 and BS 3506, Class 'C'; 6m lengths; compression joints with rubber ring; Nominal bore 300mm	m	0.13	14.00	8.70	128.72	151.42	*21.60*
I5.2.4	In trenches, depth: 2 - 2.5m							
I5.2.4.01	Unplasticised PVC pipes, BS EN 1452 and BS 3506, Class 'C'; 6m lengths; compression joints with rubber ring; Nominal bore 300mm	m	0.15	16.15	10.04	128.72	154.91	*22.12*
I5.2.5	In trenches, depth: 2.5 - 3m							
I5.2.5.01	Unplasticised PVC pipes, BS EN 1452 and BS 3506, Class 'C'; 6m lengths; compression joints with rubber ring; Nominal bore 300mm	m	0.18	19.38	12.04	128.72	160.14	*22.91*
I5.2.6	In trenches, depth: 3 - 3.5m							
I5.2.6.01	Unplasticised PVC pipes, BS EN 1452 and BS 3506, Class 'C'; 6m lengths; compression joints with rubber ring; Nominal bore 300mm	m	0.18	31.18	16.06	128.72	175.96	*24.61*
I5.2.7	In trenches, depth: 3.5 - 4m							
I5.2.7.01	Unplasticised PVC pipes, BS EN 1452 and BS 3506, Class 'C'; 6m lengths; compression joints with rubber ring; Nominal bore 300mm	m	0.22	38.11	19.62	128.72	186.45	*26.03*
I5.2.8	In trenches, depth: exceeding 4m							
I5.2.8.01	Unplasticised PVC pipes, BS EN 1452 and BS 3506, Class 'C'; 6m lengths; compression joints with rubber ring; Nominal bore 300mm; depth: 4 - 4.5m	m	0.30	51.96	26.76	128.72	207.44	*28.89*
I5.2.8.02	as above; depth: 4.5 - 5m	m	0.44	76.21	39.25	128.72	244.18	*33.89*

I8 Medium density Polyethylene pipes

		Unit	Labour Hours	Labour Net £	Plant Net £	Materials Net £	Unit Net £	CO_2 Kg
I8.1	**Nominal bore: not exceeding 200mm**							
I8.1.2	In trenches, depth: not exceeding 1.5m							
I8.1.2.01	Blue MDPE (SDR 11) water supply pipe systems, to WIS 4-32-03, 6m lengths, butt welded joints; Outside diameter 90mm	m	0.06	6.46	6.82	4.52	**17.80**	*5.09*
I8.1.2.02	as above; Outside diameter 125mm	m	0.07	7.54	7.96	8.68	**24.18**	*7.95*
I8.1.2.03	as above; Outside diameter 160mm	m	0.08	8.61	9.09	14.16	**31.86**	*11.60*
I8.1.2.04	as above; Outside diameter 180mm	m	0.09	9.69	10.23	17.94	**37.86**	*14.22*
I8.1.3	In trenches, depth: 1.5 - 2m							
I8.1.3.01	Blue MDPE (SDR 11) water supply pipe systems, to WIS 4-32-03, 6m lengths, butt welded joints; Outside diameter 90mm	m	0.07	7.54	7.96	4.52	**20.02**	*5.50*
I8.1.3.02	as above; Outside diameter 125mm	m	0.09	9.69	10.23	8.68	**28.60**	*8.77*
I8.1.3.03	as above; Outside diameter 160mm	m	0.11	11.84	12.50	14.16	**38.50**	*12.83*
I8.1.3.04	as above; Outside diameter 180mm	m	0.11	11.84	12.50	17.94	**42.28**	*15.04*
I8.1.4	In trenches, depth: 2 - 2.5m							
I8.1.4.01	Blue MDPE (SDR 11) water supply pipe systems, to WIS 4-32-03, 6m lengths, butt welded joints; Outside diameter 90mm	m	0.10	10.77	11.37	4.52	**26.66**	*6.73*
I8.1.4.02	as above; Outside diameter 125mm	m	0.12	12.92	13.64	8.68	**35.24**	*10.00*
I8.1.4.03	as above; Outside diameter 160mm	m	0.13	14.00	14.78	14.16	**42.94**	*13.65*
I8.1.4.04	as above; Outside diameter 180mm	m	0.13	14.00	14.78	17.94	**46.72**	*15.86*
I8.1.5	In trenches, depth: 2.5 - 3m							
I8.1.5.01	Blue MDPE (SDR 11) water supply pipe systems, to WIS 4-32-03, 6m lengths, butt welded joints; Outside diameter 90mm	m	0.12	12.92	13.64	4.52	**31.08**	*7.55*
I8.1.5.02	as above; Outside diameter 125mm	m	0.14	15.07	15.91	8.68	**39.66**	*10.82*
I8.1.5.03	as above; Outside diameter 160mm	m	0.15	16.15	17.05	14.16	**47.36**	*14.47*
I8.1.5.04	as above; Outside diameter 180mm	m	0.15	16.15	17.05	17.94	**51.14**	*16.68*
I8.1.6	In trenches, depth: 3 - 3.5m							
I8.1.6.01	Blue MDPE (SDR 11) water supply pipe systems, to WIS 4-32-03, 6m lengths, butt welded joints; Outside diameter 90mm	m	0.12	20.79	13.64	4.52	**38.95**	*7.55*
I8.1.6.02	as above; Outside diameter 125mm	m	0.14	24.25	15.91	8.68	**48.84**	*10.82*
I8.1.6.03	as above; Outside diameter 160mm	m	0.15	25.98	17.05	14.16	**57.19**	*14.47*
I8.1.6.04	as above; Outside diameter 180mm	m	0.15	25.98	17.05	17.94	**60.97**	*16.68*

I8 Medium density Polyethylene pipes continued...

		Unit	Labour Hours	Labour Net £	Plant Net £	Materials Net £	Unit Net £	CO_2 Kg
I8.1	**Nominal bore: not exceeding 200mm**							
I8.1.7	In trenches, depth: 3.5 - 4m							
I8.1.7.01	Blue MDPE (SDR 11) water supply pipe systems, to WIS 4-32-03, 6m lengths, butt welded joints; Outside diameter 90mm	m	0.14	24.25	15.91	4.52	**44.68**	*8.37*
I8.1.7.02	as above; Outside diameter 125mm	m	0.16	27.71	18.19	8.68	**54.58**	*11.64*
I8.1.7.03	as above; Outside diameter 160mm	m	0.18	31.18	20.46	14.16	**65.80**	*15.70*
I8.1.7.04	as above; Outside diameter 180mm	m	0.19	32.91	21.60	17.94	**72.45**	*18.32*
I8.1.8	In trenches, depth: exceeding 4m							
I8.1.8.01	Blue MDPE (SDR 11) water supply pipe systems, to WIS 4-32-03, 6m lengths, butt welded joints; Outside diameter 90mm; depth: 4 - 4.5m	m	0.17	29.45	19.32	4.52	**53.29**	*9.60*
I8.1.8.02	as above; depth: 4.5 - 5m	m	0.21	36.37	23.87	4.52	**64.76**	*11.24*
I8.1.8.03	as above; Outside diameter 125mm; depth: 4 - 4.5m	m	0.20	34.64	22.73	8.68	**66.05**	*13.28*
I8.1.8.04	as above; depth: 4.5 - 5m	m	0.26	45.03	29.55	8.68	**83.26**	*15.74*
I8.1.8.05	as above; Outside diameter 160mm; depth: 4 - 4.5m	m	0.23	39.84	26.14	14.16	**80.14**	*17.75*
I8.1.8.06	as above; depth: 4.5 - 5m	m	0.31	53.70	35.24	14.16	**103.10**	*21.03*
I8.1.8.07	as above; Outside diameter 180mm; depth: 4 - 4.5m	m	0.24	41.57	27.28	17.94	**86.79**	*20.37*
I8.1.8.08	as above; depth: 4.5 - 5m	m	0.33	57.16	37.51	17.94	**112.61**	*24.06*
I8.2	**Nominal bore: 200 - 300mm**							
I8.2.2	In trenches, depth: not exceeding 1.5m							
I8.2.2.01	Blue MDPE (SDR 11) water supply pipe systems, to WIS 4-32-03, 6m lengths, butt welded joints; Outside diameter 250mm	m	0.10	10.77	11.37	34.47	**56.61**	*24.41*
I8.2.3	In trenches, depth: 1.5 - 2m							
I8.2.3.01	Blue MDPE (SDR 11) water supply pipe systems, to WIS 4-32-03, 6m lengths, butt welded joints; Outside diameter 250mm	m	0.12	12.92	13.64	34.47	**61.03**	*25.23*
I8.2.4	In trenches, depth: 2 - 2.5m							
I8.2.4.01	Blue MDPE (SDR 11) water supply pipe systems, to WIS 4-32-03, 6m lengths, butt welded joints; Outside diameter 250mm	m	0.14	15.07	15.91	34.47	**65.45**	*26.05*
I8.2.5	In trenches, depth: 2.5 - 3m							
I8.2.5.01	Blue MDPE (SDR 11) water supply pipe systems, to WIS 4-32-03, 6m lengths, butt welded joints; Outside diameter 250mm	m	0.17	18.30	19.32	34.47	**72.09**	*27.28*
I8.2.6	In trenches, depth: 3 - 3.5m							
I8.2.6.01	Blue MDPE (SDR 11) water supply pipe systems, to WIS 4-32-03, 6m lengths, butt welded joints; Outside diameter 250mm	m	0.17	29.45	19.32	34.47	**83.24**	*27.28*

I8 Medium density Polyethylene pipes continued...

		Unit	Labour Hours	Labour Net £	Plant Net £	Materials Net £	Unit Net £	CO_2 Kg
I8.2	**Nominal bore: 200 - 300mm**							
I8.2.7	In trenches, depth: 3.5 - 4m							
I8.2.7.01	Blue MDPE (SDR 11) water supply pipe systems, to WIS 4-32-03, 6m lengths, butt welded joints; Outside diameter 250mm	m	0.21	36.37	23.87	34.47	**94.71**	*28.92*
I8.2.8	In trenches, depth: exceeding 4m							
I8.2.8.01	Blue MDPE (SDR 11) water supply pipe systems, to WIS 4-32-03, 6m lengths, butt welded joints; Outside diameter 250mm; depth: 4 - 4.5m	m	0.27	46.77	30.69	34.47	**111.93**	*31.38*
I8.2.8.02	as above; depth: 4.5 - 5m	m	0.39	67.55	44.33	34.47	**146.35**	*36.30*
I8.3	**Nominal bore: 300 - 600mm**							
I8.3.2	In trenches, depth: not exceeding 1.5m							
I8.3.2.01	Blue MDPE (SDR 11) water supply pipe systems, to WIS 4-32-03, 6m lengths, butt welded joints; Outside diameter 315mm	m	0.11	11.84	12.50	54.69	**79.03**	*36.96*
I8.3.2.02	as above; Outside diameter 335mm	m	0.12	12.92	13.64	69.50	**96.06**	*47.04*
I8.3.2.03	as above; Outside diameter 400mm	m	0.13	14.00	14.78	88.21	**116.99**	*57.33*
I8.3.3	In trenches, depth: 1.5 - 2m							
I8.3.3.01	Blue MDPE (SDR 11) water supply pipe systems, to WIS 4-32-03, 6m lengths, butt welded joints; Outside diameter 315mm	m	0.13	14.00	14.78	54.69	**83.47**	*37.78*
I8.3.3.02	as above; Outside diameter 335mm	m	0.13	14.00	14.78	69.50	**98.28**	*47.45*
I8.3.3.03	as above; Outside diameter 400mm	m	0.14	15.07	15.91	88.21	**119.19**	*57.74*
I8.3.4	In trenches, depth: 2 - 2.5m							
I8.3.4.01	Blue MDPE (SDR 11) water supply pipe systems, to WIS 4-32-03, 6m lengths, butt welded joints; Outside diameter 315mm	m	0.15	16.15	17.05	54.69	**87.89**	*38.60*
I8.3.4.02	as above; Outside diameter 335mm	m	0.16	17.23	18.19	69.50	**104.92**	*48.68*
I8.3.4.03	as above; Outside diameter 400mm	m	0.16	17.23	18.19	88.21	**123.63**	*58.56*
I8.3.5	In trenches, depth: 2.5 - 3m							
I8.3.5.01	Blue MDPE (SDR 11) water supply pipe systems, to WIS 4-32-03, 6m lengths, butt welded joints; Outside diameter 315mm	m	0.18	19.38	20.46	54.69	**94.53**	*39.83*
I8.3.5.02	as above; Outside diameter 335mm	m	0.19	20.46	21.60	69.50	**111.56**	*49.91*
I8.3.5.03	as above; Outside diameter 400mm	m	0.20	21.53	22.73	88.21	**132.47**	*60.20*
I8.3.6	In trenches, depth: 3 - 3.5m							
I8.3.6.01	Blue MDPE (SDR 11) water supply pipe systems, to WIS 4-32-03, 6m lengths, butt welded joints; Outside diameter 315mm	m	0.18	31.18	20.46	54.69	**106.33**	*39.83*

I8 Medium density Polyethylene pipes continued...

		Unit	Labour Hours	Labour Net £	Plant Net £	Materials Net £	**Unit Net £**	*CO_2 Kg*
I8.3	**Nominal bore: 300 - 600mm**							
I8.3.6	In trenches, depth: 3 - 3.5m							
I8.3.6.02	as previous item; Outside diameter 335mm	m	0.19	32.91	21.60	69.50	**124.01**	*49.91*
I8.3.6.03	as above; Outside diameter 400mm	m	0.20	34.64	22.73	88.21	**145.58**	*60.20*
I8.3.7	In trenches, depth: 3.5 - 4m							
I8.3.7.01	Blue MDPE (SDR 11) water supply pipe systems, to WIS 4-32-03, 6m lengths, butt welded joints; Outside diameter 315mm	m	0.23	39.84	26.14	54.69	**120.67**	*41.88*
I8.3.7.02	as above; Outside diameter 335mm	m	0.24	41.57	27.28	69.50	**138.35**	*51.96*
I8.3.7.03	as above; Outside diameter 400mm	m	0.25	43.30	28.42	88.21	**159.93**	*62.25*
I8.3.8	In trenches, depth: exceeding 4m							
I8.3.8.01	Blue MDPE (SDR 11) water supply pipe systems, to WIS 4-32-03, 6m lengths, butt welded joints; Outside diameter 315mm; depth: 4 - 4.5m	m	0.30	51.96	34.10	54.69	**140.75**	*44.75*
I8.3.8.02	as above; depth: 4.5 - 5m	m	0.46	79.68	52.29	54.69	**186.66**	*51.31*
I8.3.8.03	as above; Outside diameter 335mm; depth: 4 - 4.5m	m	0.32	55.43	36.37	69.50	**161.30**	*55.24*
I8.3.8.04	as above; depth: 4.5 - 5m	m	0.50	86.61	56.84	69.50	**212.95**	*62.62*
I8.3.8.05	as above; Outside diameter 400mm; depth: 4 - 4.5m	m	0.35	60.62	39.78	88.21	**188.61**	*66.35*
I8.3.8.06	as above; depth: 4.5 - 5m	m	0.54	93.53	61.38	88.21	**243.12**	*74.14*

CLASS J:

PIPEWORK - FITTINGS & VALVES

Calculations used throughout Class J - Pipework - Fittings & Valves

Labour

		Qty		Rate		Total
L A0183ICE	**Lay and joint pipe fitting Labour Gang**					
	Labourer (General Operative)	1	x	12.56	=	£12.56
	Pipelayer (standard rate)	1	x	14.34	=	£14.34
	Total hourly cost of gang				**=**	**£26.90**
L A0184ICE	**Small bore pipes in shallow trenches Labour Gang**					
	Banksman	1	x	13.53	=	£13.53
	Ganger	1	x	16.99	=	£16.99
	Pipelayer (standard rate)	1	x	14.34	=	£14.34
	Labourer (General Operative)	5	x	12.56	=	£62.80
	Total hourly cost of gang				**=**	**£107.66**
L A0186ICE	**Large bore pipes in shallow trench Labour Gang**					
	Ganger	1	x	16.99	=	£16.99
	Pipelayer (large pipes)	1	x	15.91	=	£15.91
	Labourer (General Operative)	5	x	12.56	=	£62.80
	Banksman	1	x	13.53	=	£13.53
	Total hourly cost of gang				**=**	**£109.23**
L A0188ICE	**Small bore steel pipes in shallow trench Labour Gang**					
	Ganger	1	x	16.99	=	£16.99
	Fitters and Welders	1	x	16.68	=	£16.68
	Labourer (Skill Rate 3)	3	x	14.34	=	£43.02
	Banksman	1	x	13.53	=	£13.53
	Labourer (General Operative)	5	x	12.56	=	£62.80
	Total hourly cost of gang				**=**	**£153.02**

Plant

		Qty		Rate		Total
P A1184ICE	**Small bore pipes in shallow trench Plant Gang**					
	Hydraulic Excavator - Cat 320 96kW	1	x	33.98	=	£33.98
	Pump - Godwin ET50 23m3/h 4 inches	1	x	2.74	=	£2.74
	Vibrating Plate Diesel 24kN	1	x	2.36	=	£2.36
	Trench Sheets	90	x	0.08	=	£7.15
	Acrow Props	70	x	0.08	=	£5.56
	Landrover 4WD	1	x	15.10	=	£15.10
	Total hourly cost of gang				**=**	**£66.89**
P A1186ICE	**Large bore in shallow trench Plant Gang**					
	Hydraulic Excavator - Cat 166kW	1	x	41.41	=	£41.41
	Pump - Godwin ET50 23m3/h 4 inches	1	x	2.74	=	£2.74
	Vibrating Plate Diesel 24kN	1	x	2.36	=	£2.36
	Trench Sheets	90	x	0.08	=	£7.15
	Acrow Props	70	x	0.08	=	£5.56
	Cranes Crawler - 22RB - 15t	1	x	38.37	=	£38.37
	Landrover 4WD	1	x	15.10	=	£15.10
	Total hourly cost of gang				**=**	**£112.69**
P A1188ICE	**Small bore steel pipes in shallow trench Plant Gang**					
	Hydraulic Excavator - Cat 320 96kW	1	x	33.98	=	£33.98
	Pump - Godwin ET50 23m3/h 4 inches	1	x	2.74	=	£2.74
	Vibrating Plate Diesel 24kN	1	x	2.36	=	£2.36
	Trench Sheets	90	x	0.08	=	£7.15
	Acrow Props	70	x	0.08	=	£5.56
	Landrover 4WD	1	x	15.10	=	£15.10
	Welding Set - 300 amp Diesel Electric Start Sil	1	x	4.18	=	£4.18
	Crawler Tractor / Dozer - Cat 561 Sideboom	1	x	41.44	=	£41.44
	Total hourly cost of gang				**=**	**£112.51**

Class J - Pipeworks - Fittings & Valves

Note(s): The rates included under Class J are full value and the user must take this into account when pricing fittings and valves in conjunction with lengths of pipes in trenches measured under Class I Measurement Rule M3.

J1 Clay Pipe Fittings

		Unit	Labour Hours	Labour Net £	Plant Net £	Materials Net £	Unit Net £	CO_2 Kg
J1.1	**Bends**							
J1.1.1	Nominal bore: not exceeding 200mm							
J1.1.1.01	Vitrified clay pipe fittings, BS 65, spigot & socket flexible joints; Nominal bore 100mm; 45 degree bends	Nr	0.08	2.15	-	32.36	**34.51**	*4.15*
J1.1.1.02	as above; 11.25 degree bends	Nr	0.08	2.15	-	32.36	**34.51**	*3.72*
J1.1.1.03	as above; Rest bends	Nr	0.15	4.03	-	38.83	**42.86**	*6.23*
J1.1.1.04	Vitrified clay pipe fittings, BS 65, spigot & socket flexible joints; Nominal bore 150mm; 45 degree bends	Nr	0.10	2.69	-	35.95	**38.64**	*5.54*
J1.1.1.05	as above; 11.25 degree bends	Nr	0.10	2.69	-	35.95	**38.64**	*4.95*
J1.1.1.06	as above; Rest bends	Nr	0.18	4.84	-	42.86	**47.70**	*8.31*
J1.1.1.07	Vitrified clay pipe fittings, BS 65, 'extra strength' spigot and socket flexible joints; Nominal bore 100mm; 45 degree bends	Nr	0.08	2.15	-	8.54	**10.69**	*1.69*
J1.1.1.08	as above; 11.25 degree bends	Nr	0.08	2.15	-	8.54	**10.69**	*1.56*
J1.1.1.09	as above; Rest bends	Nr	0.15	4.03	-	14.24	**18.27**	*1.58*
J1.1.1.10	Vitrified clay pipe fittings, BS 65, 'extra strength' spigot and socket flexible joints; Nominal bore 150mm; 45 degree bends	Nr	0.10	2.69	-	21.62	**24.31**	*3.61*
J1.1.1.11	as above; 11.25 degree bends	Nr	0.10	2.69	-	21.62	**24.31**	*2.74*
J1.1.1.12	as above; Rest bends	Nr	0.18	4.84	-	27.78	**32.62**	*2.99*
J1.1.1.13	Vitrified clay pipe fittings, BS 65, 'extra strength' spigot and socket flexible joints; Nominal bore 200mm; 45 degree bends	Nr	0.13	3.50	-	71.78	**75.28**	*9.02*
J1.1.1.14	as above; 11.25 degree bends	Nr	0.13	3.50	-	71.78	**75.28**	*8.84*
J1.1.1.15	Vitrified clay pipe fittings, BS 65, 'surface water' spigot and socket cement joints; Nominal bore 100mm; 45 degree bends	Nr	0.25	6.72	-	21.29	**28.01**	*3.43*
J1.1.1.16	as above; 11.25 degree bends	Nr	0.25	6.72	-	21.31	**28.03**	*3.43*
J1.1.1.17	Vitrified clay pipe fittings, BS 65, 'surface water' spigot and socket cement joints; Nominal bore 150mm; 45 degree bends	Nr	0.17	4.57	-	21.29	**25.86**	*3.43*
J1.1.1.18	as above; 11.25 degree bends	Nr	0.17	4.57	-	21.29	**25.86**	*4.19*
J1.1.1.19	Vitrified clay pipe fittings, BS 65, 'British Standard Tested' quality; spigot and socket cement joints; Nominal bore 100mm; 45 degree bends	Nr	0.25	6.72	-	4.58	**11.30**	*2.29*
J1.1.1.20	as above; 11.25 degree bends	Nr	0.25	6.72	-	4.58	**11.30**	*2.29*
J1.1.1.21	Vitrified clay pipe fittings, BS 65, 'British Standard Tested' quality; spigot and socket cement joints; Nominal bore 150mm; 45 degree bends	Nr	0.06	1.61	-	8.19	**9.80**	*3.43*
J1.1.1.22	as above; 11.25 degree bends	Nr	0.06	1.61	-	8.56	**10.17**	*3.43*

J1 Clay Pipe Fittings continued...

		Unit	Labour Hours	Labour Net £	Plant Net £	Materials Net £	Unit Net £	CO_2 Kg
J1.1	**Bends**							
J1.1.1	Nominal bore: not exceeding 200mm							
J1.1.1.23	Vitrified clay pipe fittings, BS 65, 'Perforated'; spigot and socket flexible joints; Nominal bore 100mm; 45 degree bends	Nr	0.08	2.15	-	12.46	**14.61**	*2.29*
J1.1.1.24	as above; 22.5 degree bends	Nr	0.10	2.69	-	12.46	**15.15**	*2.29*
J1.1.1.25	Vitrified clay pipe fittings, BS 65, 'Perforated'; spigot and socket flexible joints; Nominal bore 150mm; 45 degree bends	Nr	0.12	3.23	-	21.29	**24.52**	*3.43*
J1.1.1.26	as above; 22.5 degree bends	Nr	0.18	4.84	-	21.29	**26.13**	*3.43*
J1.1.2	Nominal bore: 200 - 300mm							
J1.1.2.01	Vitrified clay pipe fittings, BS 65, spigot & socket flexible joints; Nominal bore 225mm; 45 degree bends	Nr	0.14	3.77	-	73.30	**77.07**	*10.97*
J1.1.2.02	as above; Rest bends	Nr	0.25	6.72	-	102.13	**108.85**	*13.08*
J1.1.2.03	Vitrified clay pipe fittings, BS 65, spigot & socket flexible joints; Nominal bore 300mm; 45 degree bends	Nr	0.18	4.84	-	144.23	**149.07**	*24.64*
J1.1.2.04	as above; 22.5 degree bends	Nr	0.18	4.84	-	144.23	**149.07**	*19.41*
J1.1.2.05	Vitrified clay pipe fittings, BS 65, 'extra strength' spigot and socket flexible joints; Nominal bore 225mm; 45 degree bends	Nr	0.23	6.19	-	346.40	**352.59**	*38.16*
J1.1.2.06	as above; 22.5 degree bends	Nr	0.25	6.72	-	346.40	**353.12**	*43.01*
J1.1.2.07	Vitrified clay pipe fittings, BS 65, 'surface water' spigot and socket cement joints; Nominal bore 225mm; 45 degree bends	Nr	0.30	8.07	-	73.30	**81.37**	*10.97*
J1.1.2.08	as above; 11.25 degree bends	Nr	0.30	8.07	-	73.30	**81.37**	*9.53*
J1.1.2.09	as above; Rest bends	Nr	0.13	3.50	-	102.13	**105.63**	*13.08*
J1.1.2.10	Vitrified clay pipe fittings, BS 65, 'surface water' spigot and socket cement joints; Nominal bore 300mm; 45 degree bends	Nr	0.13	3.50	-	121.33	**124.83**	*6.22*
J1.1.2.11	as above; 11.25 degree bends	Nr	0.14	3.77	-	121.33	**125.10**	*7.47*
J1.1.2.12	as above; Rest bends	Nr	0.14	3.77	-	284.35	**288.12**	*9.81*
J1.1.2.13	Vitrified clay pipe fittings, BS 65, 'British Standard Tested' quality; spigot and socket cement joints; Nominal bore 225mm; 45 degree bends	Nr	0.35	9.41	-	66.77	**76.18**	*4.98*
J1.1.2.14	as above; 11.25 degree bends	Nr	0.35	9.41	-	66.77	**76.18**	*4.98*
J1.1.2.15	as above; Rest bends	Nr	0.45	12.11	-	37.62	**49.73**	*7.74*
J1.1.2.16	Vitrified clay pipe fittings, BS 65, 'British Standard Tested' quality; spigot and socket cement joints; Nominal bore 300mm; 45 degree bends	Nr	0.50	13.45	-	46.94	**60.39**	*6.22*
J1.1.2.17	as above; 11.25 degree bends	Nr	0.50	13.45	-	137.47	**150.92**	*6.22*
J1.1.2.18	as above; Rest bends	Nr	0.65	17.48	-	175.90	**193.38**	*9.81*
J1.1.2.19	Vitrified clay pipe fittings, BS 65, 'Perforated'; spigot and socket flexible joints; Nominal bore 225mm; 45 degree bends	Nr	1.00	26.90	-	66.77	**93.67**	*4.98*
J1.1.2.20	as above; 22.5 degree bends	Nr	0.75	20.17	-	66.77	**86.94**	*4.98*

J1 Clay Pipe Fittings continued...

		Unit	Labour Hours	Labour Net £	Plant Net £	Materials Net £	Unit Net £	CO_2 Kg
J1.1	**Bends**							
J1.1.2	Nominal bore: 200 - 300mm							
J1.1.2.21	Vitrified clay pipe fittings, BS 65, 'Perforated'; spigot and socket flexible joints; Nominal bore 300mm; 45 degree bends	Nr	0.60	16.14	-	121.33	**137.47**	*6.22*
J1.1.2.22	as above; 22.5 degree bends	Nr	0.17	4.57	-	121.33	**125.90**	*6.22*
J1.1.2.23	Vitrified clay pipe fittings, BS 65, spigot & socket flexible joints; Nominal bore 225mm; 22.5 degree bends	Nr	0.14	3.77	-	73.30	**77.07**	*9.53*
J1.1.3	Nominal bore: 300 - 600mm							
J1.1.3.01	Vitrified clay pipe fittings, BS 65, spigot & socket flexible joints; Nominal bore 375mm; 45 degree bends	Nr	0.23	6.19	-	346.40	**352.59**	*38.16*
J1.1.3.02	as above; 22.5 degree bends	Nr	0.23	6.19	-	346.40	**352.59**	*43.01*
J1.1.3.03	Vitrified clay pipe fittings, BS 65, spigot & socket flexible joints; Nominal bore 450mm; 45 degree bends	Nr	0.30	8.07	-	515.96	**524.03**	*69.79*
J1.1.3.04	as above; 22.5 degree bends	Nr	0.30	8.07	-	515.96	**524.03**	*56.98*
J1.1.3.05	Vitrified clay pipe fittings, BS 65, 'surface water' spigot and socket cement joints; Nominal bore 375mm; 45 degree bends	Nr	0.65	17.48	-	340.98	**358.46**	*7.40*
J1.1.3.06	as above; 11.25 degree bends	Nr	0.65	17.48	-	348.19	**365.67**	*7.40*
J1.1.3.07	Vitrified clay pipe fittings, BS 65, 'surface water' spigot and socket cement joints; Nominal bore 450mm; 45 degree bends	Nr	0.75	20.17	-	557.21	**577.38**	*7.77*
J1.1.3.08	as above; 11.25 degree bends	Nr	0.75	20.17	-	557.21	**577.38**	*12.44*
J1.1.3.09	Vitrified clay pipe fittings, BS 65, 'British Standard Tested' quality; spigot and socket cement joints; Nominal bore 375mm; 45 degree bends	Nr	0.65	17.48	-	121.33	**138.81**	*7.40*
J1.1.3.10	as above; 11.25 degree bends	Nr	0.65	17.48	-	121.33	**138.81**	*7.40*
J1.1.3.11	Vitrified clay pipe fittings, BS 65, 'British Standard Tested' quality; spigot and socket cement joints; Nominal bore 450mm; 45 degree bends	Nr	0.75	20.17	-	162.43	**182.60**	*7.77*
J1.1.3.12	as above; 11.25 degree bends	Nr	0.75	20.17	-	245.17	**265.34**	*12.44*
J1.2	**Junction and Branches**							
J1.2.1	Nominal bore: not exceeding 200mm							
J1.2.1.01	Vitrified clay pipe fittings, BS 65, spigot & socket flexible joints; Nominal bore 100mm; Single junctions	Nr	0.15	4.03	-	32.36	**36.39**	*5.74*
J1.2.1.02	as above; Double junctions (special)	Nr	0.20	5.38	-	54.05	**59.43**	*6.56*
J1.2.1.03	as above; Oblique saddles	Nr	0.75	20.17	-	35.79	**55.96**	*6.56*
J1.2.1.04	Vitrified clay pipe fittings, BS 65, spigot & socket flexible joints; Nominal bore 150mm; Single junctions	Nr	0.18	4.84	-	46.98	**51.82**	*7.65*

J1 Clay Pipe Fittings continued...

		Unit	Labour Hours	Labour Net £	Plant Net £	Materials Net £	Unit Net £	CO_2 Kg
J1.2	**Junction and Branches**							
J1.2.1	Nominal bore: not exceeding 200mm							
J1.2.1.05	as previous item; Double junctions (special)	Nr	0.25	6.72	-	125.49	132.21	8.74
J1.2.1.06	as above; Oblique saddles	Nr	1.00	26.90	-	35.68	62.58	5.10
J1.2.1.07	Vitrified clay pipe fittings, BS 65, 'extra strength' spigot and socket flexible joints; Nominal bore 100mm; Single junctions	Nr	0.15	4.03	-	18.11	22.14	2.76
J1.2.1.08	as above; Nominal bore 150mm; Single junctions	Nr	0.18	4.84	-	31.68	36.52	6.27
J1.2.1.09	Vitrified clay pipe fittings, BS 65, 'surface water' spigot and socket cement joints; Nominal bore 100mm; Single junctions	Nr	0.25	6.72	-	25.34	32.06	2.75
J1.2.1.10	as above; Double junctions (special)	Nr	0.25	6.72	-	45.24	51.96	3.66
J1.2.1.11	as above; Oblique saddles	Nr	0.33	8.88	-	22.57	31.45	3.56
J1.2.1.12	Vitrified clay pipe fittings, BS 65, 'surface water' spigot and socket cement joints; Nominal bore 150mm; 11.25 degree bends	Nr	0.75	20.17	-	41.93	62.10	5.49
J1.2.1.13	as above; Rest bends	Nr	0.35	9.41	-	103.88	113.29	5.49
J1.2.1.14	as above; 45 degree bends	Nr	0.45	12.11	-	18.72	30.83	5.33
J1.2.1.15	Vitrified clay pipe fittings, BS 65, 'British Standard Tested' quality; spigot and socket cement joints; Nominal bore 100mm; Single junctions	Nr	1.00	26.90	-	10.96	37.86	2.75
J1.2.1.16	as above; Double junctions (special)	Nr	0.25	6.72	-	20.79	27.51	3.66
J1.2.1.17	as above; Oblique saddles	Nr	0.33	8.88	-	10.96	19.84	3.56
J1.2.1.18	Vitrified clay pipe fittings, BS 65, 'British Standard Tested' quality; spigot and socket cement joints; Nominal bore 150mm; Single junctions	Nr	0.75	20.17	-	18.72	38.89	4.12
J1.2.1.19	as above; Double junctions (special)	Nr	0.35	9.41	-	35.14	44.55	5.49
J1.2.1.20	as above; Oblique saddles	Nr	0.45	12.11	-	18.72	30.83	5.33
J1.2.1.21	Vitrified clay pipe fittings, BS 65, 'Perforated'; spigot and socket flexible joints; Nominal bore 100mm; Square junctions	Nr	0.13	3.50	-	22.87	26.37	3.66
J1.2.1.22	as above; Oblique junctions	Nr	0.12	3.23	-	22.87	26.10	3.56
J1.2.1.23	Vitrified clay pipe fittings, BS 65, 'Perforated'; spigot and socket flexible joints; Nominal bore 150mm; Oblique junctions	Nr	0.65	17.48	-	39.12	56.60	5.33
J1.2.1.24	Unglazed clay pipe fittings, BS 1196, plain butt joints; Nominal bore 75mm; Single junctions	Nr	0.08	2.15	-	13.73	15.88	2.74
J1.2.1.25	as above; Nominal bore 100mm; Single junctions	Nr	0.13	3.50	-	18.23	21.73	3.66
J1.2.1.26	as above; Nominal bore 150mm; Single junctions	Nr	0.25	6.72	-	22.45	29.17	5.49
J1.2.2	Nominal bore: 200 - 300mm							
J1.2.2.01	Unglazed clay pipe fittings, BS 1196, plain butt joints; Nominal bore 225mm; Single junctions	Nr	0.10	2.69	-	58.98	61.67	7.32

J1 Clay Pipe Fittings continued...

		Unit	Labour Hours	Labour Net £	Plant Net £	Materials Net £	Unit Net £	CO_2 Kg
J1.2	**Junction and Branches**							
J1.2.2	Nominal bore: 200 - 300mm							
J1.2.2.02	Vitrified clay pipe fittings, BS 65, spigot & socket flexible joints; Nominal bore 225mm; Single junctions	Nr	0.25	6.72	-	110.27	116.99	*18.51*
J1.2.2.03	as above; Double junctions (special)	Nr	0.35	9.41	-	271.41	280.82	*20.17*
J1.2.2.04	as above; Oblique saddles	Nr	1.50	40.35	-	85.31	125.66	*7.76*
J1.2.2.05	Vitrified clay pipe fittings, BS 65, spigot & socket flexible joints; Nominal bore 300mm; Single junctions	Nr	0.35	9.41	-	227.30	236.71	*41.07*
J1.2.2.06	as above; Double junctions (special)	Nr	0.50	13.45	-	547.33	560.78	*48.53*
J1.2.2.07	as above; Oblique saddles	Nr	2.00	53.80	-	223.54	277.34	*13.07*
J1.2.2.08	Vitrified clay pipe fittings, BS 65, 'extra strength' spigot and socket flexible joints; Nominal bore 225mm; Single junctions	Nr	0.45	12.11	-	486.54	498.65	*75.72*
J1.2.2.09	Vitrified clay pipe fittings, BS 65, 'surface water' spigot and socket cement joints; Nominal bore 225mm; Single junctions	Nr	0.50	13.45	-	116.51	129.96	*5.98*
J1.2.2.10	as above; Double junctions (special)	Nr	0.60	16.14	-	271.41	287.55	*20.17*
J1.2.2.11	as above; Oblique saddles	Nr	0.25	6.72	-	85.31	92.03	*7.76*
J1.2.2.12	Vitrified clay pipe fittings, BS 65, 'surface water' spigot and socket cement joints; Nominal bore 300mm; Single junctions	Nr	0.50	13.45	-	116.51	129.96	*5.98*
J1.2.2.13	as above; Double junctions (special)	Nr	0.60	16.14	-	238.92	255.06	*7.97*
J1.2.2.14	as above; Oblique saddles	Nr	1.50	40.35	-	119.65	160.00	*7.74*
J1.2.2.15	Vitrified clay pipe fittings, BS 65, 'British Standard Tested' quality; spigot and socket cement joints; Nominal bore 225mm; Single junctions	Nr	0.65	17.48	-	52.31	69.79	*5.98*
J1.2.2.16	as above; Double junctions (special)	Nr	0.80	21.52	-	106.94	128.46	*7.97*
J1.2.2.17	as above; Oblique saddles	Nr	2.00	53.80	-	90.16	143.96	*7.85*
J1.2.2.18	Vitrified clay pipe fittings, BS 65, 'British Standard Tested' quality; spigot and socket cement joints; Nominal bore 300mm; Single junctions	Nr	0.85	22.86	-	137.47	160.33	*7.47*
J1.2.2.19	as above; Double junctions (special)	Nr	1.00	26.90	-	173.31	200.21	*9.68*
J1.2.2.20	as above; Oblique saddles	Nr	2.50	67.25	-	160.68	227.93	*9.67*
J1.2.2.21	Vitrified clay pipe fittings, BS 65, 'Perforated'; spigot and socket flexible joints; Nominal bore 225mm; Square junctions	Nr	0.75	20.17	-	89.12	109.29	*7.97*
J1.2.2.22	as above; Oblique junctions	Nr	0.50	13.45	-	89.12	102.57	*7.74*
J1.2.2.23	Vitrified clay pipe fittings, BS 65, 'Perforated'; spigot and socket flexible joints; Nominal bore 300mm; Square junctions	Nr	0.24	6.46	-	89.12	95.58	*7.97*
J1.2.2.24	as above; Oblique junctions	Nr	0.24	6.46	-	89.12	95.58	*7.74*

J1 Clay Pipe Fittings continued...

		Unit	Labour Hours	Labour Net £	Plant Net £	Materials Net £	Unit Net £	CO_2 Kg
J1.2	**Junction and Branches**							
J1.2.3	Nominal bore: 300 - 600mm							
J1.2.3.01	Vitrified clay pipe fittings, BS 65, 'surface water' spigot and socket cement joints; Nominal bore 375mm; Single junctions	Nr	0.85	22.86	-	340.98	**363.84**	*11.32*
J1.2.3.02	as above; Double junctions (special)	Nr	1.00	26.90	-	719.98	**746.88**	*12.04*
J1.2.3.03	as above; Oblique saddles	Nr	2.50	67.25	-	432.34	**499.59**	*11.51*
J1.2.3.04	Vitrified clay pipe fittings, BS 65, spigot & socket flexible joints; Nominal bore 375mm; Single junctions	Nr	0.45	12.11	-	486.54	**498.65**	*75.72*
J1.2.3.05	as above; Double junctions (special)	Nr	0.65	17.48	-	772.64	**790.12**	*90.86*
J1.2.3.06	Vitrified clay pipe fittings, BS 65, spigot & socket flexible joints; Nominal bore 450mm; Single junctions	Nr	0.60	16.14	-	618.49	**634.63**	*123.67*
J1.2.3.07	Vitrified clay pipe fittings, BS 65, 'surface water' spigot and socket cement joints; Nominal bore 450mm; Single junctions	Nr	1.00	26.90	-	610.25	**637.15**	*12.09*
J1.2.3.08	as above; Oblique saddles	Nr	3.00	80.70	-	610.25	**690.95**	*12.08*
J1.2.3.09	Vitrified clay pipe fittings, BS 65, 'British Standard Tested' quality; spigot and socket cement joints; Nominal bore 375mm; Single junctions	Nr	0.85	22.86	-	147.54	**170.40**	*11.32*
J1.2.3.10	as above; Double junctions (special)	Nr	1.00	26.90	-	194.44	**221.34**	*12.04*
J1.2.3.11	as above; Oblique saddles	Nr	2.50	67.25	-	148.81	**216.06**	*11.51*
J1.2.3.12	Vitrified clay pipe fittings, BS 65, 'British Standard Tested' quality; spigot and socket cement joints; Nominal bore 450mm; Single junctions	Nr	1.00	26.90	-	268.50	**295.40**	*12.09*
J1.2.3.13	as above; Oblique saddles	Nr	3.00	80.70	-	268.50	**349.20**	*12.08*
J1.3	**Tapers**							
J1.3.1	Nominal bore: not exceeding 200mm							
J1.3.1.01	Vitrified clay pipe fittings, BS 65, spigot & socket flexible joints; Nominal bore 150mm; Tapers	Nr	0.10	2.69	-	84.80	**87.49**	*4.37*
J1.3.1.02	Vitrified clay pipe fittings, BS 65, 'extra strength' spigot and socket flexible joints; Nominal bore 150mm; Tapers	Nr	0.10	2.69	-	72.94	**75.63**	*2.98*
J1.3.1.03	as above; Nominal bore 200mm; Tapers	Nr	0.13	3.50	-	79.37	**82.87**	*6.86*
J1.3.1.04	Vitrified clay pipe fittings, BS 65, 'surface water' spigot and socket cement joints; Nominal bore 150mm; Tapers	Nr	0.25	6.72	-	24.53	**31.25**	*5.49*
J1.3.1.05	Vitrified clay pipe fittings, BS 65, 'British Standard Tested' quality; spigot and socket cement joints; Nominal bore 150mm; Tapers	Nr	0.25	6.72	-	24.53	**31.25**	*5.49*

J1 Clay Pipe Fittings continued...

		Unit	Labour Hours	Labour Net £	Plant Net £	Materials Net £	Unit Net £	CO_2 Kg
J1.3	**Tapers**							
J1.3.2	Nominal bore: 200 - 300mm							
J1.3.2.01	Vitrified clay pipe fittings, BS 65, spigot & socket flexible joints; Nominal bore 225mm; Tapers	Nr	0.14	3.77	-	284.05	**287.82**	*9.98*
J1.3.2.02	as above; Nominal bore 300mm; Tapers	Nr	0.18	4.84	-	269.73	**274.57**	*18.67*
J1.3.2.03	Vitrified clay pipe fittings, BS 65, 'extra strength' spigot and socket flexible joints; Nominal bore 225mm; Tapers	Nr	0.23	6.19	-	345.54	**351.73**	*33.32*
J1.3.2.04	Vitrified clay pipe fittings, BS 65, 'surface water' spigot and socket cement joints; Nominal bore 225mm; Tapers	Nr	0.13	3.50	-	284.05	**287.55**	*9.98*
J1.3.2.05	as above; Nominal bore 300mm; Tapers	Nr	0.14	3.77	-	215.34	**219.11**	*9.58*
J1.3.2.06	Vitrified clay pipe fittings, BS 65, 'British Standard Tested' quality; spigot and socket cement joints; Nominal bore 225mm; Tapers	Nr	0.35	9.41	-	61.10	**70.51**	*7.74*
J1.3.2.07	as above; Nominal bore 300mm; Tapers	Nr	0.50	13.45	-	98.91	**112.36**	*9.58*
J1.3.3	Nominal bore: 300 - 600mm							
J1.3.3.01	Vitrified clay pipe fittings, BS 65, spigot & socket flexible joints; Nominal bore 375mm; Tapers	Nr	0.23	6.19	-	345.54	**351.73**	*33.32*
J1.3.3.02	Vitrified clay pipe fittings, BS 65, 'surface water' spigot and socket cement joints; Nominal bore 375mm; Tapers	Nr	0.65	17.48	-	344.17	**361.65**	*11.39*
J1.3.3.03	as above; Nominal bore 450mm; Tapers	Nr	0.75	20.17	-	633.51	**653.68**	*11.96*
J1.3.3.04	Vitrified clay pipe fittings, BS 65, 'British Standard Tested' quality; spigot and socket cement joints; Nominal bore 375mm; Tapers	Nr	0.65	17.48	-	132.61	**150.09**	*11.39*
J1.3.3.05	as above; Nominal bore 450mm; Tapers	Nr	0.75	20.17	-	278.74	**298.91**	*11.96*

J2 Concrete Pipe Fittings

		Unit	Labour Hours	Labour Net £	Plant Net £	Materials Net £	Unit Net £	CO_2 Kg
J2.1	**Bends**							
J2.1.2	Nominal bore: 200 - 300mm							
J2.1.2.01	BS 5911, Class '120'; rebated flexible joints with mastic sealant to internal faces; Nominal bore 300mm; Bends	Nr	0.30	8.07	-	122.82	**130.89**	*21.93*
J2.1.3	Nominal bore: 300 - 600mm							
J2.1.3.01	BS 5911, Class '120'; rebated flexible joints with mastic sealant to internal faces; Nominal bore 375mm; Bends	Nr	0.36	9.68	-	142.84	**152.52**	*26.19*
J2.1.3.02	as above; Nominal bore 450mm; Bends	Nr	0.50	13.45	-	164.55	**178.00**	*36.64*
J2.1.3.03	as above; Nominal bore 600mm; Bends	Nr	0.10	10.92	11.27	238.39	**260.58**	*66.43*

J2 Concrete Pipe Fittings continued...

		Unit	Labour Hours	Labour Net £	Plant Net £	Materials Net £	Unit Net £	CO_2 Kg
J2.1	**Bends**							
J2.1.4	Nominal bore: 600 - 900mm							
J2.1.4.01	BS 5911, Class '120'; rebated flexible joints with mastic sealant to internal faces; Nominal bore 750mm; Bends	Nr	0.13	14.20	14.65	777.14	**805.99**	*133.86*
J2.1.4.02	as above; Nominal bore 900mm; Bends	Nr	0.20	21.85	22.54	1,043.65	**1,088.04**	*181.62*
J2.1.5	Nominal bore: 900 - 1200mm							
J2.1.5.01	BS 5911, Class '120'; rebated flexible joints with mastic sealant to internal faces; Nominal bore 1200mm; Bends	Nr	0.26	28.40	29.30	1,793.69	**1,851.39**	*385.96*
J2.1.6	Nominal bore: 1200 - 1500mm							
J2.1.6.01	BS 5911, Class '120'; rebated flexible joints with mastic sealant to internal faces; Nominal bore 1500mm; Bends	Nr	0.32	34.95	36.06	3,158.16	**3,229.17**	*581.70*
J2.1.7	Nominal bore: 1500 - 1800mm							
J2.1.7.01	BS 5911, Class '120'; rebated flexible joints with mastic sealant to internal faces; Nominal bore 1800mm; Bends	Nr	0.40	43.69	45.08	4,390.50	**4,479.27**	*778.19*
J2.2	**Junction and Branches**							
J2.2.1	Nominal bore: not exceeding 200mm							
J2.2.1.01	Concrete porous pipe fittings, BS 5911, Ogee joints; Nominal bore 100mm; Single junctions	Nr	0.20	5.38	-	22.43	**27.81**	*3.21*
J2.2.1.02	as above; Nominal bore 150mm; Single junctions	Nr	0.30	8.07	-	32.93	**41.00**	*3.78*
J2.2.2	Nominal bore: 200 - 300mm							
J2.2.2.01	BS 5911, Class '120'; rebated flexible joints with mastic sealant to internal faces; Nominal bore 300mm; Single junction 150mm	Nr	0.45	12.11	-	80.36	**92.47**	*11.33*
J2.2.2.02	as above; Double junctions	Nr	0.55	14.80	-	246.47	**261.27**	*21.93*
J2.2.3	Nominal bore: 300 - 600mm							
J2.2.3.01	BS 5911, Class '120'; rebated flexible joints with mastic sealant to internal faces; Nominal bore 375mm; Single junction 150mm	Nr	0.50	13.45	-	83.28	**96.73**	*15.28*
J2.2.3.02	as above; Double junctions	Nr	0.65	17.48	-	178.63	**196.11**	*30.55*
J2.2.3.03	BS 5911, Class '120'; rebated flexible joints with mastic sealant to internal faces; Nominal bore 450mm; Single junction 150mm	Nr	0.75	20.17	-	104.56	**124.73**	*21.98*
J2.2.3.04	as above; Nominal bore 600mm; Single junction 150mm	Nr	0.15	16.38	16.91	136.25	**169.54**	*45.31*
J2.2.4	Nominal bore: 600 - 900mm							
J2.2.4.01	BS 5911, Class '120'; rebated flexible joints with mastic sealant to internal faces; Nominal bore 750mm; Single junction 150mm	Nr	0.20	21.85	22.54	765.15	**809.54**	*136.47*

J3 Iron or Steel Pipe Fittings

		Unit	Labour Hours	Labour Net £	Plant Net £	Materials Net £	Unit Net £	CO_2 Kg
J3.1	**Bends**							
J3.1.1	Nominal bore: not exceeding 200mm							
J3.1.1.01	Ductile spun iron fittings, BS EN 598, spigot and socket joints; Nominal bore 100mm; 22.5 degree bends	Nr	0.20	5.38	-	22.62	28.00	*21.97*
J3.1.1.02	as above; 45 degree bends	Nr	0.25	6.72	-	27.56	34.28	*21.97*
J3.1.1.03	as above; 90 degree bends	Nr	0.35	9.41	-	29.31	38.72	*22.92*
J3.1.1.04	as above; 90 degree flanged bends	Nr	0.60	16.14	-	34.03	50.17	*22.92*
J3.1.1.05	Ductile spun iron fittings, BS EN 598, spigot and socket joints; Nominal bore 150mm; 22.5 degree bends	Nr	0.30	8.07	-	77.65	85.72	*34.38*
J3.1.1.06	as above; 45 degree bends	Nr	0.35	9.41	-	84.82	94.23	*35.34*
J3.1.1.07	as above; 90 degree bends	Nr	0.45	12.11	-	132.47	144.58	*42.98*
J3.1.1.08	as above; 90 degree double flanged bends	Nr	0.80	21.52	-	98.63	120.15	*42.98*
J3.1.1.09	Carbon steel pipe fittings, butt welded joints, BS 5135; Not in trenches; fixed to pipes on pipe supports; Nominal bore 100mm; 45 degree elbows	Nr	0.28	42.85	31.51	11.10	85.46	*20.25*
J3.1.1.10	as above; 90 degree elbows	Nr	0.29	44.38	32.63	13.32	90.33	*27.93*
J3.1.1.11	Carbon steel pipe fittings, butt welded joints, BS 5135; Not in trenches; fixed to pipes on pipe supports; Nominal bore 150mm; 45 degree elbows	Nr	0.42	64.27	47.26	27.41	138.94	*40.22*
J3.1.1.12	as above; 90 degree elbows	Nr	0.44	67.33	49.51	32.47	149.31	*61.80*
J3.1.2	Nominal bore: 200 - 300mm							
J3.1.2.01	Ductile spun iron fittings, BS EN 598, spigot and socket joints; Nominal bore 300mm; 22.5 degree bends	Nr	0.10	10.92	11.27	313.59	335.78	*110.70*
J3.1.2.02	as above; 45 degree bends	Nr	0.11	12.02	12.40	356.70	381.12	*116.80*
J3.1.2.03	as above; 90 degree bends	Nr	0.12	13.11	13.52	510.81	537.44	*136.27*
J3.1.2.04	as above; 90 degree flanged bends	Nr	0.21	22.94	23.67	423.41	470.02	*139.64*
J3.1.3	Nominal bore: 300 - 600mm							
J3.1.3.01	Ductile spun iron fittings, BS EN 598, spigot and socket joints; Nominal bore 450mm; 22.5 degree bends	Nr	0.18	19.66	20.29	978.74	1,018.69	*415.46*
J3.1.3.02	as above; 45 degree bends	Nr	0.20	21.85	22.54	1,066.00	1,110.39	*412.39*
J3.1.3.03	as above; 90 degree bends	Nr	0.22	24.03	24.79	1,327.33	1,376.15	*248.88*
J3.1.3.04	as above; 90 degree flanged bends	Nr	0.36	39.32	40.57	1,425.37	1,505.26	*254.11*
J3.1.3.05	Ductile spun iron fittings, BS EN 598, spigot and socket joints; Nominal bore 600mm; 22.5 degree bends	Nr	0.23	25.12	25.92	1,376.46	1,427.50	*518.56*
J3.1.3.06	as above; 45 degree bends	Nr	0.25	27.31	28.18	1,536.65	1,592.14	*513.58*
J3.1.3.07	as above; 90 degree bends	Nr	0.27	29.49	30.43	2,527.92	2,587.84	*628.93*
J3.1.3.08	as above; 90 degree flanged bends	Nr	0.47	51.34	52.97	2,574.59	2,678.90	*636.40*

J3 Iron or Steel Pipe Fittings continued...

		Unit	Labour Hours	Labour Net £	Plant Net £	Materials Net £	Unit Net £	CO_2 Kg
J3.1	**Bends**							
J3.1.4	Nominal bore: 600 - 900mm							
J3.1.4.02	as above; 45 degree bends	Nr	0.30	32.77	33.81	3,804.02	3,870.60	*651.06*
J3.1.4.03	as above; 90 degree bends	Nr	0.33	36.05	37.19	5,030.29	5,103.53	*820.26*
J3.1.4.04	as above; 90 degree double flanged bends	Nr	0.57	62.26	64.24	2,743.84	2,870.34	*829.22*
J3.1.4.05	Ductile spun iron fittings, BS EN 598, spigot and socket joints; Nominal bore 800mm; 22.5 degree bends	Nr	0.34	37.14	38.32	3,080.61	3,156.07	*868.38*
J3.1.4.06	as above; 45 degree bends	Nr	0.37	40.42	41.70	4,397.01	4,479.13	*861.86*
J3.1.4.07	as above; 90 degree bends	Nr	0.41	44.78	46.21	9,511.56	9,602.55	*1,105.93*
J3.1.4.08	as above; 90 degree double flanged bends	Nr	0.70	76.46	78.89	5,329.23	5,484.58	*1,116.76*
J3.1.4.09	Ductile spun iron fittings, BS EN 598, spigot and socket joints; Nominal bore 900mm; 22.5 degree bends	Nr	0.40	43.69	45.08	5,954.64	6,043.41	*1,138.02*
J3.1.4.10	as above; 45 degree bends	Nr	0.43	46.97	48.46	6,975.67	7,071.10	*1,116.22*
J3.1.4.11	as above; 90 degree bends	Nr	0.48	52.43	54.10	10,800.95	10,907.48	*1,450.43*
J3.1.4.12	as above; 90 degree flanged bends	Nr	0.82	89.57	92.41	5,818.07	6,000.05	*1,463.13*
J3.1.5	Nominal bore: 900 - 1200mm							
J3.1.5.01	Ductile spun iron fittings, BS EN 598, spigot and socket joints; Nominal bore 1000mm; 22.5 degree bends	Nr	0.47	51.34	52.97	6,519.12	6,623.43	*1,196.79*
J3.1.5.02	as above; 45 degree bends	Nr	0.50	54.62	56.35	7,694.04	7,805.01	*1,173.85*
J3.1.5.03	as above; 90 degree bends	Nr	0.56	61.17	63.11	12,320.49	12,444.77	*1,525.05*
J3.1.5.04	as above; 90 degree flanged bends	Nr	0.96	104.86	108.19	6,523.06	6,736.11	*1,539.99*
J3.1.5.05	Ductile spun iron fittings, BS EN 598, spigot and socket joints; Nominal bore 1200mm; 22.5 degree bends	Nr	0.68	74.28	76.64	14,938.56	15,089.48	*2,292.57*
J3.1.5.06	as above; 45 degree bends	Nr	0.76	83.01	85.65	18,250.08	18,418.74	*3,032.82*
J3.1.5.07	as above; 90 degree bends	Nr	1.30	142.00	146.51	16,018.42	16,306.93	*3,053.00*
J3.1.5.08	as above; 90 degree double flanged bends	Nr	0.76	83.01	85.65	19,502.13	19,670.79	*3,953.44*
J3.2	**Junction and Branches**							
J3.2.1	Nominal bore: not exceeding 200mm							
J3.2.1.01	Ductile spun iron fittings, BS EN 598, spigot and socket joints; Nominal bore 100mm; Equal tees	Nr	0.50	13.45	-	39.36	52.81	*23.88*
J3.2.1.02	as above; Flanged equal tees	Nr	1.00	26.90	-	83.91	110.81	*36.29*
J3.2.1.03	Ductile spun iron fittings, BS EN 598, spigot and socket joints; Nominal bore 150mm; Equal tees	Nr	0.65	17.48	-	160.72	178.20	*56.35*
J3.2.1.04	as above; Flanged equal tees	Nr	1.40	37.66	-	155.14	192.80	*56.35*
J3.2.1.05	Carbon steel pipe fittings, butt welded joints, BS 5135; Not in trenches; fixed to pipes on pipe supports; Nominal bore 100mm; Equal tees	Nr	0.38	58.15	42.76	57.38	158.29	*39.33*
J3.2.1.06	as above; Nominal bore 150mm; Equal tees	Nr	0.57	87.22	64.14	126.39	277.75	*88.51*

J3 Iron or Steel Pipe Fittings continued...

		Unit	Labour Hours	Labour Net £	Plant Net £	Materials Net £	Unit Net £	CO_2 Kg
J3.2	**Junction and Branches**							
J3.2.2	Nominal bore: 200 - 300mm							
J3.2.2.01	Ductile spun iron fittings, BS EN 598, spigot and socket joints; Nominal bore 300mm; Equal tees	Nr	0.12	13.11	13.52	540.57	**567.20**	*166.83*
J3.2.2.02	as above; Flanged equal tees	Nr	0.30	32.77	33.81	564.05	**630.63**	*173.56*
J3.2.3	Nominal bore: 300 - 600mm							
J3.2.3.01	Ductile spun iron fittings, BS EN 598, spigot and socket joints; Nominal bore 450mm; Equal tees	Nr	0.22	24.03	24.79	1,808.51	**1,857.33**	*378.76*
J3.2.3.02	as above; Flanged equal tees	Nr	0.45	49.15	50.72	2,078.02	**2,177.89**	*387.35*
J3.2.3.03	Ductile spun iron fittings, BS EN 598, spigot and socket joints; Nominal bore 600mm; Equal tees	Nr	0.27	29.49	30.43	3,292.61	**3,352.53**	*863.86*
J3.2.3.04	as above; Flanged equal tees	Nr	0.70	76.46	78.89	2,934.70	**3,090.05**	*879.92*
J3.2.4	Nominal bore: 600 - 900mm							
J3.2.4.01	Ductile spun iron fittings, BS EN 598, spigot and socket joints; Nominal bore 700mm; Equal tees	Nr	0.33	36.05	37.19	4,725.94	**4,799.18**	*1,059.01*
J3.2.4.02	as above; Flanged equal tees	Nr	0.85	92.85	95.80	4,237.60	**4,426.25**	*1,078.43*
J3.2.4.03	Ductile spun iron fittings, BS EN 598, spigot and socket joints; Nominal bore 800mm; Equal tees	Nr	0.41	44.78	46.21	6,034.13	**6,125.12**	*1,114.33*
J3.2.4.04	as above; Flanged equal tees	Nr	1.05	114.69	118.34	5,755.92	**5,988.95**	*1,138.24*
J3.2.4.05	Ductile spun iron fittings, BS EN 598, spigot and socket joints; Nominal bore 900mm; Equal tees	Nr	0.48	52.43	54.10	13,955.26	**14,061.79**	*1,878.27*
J3.2.4.06	as above; Flanged equal tees	Nr	1.23	134.35	138.62	11,386.07	**11,659.04**	*1,906.29*
J3.2.5	Nominal bore: 900 - 1200mm							
J3.2.5.01	Ductile spun iron fittings, BS EN 598, spigot and socket joints; Nominal bore 1000mm; Equal tees	Nr	0.56	61.17	63.11	14,038.53	**14,162.81**	*1,974.28*
J3.2.5.02	as above; Flanged equal tees	Nr	1.44	157.29	162.29	12,809.08	**13,128.66**	*2,007.15*
J3.2.5.03	Ductile spun iron fittings, BS EN 598, spigot and socket joints; Nominal bore 1200mm; Equal tees	Nr	1.95	213.00	112.70	19,502.13	**19,827.83**	*3,962.41*
J3.2.5.04	as above; Flanged equal tees	Nr	1.95	213.00	219.76	21,777.77	**22,210.53**	*3,997.90*
J3.3	**Tapers**							
J3.3.1	Nominal bore: not exceeding 200mm							
J3.3.1.01	Carbon steel pipe fittings, butt welded joints, BS 5135; Not in trenches; fixed to pipes on pipe supports; Nominal bore 100mm; Concentric reducers, 100 - 50mm	Nr	0.27	41.32	30.38	20.79	**92.49**	*27.40*
J3.3.1.02	as above; Eccentric reducers, 100 - 50mm	Nr	0.27	41.32	30.38	34.18	**105.88**	*27.40*

J3 Iron or Steel Pipe Fittings continued...

		Unit	Labour Hours	Labour Net £	Plant Net £	Materials Net £	Unit Net £	CO_2 Kg
J3.3	**Tapers**							
J3.3.1	Nominal bore: not exceeding 200mm							
J3.3.1.03	Carbon steel pipe fittings, butt welded joints, BS 5135; Not in trenches; fixed to pipes on pipe supports; Nominal bore 150mm; Concentric reducers, 100 - 50mm	Nr	0.41	62.74	46.14	26.32	135.20	*35.35*
J3.3.1.04	as above; Eccentric reducers, 100 - 50mm	Nr	0.41	62.74	46.14	49.19	158.07	*36.78*
J3.5	**Adaptors**							
J3.5.1	Nominal bore: not exceeding 200mm							
J3.5.1.01	Ductile spun iron fittings, BS EN 598, spigot and socket joints; Nominal bore 100mm; Flange and socket pieces	Nr	0.40	10.76	-	51.61	62.37	*25.31*
J3.5.1.02	as above; Flange and spigot pieces	Nr	0.70	18.83	-	137.34	156.17	*59.69*
J3.5.1.03	Ductile spun iron fittings, BS EN 598, spigot and socket joints; Nominal bore 150mm; Flange and socket pieces	Nr	0.55	14.80	-	82.11	96.91	*36.29*
J3.5.1.04	as above; Flange and spigot pieces	Nr	0.95	25.56	-	173.47	199.03	*75.45*
J3.5.2	Nominal bore: 200 - 300mm							
J3.5.2.01	Ductile spun iron fittings, BS EN 598, spigot and socket joints; Nominal bore 300mm; Flange and socket pieces	Nr	0.20	21.85	22.54	251.92	296.31	*93.42*
J3.5.2.02	as above; Flange and spigot pieces	Nr	0.20	21.85	22.54	241.57	285.96	*87.69*
J3.5.3	Nominal bore: 300 - 600mm							
J3.5.3.01	Ductile spun iron fittings, BS EN 598, spigot and socket joints; Nominal bore 450mm; Flange and socket pieces	Nr	0.27	29.49	30.43	563.92	623.84	*267.94*
J3.5.3.02	as above; Flange and spigot pieces	Nr	0.27	29.49	30.43	510.79	570.71	*267.94*
J3.5.3.03	Ductile spun iron fittings, BS EN 598, spigot and socket joints; Nominal bore 600mm; Flange and socket pieces	Nr	0.35	38.23	39.45	966.19	1,043.87	*471.48*
J3.5.3.04	as above; Flange and spigot pieces	Nr	0.35	38.23	39.45	1,145.29	1,222.97	*471.48*
J3.5.4	Nominal bore: 600 - 900mm							
J3.5.4.01	Ductile spun iron fittings, BS EN 598, spigot and socket joints; Nominal bore 700mm; Flange and socket pieces	Nr	0.42	45.88	47.33	2,378.69	2,471.90	*699.47*
J3.5.4.02	as above; Flange and spigot pieces	Nr	0.42	45.88	47.33	1,580.38	1,673.59	*699.47*
J3.5.4.03	Ductile spun iron fittings, BS EN 598, spigot and socket joints; Nominal bore 800mm; Flange and socket pieces	Nr	0.52	56.80	58.60	4,347.84	4,463.24	*737.40*
J3.5.4.04	as above; Flange and spigot pieces	Nr	0.52	56.80	58.60	1,711.47	1,826.87	*737.40*
J3.5.4.05	Ductile spun iron fittings, BS EN 598, spigot and socket joints; Nominal bore 900mm; Flange and socket pieces	Nr	0.61	66.63	68.75	4,817.07	4,952.45	*1,271.93*
J3.5.4.06	as above; Flange and spigot pieces	Nr	0.61	66.63	68.75	3,163.64	3,299.02	*1,271.93*

J3 Iron or Steel Pipe Fittings continued...

		Unit	Labour Hours	Labour Net £	Plant Net £	Materials Net £	Unit Net £	CO_2 Kg
J3.5	**Adaptors**							
J3.5.5	Nominal bore: 900 - 1200mm							
J3.5.5.01	Ductile spun iron fittings, BS EN 598, spigot and socket joints; Nominal bore 1000mm; Flange and socket pieces	Nr	0.71	77.55	80.02	5,289.69	**5,447.26**	*1,338.12*
J3.5.5.02	as above; Flange and spigot pieces	Nr	0.71	77.55	80.02	4,224.82	**4,382.39**	*1,338.12*
J3.5.5.03	Ductile spun iron fittings, BS EN 598, spigot and socket joints; Nominal bore 1200mm; Flange and socket pieces	Nr	0.96	104.86	108.19	7,633.86	**7,846.91**	*1,687.85*
J3.5.5.04	as above; Flange and spigot pieces	Nr	0.64	69.91	72.13	9,610.06	**9,752.10**	*2,340.74*

J4 Polyvinyl Chloride Pipe Fittings

		Unit	Labour Hours	Labour Net £	Plant Net £	Materials Net £	Unit Net £	CO_2 Kg
J4.1	**Bends**							
J4.1.1	Nominal bore: not exceeding 200mm							
J4.1.1.01	Unplasticised PVC pipe fittings, BS EN 1452; solvent cement joints; Nominal bore 50mm; 45 degree elbows	Nr	0.20	5.38	-	22.62	**28.00**	*21.97*
J4.1.1.02	as above; 90 degree elbows	Nr	0.40	10.76	-	51.61	**62.37**	*25.31*
J4.1.1.03	Unplasticised PVC pipe fittings, BS EN 1452; solvent cement joints; Nominal bore 100mm; 45 degree elbows	Nr	0.30	8.07	-	77.65	**85.72**	*34.38*
J4.1.1.04	as above; 90 degree elbows	Nr	0.55	14.80	-	82.11	**96.91**	*36.29*
J4.1.1.05	Unplasticised PVC pipe fittings, BS EN 1452; solvent cement joints; Not in trenches; fixed to pipes on pipe supports; Nominal bore 50mm; 45 degree elbows	Nr	0.25	6.72	-	27.56	**34.28**	*21.97*
J4.1.1.06	as above; 90 degree elbows	Nr	0.35	9.41	-	29.31	**38.72**	*22.92*
J4.1.1.07	Unplasticised PVC pipe fittings, BS EN 1452; solvent cement joints; Not in trenches; fixed to pipes on pipe supports; Nominal bore 100mm; 45 degree elbows	Nr	0.35	9.41	-	84.82	**94.23**	*35.34*
J4.1.1.08	as above; 90 degree elbows	Nr	0.45	12.11	-	132.47	**144.58**	*42.98*
J4.3	**Tapers**							
J4.3.1	Nominal bore: not exceeding 200mm							
J4.3.1.01	Unplasticised PVC pipe fittings, BS EN 1452; solvent cement joints; Nominal bore 50mm; Reducing sockets	Nr	0.60	16.14	-	34.03	**50.17**	*22.92*
J4.3.1.02	as above; Nominal bore 100mm; Reducing sockets	Nr	0.80	21.52	-	98.63	**120.15**	*42.98*
J4.3.1.03	Unplasticised PVC pipe fittings, BS EN 1452; solvent cement joints; Not in trenches; fixed to pipes on pipe supports; Nominal bore 50mm; Reducing sockets	Nr	0.40	10.76	-	54.24	**65.00**	*23.40*
J4.3.1.04	as above; Nominal bore 100mm; Reducing sockets	Nr	0.55	14.80	-	62.88	**77.68**	*33.43*

J7 Medium Density Polyethylene Pipe Fittings

		Unit	Labour Hours	Labour Net £	Plant Net £	Materials Net £	Unit Net £	CO_2 Kg
J7.1	**Bends**							
J7.1.1	Nominal bore: not exceeding 200mm							
J7.1.1.01	Blue MDPE (SDR 11) water supply pupped fittings, to WIS 4-32-03; 90 mm outside diameter; 45 degree pupped elbow	Nr	0.14	15.07	-	24.57	**39.64**	*1.07*
J7.1.1.02	as above; 90 degree pupped elbow	Nr	0.14	15.07	-	25.99	**41.06**	*1.07*
J7.1.1.03	Blue MDPE (SDR 11) water supply pupped fittings, to WIS 4-32-03; 125 mm outside diameter; 45 degree pupped elbow	Nr	0.17	18.30	-	36.74	**55.04**	*2.05*
J7.1.1.04	as above; 90 degree pupped elbow	Nr	0.17	18.30	-	42.69	**60.99**	*2.05*
J7.1.1.05	Blue MDPE (SDR 11) water supply pupped fittings, to WIS 4-32-03; 180 mm outside diameter; 45 degree pupped elbow	Nr	0.23	24.76	-	75.35	**100.11**	*4.23*
J7.1.1.06	as above; 90 degree pupped elbow	Nr	0.23	24.76	-	115.81	**140.57**	*4.23*
J7.1.2	Nominal bore: 200 - 300mm							
J7.1.2.01	Blue MDPE (SDR 11) water supply pupped fittings, to WIS 4-32-03; 250 mm outside diameter; 45 degree pupped elbow	Nr	0.30	32.30	-	113.96	**146.26**	*8.12*
J7.1.2.02	as above; 90 degree pupped elbow	Nr	0.30	32.30	-	170.37	**202.67**	*8.12*
J7.1.3	Nominal bore: 300 - 600mm							
J7.1.3.01	Blue MDPE (SDR 11) water supply pupped fittings, to WIS 4-32-03; 315 mm outside diameter; 45 degree pupped elbow	Nr	0.37	39.83	-	199.33	**239.16**	*12.89*
J7.1.3.02	as above; 90 degree pupped elbow	Nr	0.37	39.83	-	345.95	**385.78**	*12.89*
J7.2	**Junction and Branches**							
J7.2.1	Nominal bore: not exceeding 200mm							
J7.2.1.01	Blue MDPE (SDR 11) water supply pupped fittings, to WIS 4-32-03; 90 mm outside diameter; 90 degree pupped equal tee	Nr	0.14	15.07	-	33.26	**48.33**	*1.49*
J7.2.1.02	as above; 90 degree pupped reducing branch tee (90 x 63)	Nr	0.14	15.07	-	48.78	**63.85**	*1.49*
J7.2.1.03	Blue MDPE (SDR 11) water supply pupped fittings, to WIS 4-32-03; 125 mm outside diameter; 90 degree pupped equal tee	Nr	0.17	18.30	-	61.62	**79.92**	*2.86*
J7.2.1.04	as above; 90 degree pupped reducing branch tee (125 x 90)	Nr	0.17	18.30	-	90.53	**108.83**	*2.86*
J7.2.1.05	Blue MDPE (SDR 11) water supply pupped fittings, to WIS 4-32-03; 180 mm outside diameter; 90 degree pupped equal tee	Nr	0.23	24.76	-	114.70	**139.46**	*5.92*

J7 Medium Density Polyethylene Pipe Fittings continued...

		Unit	Labour Hours	Labour Net £	Plant Net £	Materials Net £	Unit Net £	CO_2 Kg
J7.2	**Junction and Branches**							
J7.2.1	Nominal bore: not exceeding 200mm							
J7.2.1.06	as previous item; 90 degree pupped reducing branch tee (180 x 125)	Nr	0.23	24.76	-	162.62	**187.38**	*5.92*
J7.2.2	Nominal bore: 200 - 300mm							
J7.2.2.01	Blue MDPE (SDR 11) water supply pupped fittings, to WIS 4-32-03; 250 mm outside diameter; 90 degree pupped equal tee	Nr	0.30	32.30	-	207.39	**239.69**	*11.37*
J7.2.2.02	as above; 90 degree pupped reducing branch tee (250 x 180)	Nr	0.30	32.30	-	303.77	**336.07**	*11.37*
J7.2.3	Nominal bore: 300 - 600mm							
J7.2.3.01	Blue MDPE (SDR 11) water supply pupped fittings, to WIS 4-32-03; 315 mm outside diameter; 90 degree pupped equal tee	Nr	0.37	39.83	-	518.92	**558.75**	*18.04*
J7.2.3.02	as above; 90 degree pupped reducing branch tee (315 x 250)	Nr	0.37	39.83	-	600.10	**639.93**	*18.04*
J7.3	**Tapers**							
J7.3.1	Nominal bore: not exceeding 200mm							
J7.3.1.01	Blue MDPE (SDR 11) water supply pupped fittings, to WIS 4-32-03; 90 mm outside diameter; Pupped reducer (90 x 63)	Nr	0.14	15.07	-	20.18	**35.25**	*1.40*
J7.3.1.02	as above; 125 mm outside diameter; Pupped reducer (125 x 90)	Nr	0.17	18.30	-	18.79	**37.09**	*1.88*
J7.3.1.03	as above; 180 mm outside diameter; Pupped reducer (180 x 125)	Nr	0.23	24.76	-	55.23	**79.99**	*3.89*
J7.3.2	Nominal bore: 200 - 300mm							
J7.3.2.01	Blue MDPE (SDR 11) water supply pupped fittings, to WIS 4-32-03; 250 mm outside diameter; Pupped reducer (250 x 180)	Nr	0.30	32.30	-	91.83	**124.13**	*7.47*
J7.3.3	Nominal bore: 300 - 600mm							
J7.3.3.01	Blue MDPE (SDR 11) water supply pupped fittings, to WIS 4-32-03; 315 mm outside diameter; Pupped reducer (315 x 250)	Nr	0.37	39.83	-	128.81	**168.64**	*11.85*

J8 Valves and Penstocks

		Unit	Labour Hours	Labour Net £	Plant Net £	Materials Net £	Unit Net £	CO_2 Kg
J8.1	**Gate Valves: Hand Operated**							
J8.1.1	Nominal bore: not exceeding 200mm							
J8.1.1.01	Flanged Ductile iron valves; BS 5150 and 5163, Euro 16 sluice valve; right hand closing; Nominal bore; 80mm; with cap	Nr	0.15	16.15	10.04	141.76	**167.95**	*45.97*
J8.1.1.02	as above; Nominal bore; 80mm; with handwheel	Nr	0.18	19.38	12.04	166.42	**197.84**	*48.86*

J8 Valves and Penstocks continued...

		Unit	Labour Hours	Labour Net £	Plant Net £	Materials Net £	Unit Net £	CO_2 Kg
J8.1	**Gate Valves: Hand Operated**							
J8.1.1	Nominal bore: not exceeding 200mm							
J8.1.1.03	as previous item; Nominal bore; 100mm; with cap	Nr	0.19	20.46	12.71	170.29	**203.46**	*60.39*
J8.1.1.04	as above; Nominal bore; 100mm; with handwheel	Nr	0.22	23.69	14.72	189.29	**227.70**	*63.95*
J8.1.1.05	as above; Nominal bore; 150mm; with cap	Nr	0.34	36.60	22.75	259.26	**318.61**	*106.36*
J8.1.1.06	as above; Nominal bore; 150mm; with handwheel	Nr	0.37	39.83	24.76	278.27	**342.86**	*112.02*
J8.1.1.07	as above; Nominal bore; 200mm; with cap	Nr	0.46	49.52	30.78	508.34	**588.64**	*180.19*
J8.1.1.08	as above; Nominal bore; 200mm; with handwheel	Nr	0.50	53.83	33.45	533.77	**621.05**	*189.64*
J8.1.2	Nominal bore: 200 - 300mm							
J8.1.2.01	Flanged Ductile iron valves; BS 5150 and 5163, Euro 16 sluice valve; right hand closing; Nominal bore; 250mm; with cap	Nr	0.58	62.44	38.81	737.10	**838.35**	*301.76*
J8.1.2.02	as above; Nominal bore; 250mm; with handwheel	Nr	0.62	66.75	41.48	773.83	**882.06**	*317.14*
J8.1.2.03	as above; Nominal bore; 300mm; with cap	Nr	0.70	75.36	46.84	891.90	**1,014.10**	*409.97*
J8.1.2.04	as above; Nominal bore; 300mm; with handwheel	Nr	0.75	80.75	50.18	928.66	**1,059.59**	*430.87*
J8.1.3	Nominal bore: 300 - 600mm							
J8.1.3.01	Flanged Cast iron wedge valve, BS 5163/PN16, rating having gunmetal faces to body and wedge, stainless steel non-rising screw stem working in a gunmetal nut housed in the wedge; end flanges faced and drilled, BS 4504, Table PN16; body tested 24 bars; seat test and maximum working pressure 16 bar; clockwise closing; complete with cast iron cap for key operation or cast iron handwheel direct on valve; prices exclude forming holes and grouting in; Nominal bore 350mm; with cap	Nr	0.84	90.43	56.20	2,254.71	**2,401.34**	*538.87*
J8.1.3.02	as above; Nominal bore: 350mm; with handwheel	Nr	0.90	96.89	60.22	2,336.82	**2,493.93**	*530.31*
J8.1.3.03	as above; Nominal bore: 400mm; with cap	Nr	1.00	107.66	66.91	2,705.49	**2,880.06**	*628.44*
J8.1.3.04	as above; Nominal bore: 400mm; with handwheel	Nr	1.06	114.12	70.92	2,849.00	**3,034.04**	*660.13*
J8.1.3.05	as above; Nominal bore: 450mm; with cap	Nr	1.15	123.81	76.95	3,702.65	**3,903.41**	*727.89*
J8.1.3.06	as above; Nominal bore: 450mm; with handwheel	Nr	1.22	131.35	81.63	3,867.58	**4,080.56**	*759.84*
J8.1.3.07	as above; Nominal bore: 500mm; with cap	Nr	1.27	138.72	143.13	4,536.57	**4,818.42**	*840.57*
J8.1.3.08	as above; Nominal bore: 500mm; with handwheel	Nr	1.34	146.37	151.02	4,731.69	**5,029.08**	*873.29*
J8.1.3.09	as above; Nominal bore: 600mm; with cap	Nr	1.60	174.77	180.32	5,632.96	**5,988.05**	*948.40*
J8.1.3.10	as above; Nominal bore: 600mm; with handwheel	Nr	1.70	185.69	191.59	5,744.46	**6,121.74**	*982.24*

J8 Valves and Penstocks continued...

		Unit	Labour Hours	Labour Net £	Plant Net £	Materials Net £	Unit Net £	CO_2 Kg
J8.8	**Penstocks**							
J8.8.1	Nominal bore: not exceeding 200mm							
J8.8.1.01	Circular pattern cast iron penstocks suitable for on-seat pressure each comprising of cast iron frame, door and adjustable wedges; frame with flat back for wall fixing; door and frame having copper alloy sealing faces; stainless steel non-rising screw stem working in a gunmetal nut housed in door; complete with cast iron capor handwheel mounted direct on penstock framework and necessary mild steel indented type foundation bolts; prices exclude forming holes and grouting in; Nominal bore 100mm; with cap	Nr	0.20	21.53	13.38	563.30	**598.21**	*88.35*
J8.8.1.02	as above; Nominal bore: 100mm; with handwheel	Nr	0.23	24.76	15.39	747.96	**788.11**	*93.29*
J8.8.1.03	as above; Nominal bore: 150mm; with cap	Nr	0.33	35.53	22.08	666.66	**724.27**	*154.80*
J8.8.1.04	as above; Nominal bore: 150mm; with handwheel	Nr	0.36	38.76	24.09	872.24	**935.09**	*162.89*
J8.8.1.05	as above; Nominal bore: 200mm; with cap	Nr	0.50	53.83	33.45	747.12	**834.40**	*269.94*
J8.8.1.06	as above; Nominal bore: 200mm; with handwheel	Nr	0.54	58.14	36.13	996.51	**1,090.78**	*278.94*
J8.8.2	Nominal bore: 200 - 300mm							
J8.8.2.01	Circular pattern cast iron penstocks suitable for on-seat pressure each comprising of cast iron frame, door and adjustable wedges; frame with flat back for wall fixing; door and frame having copper alloy sealing faces; stainless steel non-rising screw stem working in a gunmetal nut housed in door; complete with cast iron capor handwheel mounted direct on penstock framework and necessary mild steel indented type foundation bolts; prices exclude forming holes and grouting in; Nominal bore 225mm; with cap	Nr	0.58	62.44	38.81	796.74	**897.99**	*402.04*
J8.8.2.02	as above; Nominal bore: 225mm; with handwheel	Nr	0.62	66.75	41.48	1,060.39	**1,168.62**	*422.44*
J8.8.2.03	as above; Nominal bore: 250mm; with cap	Nr	0.68	73.21	45.50	872.24	**990.95**	*447.64*
J8.8.2.04	as above; Nominal bore: 250mm; with handwheel	Nr	0.73	78.59	48.84	1,110.33	**1,237.76**	*470.45*
J8.8.2.05	as above; Nominal bore: 300mm; with cap	Nr	0.80	86.13	53.53	975.61	**1,115.27**	*608.38*
J8.8.2.06	as above; Nominal bore: 300mm; with handwheel	Nr	0.85	91.51	56.87	1,241.57	**1,389.95**	*639.06*

J8 Valves and Penstocks continued...

		Unit	Labour Hours	Labour Net £	Plant Net £	Materials Net £	Unit Net £	CO_2 Kg
J8.8	**Penstocks**							
J8.8.3	Nominal bore: 300 - 600mm							
J8.8.3.01	Circular pattern cast iron penstocks suitable for on-seat pressure each comprising of cast iron frame, door and adjustable wedges; frame with flat back for wall fixing; door and frame having copper alloy sealing faces; stainless steel non-rising screw stem working in a gunmetal nut housed in door; complete with cast iron capor handwheel mounted direct on penstock framework and necessary mild steel indented type foundation bolts; prices exclude forming holes and grouting in; Nominal bore 350mm; with cap	Nr	1.00	107.66	66.91	1,077.81	**1,252.38**	*684.93*
J8.8.3.02	as above; Nominal bore: 350mm; with handwheel	Nr	1.06	114.12	70.92	1,372.82	**1,557.86**	*787.84*
J8.8.3.03	as above; Nominal bore: 400mm; with cap	Nr	1.20	129.19	80.29	1,168.40	**1,377.88**	*934.77*
J8.8.3.04	as above; Nominal bore: 400mm; with handwheel	Nr	1.27	136.73	84.98	1,475.02	**1,696.73**	*981.77*
J8.8.3.05	as above; Nominal bore: 500mm; with cap	Nr	1.60	174.77	180.32	1,349.59	**1,704.68**	*1,249.46*
J8.8.3.06	as above; Nominal bore: 500mm; with handwheel	Nr	1.70	185.69	191.59	1,677.51	**2,054.79**	*1,298.36*
J8.8.3.07	as above; Nominal bore: 600mm; with cap	Nr	1.95	213.00	219.76	1,764.35	**2,197.11**	*1,409.61*
J8.8.3.08	as above; Nominal bore: 600mm; with handwheel	Nr	2.05	223.92	231.04	1,881.52	**2,336.48**	*1,454.68*
J8.8.4	Nominal bore: 600 - 900mm							
J8.8.4.01	Circular pattern cast iron penstocks suitable for on-seat pressure each comprising of cast iron frame, door and adjustable wedges; frame with flat back for wall fixing; door and frame having copper alloy sealing faces; stainless steel non-rising screw stem working in a gunmetal nut housed in door; complete with cast iron capor handwheel mounted direct on penstock framework and necessary mild steel indented type foundation bolts; prices exclude forming holes and grouting in; Nominal bore 700mm; with cap	Nr	2.30	251.23	259.21	1,711.66	**2,222.10**	*1,388.23*
J8.8.4.02	as above; Nominal bore: 700mm; with handwheel	Nr	2.40	262.15	270.48	2,084.78	**2,617.41**	*1,536.67*
J8.8.4.03	as above; Nominal bore: 750mm; with cap	Nr	2.53	276.35	285.13	1,801.97	**2,363.45**	*1,461.94*
J8.8.4.04	as above; Nominal bore: 750mm; with handwheel	Nr	2.65	289.46	298.65	2,113.23	**2,701.34**	*1,618.35*
J8.8.4.05	as above; Nominal bore: 800mm; with cap	Nr	2.65	289.46	298.65	1,892.56	**2,480.67**	*1,534.79*
J8.8.4.06	as above; Nominal bore: 800mm; with handwheel	Nr	2.77	302.57	312.18	2,288.61	**2,903.36**	*1,698.81*

J8 Valves and Penstocks continued...

		Unit	Labour Hours	Labour Net £	Plant Net £	Materials Net £	Unit Net £	CO_2 Kg
J8.8	**Penstocks**							
J8.8.4	Nominal bore: 600 - 900mm							
J8.8.4.07	as previous item; Nominal bore: 900mm; with cap	Nr	3.00	327.69	338.10	2,073.16	**2,738.95**	*1,619.66*
J8.8.4.08	as above; Nominal bore: 900mm; with handwheel	Nr	3.15	344.07	355.01	2,491.86	**3,190.94**	*1,792.77*
J8.8.5	Nominal bore: 900 - 1200mm							
J8.8.5.01	Circular pattern cast iron penstocks suitable for on-seat pressure each comprising of cast iron frame, door and adjustable wedges; frame with flat back for wall fixing; door and frame having copper alloy sealing faces; stainless steel non-rising screw stem working in a gunmetal nut housed in door; complete with cast iron capor handwheel mounted direct on penstock framework and necessary mild steel indented type foundation bolts; prices exclude forming holes and grouting in; Nominal bore 1000mm; with cap	Nr	3.35	365.92	377.55	2,254.64	**2,998.11**	*1,677.96*
J8.8.5.02	as above; Nominal bore: 1000mm; with handwheel	Nr	3.50	382.31	394.45	2,695.69	**3,472.45**	*1,856.10*

CLASS K:

PIPEWORK - MANHOLES AND PIPEWORK ANCILLARIES

Calculations used throughout Class K - Pipework - Manholes and Pipework Ancillaries

Labour

		Qty		Rate		Total
L K0200ICE	**Manholes Labour Gang**					
	Ganger	1	x	16.99	=	£16.99
	Labourer (General Operative)	3	x	12.56	=	£37.68
	Craftsman WRA	1	x	16.68	=	£16.68
	Total hourly cost of gang				**=**	**£71.35**
L K0202ICE	**Gullies Labour Gang**					
	Ganger	1	x	16.99	=	£16.99
	Labourer (General Operative)	2	x	12.56	=	£25.12
	Total hourly cost of gang				**=**	**£42.11**
L K0203ICE	**French and rubble drains Labour Gang**					
	Ganger	1	x	16.99	=	£16.99
	Labourer (General Operative)	3	x	12.56	=	£37.68
	Pipelayer (standard rate)	1	x	14.34	=	£14.34
	Total hourly cost of gang				**=**	**£69.01**
L K0205ICE	**Topsoil stripping and reinstatement Labour Gang**					
	Labourer (General Operative)	1	x	12.56	=	£12.56
	Total hourly cost of gang				**=**	**£12.56**
L K0206ICE	**Building in pipes to manholes etc. Labour Gang**					
	Ganger	1	x	16.99	=	£16.99
	Labourer (General Operative)	1	x	12.56	=	£12.56
	Total hourly cost of gang				**=**	**£29.55**

Plant

P K1200ICE	**Precast concrete manholes (shallow) Plant Gang**					
	Hydraulic Excavator - Cat 320 96kW	1	x	33.98	=	£33.98
	Pump - Godwin ET50 23m3/h 4 inches	1	x	2.74	=	£2.74
	Wheeled Tractor / Grader - Ford 3190H	1	x	23.52	=	£23.52
	Trailer - Massey Tipping	1	x	1.69	=	£1.69
	Dumper - 1.50t 2WD	1	x	2.75	=	£2.75
	Trench Sheets	72	x	0.08	=	£5.72
	Acrow Props	50	x	0.08	=	£3.97
	Concrete Mixer - 4/3 Petrol	1	x	2.04	=	£2.04
	Total hourly cost of gang				**=**	**£76.41**
P K1201ICE	**Precast concrete manholes (deep) Plant Gang**					
	Hydraulic Excavator - Cat 166kW	1	x	41.41	=	£41.41
	Pump - Godwin ET75 74m3/h 4 inches	1	x	4.12	=	£4.12
	Wheeled Tractor / Grader - Ford 3190H	1	x	23.52	=	£23.52
	Trailer - Massey Tipping	1	x	1.69	=	£1.69
	Dumper - 1.50t 2WD	1	x	2.75	=	£2.75
	Trench Sheets	96	x	0.08	=	£7.63
	Acrow Props	60	x	0.08	=	£4.77
	Concrete Mixer - 4/3 Petrol	1	x	2.04	=	£2.04
	Total hourly cost of gang				**=**	**£87.93**
P K1202ICE	**Gullies Plant Gang**					
	Hydraulic Excavator - JCB 3CX Sitemaster	1	x	27.01	=	£27.01
	Dumper - 1.50t 2WD	1	x	2.75	=	£2.75
	Concrete Mixer - 4/3 Petrol	1	x	2.04	=	£2.04
	Total hourly cost of gang				**=**	**£31.80**

P K1203ICE	**French and rubble drains**					
	Hydraulic Excavator - Cat 320 96kW	1	x	33.98	=	£33.98
	Pump - Godwin ET50 23m3/h 4 inches	1	x	2.74	=	£2.74
	Dumper - 1.50t 2WD	1	x	2.75	=	£2.75
	Vibrating Plate Diesel 33.5kN	1	x	2.76	=	£2.76
	Total hourly cost of gang				**=**	**£42.23**
P K1204ICE	**Breaking up and temporary reinstatement of roads and footpaths Plant Gang**					
	Compressor - 2-Tool (Complete)	1	x	4.86	=	£4.86
	Thor 16D / Maco SK8 Medium Duty Breaker	2	x	0.77	=	£1.54
	Dumper - 1.50t 2WD	1	x	2.75	=	£2.75
	Roller - 28 inch Vibratory Roller 0.37t	1	x	2.04	=	£2.04
	Rammer Benjo	1	x	1.49	=	£1.49
	Traffic Lights - Main Generator 2-Way with 100m Cables	1	x	3.00	=	£3.00
	Total hourly cost of gang				**=**	**£15.68**
P K1205ICE	**Topsoil, stripping and reinstatement Plant Gang**					
	Crawler Tractor / Dozer - Cat D6R LGP 138kW	1	x	45.76	=	£45.76
	Total hourly cost of gang				**=**	**£45.76**

Class K - Pipework - Manholes and Pipework Ancillaries

K1 Manholes

		Unit	Labour Hours	Labour Net £	Plant Net £	Materials Net £	Unit Net £	CO_2 Kg
K1.1	**Brick**							
K1.1.1	Depth: not exceeding 1.5m							
K1.1.1.01	Brick manholes 900 x 675mm internally with 150mm in situ concrete, grade 20 base with fair faced engineering Class 'B' brick walls 215mm thick in cement mortar (1:3), 150mm precast concrete cover slab on 3 course brick kerb, 150mm vitrified clay straight main channel and 1nr 3/4 section branch, concrete benching and 600 x 450mm grade 'B' single seal cast iron cover and frame including excavating in firm ground by machine and filling by hand and spreading surplus excavated material by hand on site average 25m distance from excavation; Depth: 1m; total cost of one manhole	Nr	7.85	560.10	599.90	464.57	**1,624.57**	*1,549.96*
K1.1.2	Depth: 1.5 - 2m							
K1.1.2.01	Brick manholes 900 x 675mm internally with 150mm in situ concrete, grade 20 base with fair faced engineering Class 'B' brick walls 215mm thick in cement mortar (1:3), 150mm precast concrete cover slab on 3 course brick kerb, 150mm vitrified clay straight main channel and 1nr 3/4 section branch, concrete benching and 600 x 450mm grade 'B' single seal cast iron cover and frame including excavating in firm ground by machine and filling by hand and spreading surplus excavated material by hand on site average 25m distance from excavation; Depth: 2m; total cost of one manhole	Nr	12.90	920.41	985.82	678.14	**2,584.37**	*2,747.76*

K1 Manholes continued...

		Unit	Labour Hours	Labour Net £	Plant Net £	Materials Net £	Unit Net £	CO_2 Kg
K1.2	**Brick with backdrop**							
K1.2.2	Depth: 1.5 - 2m							
K1.2.2.01	Brick manholes 1200 x 1050mm internally with 150mm in situ concrete, grade 20 base with fair faced engineering Class 'B' brick walls 215mm thick in cement mortar (1:3), 150mm precast concrete cover slab on 3 course brick kerb, 150mm diameter vitrified clay pipe and 1nr 150 x 150mm junction forming backdrop commencing 1m above invert encased in concrete, grade 20, with cast iron cover and frame and 1nr 3/4 section branch channel bend, concrete benching and 600 x 600mm grade 'B' single seal cast iron cover and frame, including excavating and filling in firm ground by machine, removing surplus from site; Depth: 2m; total cost of one manhole	Nr	18.47	1,317.83	1,411.48	995.49	**3,724.80**	*3,867.03*
K1.2.4	Depth: 2.5 - 3m							
K1.2.4.01	Brick manholes 1200 x 1050mm internally with 150mm in situ concrete, grade 20 base with fair faced engineering Class 'B' brick walls 215mm thick in cement mortar (1:3), 150mm precast concrete cover slab on 3 course brick kerb, 150mm diameter vitrified clay pipe and 1nr 150 x 150mm junction forming backdrop commencing 1m above invert encased in concrete, grade 20, with cast iron cover and frame and 1nr 3/4 section branch channel bend, concrete benching and 600 x 600mm grade 'B' single seal cast iron cover and frame, including excavating and filling in firm ground by machine, removing surplus from site; Depth: 4m, backdrop commencing 2.5m above invert; total cost of one manhole	Nr	32.10	2,290.34	2,453.08	1,595.33	**6,338.75**	*7,222.36*
K1.5	**Precast concrete**							
K1.5.1	Depth: not exceeding 1.5m							
K1.5.1.01	Precast concrete manholes; excavation and backfilling in natural material; in situ concrete grade 20 in 300mm base; 300/150mm branch junction channel; 150mm diameter half round bend channel; cement mortar benching (1:3); precast concrete manhole rings and cover slab, BS 5911; 150mm in situ concrete grade 20 surround to rings; 600mm diameter heavy duty cast iron access cover and frame; galvanised malleable step irons BS 1247 at 305mm centres cast into sides of chamber rings; 675mm nominal internal diameter manhole rings; Depth: 1.5m; total cost of one manhole	Nr	3.95	281.83	290.40	776.88	**1,349.11**	*905.63*

K1 Manholes continued...

		Unit	Labour Hours	Labour Net £	Plant Net £	Materials Net £	Unit Net £	CO_2 Kg
K1.5	**Precast concrete**							
K1.5.1	Depth: not exceeding 1.5m							
K1.5.1.02	as previous item; 900mm nominal internal diameter manhole rings; Depth: 1.5m; total cost of one manhole	Nr	4.41	314.65	325.55	626.86	1,267.06	*976.70*
K1.5.1.03	as above; 1050mm nominal internal diameter manhole rings; Depth: 1.5m; total cost of one manhole	Nr	5.32	379.58	395.09	632.08	1,406.75	*1,092.09*
K1.5.1.04	as above; 1200mm nominal internal diameter manhole rings; Depth: 1.5m; total cost of one manhole	Nr	6.24	445.22	465.40	734.03	1,644.65	*1,412.82*
K1.5.1.05	as above; 1350mm nominal internal diameter manhole rings; Depth: 1.5m; total cost of one manhole	Nr	7.18	512.29	537.23	835.14	1,884.66	*1,661.56*
K1.5.1.06	as above; 1500mm nominal internal diameter manhole rings; Depth: 1.5m; total cost of one manhole	Nr	8.14	580.79	702.48	894.66	2,177.93	*1,929.27*
K1.5.1.07	as above; 1800mm nominal internal diameter manhole rings; Depth: 1.5m; total cost of one manhole	Nr	10.08	719.21	873.05	1,131.41	2,723.67	*2,347.44*
K1.5.2	Depth: 1.5 - 2m							
K1.5.2.01	Precast concrete manholes; excavation and backfilling in natural material; in situ concrete grade 20 in 300mm base; 300/150mm branch junction channel; 150mm diameter half round bend channel; cement mortar benching (1:3); precast concrete manhole rings and cover slab, BS 5911; 150mm in situ concrete grade 20 surround to rings; 600mm diameter heavy duty cast iron access cover and frame; galvanised malleable step irons BS 1247 at 305mm centres cast into sides of chamber rings; 675mm nominal internal diameter manhole rings; Depth: 2m; total cost of one manhole	Nr	3.75	267.56	275.11	612.39	1,155.06	*914.14*
K1.5.2.02	as above; 900mm nominal internal diameter manhole rings; Depth: 2m; total cost of one manhole	Nr	5.21	371.73	386.69	685.27	1,443.69	*1,150.68*
K1.5.2.03	as above; 1050mm nominal internal diameter manhole rings; Depth: 2m; total cost of one manhole	Nr	6.33	451.65	472.28	720.14	1,644.07	*1,359.39*
K1.5.2.04	as above; 1200mm nominal internal diameter manhole rings; Depth: 2m; total cost of one manhole	Nr	7.49	534.41	560.92	795.87	1,891.20	*1,632.47*
K1.5.2.05	as above; 1350mm nominal internal diameter manhole rings; Depth: 2m; total cost of one manhole	Nr	8.68	619.32	651.86	932.14	2,203.32	*1,974.73*

K1 Manholes continued...

		Unit	Labour Hours	Labour Net £	Plant Net £	Materials Net £	Unit Net £	CO_2 Kg
K1.5	**Precast concrete**							
K1.5.2	Depth: 1.5 - 2m							
K1.5.2.06	as previous item; 1500mm nominal internal diameter manhole rings; Depth: 2m; total cost of one manhole	Nr	9.89	705.65	856.34	1,052.55	**2,614.54**	*2,314.61*
K1.5.2.07	as above; 1800mm nominal internal diameter manhole rings; Depth: 2m; total cost of one manhole	Nr	12.32	879.03	1,069.99	1,276.42	**3,225.44**	*2,810.44*
K1.5.2.08	as above; 1200mm nominal internal diameter manhole chamber rings tapering to 900mm nominal internal diameter shaft rings at 1.5m above channel invert; Depth: 2m; total cost of one manhole	Nr	7.02	500.88	525.01	871.67	**1,897.56**	*1,602.27*
K1.5.2.09	as above; 1350mm nominal internal diameter manhole chamber rings tapering to 900mm nominal internal diameter shaft rings at 1.5m above channel invert; Depth: 2m; total cost of one manhole	Nr	7.92	565.09	593.78	951.06	**2,109.93**	*1,814.56*
K1.5.2.10	as above; 1500mm nominal internal diameter manhole chamber rings tapering to 900mm nominal internal diameter shaft rings at 1.5m above channel invert; Depth: 2m; total cost of one manhole	Nr	9.13	651.43	789.52	1,073.44	**2,514.39**	*2,158.55*
K1.5.2.11	as above; 1800mm nominal internal diameter manhole chamber rings tapering to 900mm nominal internal diameter shaft rings at 1.5m above channel invert; Depth: 2m; total cost of one manhole	Nr	11.24	801.97	975.03	1,267.70	**3,044.70**	*2,609.48*
K1.5.4	Depth: 2.5 - 3m							
K1.5.4.01	Precast concrete manholes; excavation and backfilling in natural material; in situ concrete grade 20 in 300mm base; 300/150mm branch junction channel; 150mm diameter half round bend channel; cement mortar benching (1:3); precast concrete manhole rings and cover slab, BS 5911; 150mm in situ concrete grade 20 surround to rings; 600mm diameter heavy duty cast iron access cover and frame; galvanised malleable step irons BS 1247 at 305mm centres cast into sides of chamber rings; 675mm nominal internal diameter manhole rings; Depth: 3m; total cost of one manhole	Nr	4.81	343.19	352.30	718.87	**1,414.36**	*1,199.56*
K1.5.4.02	as above; 900mm nominal internal diameter manhole rings; Depth: 3m; total cost of one manhole	Nr	6.97	497.31	517.36	811.45	**1,826.12**	*1,512.93*

K1 Manholes continued...

		Unit	Labour Hours	Labour Net £	Plant Net £	Materials Net £	Unit Net £	CO_2 Kg
K1.5	**Precast concrete**							
K1.5.4	Depth: 2.5 - 3m							
K1.5.4.03	as previous item; 1050mm nominal internal diameter manhole rings; Depth: 3m; total cost of one manhole	Nr	8.62	615.04	643.46	858.00	**2,116.50**	*1,800.57*
K1.5.4.04	as above; 1200mm nominal internal diameter manhole rings; Depth: 3m; total cost of one manhole	Nr	10.19	727.06	763.44	963.80	**2,454.30**	*2,192.08*
K1.5.4.05	as above; 1200mm nominal internal diameter manhole chamber rings tapering to 900mm nominal internal diameter shaft rings at 1.5m above channel invert; Depth: 3m; total cost of one manhole	Nr	7.84	559.38	583.85	822.26	**1,965.49**	*1,298.98*
K1.5.4.06	as above; 1350mm nominal internal diameter manhole rings; Depth: 3m; total cost of one manhole	Nr	11.97	854.06	899.46	1,135.49	**2,889.01**	*2,618.97*
K1.5.4.07	as above; 1350mm nominal internal diameter manhole chamber rings tapering to 900mm nominal internal diameter shaft rings at 1.5m above channel invert; Depth: 3m; total cost of one manhole	Nr	9.91	707.08	742.04	1,119.96	**2,569.08**	*2,287.87*
K1.5.4.08	as above; 1500mm nominal internal diameter manhole rings; Depth: 3m; total cost of one manhole	Nr	13.59	969.65	1,177.25	1,273.09	**3,419.99**	*3,053.09*
K1.5.4.09	as above; 1500mm nominal internal diameter manhole chamber rings tapering to 900mm nominal internal diameter shaft rings at 1.5m above channel invert; Depth: 3m; total cost of one manhole	Nr	11.10	791.98	958.33	1,256.97	**3,007.28**	*2,623.17*
K1.5.4.10	as above; 1800mm nominal internal diameter manhole rings; Depth: 3m; total cost of one manhole	Nr	16.94	1,208.67	1,478.81	1,567.28	**4,254.76**	*3,722.55*
K1.5.4.11	as above; 1800mm nominal internal diameter manhole chamber rings tapering to 900mm nominal internal diameter shaft rings at 1.5m above channel invert; Depth: 3m; total cost of one manhole	Nr	13.53	965.37	1,171.97	1,411.28	**3,548.62**	*3,053.80*

K1 Manholes continued...

		Unit	Labour Hours	Labour Net £	Plant Net £	Materials Net £	Unit Net £	CO_2 Kg
K1.5	**Precast concrete**							
K1.5.6	Depth: 3.5 - 4m							
K1.5.6.01	Precast concrete manholes; excavation and backfilling in natural material; in situ concrete grade 20 in 300mm base; 300/150mm branch junction channel; 150mm diameter half round bend channel; cement mortar benching (1:3); precast concrete manhole rings and cover slab, BS 5911; 150mm in situ concrete grade 20 surround to rings; 600mm diameter heavy duty cast iron access cover and frame; galvanised malleable step irons BS 1247 at 305mm centres cast into sides of chamber rings; 675mm nominal internal diameter manhole rings; Depth: 4m; total cost of one manhole	Nr	5.90	420.96	427.95	820.67	**1,669.58**	*1,478.79*
K1.5.6.02	as above; 900mm nominal internal diameter manhole rings; Depth: 4m; total cost of one manhole	Nr	8.71	621.46	642.69	932.94	**2,197.09**	*1,867.62*
K1.5.6.03	as above; 1050mm nominal internal diameter manhole rings; Depth: 4m; total cost of one manhole	Nr	10.72	764.87	796.30	995.44	**2,556.61**	*2,245.09*
K1.5.6.04	as above; 1200mm nominal internal diameter manhole rings; Depth: 4m; total cost of one manhole	Nr	12.89	919.70	962.13	1,114.28	**2,996.11**	*2,697.87*
K1.5.6.05	as above; 1200mm nominal internal diameter manhole chamber rings tapering to 900mm nominal internal diameter shaft rings at 1.5m above channel invert; Depth: 4m; total cost of one manhole	Nr	10.02	714.93	742.80	1,114.07	**2,571.80**	*2,289.80*
K1.5.6.06	as above; 1350mm nominal internal diameter manhole rings; Depth: 4m; total cost of one manhole	Nr	15.74	1,123.05	1,348.69	1,424.85	**3,896.59**	*3,685.69*
K1.5.6.07	as above; 1350mm nominal internal diameter manhole chamber rings tapering to 900mm nominal internal diameter shaft rings at 1.5m above channel invert; Depth: 4m; total cost of one manhole	Nr	11.37	811.25	845.97	1,232.94	**2,890.16**	*2,603.63*
K1.5.6.08	as above; 1500mm nominal internal diameter manhole rings; Depth: 4m; total cost of one manhole	Nr	17.29	1,233.64	1,493.76	1,488.95	**4,216.35**	*3,784.16*
K1.5.6.09	as above; 1500mm nominal internal diameter manhole chamber rings tapering to 900mm nominal internal diameter shaft rings at 1.5m above channel invert; Depth: 4m; total cost of one manhole	Nr	12.64	901.86	1,084.93	1,369.95	**3,356.74**	*2,952.53*

K1 Manholes continued...

		Unit	Labour Hours	Labour Net £	Plant Net £	Materials Net £	Unit Net £	*CO 2 Kg*
K1.5	**Precast concrete**							
K1.5.6	Depth: 3.5 - 4m							
K1.5.6.10	as previous item; 1800mm nominal internal diameter manhole rings; Depth: 4m; total cost of one manhole	Nr	21.72	1,549.72	1,883.25	1,853.47	**5,286.44**	*4,627.25*
K1.5.6.11	as above; 1800mm nominal internal diameter manhole chamber rings tapering to 900mm nominal internal diameter shaft rings at 1.5m above channel invert; Depth: 4m; total cost of one manhole	Nr	15.25	1,088.09	1,314.40	1,535.53	**3,938.02**	*3,410.61*
K1.5.7	Depth: stated exceeding 4m							
K1.5.7.01	Precast concrete manholes; excavation and backfilling in natural material; in situ concrete grade 20 in 300mm base; 300/150mm branch junction channel; 150mm diameter half round bend channel; cement mortar benching (1:3); precast concrete manhole rings and cover slab, BS 5911; 150mm in situ concrete grade 20 surround to rings; 600mm diameter heavy duty cast iron access cover and frame; galvanised malleable step irons BS 1247 at 305mm centres cast into sides of chamber rings; 900mm nominal internal diameter manhole rings; Depth: 5m; total cost of one manhole	Nr	10.46	746.32	884.48	1,055.63	**2,686.43**	*2,309.16*
K1.5.7.02	as above; 1050mm nominal internal diameter manhole rings; Depth: 5m; total cost of one manhole	Nr	13.08	933.26	1,114.83	1,128.62	**3,176.71**	*2,781.45*
K1.5.7.03	as above; 1200mm nominal internal diameter manhole rings; Depth: 5m; total cost of one manhole	Nr	15.74	1,123.05	1,348.69	1,273.28	**3,745.02**	*3,360.28*
K1.5.7.04	as above; 1200mm nominal internal diameter manhole chamber rings tapering to 900mm nominal internal diameter shaft rings at 1.5m above channel invert; Depth: 5m; total cost of one manhole	Nr	11.45	816.96	971.52	1,184.47	**2,972.95**	*2,536.11*
K1.5.7.05	as above; 1350mm nominal internal diameter manhole rings; Depth: 5m; total cost of one manhole	Nr	18.42	1,314.27	1,584.32	1,356.27	**4,254.86**	*3,941.45*
K1.5.7.06	as above; 1350mm nominal internal diameter manhole chamber rings tapering to 900mm nominal internal diameter shaft rings at 1.5m above channel invert; Depth: 5m; total cost of one manhole	Nr	12.86	917.56	1,095.48	1,345.92	**3,358.96**	*3,018.75*

K1 Manholes continued...

		Unit	Labour Hours	Labour Net £	Plant Net £	Materials Net £	Unit Net £	CO_2 Kg
K1.5	**Precast concrete**							
K1.5.7	Depth: stated exceeding 4m							
K1.5.7.07	as previous item; 1500mm nominal internal diameter manhole rings; Depth: 5m; total cost of one manhole	Nr	21.10	1,505.48	1,819.94	1,709.07	**5,034.49**	*4,534.73*
K1.5.7.08	as above; 1500mm nominal internal diameter manhole chamber rings tapering to 900mm nominal internal diameter shaft rings at 1.5m above channel invert; Depth: 5m; total cost of one manhole	Nr	14.23	1,015.31	1,215.93	1,482.93	**3,714.17**	*3,283.66*
K1.5.7.09	as above; 1800mm nominal internal diameter manhole rings; Depth: 5m; total cost of one manhole	Nr	26.52	1,892.20	2,296.47	2,148.17	**6,336.84**	*5,566.70*
K1.5.7.10	as above; 1800mm nominal internal diameter manhole chamber rings tapering to 900mm nominal internal diameter shaft rings at 1.5m above channel invert; Depth: 5m; total cost of one manhole	Nr	17.01	1,213.66	1,460.35	1,648.51	**4,322.52**	*3,747.78*

K3 Gullies

		Unit	Labour Hours	Labour Net £	Plant Net £	Materials Net £	Unit Net £	CO_2 Kg
K3.1	**Clay**							
K3.1.1	Vitrified clay road gully; concrete grade 20 surround 150mm thick; 3 courses class 'B' engineering brick in cement mortar (1:3); 400 x 349mm cast iron grating and frame; BS EN 124, grade 'A' bedded in cement mortar (1:3)							
K3.1.1.01	450mm diameter x 900mm deep	Nr	2.03	85.48	64.55	296.58	**446.61**	*350.35*
K3.6	**Precast concrete trapped**							
K3.6.1	Precast concrete gully, BS 5911; 150mm trapped outlet; rodding eye with stopper and galvanised chain; concrete grade 20 surround 150mm thick; 3 courses class 'B' engineering brick in cement mortar (1:3); 400 x 349mm cast iron grating and frame, BS EN 124, grade 'A' bedded in cement mortar (1:3)							
K3.6.1.01	375mm diameter x 900mm deep	Nr	1.68	70.74	53.42	178.53	**302.69**	*372.23*
K3.7	**Plastics**							
K3.7.1	Polypropylene road gully; concrete grade 20 surround 150mm thick; 3 courses class 'B' engineering bricks in cement mortar (1:3); 502 x 349mm cast iron grating and frame, BS EN 124, grade 'A' bedded in cement mortar (1:3)							
K3.7.1.01	500mm diameter x 900mm deep	Nr	2.25	94.75	71.55	216.01	**382.31**	*402.02*

K4 French Drains, Rubble Drains, Ditches and Trenches

Note(s): Items for Filling of French and rubble drains are exclusive of disposal of excavated material which is included in class 'I': Pipes.

		Unit	Labour Hours	Labour Net £	Plant Net £	Materials Net £	Unit Net £	CO_2 Kg
K4.1	**Filling french and rubble drains with graded material**							
K4.1.1	14mm limestone aggregate fill							
K4.1.1.01	Generally	m^3	0.18	12.42	7.60	20.38	**40.40**	*10.66*

K4 French Drains, Rubble Drains, Ditches and Trenches continued...

		Unit	Labour Hours	Labour Net £	Plant Net £	Materials Net £	Unit Net £	CO_2 Kg
K4.2	**Filling french and rubble drains with rubble**							
K4.2.1	Broken brick fill							
K4.2.1.01	Generally	m^3	0.20	13.80	8.44	11.75	33.99	*285.34*
K4.3	**Trenches for unpiped rubble drains**							
K4.3.1	Cross-sectional area: not exceeding $0.25m^2$							
K4.3.1.01	Generally	m	0.03	1.73	2.11	3.40	7.24	*2.68*
K4.3.2	Cross-sectional area: 0.25 – $0.5m^2$							
K4.3.2.01	Generally	m	0.04	2.76	3.38	5.15	11.29	*4.14*
K4.3.3	Cross-sectional area: 0.5 – $0.75m^2$							
K4.3.3.01	Generally	m	0.06	4.14	5.07	8.55	17.76	*6.64*
K4.3.4	Cross-sectional area: 0.75 – $1m^2$							
K4.3.4.01	Generally	m	0.09	5.87	7.18	11.96	25.01	*9.33*
K4.3.5	Cross-sectional area: 1 – $1.5m^2$							
K4.3.5.01	Generally	m	0.11	7.25	8.87	17.01	33.13	*12.67*
K4.3.6	Cross-sectional area: 1.5 – $2m^2$							
K4.3.6.01	Generally	m	0.13	8.63	10.56	23.81	43.00	*16.92*
K4.3.7	Cross-sectional area: 2 – $3m^2$							
K4.3.7.01	Generally	m	0.19	13.11	16.04	34.02	63.17	*24.60*
K4.3.8	Cross-sectional area: exceeding $3m^2$							
K4.3.8.01	Generally;cross-sectional area: $5m^2$	m	0.34	23.12	28.29	68.04	119.45	*47.51*
K4.4	**Rectangular section ditches: unlined**							
K4.4.1	Cross-sectional area: not exceeding $0.25m^2$							
K4.4.1.01	Generally	m	0.03	1.86	2.32	3.40	7.58	*2.78*
K4.4.2	Cross-sectional area: 0.25 – $0.5m^2$							
K4.4.2.01	Generally	m	0.04	3.04	3.72	5.15	11.91	*4.29*
K4.4.3	Cross-sectional area: 0.5 – $0.75m^2$							
K4.4.3.01	Generally	m	0.07	4.55	5.57	8.55	18.67	*6.87*
K4.4.4	Cross-sectional area: 0.75 – $1m^2$							
K4.4.4.01	Generally	m	0.09	6.49	7.90	11.96	26.35	*9.64*
K4.4.5	Cross-sectional area: 1 – $1.5m^2$							
K4.4.5.01	Generally	m	0.12	8.01	9.75	17.01	34.77	*13.06*
K4.4.6	Cross-sectional area: 1.5 – $2m^2$							
K4.4.6.01	Generally	m	0.14	9.52	11.61	23.81	44.94	*17.39*
K4.4.7	Cross-sectional area: 2 – $3m^2$							
K4.4.7.01	Generally	m	0.21	14.42	17.65	34.02	66.09	*25.31*
K4.4.8	Cross-sectional area: exceeding $3m^2$							
K4.4.8.01	Generally;cross-sectional area: $5m^2$	m	0.37	25.40	31.12	68.04	124.56	*48.77*
K4.5	**Rectangular section ditches: lined**							
K4.5.1	Cross-sectional area: not exceeding $0.25m^2$							
K4.5.1.01	100mm thick weak mix concrete grade 15, 20mm aggregate; Generally	m	0.06	3.80	4.20	15.06	23.06	*50.07*

K4 French Drains, Rubble Drains, Ditches and Trenches continued...

		Unit	Labour Hours	Labour Net £	Plant Net £	Materials Net £	Unit Net £	*CO_2 Kg*
K4.5	**Rectangular section ditches: lined**							
K4.5.2	Cross-sectional area: 0.25 – 0.5m²							
K4.5.2.01	100mm thick weak mix concrete grade 15, 20mm aggregate; Generally	m	0.09	6.07	6.72	19.91	**32.70**	*64.36*
K4.5.3	Cross-sectional area: 0.5 – 0.75m²							
K4.5.3.01	100mm thick weak mix concrete grade 15, 20mm aggregate; Generally	m	0.13	9.11	10.09	27.20	**46.40**	*82.92*
K4.5.4	Cross-sectional area: 0.75 – 1m²							
K4.5.4.01	100mm thick weak mix concrete grade 15, 20mm aggregate; Generally	m	0.19	12.90	14.29	33.71	**60.90**	*98.67*
K4.5.5	Cross-sectional area: 1 – 1.5m²							
K4.5.5.01	100mm thick weak mix concrete grade 15, 20mm aggregate; Generally	m	0.23	15.94	17.65	43.43	**77.02**	*121.20*
K4.5.6	Cross-sectional area: 1.5 – 2m²							
K4.5.6.01	100mm thick weak mix concrete grade 15, 20mm aggregate; Generally	m	0.28	18.98	21.02	54.89	**94.89**	*144.63*
K4.5.7	Cross-sectional area: 2 – 3m²							
K4.5.7.01	100mm thick weak mix concrete grade 15, 20mm aggregate; Generally	m	0.42	28.85	31.94	70.54	**131.33**	*175.67*
K4.5.8	Cross-sectional area: exceeding 3m²							
K4.5.8.01	100mm thick weak mix concrete grade 15, 20mm aggregate; Generally	m	0.74	50.86	56.32	120.10	**227.28**	*264.36*
K4.6	**Vee section ditches: unlined**							
K4.6.1	Cross-sectional area: not exceeding 0.25m²							
K4.6.1.01	Generally	m	0.03	2.07	4.59	3.40	**10.06**	*3.40*
K4.6.2	Cross-sectional area: 0.25 – 0.5m²							
K4.6.2.01	Generally	m	0.05	3.31	7.34	5.15	**15.80**	*5.30*
K4.6.3	Cross-sectional area: 0.5 – 0.75m²							
K4.6.3.01	Generally	m	0.07	4.97	11.00	8.55	**24.52**	*8.37*
K4.6.4	Cross-sectional area: 0.75 – 1m²							
K4.6.4.01	Generally	m	0.10	7.04	15.59	11.96	**34.59**	*11.77*
K4.6.5	Cross-sectional area: 1 – 1.5m²							
K4.6.5.01	Generally	m	0.13	8.70	19.26	17.01	**44.97**	*15.70*
K4.6.6	Cross-sectional area: 1.5 – 2m²							
K4.6.6.01	Generally	m	0.15	10.35	22.93	23.81	**57.09**	*20.52*
K4.6.7	Cross-sectional area: 2 – 3m²							
K4.6.7.01	Generally	m	0.23	15.73	34.85	34.02	**84.60**	*30.07*
K4.6.8	Cross-sectional area: exceeding 3m²							
K4.6.8.01	Generally	m	0.40	27.74	61.44	68.04	**157.22**	*57.17*

K4 French Drains, Rubble Drains, Ditches and Trenches continued...

		Unit	Labour Hours	Labour Net £	Plant Net £	Materials Net £	Unit Net £	CO_2 Kg
K4.7	**Vee section ditches: lined**							
K4.7.1	Cross-sectional area: not exceeding 0.25m²							
K4.7.1.01	100mm thick weak mix concrete grade 15, 20mm aggregate; Generally	m	0.06	4.14	4.59	15.06	**23.79**	*50.20*
K4.7.2	Cross-sectional area: 0.25 – 0.5m²							
K4.7.2.01	100mm thick weak mix concrete grade 15, 20mm aggregate; Generally	m	0.10	6.62	7.34	19.91	**33.87**	*64.58*
K4.7.3	Cross-sectional area: 0.5 – 0.75m²							
K4.7.3.01	100mm thick weak mix concrete grade 15, 20mm aggregate; Generally	m	0.14	9.94	11.00	27.20	**48.14**	*83.25*
K4.7.4	Cross-sectional area: 0.75 – 1m²							
K4.7.4.01	100mm thick weak mix concrete grade 15, 20mm aggregate; Generally	m	0.20	14.08	15.59	33.71	**63.38**	*99.13*
K4.7.5	Cross-sectional area: 1 – 1.5m²							
K4.7.5.01	100mm thick weak mix concrete grade 15, 20mm aggregate; Generally	m	0.25	17.39	19.26	43.43	**80.08**	*121.78*
K4.7.6	Cross-sectional area: 1.5 – 2m²							
K4.7.6.01	100mm thick weak mix concrete grade 15, 20mm aggregate; Generally	m	0.30	20.70	22.93	54.89	**98.52**	*145.32*
K4.7.7	Cross-sectional area: 2 – 3m²							
K4.7.7.01	100mm thick weak mix concrete grade 15, 20mm aggregate; Generally	m	0.46	31.47	34.85	70.54	**136.86**	*176.71*
K4.7.8	Cross-sectional area: exceeding 3m²							
K4.7.8.01	100mm thick weak mix concrete grade 15, 20mm aggregate; Generally	m	0.80	55.48	61.44	120.10	**237.02**	*266.21*
K4.8	**Trenches for pipes or cables not to be laid by the contractor**							
K4.8.1	Cross-sectional area: not exceeding 0.25m²							
K4.8.1.01	100mm thick weak mix concrete grade 15, 20mm aggregate; Generally	m	0.03	2.07	4.59	3.40	**10.06**	*3.40*
K4.8.2	Cross-sectional area: 0.25 – 0.5m²							
K4.8.2.01	100mm thick weak mix concrete grade 15, 20mm aggregate; Generally	m	0.05	3.31	7.34	5.15	**15.80**	*5.30*
K4.8.3	Cross-sectional area: 0.5 – 0.75m²							
K4.8.3.01	100mm thick weak mix concrete grade 15, 20mm aggregate; Generally	m	0.07	4.97	11.00	8.55	**24.52**	*8.37*
K4.8.4	Cross-sectional area: 0.75 – 1m²							
K4.8.4.01	100mm thick weak mix concrete grade 15, 20mm aggregate; Generally	m	0.10	7.04	15.59	11.96	**34.59**	*11.77*

K4 French Drains, Rubble Drains, Ditches and Trenches continued...

		Unit	Labour Hours	Labour Net £	Plant Net £	Materials Net £	Unit Net £	CO_2 Kg
K4.8	**Trenches for pipes or cables not to be laid by the contractor**							
K4.8.5	Cross-sectional area: 1 – 1.5m²							
K4.8.5.01	100mm thick weak mix concrete grade 15, 20mm aggregate; Generally	m	0.13	8.70	19.26	17.01	**44.97**	*15.70*
K4.8.6	Cross-sectional area: 1.5 – 2m²							
K4.8.6.01	100mm thick weak mix concrete grade 15, 20mm aggregate; Generally	m	0.15	10.35	22.93	23.81	**57.09**	*20.52*
K4.8.7	Cross-sectional area: 2 – 3m²							
K4.8.7.01	100mm thick weak mix concrete grade 15, 20mm aggregate; Generally	m	0.23	15.73	34.85	34.02	**84.60**	*30.07*
K4.8.8	Cross-sectional area: exceeding 3m²							
K4.8.8.01	100mm thick weak mix concrete grade 15, 20mm aggregate; Generally	m	0.40	27.74	61.44	68.04	**157.22**	*57.17*

K5 Dust and Metal Culverts

		Unit	Labour Hours	Labour Net £	Plant Net £	Materials Net £	Unit Net £	CO_2 Kg
K5.1	**Cable ducts: 1 way**							
K5.1.2	In trenches, depth: not exceeding 1.5m							
K5.1.2.01	clay ducts, BS 65; 100mm diameter	m	0.08	5.52	3.38	7.84	**16.74**	*2.13*
K5.1.2.02	as above; 150mm diameter	m	0.09	6.21	3.80	17.11	**27.12**	*2.95*
K5.1.3	In trenches, depth: 1.5 – 2m							
K5.1.3.01	clay ducts, BS 65; 100mm diameter	m	0.12	8.28	5.07	7.84	**21.19**	*2.87*
K5.1.3.02	as above; 150mm diameter	m	0.14	9.66	5.91	17.11	**32.68**	*3.88*
K5.1.4	In trenches, depth: 2 – 2.5m							
K5.1.4.01	clay ducts, BS 65; 100mm diameter	m	0.18	12.42	7.60	7.84	**27.86**	*4.00*
K5.1.4.02	as above; 150mm diameter	m	0.20	13.80	8.44	17.11	**39.35**	*5.00*
K5.1.5	In trenches, depth: 2.5 – 3m							
K5.1.5.01	clay ducts, BS 65; 100mm diameter	m	0.25	17.25	10.56	7.84	**35.65**	*5.30*
K5.1.5.02	as above; 150mm diameter	m	0.28	19.32	11.82	17.11	**48.25**	*6.49*
K5.1.6	In trenches, depth: 3 – 3.5m							
K5.1.6.01	clay ducts, BS 65; 100mm diameter	m	0.33	22.77	13.93	7.84	**44.54**	*6.80*
K5.1.6.02	as above; 150mm diameter	m	0.37	25.53	15.62	17.11	**58.26**	*8.18*
K5.1.7	In trenches, depth: 3.5 – 4m							
K5.1.7.01	clay ducts, BS 65; 100mm diameter	m	0.42	28.98	17.73	7.84	**54.55**	*8.48*
K5.1.7.02	as above; 150mm diameter	m	0.47	32.43	19.84	17.11	**69.38**	*10.04*

K5 Dust and Metal Culverts continued...

		Unit	Labour Hours	Labour Net £	Plant Net £	Materials Net £	Unit Net £	*CO_2 Kg*
K5.5	**Sectional corrugated metal culverts, nominal internal diameter: not exceeding 0.5m**							
K5.5.1	Not in trenches							
K5.5.1.01	Sections corrugated, galvanised and bitumen coated steel culverts; 1.5mm thickness; 3m length jointed with coupling bands; Nominal internal diameter 0.5m	m	0.08	3.37	1.27	-	4.64	*0.47*
K5.5.2	In trenches, depth: not exceeding 1.5m							
K5.5.2.01	Sections corrugated, galvanised and bitumen coated steel culverts; 1.5mm thickness; 3m length jointed with coupling bands; Nominal internal diameter 0.5m	m	0.21	8.84	6.68	80.95	96.47	*180.87*
K5.5.3	In trenches, depth: 1.5 – 2m							
K5.5.3.01	Sections corrugated, galvanised and bitumen coated steel culverts; 1.5mm thickness; 3m length jointed with coupling bands; Nominal internal diameter 0.5m	m	0.25	10.53	7.95	80.95	99.43	*181.33*
K5.5.4	In trenches, depth: 2 – 2.5m							
K5.5.4.01	Sections corrugated, galvanised and bitumen coated steel culverts; 1.5mm thickness; 3m length jointed with coupling bands; Nominal internal diameter 0.5m	m	0.30	12.63	9.54	80.95	103.12	*181.92*
K5.5.5	In trenches, depth: 2.5 – 3m							
K5.5.5.01	Sections corrugated, galvanised and bitumen coated steel culverts; 1.5mm thickness; 3m length jointed with coupling bands; Nominal internal diameter 0.5m	m	0.36	15.16	11.45	80.95	107.56	*182.61*
K5.5.6	In trenches, depth: 3 – 3.5m							
K5.5.6.01	Sections corrugated, galvanised and bitumen coated steel culverts; 1.5mm thickness; 3m length jointed with coupling bands; Nominal internal diameter 0.5m	m	0.44	18.53	13.99	80.95	113.47	*183.54*
K5.5.7	In trenches, depth: 3.5 – 4m							
K5.5.7.01	Sections corrugated, galvanised and bitumen coated steel culverts; 1.5mm thickness; 3m length jointed with coupling bands; Nominal internal diameter 0.5m	m	0.54	22.74	17.17	80.95	120.86	*184.71*
K5.6	**Sectional corrugated metal culverts, nominal internal diameter: 0.5 - 1m**							
K5.6.1	Not in trenches							
K5.6.1.01	Sections corrugated, galvanised and bitumen coated steel culverts; 1.5mm thickness; 3m length jointed with coupling bands; Nominal internal diameter 1.0m	m	0.12	5.05	1.91	161.89	168.85	*357.55*

K5 Dust and Metal Culverts continued...

		Unit	Labour Hours	Labour Net £	Plant Net £	Materials Net £	Unit Net £	CO_2 Kg
K5.6	**Sectional corrugated metal culverts, nominal internal diameter: 0.5 - 1m**							
K5.6.2	In trenches, depth: not exceeding 1.5m							
K5.6.2.01	Sections corrugated, galvanised and bitumen coated steel culverts; 1.5mm thickness; 3m length jointed with coupling bands; Nominal internal diameter 1.0m	m	0.25	10.53	7.95	161.89	**180.37**	*359.76*
K5.6.3	In trenches, depth: 1.5 – 2m							
K5.6.3.01	Sections corrugated, galvanised and bitumen coated steel culverts; 1.5mm thickness; 3m length jointed with coupling bands; Nominal internal diameter 1.0m	m	0.32	13.48	10.18	161.89	**185.55**	*360.58*
K5.6.4	In trenches, depth: 2 – 2.5m							
K5.6.4.01	Sections corrugated, galvanised and bitumen coated steel culverts; 1.5mm thickness; 3m length jointed with coupling bands; Nominal internal diameter 1.0m	m	0.41	17.27	13.04	161.89	**192.20**	*361.62*
K5.6.5	In trenches, depth: 2.5 – 3m							
K5.6.5.01	Sections corrugated, galvanised and bitumen coated steel culverts; 1.5mm thickness; 3m length jointed with coupling bands; Nominal internal diameter 1.0m	m	0.51	21.48	16.22	133.30	**171.00**	*345.95*
K5.6.6	In trenches, depth: 3 – 3.5m							
K5.6.6.01	Sections corrugated, galvanised and bitumen coated steel culverts; 1.5mm thickness; 3m length jointed with coupling bands; Nominal internal diameter 1.0m	m	0.62	26.11	19.72	161.89	**207.72**	*364.06*
K5.6.7	In trenches, depth: 3.5 – 4m							
K5.6.7.01	Sections corrugated, galvanised and bitumen coated steel culverts; 1.5mm thickness; 3m length jointed with coupling bands; Nominal internal diameter 1.0m	m	0.74	31.16	23.53	161.89	**216.58**	*365.46*
K5.7	**Sectional corrugated metal culverts, nominal internal diameter: 1 - 1.5m**							
K5.7.1	Not in trenches							
K5.7.1.01	Sections corrugated, galvanised and bitumen coated steel culverts; 1.5mm thickness; 3m length jointed with coupling bands; Nominal internal diameter 1.0m	m	0.20	8.42	3.18	300.28	**311.88**	*536.45*
K5.7.2	In trenches, depth: not exceeding 1.5m							
K5.7.2.01	Sections corrugated, galvanised and bitumen coated steel culverts; 1.5mm thickness; 3m length jointed with coupling bands; Nominal internal diameter 1.0m	m	0.49	20.63	15.58	300.28	**336.49**	*540.98*

K5 Dust and Metal Culverts continued...

		Unit	Labour Hours	Labour Net £	Plant Net £	Materials Net £	Unit Net £	CO_2 Kg
K5.7	**Sectional corrugated metal culverts, nominal internal diameter: 1 - 1.5m**							
K5.7.3 K5.7.3.01	In trenches, depth: 1.5 – 2m Sections corrugated, galvanised and bitumen coated steel culverts; 1.5mm thickness; 3m length jointed with coupling bands; Nominal internal diameter 1.0m	m	0.41	17.27	13.04	300.28	**330.59**	*540.05*
K5.7.4 K5.7.4.01	In trenches, depth: 2 – 2.5m Sections corrugated, galvanised and bitumen coated steel culverts; 1.5mm thickness; 3m length jointed with coupling bands; Nominal internal diameter 1.0m	m	0.63	26.53	20.03	300.28	**346.84**	*542.61*
K5.7.5 K5.7.5.01	In trenches, depth: 2.5 – 3m Sections corrugated, galvanised and bitumen coated steel culverts; 1.5mm thickness; 3m length jointed with coupling bands; Nominal internal diameter 1.0m	m	0.77	32.42	24.49	300.28	**357.19**	*544.24*
K5.7.6 K5.7.6.01	In trenches, depth: 3 – 3.5m Sections corrugated, galvanised and bitumen coated steel culverts; 1.5mm thickness; 3m length jointed with coupling bands; Nominal internal diameter 1.0m	m	0.91	38.32	28.94	300.28	**367.54**	*545.86*
K5.7.7 K5.7.7.01	In trenches, depth: 3.5 – 4m Sections corrugated, galvanised and bitumen coated steel culverts; 1.5mm thickness; 3m length jointed with coupling bands; Nominal internal diameter 1.0m	m	1.05	44.22	33.39	300.28	**377.89**	*547.49*
K5.8	**Sectional corrugated metal culverts, nominal internal diameter: exceeding 1.5m**							
K5.8.1 K5.8.1.01	Not in trenches Sections corrugated, galvanised and bitumen coated steel culverts; 1.5mm thickness; 3m length jointed with coupling bands; Nominal internal diameter 2.0m	m	0.27	11.37	4.29	430.84	**446.50**	*715.28*
K5.8.2 K5.8.2.01	In trenches, depth: not exceeding 1.5m Sections corrugated, galvanised and bitumen coated steel culverts; 1.5mm thickness; 3m length jointed with coupling bands; Nominal internal diameter 2.0m	m	0.36	15.16	11.45	430.84	**457.45**	*717.90*
K5.8.3 K5.8.3.01	In trenches, depth: 1.5 – 2m Sections corrugated, galvanised and bitumen coated steel culverts; 1.5mm thickness; 3m length jointed with coupling bands; Nominal internal diameter 2.0m	m	0.47	19.79	14.95	430.84	**465.58**	*719.18*

K5 Dust and Metal Culverts continued...

		Unit	Labour Hours	Labour Net £	Plant Net £	Materials Net £	Unit Net £	*CO_2 Kg*
K5.8	**Sectional corrugated metal culverts, nominal internal diameter: exceeding 1.5m**							
K5.8.4	In trenches, depth: 2 – 2.5m							
K5.8.4.01	Sections corrugated, galvanised and bitumen coated steel culverts; 1.5mm thickness; 3m length jointed with coupling bands; Nominal internal diameter 2.0m	m	0.62	26.11	19.72	430.84	**476.67**	*720.92*
K5.8.5	In trenches, depth: 2.5 – 3m							
K5.8.5.01	Sections corrugated, galvanised and bitumen coated steel culverts; 1.5mm thickness; 3m length jointed with coupling bands; Nominal internal diameter 2.0m	m	0.79	33.27	25.12	430.84	**489.23**	*722.90*
K5.8.6	In trenches, depth: 3 – 3.5m							
K5.8.6.01	Sections corrugated, galvanised and bitumen coated steel culverts; 1.5mm thickness; 3m length jointed with coupling bands; Nominal internal diameter 2.0m	m	0.95	40.00	30.21	430.84	**501.05**	*724.76*
K5.8.7	In trenches, depth: 3.5 – 4m							
K5.8.7.01	Sections corrugated, galvanised and bitumen coated steel culverts; 1.5mm thickness; 3m length jointed with coupling bands; Nominal internal diameter 2.0m	m	1.12	47.16	35.62	430.84	**513.62**	*726.73*

K7 Reinstatement

Note(s): Reinstatement of Roads and Footpaths - There are numerous specifications used in road construction and the following items are provided as a guide only. Many highway authorities do not permit contractors to carry out permanent reinstatement of trenches; they carry this out themselves or use their own contractors and charge the cost to Permanent reinstatement. The rates quoted should be used with care as they are for a median situation - continuous trench work in urban areas will be cheaper because of the greater lengths involved; crossings of narrow country roads will be dearer because of the mobilisation and set up costs for a short measured length.

Reinstatement of land - Because of the very wide range of types of terrain likely to be encountered in the construction of a pipline it is not possible to give examples of cost. In addition, the cost will be dependant on the time of year and construction methods used. The following, however, are the factors to be considered:

1) recovery of all surplus construction materials, consumables and rubbish

2) restoration of original ground levels and profiles (ridge and furrow fields can prove particularly expensive)

3) cleaning, recovery of any bridging or flushing pipes, and the restoration of banks to field ditches and other minor water courses

4) removal of any temporary fences and gates (if not measured elsewhere)

5) liaison with farmers and landowners

		Unit	Labour Hours	Labour Net £	Plant Net £	Materials Net £	Unit Net £	CO_2 Kg
K7.1	**Breaking up and temporary reinstatement of roads**							
K7.1.1	Pipe bore: not exceeding 300mm							
K7.1.1.01	100mm macadam base course; 50mm bituminous macadam wearing course; temporary reinstatement with 150mm lean mix; 40mm bituminous macadam base course (20mm aggregate) and 10mm bituminous macadam wearing course (10mm aggregate); pipe nominal bore; 300mm	m	0.62	26.11	9.72	19.82	**55.65**	*61.53*
K7.1.1.02	200mm granular sub-base; 100mm bituminous macadam basecourse; 25mm wearing course; temporary reinstatement with 200mm lean mix; 85mm bituminous macadam base course (40mm aggregate) and 15mm bituminous macadam wearing course (10mm aggregate); pipe nominal nominal bore; 300mm	m	0.91	38.32	14.26	32.66	**85.24**	*93.88*
K7.1.1.03	100mm granular sub-base; 150mm concrete pavement; temporary reinstatement with 150mm lean mix; 150mm concrete grade 20; pipe nominal bore; 300mm	m	0.81	34.11	12.69	16.41	**63.21**	*72.76*
K7.1.1.04	150mm granular sub-base; 150mm reinforced concrete pavement; temporary reinstatement with 200mm lean mix; 150mm concrete grade 20; 1 layer mesh reinforcement (ref A252); pipe nominal bore; 300mm	m	0.96	40.43	15.04	19.56	**75.03**	*86.87*

K7 Reinstatement continued...

		Unit	Labour Hours	Labour Net £	Plant Net £	Materials Net £	Unit Net £	CO_2 Kg
K7.1	**Breaking up and temporary reinstatement of roads**							
K7.1.2	Pipe bore: 300 - 900mm							
K7.1.2.01	100mm macadam base course; 50mm bituminous macadam wearing course; temporary reinstatement with 150mm lean mix; 40mm bituminous macadam base course (20mm aggregate) and 10mm bituminous macadam wearing course (10mm aggregate); pipe nominal bore; 600mm	m	0.71	29.90	11.13	25.95	**66.98**	*80.76*
K7.1.2.02	100mm macadam base course; 50mm bituminous macadam wearing course; temporary reinstatement with 150mm lean mix; 40mm bituminous macadam base course (20mm aggregate) and 10mm bituminous macadam wearing course (10mm aggregate); pipe nominal bore; 900mm	m	0.83	34.95	13.01	32.08	**80.04**	*100.38*
K7.1.2.03	200mm granular sub-base; 100mm bituminous macadam basecourse; 25mm wearing course; temporary reinstatement with 200mm lean mix; 85mm bituminous macadam base course (40mm aggregate) and 15mm bituminous macadam wearing course (10mm aggregate); pipe nominal nominal bore; 600mm	m	1.03	43.37	16.14	45.34	**104.85**	*129.54*
K7.1.2.04	200mm granular sub-base; 100mm bituminous macadam basecourse; 25mm wearing course; temporary reinstatement with 200mm lean mix; 85mm bituminous macadam base course (40mm aggregate) and 15mm bituminous macadam wearing course (10mm aggregate); pipe nominal nominal bore; 900mm	m	1.24	52.22	19.43	56.60	**128.25**	*163.55*
K7.1.2.05	100mm granular sub-base; 150mm concrete pavement; temporary reinstatement with 150mm lean mix; 150mm concrete grade 20; pipe nominal bore; 600mm	m	0.94	39.58	14.73	22.98	**77.29**	*99.39*
K7.1.2.06	100mm granular sub-base; 150mm concrete pavement; temporary reinstatement with 150mm lean mix; 150mm concrete grade 20; pipe nominal bore; 900mm	m	1.14	48.01	17.86	29.54	**95.41**	*126.91*

K7 Reinstatement continued...

		Unit	Labour Hours	Labour Net £	Plant Net £	Materials Net £	Unit Net £	CO_2 Kg
K7.1	**Breaking up and temporary reinstatement of roads**							
K7.1.2	Pipe bore: 300 - 900mm							
K7.1.2.07	150mm granular sub-base; 150mm reinforced concrete pavement; temporary reinstatement with 200mm lean mix; 150mm concrete grade 20; 1 layer mesh reinforcement (ref A252); pipe nominal bore; 600mm	m	1.12	47.16	17.55	27.70	**92.41**	*120.12*
K7.1.2.08	150mm granular sub-base; 150mm reinforced concrete pavement; temporary reinstatement with 200mm lean mix; 150mm concrete grade 20; 1 layer mesh reinforcement (ref A252); pipe nominal bore; 900mm	m	1.36	57.27	21.31	35.85	**114.43**	*154.39*
K7.1.3	Pipe bore: 900 - 1800mm							
K7.1.3.01	100mm macadam base course; 50mm bituminous macadam wearing course; temporary reinstatement with 150mm lean mix; 40mm bituminous macadam base course (20mm aggregate) and 10mm bituminous macadam wearing course (10mm aggregate); pipe nominal bore; 1200mm	m	0.95	40.00	14.89	38.99	**93.88**	*123.12*
K7.1.3.02	200mm granular sub-base; 100mm bituminous macadam basecourse; 25mm wearing course; temporary reinstatement with 200mm lean mix; 85mm bituminous macadam base course (40mm aggregate) and 15mm bituminous macadam wearing course (10mm aggregate); pipe nominal bore; 1200mm	m	1.45	61.06	22.72	68.51	**152.29**	*198.95*
K7.1.3.03	100mm granular sub-base; 150mm concrete pavement; temporary reinstatement with 150mm lean mix; 150mm concrete grade 20; pipe nominal bore; 1200mm	m	1.33	56.01	20.84	37.75	**114.60**	*160.54*
K7.1.3.04	150mm granular sub-base; 150mm reinforced concrete pavement; temporary reinstatement with 200mm lean mix; 150mm concrete grade 20; 1 layer mesh reinforcement (ref A252); pipe nominal bore; 1200mm	m	1.60	67.38	25.07	44.84	**137.29**	*191.78*

K7 Reinstatement continued...

		Unit	Labour Hours	Labour Net £	Plant Net £	Materials Net £	Unit Net £	CO_2 Kg
K7.2	**Breaking up and temporary reinstatement of footpaths**							
K7.2.1	Pipe bore: not exceeding 300mm							
K7.2.1.01	100mm granular base; 50mm wearing course; temporary reinstatement with 50mm bituminous macadam; pipe nominal bore; 300mm	m	0.52	21.90	8.15	10.07	40.12	*24.85*
K7.2.1.02	100mm granular base; 50mm precast concrete paving slabs; pipe nominal bore; 300mm	m	0.52	21.90	-	-	21.90	-
K7.2.2	Pipe bore: 300 - 900mm							
K7.2.2.01	100mm granular base; 50mm wearing course; temporary reinstatement with 50mm bituminous macadam; pipe nominal bore; 600mm	m	0.61	25.69	9.56	13.95	49.20	*33.00*
K7.2.2.02	as above; pipe nominal bore; 900mm	m	0.72	30.32	11.28	17.82	59.42	*41.41*
K7.2.2.03	100mm granular base; 50mm precast concrete paving slabs; pipe nominal bore; 600mm	m	0.61	25.69	9.56	-	35.25	*7.80*
K7.2.2.04	as above; pipe nominal bore; 900mm	m	0.72	30.32	11.28	-	41.60	*9.21*
K7.2.3	Pipe bore: 900 - 1800mm							
K7.2.3.01	100mm granular base; 50mm wearing course; temporary reinstatement with 50mm bituminous macadam; pipe nominal bore; 1200mm	m	0.84	35.37	13.16	22.47	71.00	*51.35*
K7.2.3.02	100mm granular base; 50mm precast concrete paving slabs; pipe nominal bore; 1200mm	m	0.84	35.37	13.16	-	48.53	*10.75*
K7.6	**Strip topsoil from easement and reinstate**							
K7.6.1	Storing and protecting for re-use (225mm depth)							
K7.6.1.01	Width: 5m	m	0.02	0.26	0.96	-	1.22	*0.50*
K7.6.1.02	Width: 10m	m	0.04	0.49	1.78	-	2.27	*0.93*

K8 Other Pipework Ancillaries

		Unit	Labour Hours	Labour Net £	Plant Net £	Materials Net £	Unit Net £	CO_2 Kg
K8.2	**Marker posts**							
K8.2.1	Fix only							
K8.2.1.01	Precast concrete marker post including excavation and setting base in concrete	Nr	1.25	52.64	-	-	52.64	-
K8.5	**Connection to existing manholes and other chambers**							
K8.5.1	Pipe bore: not exceeding 200mm							
K8.5.1.01	Building in ends of pipes to existing 215mm brick manhole in engineering class 'B' bricks and make good with cement mortar (1:3); 2m below ground level; pipe nominal bore; 150mm	Nr	2.50	73.88	-	2.99	76.87	*17.57*
K8.5.1.02	as above; 4m below ground level; pipe nominal bore; 150mm	Nr	3.00	88.65	-	2.99	91.64	*17.57*

K8 Other Pipework Ancillaries continued...

		Unit	Labour Hours	Labour Net £	Plant Net £	Materials Net £	Unit Net £	CO_2 Kg
K8.5	**Connection to existing manholes and other chambers**							
K8.5.1	Pipe bore: not exceeding 200mm							
K8.5.1.03	Building in ends of pipes to existing 675mm precast concrete manhole chamber and make good with cement mortar (1:3); 2m below ground level; pipe nominal bore; 150mm	Nr	1.00	29.55	-	2.99	**32.54**	*17.57*
K8.5.1.04	as above; 4m below ground level; pipe nominal bore; 150mm	Nr	1.20	35.46	-	2.99	**38.45**	*17.57*
K8.5.2	Pipe bore: 200 - 300mm							
K8.5.2.01	Building in ends of pipes to existing 215mm brick manhole in engineering class 'B' bricks and make good with cement mortar (1:3); 2m below ground level; pipe nominal bore; 300mm	Nr	4.00	118.20	-	3.58	**121.78**	*21.09*
K8.5.2.02	as above; 4m below ground level; pipe nominal bore; 300mm	Nr	4.80	141.84	-	3.58	**145.42**	*21.09*
K8.5.2.03	Building in ends of pipes to existing 675mm precast concrete manhole chamber and make good with cement mortar (1:3); 2m below ground level; pipe nominal bore; 300mm	Nr	2.00	59.10	-	3.58	**62.68**	*21.09*
K8.5.2.04	as above; 4m below ground level; pipe nominal bore; 300mm	Nr	2.40	70.92	-	3.58	**74.50**	*21.09*
K8.5.3	Pipe bore: 300 - 600mm							
K8.5.3.01	Building in ends of pipes to existing 215mm brick manhole in engineering class 'B' bricks and make good with cement mortar (1:3); 2m below ground level; pipe nominal bore; 450mm	Nr	6.50	192.08	-	4.18	**196.26**	*24.60*
K8.5.3.02	as above; 2m below ground level; pipe nominal bore; 600mm	Nr	9.50	280.73	-	5.97	**286.70**	*35.15*
K8.5.3.03	as above; 4m below ground level; pipe nominal bore; 450mm	Nr	7.80	230.49	-	4.18	**234.67**	*24.60*
K8.5.3.04	as above; 4m below ground level; pipe nominal bore; 600mm	Nr	11.40	336.87	-	5.97	**342.84**	*35.15*
K8.5.3.05	Building in ends of pipes to existing 675mm precast concrete manhole chamber and make good with cement mortar (1:3); 2m below ground level; pipe nominal bore; 450mm	Nr	2.75	81.26	-	4.18	**85.44**	*24.60*
K8.5.3.06	as above; 2m below ground level; pipe nominal bore; 600mm	Nr	3.50	103.43	-	5.97	**109.40**	*35.15*
K8.5.3.07	as above; 4m below ground level; pipe nominal bore; 450mm	Nr	3.30	97.52	-	4.18	**101.70**	*24.60*
K8.5.3.08	as above; 4m below ground level; pipe nominal bore; 600mm	Nr	4.20	124.11	-	5.97	**130.08**	*35.15*

K8 Other Pipework Ancillaries continued...

		Unit	Labour Hours	Labour Net £	Plant Net £	Materials Net £	**Unit Net £**	*CO_2 Kg*
K8.6	**Connection to existing pipes, ducts and culverts**							
K8.6.1	Pipe bore: not excedding 200mm							
K8.6.1.01	Building new clay pipe into existing 450mm diameter clay main; including all cutting installation of saddle building in and making good upon completion; pipe nominal bore; 150mm	Nr	1.00	29.55	-	25.73	**55.28**	*5.81*
K8.6.1.02	Building in new concrete pipe into existing 750mm diameter concrete main; including all cutting, building in and making good upon completion; pipe nominal bore; 150mm	Nr	1.50	44.33	-	1.19	**45.52**	*7.03*
K8.6.2	Pipe bore: 200 - 300mm							
K8.6.2.01	Building new clay pipe into existing 450mm diameter clay main; including all cutting installation of saddle building in and making good upon completion; pipe nominal bore; 225mm	Nr	1.50	44.33	-	90.40	**134.73**	*12.01*
K8.6.2.02	as above; pipe nominal bore; 300mm	Nr	2.10	62.06	-	158.23	**220.29**	*25.04*
K8.6.2.03	Building in new concrete pipe into existing 750mm diameter concrete main; including all cutting, building in and making good upon completion; pipe nominal bore; 225mm	Nr	2.10	62.06	-	2.99	**65.05**	*17.57*
K8.6.3	Pipe bore: 300 - 600mm							
K8.6.3.01	Building in new concrete pipe into existing 750mm diameter concrete main; including all cutting, building in and making good upon completion; pipe nominal bore; 375mm	Nr	2.80	82.74	-	3.58	**86.32**	*21.09*
K8.6.3.02	as above; pipe nominal bore; 450mm	Nr	3.50	103.43	-	4.78	**108.21**	*28.12*
K8.6.3.03	as above; pipe nominal bore; 525mm	Nr	4.25	125.59	-	5.97	**131.56**	*35.15*

CLASS L:

PIPEWORK - SUPPORTS & PROTECTION, ANCILLARIES TO LAYING & EXCAVATION

Calculations used throughout Class L - Pipework - Supports & Protection, Ancillaries to Laying & Excavation

Labour

		Qty		Rate		Total
L A0184ICE	**Small bore pipes in shallow trenches Labour Gang**					
	Banksman	1	x	13.53	=	£13.53
	Ganger	1	x	16.99	=	£16.99
	Pipelayer (standard rate)	1	x	14.34	=	£14.34
	Labourer (General Operative)	5	x	12.56	=	£62.80
	Total hourly cost of gang				**=**	**£107.66**
L A0212ICE	**Breaking out rock, concrete etc. Labour Gang**					
	Labourer (General Operative)	2	x	12.56	=	£25.12
	Total hourly cost of gang				**=**	**£25.12**
L A0213ICE	**Breaking out rock, concrete etc in headings and pipe jacking**					
	Miners	2	x	39.86	=	£79.73
	Total hourly cost of gang				**=**	**£79.73**
L A0214ICE	**Placing materials in beds, haunches and surrounds Labour Gang**					
	Labourer (General Operative)	2	x	12.56	=	£25.12
	Ganger	0.5	x	16.99	=	£8.49
	Total hourly cost of gang				**=**	**£33.61**
L L0001ICE	**Pipework Jacking Labour Gang**					
	Labourer (Skill Rate 3)	2	x	14.34	=	£28.68
	Ganger	1	x	16.99	=	£16.99
	Banksman	1	x	13.53	=	£13.53
	Miners	2	x	39.86	=	£79.73
	Total hourly cost of gang				**=**	**£138.93**
L L0002ICE	**Pipework Thrust Boring Labour Gang**					
	Labourer (Skill Rate 3)	2	x	14.34	=	£28.68
	Ganger	1	x	16.99	=	£16.99
	Banksman	1	x	13.53	=	£13.53
	Miners	2	x	39.86	=	£79.73
	Fitters and Welders	1	x	16.68	=	£16.68
	Total hourly cost of gang				**=**	**£155.61**

Plant

		Qty		Rate		Total
P A1184ICE	**Small bore pipes in shallow trench Plant Gang**					
	Hydraulic Excavator - Cat 320 96kW	1	x	33.98	=	£33.98
	Pump - Godwin ET50 23m3/h 4 inches	1	x	2.74	=	£2.74
	Vibrating Plate Diesel 24kN	1	x	2.36	=	£2.36
	Trench Sheets	90	x	0.079	=	£7.15
	Acrow Props	70	x	0.079	=	£5.56
	Landrover 4WD	1	x	15.10	=	£15.10
	Total hourly cost of gang				**=**	**£66.89**
P A1192ICE	**Breaking out rock, concrete etc. Plant Gang**					
	Compressor - 250 cfm	1	x	10.81	=	£10.81
	Thor 16D / Maco SK8 Medium Duty Breaker	2	x	0.77	=	£1.54
	Total hourly cost of gang				**=**	**£12.35**
P A1194ICE	**Placing materials in bed, haunches and surrounds Plant Gang**					
	Vibrating Plate Diesel 33.5kN	1	x	2.8	=	£2.76
	Crawler Tractor / Dozer - Cat 941	0.5	x	35.36	=	£17.68
	Total hourly cost of gang				**=**	**£20.44**

Class L - Pipework - Supports & Protection, Ancillaries to Laying & Excavation

Note(s): 1) Prices for imported materials in trenches do not allow for double handling by off highway dumpers. Good access for road vehicles is assumed.

2) Price for items dealing with 'rock' are guide prices only and may vary considerably.

3) Granular material shrinkage and compaction; the conversion factor from tonne to cubic metres for granular materials allows for shrinkage, compaction and high wastage to take account of 'ragged' trenches. The conversion for sand has been calculated as follows:

tonnes per cubic metres	1.70
shrinkage and compaction 10%	0.17
wastage 15%	1.87
conversion factor for sand	2.15t per m^3

4) Prices include for spreading surplus excavated material at sides of excavation. No allowance has been made for disposal of excavated rock, concrete or the like from site.

L1 Extras to Excavation and Backfilling

		Unit	Labour Hours	Labour Net £	Plant Net £	Materials Net £	Unit Net £	CO_2 Kg
L1.1	**In pipe trenches**							
L1.1.1	Excavation of rock							
L1.1.1.01	Generally	m^3	2.00	50.24	24.70	-	**74.94**	*30.41*
L1.1.2	Excavation of mass concrete							
L1.1.2.01	Generally	m^3	2.75	69.08	33.96	-	**103.04**	*41.82*
L1.1.3	Excavation of reinforced concrete							
L1.1.3.01	Generally	m^3	3.85	96.71	47.55	-	**144.26**	*58.55*
L1.1.4	Excavation of other artificial hard material							
L1.1.4.01	Old brick foundations	m^3	1.25	31.40	15.44	-	**46.84**	*19.01*
L1.1.5	Backfilling above the Final Surface with concrete							
L1.1.5.01	Grade 15, 20mm aggregate	m^3	0.05	5.38	3.35	83.62	**92.35**	*287.32*
L1.1.6	Backfilling above the Final Surface with stated material other than concrete							
L1.1.6.01	Pea gravel	m^3	0.05	5.38	3.35	38.45	**47.18**	*9.32*
L1.1.7	Excavation of natural material below the Final Surface and backfilling with concrete							
L1.1.7.01	Grade 15, 20mm aggregate	m^3	0.12	12.92	8.03	83.62	**104.57**	*289.16*
L1.1.8	Excavation of natural material below the Final Surface and backfilling with stated material other than concrete							
L1.1.8.01	Pea gravel	m^3	0.12	12.92	8.03	38.45	**59.40**	*11.16*
L1.2	**In manholes and other chambers**							
L1.2.1	Excavation of rock							
L1.2.1.01	Generally	m^3	2.00	50.24	24.70	-	**74.94**	*30.41*
L1.2.2	Excavation of mass concrete							
L1.2.2.01	Generally	m^3	2.75	69.08	33.96	-	**103.04**	*41.82*
L1.2.3	Excavation of reinforced concrete							
L1.2.3.01	Generally	m^3	3.85	96.71	47.55	-	**144.26**	*58.55*
L1.2.4	Excavation of other artificial hard material							
L1.2.4.01	Old brick foundations	m^3	1.25	31.40	15.44	-	**46.84**	*19.01*
L1.2.5	Backfilling above the Final Surface with concrete							
L1.2.5.01	Grade 15, 20mm aggregate	m^3	0.06	6.46	4.01	83.62	**94.09**	*287.58*

L1 Extras to Excavation and Backfilling continued...

		Unit	Labour Hours	Labour Net £	Plant Net £	Materials Net £	Unit Net £	CO_2 Kg
L1.2	**In manholes and other chambers**							
L1.2.6	Backfilling above the Final Surface with stated material other than concrete							
L1.2.6.01	Pea gravel	m^3	0.06	6.46	4.01	38.45	**48.92**	*9.58*
L1.2.7	Excavation of natural material below the Final Surface and backfilling with concrete							
L1.2.7.01	Grade 15, 20mm aggregate	m^3	0.13	14.00	8.70	83.62	**106.32**	*289.42*
L1.2.8	Excavation of natural material below the Final Surface and backfilling with stated material other than concrete							
L1.2.8.01	Pea gravel	m^3	0.13	14.00	8.70	38.45	**61.15**	*11.42*
L1.3	**In headings**							
L1.3.1	Excavation of rock							
L1.3.1.01	Generally	m^3	6.00	478.38	74.10	-	**552.48**	*91.24*
L1.3.5	Backfilling above the Final Surface with concrete							
L1.3.5.01	Grade 15, 20mm aggregate	m^3	2.00	159.46	24.70	83.62	**267.78**	*316.41*
L1.3.6	Backfilling above the Final Surface with stated material other than concrete							
L1.3.6.01	Pea gravel	m^3	2.00	159.46	24.70	38.45	**222.61**	*38.41*
L1.3.7	Excavation of natural material below the Final Surface and backfilling with concrete							
L1.3.7.01	Grade 15, 20mm aggregate	m^3	4.00	318.92	49.40	83.62	**451.94**	*346.83*
L1.3.8	Excavation of natural material below the Final Surface and backfilling with stated material other than concrete							
L1.3.8.01	Pea gravel	m^3	4.00	318.92	49.40	38.45	**406.77**	*68.83*
L1.5	**In pipe jacking**							
L1.5.1	Excavation of rock							
L1.5.1.01	Generally	m^3	6.00	478.38	74.10	-	**552.48**	*91.24*
L1.5.5	Backfilling above the Final Surface with concrete							
L1.5.5.01	Grade 15, 20mm aggregate	m^3	2.00	159.46	24.70	83.62	**267.78**	*316.41*
L1.5.6	Backfilling above the Final Surface with stated material other than concrete							
L1.5.6.01	Pea gravel	m^3	2.00	159.46	24.70	38.45	**222.61**	*38.41*
L1.5.7	Excavation of natural material below the Final Surface and backfilling with concrete							
L1.5.7.01	Grade 15, 20mm aggregate	m^3	4.00	318.92	49.40	83.62	**451.94**	*346.83*
L1.5.8	Excavation of natural material below the Final Surface and backfilling with stated material other than concrete							
L1.5.8.01	Pea gravel	m^3	4.00	318.92	49.40	38.45	**406.77**	*68.83*

L2 Special Pipelaying Methods

Note(s): The following prices for guide purposes only and assume a typical bore length of 25 metres. Rates do not include allowances for:

1) Removal of top soil; locating services; cutting, welding and wrapping pipe; backfilling or reinstatement of pits; specialised water pumping, grouting or supports; or fencing around pits;

2) Mobilisation and demobilisation;

3) Working and reception pits;

4) Aborted bores due to excessively bad ground conditions will be charged at S/E cost, pit cost, intersite move cost, sleeve cost, and 2/3 of length to be bored;

5) Daywork or standing time charged at £125 per hour;

6) Trench sheets and supports left in place for more than two weeks will be charged at cost plus 15%;

7) Main contractor to allow for maintaining pits, withdrawing support and holding upon completion;

8) As ground conditions are a major contributor to prices it is recommended that advice on prices is sought from a specialist sub-contractor.

		Unit	Labour Hours	Labour Net £	Plant Net £	Materials Net £	Unit Net £	CO_2 Kg
L2.2	**Thrust boring**							
L2.2.2	Nominal bore: 200 - 300mm							
L2.2.2.01	Installing steel pipes by auger thrust boring; Steel pipes, BS 3601; ends bevelled; 7.3m average length; welded joints to, BS 5135; minimum 9.5mm wall thickness; Nominal bore: 250mm	m	0.16	24.90	152.37	70.99	**248.26**	*139.30*
L2.2.2.02	as above; Nominal bore: 300mm	m	0.16	24.90	152.37	102.76	**280.03**	*171.70*
L2.2.3	Nominal bore: 300 - 600mm							
L2.2.3.01	Installing steel pipes by auger thrust boring; Steel pipes, BS 3601; ends bevelled; 7.3m average length; welded joints to, BS 5135; minimum 9.5mm wall thickness; Nominal bore: 400mm	m	0.16	24.90	152.37	170.63	**347.90**	*204.20*
L2.2.3.02	as above; Nominal bore: 450mm	m	0.16	24.90	152.37	329.43	**506.70**	*236.66*
L2.2.3.03	as above; Nominal bore: 600mm	m	0.16	24.90	152.37	360.34	**537.61**	*395.50*
L2.2.4	Nominal bore: 600 - 900mm							
L2.2.4.01	Installing steel pipes by auger thrust boring; Steel pipes, BS 3601; ends bevelled; 7.3m average length; welded joints to, BS 5135; minimum 9.5mm wall thickness; Nominal bore: 750mm	m	0.16	24.90	152.37	576.76	**754.03**	*573.86*
L2.2.4.02	as above; Nominal bore: 900mm	m	0.16	24.90	152.37	709.86	**887.13**	*679.16*
L2.3	**Pipe jacking**							
L2.3.4	Nominal bore: 600 - 900mm							
L2.3.4.01	Concrete pipes, BS 5911, Part 1: Class H; 2.44m long; rebated joint with rubber sealing ring; Nominal bore: 900mm	m	2.11	293.54	463.31	205.00	**961.85**	*271.20*
L2.3.5	Nominal bore: 900 - 1200mm							
L2.3.5.01	Concrete pipes, BS 5911, Part 1: Class H; 2.44m long; rebated joint with rubber sealing ring; Nominal bore: 1050mm	m	2.11	293.54	463.31	270.00	**1,026.85**	*334.62*
L2.3.5.02	as above; Nominal bore: 1200mm	m	2.11	293.54	463.31	335.00	**1,091.85**	*398.04*

L2 Special Pipelaying Methods continued...

		Unit	Labour Hours	Labour Net £	Plant Net £	Materials Net £	Unit Net £	*CO_2 Kg*
L2.3	**Pipe jacking**							
L2.3.6	Nominal bore: 1200 - 1500mm							
L2.3.6.01	Concrete pipes, BS 5911, Part 1: Class H; 2.44m long; rebated joint with rubber sealing ring; Nominal bore: 1350mm	m	2.11	293.54	463.31	400.00	1,156.85	*475.44*
L2.3.6.02	as above; Nominal bore: 1500mm	m	2.11	293.54	463.31	465.00	1,221.85	*552.84*
L2.3.7	Nominal bore: 1500 - 1800mm							
L2.3.7.01	Concrete pipes, BS 5911, Part 1: Class H; 2.44m long; rebated joint with rubber sealing ring; Nominal bore: 1650mm	m	2.11	293.54	463.31	530.00	1,286.85	*563.01*
L2.3.7.02	as above; Nominal bore: 1800mm	m	2.11	293.54	463.31	595.00	1,351.85	*609.88*
L2.3.8	Nominal bore: stated exceeding 1800mm							
L2.3.8.01	Concrete pipes, BS 5911, Part 1: Class H; 2.44m long; rebated joint with rubber sealing ring; Nominal bore: 2100mm	m	2.11	293.54	463.31	650.00	1,406.85	*707.64*

L3 Beds

		Unit	Labour Hours	Labour Net £	Plant Net £	Materials Net £	Unit Net £	*CO_2 Kg*
L3.1	**Sand**							
L3.1.1	Nominal bore: not exceeding 200mm							
L3.1.1.01	Depth 100mm; Nominal bore: 100mm	m	0.06	2.02	1.23	2.61	5.86	*1.10*
L3.1.1.02	Depth 100mm; Nominal bore: 150mm	m	0.07	2.35	1.43	2.81	6.59	*1.22*
L3.1.1.03	Depth 150mm; Nominal bore: 100mm	m	0.09	3.02	1.84	3.82	8.68	*1.62*
L3.1.1.04	Depth 150mm; Nominal bore: 150mm	m	0.10	3.36	2.04	4.22	9.62	*1.79*
L3.1.2	Nominal bore: 200 - 300mm							
L3.1.2.01	Depth 100mm; Nominal bore: 225mm	m	0.08	2.69	1.64	3.22	7.55	*1.39*
L3.1.2.02	Depth 100mm; Nominal bore: 300mm	m	0.09	3.02	1.84	3.42	8.28	*1.52*
L3.1.2.03	Depth 150mm; Nominal bore: 225mm	m	0.12	4.03	2.45	4.62	11.10	*2.04*
L3.1.2.04	Depth 150mm; Nominal bore: 300mm	m	0.13	4.37	2.66	5.23	12.26	*2.26*
L3.1.3	Nominal bore: 300 - 600mm							
L3.1.3.01	Depth 100mm; Nominal bore: 375mm	m	0.10	3.36	2.04	4.52	9.92	*1.87*
L3.1.3.02	Depth 100mm; Nominal bore: 450mm	m	0.11	3.70	2.25	4.02	9.97	*1.82*
L3.1.3.03	Depth 100mm; Nominal bore: 600mm	m	0.13	4.37	2.66	4.82	11.85	*2.16*
L3.1.3.04	Depth 150mm; Nominal bore: 375mm	m	0.15	5.04	3.07	5.63	13.74	*2.51*
L3.1.3.05	Depth 150mm; Nominal bore: 450mm	m	0.16	5.38	3.27	6.23	14.88	*2.74*
L3.1.3.06	Depth 150mm; Nominal bore: 600mm	m	0.20	6.72	4.09	7.04	17.85	*3.23*
L3.1.4	Nominal bore: 600 - 900mm							
L3.1.4.01	Depth 100mm; Nominal bore: 675mm	m	0.14	4.71	2.86	5.03	12.60	*2.29*

L3 Beds continued...

		Unit	Labour Hours	Labour Net £	Plant Net £	Materials Net £	Unit Net £	CO_2 Kg
L3.1	**Sand**							
L3.1.4	Nominal bore: 600 - 900mm							
L3.1.4.02	Depth 100mm; Nominal bore: 750mm	m	0.15	5.04	3.07	5.43	**13.54**	*2.46*
L3.1.4.03	Depth 100mm; Nominal bore: 800mm	m	0.15	5.04	3.07	5.63	**13.74**	*2.51*
L3.1.4.04	Depth 100mm; Nominal bore: 900mm	m	0.17	5.71	3.47	6.03	**15.21**	*2.76*
L3.1.4.05	Depth 150mm; Nominal bore: 675mm	m	0.21	7.06	4.29	7.64	**18.99**	*3.46*
L3.1.4.06	Depth 150mm; Nominal bore: 750mm	m	0.23	7.73	4.70	8.04	**20.47**	*3.71*
L3.1.4.07	Depth 150mm; Nominal bore: 800mm	m	0.24	8.07	4.91	8.44	**21.42**	*3.88*
L3.1.4.08	Depth 150mm; Nominal bore: 900mm	m	0.25	8.40	5.11	9.05	**22.56**	*4.11*
L3.1.5	Nominal bore: 900 - 1200mm							
L3.1.5.01	Depth 100mm; Nominal bore: 1200mm	m	0.20	6.72	4.09	8.44	**19.25**	*3.58*
L3.1.5.02	Depth 150mm; Nominal bore: 1200mm	m	0.30	10.08	6.13	12.66	**28.87**	*5.38*
L3.1.6	Nominal bore: 1200 - 1500mm							
L3.1.6.01	Depth 100mm; Nominal bore: 1500mm	m	0.23	7.73	4.70	9.65	**22.08**	*4.11*
L3.1.6.02	Depth 150mm; Nominal bore: 1500mm	m	0.34	11.43	6.95	14.67	**33.05**	*6.17*
L3.1.7	Nominal bore: 1500 - 1800mm							
L3.1.7.01	Depth 100mm; Nominal bore: 1800mm	m	0.26	8.74	5.31	11.06	**25.11**	*4.68*
L3.1.7.02	Depth 150mm; Nominal bore: 1800mm	m	0.39	13.11	7.97	16.48	**37.56**	*6.99*
L3.2	**Selected excavated granular material**							
L3.2.1	Nominal bore: not exceeding 200mm							
L3.2.1.01	Depth 100mm; Nominal bore: 100mm	m	0.09	3.02	1.84	-	**4.86**	*0.67*
L3.2.1.02	Depth 100mm; Nominal bore: 150mm	m	0.10	3.36	2.04	-	**5.40**	*0.74*
L3.2.1.03	Depth 150mm; Nominal bore: 100mm	m	0.13	4.37	2.66	-	**7.03**	*0.96*
L3.2.1.04	Depth 150mm; Nominal bore: 150mm	m	0.15	5.04	3.07	-	**8.11**	*1.11*
L3.2.2	Nominal bore: 200 - 300mm							
L3.2.2.01	Depth 100mm; Nominal bore: 225mm	m	0.12	4.03	2.45	-	**6.48**	*0.89*
L3.2.2.02	Depth 100mm; Nominal bore: 300mm	m	0.13	4.37	2.66	-	**7.03**	*0.96*
L3.2.2.03	Depth 150mm; Nominal bore: 225mm	m	0.16	5.38	3.27	-	**8.65**	*1.19*
L3.2.2.04	Depth 150mm; Nominal bore: 300mm	m	0.19	6.39	3.88	-	**10.27**	*1.41*
L3.2.3	Nominal bore: 300 - 600mm							
L3.2.3.01	Depth 100mm; Nominal bore: 375mm	m	0.15	5.04	3.07	-	**8.11**	*1.11*
L3.2.3.02	Depth 100mm; Nominal bore: 450mm	m	0.16	5.38	3.27	-	**8.65**	*1.19*

L3 Beds continued...

		Unit	Labour Hours	Labour Net £	Plant Net £	Materials Net £	Unit Net £	CO_2 Kg
L3.2	**Selected excavated granular material**							
L3.2.3	Nominal bore: 300 - 600mm							
L3.2.3.03	Depth 100mm; Nominal bore: 600mm	m	0.20	6.72	4.09	-	10.81	*1.48*
L3.2.3.04	Depth 150mm; Nominal bore: 375mm	m	0.22	7.39	4.50	-	11.89	*1.63*
L3.2.3.05	Depth 150mm; Nominal bore: 450mm	m	0.24	8.07	4.91	-	12.98	*1.78*
L3.2.3.06	Depth 150mm; Nominal bore: 600mm	m	0.30	10.08	6.13	-	16.21	*2.23*
L3.2.4	Nominal bore: 600 - 900mm							
L3.2.4.01	Depth 100mm; Nominal bore: 675mm	m	0.21	7.06	4.29	-	11.35	*1.56*
L3.2.4.02	Depth 100mm; Nominal bore: 750mm	m	0.23	7.73	4.70	-	12.43	*1.71*
L3.2.4.03	Depth 100mm; Nominal bore: 800mm	m	0.24	8.07	4.91	-	12.98	*1.78*
L3.2.4.04	Depth 100mm; Nominal bore: 900mm	m	0.25	8.40	5.11	-	13.51	*1.86*
L3.2.4.05	Depth 150mm; Nominal bore: 675mm	m	0.32	10.76	6.54	-	17.30	*2.38*
L3.2.4.06	Depth 150mm; Nominal bore: 750mm	m	0.35	11.76	7.15	-	18.91	*2.60*
L3.2.4.07	Depth 150mm; Nominal bore: 800mm	m	0.36	12.10	7.36	-	19.46	*2.67*
L3.2.4.08	Depth 150mm; Nominal bore: 900mm	m	0.38	12.77	7.77	-	20.54	*2.82*
L3.2.5	Nominal bore: 900 - 1200mm							
L3.2.5.01	Depth 100mm; Nominal bore: 1200mm	m	0.30	10.08	6.13	-	16.21	*2.23*
L3.2.5.02	Depth 150mm; Nominal bore: 1200mm	m	0.45	15.12	9.20	-	24.32	*3.34*
L3.2.6	Nominal bore: 1200 - 1500mm							
L3.2.6.01	Depth 100mm; Nominal bore: 1500mm	m	0.34	11.43	6.95	-	18.38	*2.52*
L3.2.6.02	Depth 150mm; Nominal bore: 1500mm	m	0.51	17.14	10.42	-	27.56	*3.79*
L3.2.7	Nominal bore: 1500 - 1800mm							
L3.2.7.01	Depth 100mm; Nominal bore: 1800mm	m	0.39	13.11	7.97	-	21.08	*2.89*
L3.2.7.02	Depth 150mm; Nominal bore: 1800mm	m	0.59	19.83	12.06	-	31.89	*4.38*
L3.3	**Imported granular material**							
L3.3.1	Nominal bore: not exceeding 200mm							
L3.3.1.01	DTp clause nr. 503; Depth 100mm; Nominal bore: 100mm	m	0.06	2.02	1.23	2.34	5.59	*1.10*
L3.3.1.02	DTp clause nr. 503; Depth 100mm; Nominal bore: 150mm	m	0.07	2.35	1.43	2.52	6.30	*1.22*
L3.3.1.03	DTp clause nr. 503; Depth 150mm; Nominal bore: 100mm	m	0.09	3.02	1.84	3.43	8.29	*1.62*
L3.3.1.04	DTp clause nr. 503; Depth 150mm; Nominal bore: 150mm	m	0.10	3.36	2.04	3.79	9.19	*1.79*
L3.3.2	Nominal bore: 200 - 300mm							
L3.3.2.01	DTp clause nr. 503; Depth 100mm; Nominal bore: 225mm	m	0.08	2.69	1.64	2.88	7.21	*1.39*

L3 Beds continued...

		Unit	Labour Hours	Labour Net £	Plant Net £	Materials Net £	Unit Net £	CO_2 Kg
L3.3	**Imported granular material**							
L3.3.2	Nominal bore: 200 - 300mm							
L3.3.2.02	DTp clause nr. 503; Depth 100mm; Nominal bore: 300mm	m	0.09	3.02	1.84	3.07	**7.93**	*1.52*
L3.3.2.03	DTp clause nr. 503; Depth 150mm; Nominal bore: 225mm	m	0.12	4.03	2.45	4.15	**10.63**	*2.04*
L3.3.2.04	DTp clause nr. 503; Depth 150mm; Nominal bore: 300mm	m	0.13	4.37	2.66	4.69	**11.72**	*2.26*
L3.3.3	Nominal bore: 300 - 600mm							
L3.3.3.01	DTp clause nr. 503; Depth 100mm; Nominal bore: 375mm	m	0.10	3.36	2.04	3.43	**8.83**	*1.69*
L3.3.3.02	DTp clause nr. 503; Depth 100mm; Nominal bore: 450mm	m	0.11	3.70	2.25	3.61	**9.56**	*1.82*
L3.3.3.03	DTp clause nr. 503; Depth 100mm; Nominal bore: 600mm	m	0.13	4.37	2.66	4.33	**11.36**	*2.16*
L3.3.3.04	DTp clause nr. 503; Depth 150mm; Nominal bore: 375mm	m	0.15	5.04	3.07	5.05	**13.16**	*2.51*
L3.3.3.05	DTp clause nr. 503; Depth 150mm; Nominal bore: 450mm	m	0.16	5.38	3.27	5.59	**14.24**	*2.74*
L3.3.3.06	DTp clause nr. 503; Depth 150mm; Nominal bore: 600mm	m	0.20	6.72	4.09	6.31	**17.12**	*3.23*
L3.3.4	Nominal bore: 600 - 900mm							
L3.3.4.01	DTp clause nr. 503; Depth 100mm; Nominal bore: 675mm	m	0.14	4.71	2.86	4.51	**12.08**	*2.29*
L3.3.4.02	DTp clause nr. 503; Depth 100mm; Nominal bore: 750mm	m	0.15	5.04	3.07	4.87	**12.98**	*2.46*
L3.3.4.03	DTp clause nr. 503; Depth 100mm; Nominal bore: 800mm	m	0.15	5.04	3.07	5.05	**13.16**	*2.51*
L3.3.4.04	DTp clause nr. 503; Depth 100mm; Nominal bore: 900mm	m	0.17	5.71	3.47	5.41	**14.59**	*2.76*
L3.3.4.05	DTp clause nr. 503; Depth 150mm; Nominal bore: 675mm	m	0.21	7.06	4.29	6.85	**18.20**	*3.46*
L3.3.4.06	DTp clause nr. 503; Depth 150mm; Nominal bore: 750mm	m	0.23	7.73	4.70	7.21	**19.64**	*3.71*
L3.3.4.07	DTp clause nr. 503; Depth 150mm; Nominal bore: 800mm	m	0.24	8.07	4.91	7.57	**20.55**	*3.88*
L3.3.4.08	DTp clause nr. 503; Depth 150mm; Nominal bore: 900mm	m	0.25	8.40	5.11	8.11	**21.62**	*4.11*
L3.3.5	Nominal bore: 900 - 1200mm							
L3.3.5.01	DTp clause nr. 503; Depth 100mm; Nominal bore: 1200mm	m	0.20	6.72	4.09	7.57	**18.38**	*3.58*
L3.3.5.02	DTp clause nr. 503; Depth 150mm; Nominal bore: 1200mm	m	0.30	10.08	6.13	11.36	**27.57**	*5.38*
L3.3.6	Nominal bore: 1200 - 1500mm							
L3.3.6.01	DTp clause nr. 503; Depth 100mm; Nominal bore: 1500mm	m	0.23	7.73	4.70	8.65	**21.08**	*4.11*
L3.3.6.02	DTp clause nr. 503; Depth 150mm; Nominal bore: 1500mm	m	0.34	11.43	6.95	13.16	**31.54**	*6.17*
L3.3.7	Nominal bore: 1500 - 1800mm							
L3.3.7.01	DTp clause nr. 503; Depth 100mm; Nominal bore: 1800mm	m	0.26	8.74	5.31	9.92	**23.97**	*4.68*
L3.3.7.02	DTp clause nr. 503; Depth 150mm; Nominal bore: 1800mm	m	0.39	13.11	7.97	14.78	**35.86**	*6.99*

L3 Beds continued...

		Unit	Labour Hours	Labour Net £	Plant Net £	Materials Net £	Unit Net £	CO_2 Kg
L3.4	**Mass Concrete**							
L3.4.1	Nominal bore: not exceeding 200mm							
L3.4.1.01	Grade 15, 20mm aggregate; Depth 100mm; Nominal bore: 100mm	m	0.07	2.35	1.43	5.02	**8.80**	*17.68*
L3.4.1.02	Grade 15, 20mm aggregate; Depth 100mm; Nominal bore: 150mm	m	0.09	3.02	1.84	5.44	**10.30**	*19.26*
L3.4.1.03	Grade 15, 20mm aggregate; Depth 150mm; Nominal bore: 100mm	m	0.11	3.70	2.25	7.53	**13.48**	*26.56*
L3.4.1.04	Grade 15, 20mm aggregate; Depth 150mm; Nominal bore: 150mm	m	0.12	4.03	2.45	8.36	**14.84**	*29.49*
L3.4.2	Nominal bore: 200 - 300mm							
L3.4.2.01	Grade 15, 20mm aggregate; Depth 100mm; Nominal bore: 225mm	m	0.10	3.36	2.04	6.10	**11.50**	*21.62*
L3.4.2.02	Grade 15, 20mm aggregate; Depth 100mm; Nominal bore: 300mm	m	0.12	4.03	2.45	6.69	**13.17**	*23.77*
L3.4.2.03	Grade 15, 20mm aggregate; Depth 150mm; Nominal bore: 225mm	m	0.15	5.04	3.07	9.11	**17.22**	*32.29*
L3.4.2.04	Grade 15, 20mm aggregate; Depth 150mm; Nominal bore: 300mm	m	0.16	5.38	3.27	10.03	**18.68**	*35.51*
L3.4.3	Nominal bore: 300 - 600mm							
L3.4.3.01	Grade 15, 20mm aggregate; Depth 100mm; Nominal bore: 375mm	m	0.13	4.37	2.66	7.36	**14.39**	*26.13*
L3.4.3.02	Grade 15, 20mm aggregate; Depth 100mm; Nominal bore: 450mm	m	0.14	4.71	2.86	7.94	**15.51**	*28.21*
L3.4.3.03	Grade 15, 20mm aggregate; Depth 100mm; Nominal bore: 600mm	m	0.16	5.38	3.27	9.20	**17.85**	*32.65*
L3.4.3.04	Grade 15, 20mm aggregate; Depth 150mm; Nominal bore: 375mm	m	0.18	6.05	3.68	11.04	**20.77**	*39.09*
L3.4.3.05	Grade 15, 20mm aggregate; Depth 150mm; Nominal bore: 450mm	m	0.20	6.72	4.09	11.96	**22.77**	*42.38*
L3.4.3.06	Grade 15, 20mm aggregate; Depth 150mm; Nominal bore: 600mm	m	0.25	8.40	5.11	13.80	**27.31**	*49.05*
L3.4.4	Nominal bore: 600 - 900mm							
L3.4.4.01	Grade 15, 20mm aggregate; Depth 100mm; Nominal bore: 675mm	m	0.17	5.71	3.47	9.87	**19.05**	*35.01*
L3.4.4.02	Grade 15, 20mm aggregate; Depth 100mm; Nominal bore: 750mm	m	0.18	6.05	3.68	10.45	**20.18**	*37.09*
L3.4.4.03	Grade 15, 20mm aggregate; Depth 100mm; Nominal bore: 800mm	m	0.19	6.39	3.88	10.87	**21.14**	*38.59*
L3.4.4.04	Grade 15, 20mm aggregate; Depth 100mm; Nominal bore: 900mm	m	0.21	7.06	4.29	11.71	**23.06**	*41.60*

L3 Beds continued...

		Unit	Labour Hours	Labour Net £	Plant Net £	Materials Net £	Unit Net £	CO_2 Kg
L3.4	**Mass Concrete**							
L3.4.4	Nominal bore: 600 - 900mm							
L3.4.4.05	Grade 15, 20mm aggregate; Depth 150mm; Nominal bore: 675mm	m	0.26	8.74	5.31	14.80	**28.85**	*52.55*
L3.4.4.06	Grade 15, 20mm aggregate; Depth 150mm; Nominal bore: 750mm	m	0.29	9.75	5.93	15.72	**31.40**	*55.92*
L3.4.4.07	Grade 15, 20mm aggregate; Depth 150mm; Nominal bore: 800mm	m	0.30	10.08	6.13	16.31	**32.52**	*58.00*
L3.4.4.08	Grade 15, 20mm aggregate; Depth 150mm; Nominal bore: 900mm	m	0.32	10.76	6.54	17.56	**34.86**	*62.44*
L3.4.5	Nominal bore: 900 - 1200mm							
L3.4.5.01	Grade 15, 20mm aggregate; Depth 100mm; Nominal bore: 1200mm	m	0.25	8.40	5.11	16.31	**29.82**	*57.63*
L3.4.5.02	Grade 15, 20mm aggregate; Depth 150mm; Nominal bore: 1200mm	m	0.37	12.44	7.56	24.50	**44.50**	*86.54*
L3.4.6	Nominal bore: 1200 - 1500mm							
L3.4.6.01	Grade 15, 20mm aggregate; Depth 100mm; Nominal bore: 1500mm	m	0.29	9.75	5.93	18.81	**34.49**	*66.50*
L3.4.6.02	Grade 15, 20mm aggregate; Depth 150mm; Nominal bore: 1500mm	m	0.42	14.12	8.58	28.26	**50.96**	*99.79*
L3.4.7	Nominal bore: 1500 - 1800mm							
L3.4.7.01	Grade 15, 20mm aggregate; Depth 100mm; Nominal bore: 1800mm	m	0.33	11.09	6.75	21.32	**39.16**	*75.38*
L3.4.7.02	Grade 15, 20mm aggregate; Depth 150mm; Nominal bore: 1800mm	m	0.50	16.81	10.22	32.03	**59.06**	*113.25*
L3.5	**Reinforced concrete**							
L3.5.1	Nominal bore: not exceeding 200mm							
L3.5.1.01	Grade 25, 20mm aggregate; 1 layer A252 mesh reinforcement; Nominal bore: 100mm	m	0.10	3.36	2.04	6.84	**12.24**	*23.85*
L3.5.1.02	Grade 25, 20mm aggregate; 1 layer A252 mesh reinforcement; Nominal bore: 150mm	m	0.12	4.03	2.45	7.41	**13.89**	*25.93*
L3.5.1.03	Grade 25, 20mm aggregate; 1 layer A252 mesh reinforcement; Nominal bore: 100mm	m	0.14	4.71	2.86	9.48	**17.05**	*32.73*
L3.5.1.04	Grade 25, 20mm aggregate; 1 layer A252 mesh reinforcement; Nominal bore: 150mm	m	0.15	5.04	3.07	10.48	**18.59**	*36.16*
L3.5.2	Nominal bore: 200 - 300mm							
L3.5.2.01	Grade 25, 20mm aggregate; 1 layer A252 mesh reinforcement; Nominal bore: 225mm	m	0.14	4.71	2.86	8.32	**15.89**	*29.16*
L3.5.2.02	Grade 25, 20mm aggregate; 1 layer A252 mesh reinforcement; Nominal bore: 300mm	m	0.16	5.38	3.27	9.12	**17.77**	*32.00*

L3 Beds continued...

		Unit	Labour Hours	Labour Net £	Plant Net £	Materials Net £	Unit Net £	CO_2 Kg
L3.5	**Reinforced concrete**							
L3.5.2	Nominal bore: 200 - 300mm							
L3.5.2.03	Grade 25, 20mm aggregate; 1 layer A252 mesh reinforcement; Nominal bore: 225mm	m	0.19	6.39	3.88	11.48	**21.75**	*39.82*
L3.5.2.04	Grade 25, 20mm aggregate; 1 layer A252 mesh reinforcement; Nominal bore: 300mm	m	0.20	6.72	4.09	12.63	**23.44**	*43.74*
L3.5.3	Nominal bore: 300 - 600mm							
L3.5.3.01	Grade 25, 20mm aggregate; 1 layer A252 mesh reinforcement; Depth 100mm; Nominal bore: 375mm	m	0.17	5.71	3.47	10.03	**19.21**	*35.16*
L3.5.3.02	Grade 25, 20mm aggregate; 1 layer A252 mesh reinforcement; Depth 100mm; Nominal bore: 450mm	m	0.19	6.39	3.88	10.83	**21.10**	*38.00*
L3.5.3.03	Grade 25, 20mm aggregate; 1 layer A252 mesh reinforcement; Depth 100mm; Nominal bore: 600mm	m	0.22	7.39	4.50	-	**11.89**	*1.63*
L3.5.3.04	Grade 25, 20mm aggregate; 1 layer A252 mesh reinforcement; Depth 150mm; Nominal bore: 375mm	m	0.22	7.39	4.50	13.90	**25.79**	*48.11*
L3.5.3.05	Grade 25, 20mm aggregate; 1 layer A252 mesh reinforcement; Nominal bore: 450mm	m	0.25	8.40	5.11	15.05	**28.56**	*52.17*
L3.5.3.06	Grade 25, 20mm aggregate; 1 layer A252 mesh reinforcement; Nominal bore: 600mm	m	0.31	10.42	6.34	17.37	**34.13**	*60.40*
L3.5.4	Nominal bore: 600 - 900mm							
L3.5.4.01	Grade 25, 20mm aggregate; 1 layer A252 mesh reinforcement; Depth 100mm; Nominal bore: 675mm	m	0.23	7.73	4.70	13.45	**25.88**	*47.15*
L3.5.4.02	Grade 25, 20mm aggregate; 1 layer A252 mesh reinforcement; Depth 100mm; Nominal bore: 750mm	m	0.24	8.07	4.91	14.25	**27.23**	*49.93*
L3.5.4.03	Grade 25, 20mm aggregate; 1 layer A252 mesh reinforcement; Depth 100mm; Nominal bore: 800mm	m	0.26	8.74	5.31	14.82	**28.87**	*52.00*
L3.5.4.04	Grade 25, 20mm aggregate; 1 layer A252 mesh reinforcement; Depth 100mm; Nominal bore: 900mm	m	0.28	9.41	5.72	15.96	**31.09**	*56.00*
L3.5.4.05	Grade 25, 20mm aggregate; 1 layer A252 mesh reinforcement; Depth 150mm; Nominal bore: 675mm	m	0.32	10.76	6.54	18.63	**35.93**	*64.70*
L3.5.4.06	Grade 25, 20mm aggregate; 1 layer A252 mesh reinforcement; Depth 150mm; Nominal bore: 750mm	m	0.35	11.76	7.15	19.47	**38.38**	*67.57*
L3.5.4.07	Grade 25, 20mm aggregate; 1 layer A252 mesh reinforcement; Depth 150mm; Nominal bore: 800mm	m	0.37	12.44	7.56	20.53	**40.53**	*71.41*

L3 Beds continued...

		Unit	Labour Hours	Labour Net £	Plant Net £	Materials Net £	Unit Net £	CO_2 Kg
L3.5	**Reinforced concrete**							
L3.5.4	Nominal bore: 600 - 900mm							
L3.5.4.08	Grade 25, 20mm aggregate; 1 layer A252 mesh reinforcement; Depth 150mm; Nominal bore: 900mm	m	0.39	13.11	7.97	18.45	**39.53**	*62.95*
L3.5.5	Nominal bore: 900 - 1200mm							
L3.5.5.01	Grade 25, 20mm aggregate; 1 layer A252 mesh reinforcement; Depth 100mm; Nominal bore: 1200mm	m	0.35	11.76	7.15	22.23	**41.14**	*77.70*
L3.5.5.02	Grade 25, 20mm aggregate; 1 layer A252 mesh reinforcement; Depth 150mm; Nominal bore: 1200mm	m	0.47	15.80	9.61	30.84	**56.25**	*106.62*
L3.5.6	Nominal bore: 1200 - 1500mm							
L3.5.6.01	Grade 25, 20mm aggregate; 1 layer A252 mesh reinforcement; Depth 100mm; Nominal bore: 1500mm	m	0.40	13.44	8.18	25.65	**47.27**	*89.63*
L3.5.6.02	Grade 25, 20mm aggregate; 1 layer A252 mesh reinforcement; Depth 150mm; Nominal bore: 1500mm	m	0.53	17.81	10.83	35.58	**64.22**	*122.91*
L3.5.7	Nominal bore: 1500 - 1800mm							
L3.5.7.01	Grade 25, 20mm aggregate; 1 layer A252 mesh reinforcement; Depth 100mm; Nominal bore: 1800mm	m	0.46	15.46	9.40	29.06	**53.92**	*101.63*
L3.5.7.02	Grade 25, 20mm aggregate; 1 layer A252 mesh reinforcement; Depth 150mm; Nominal bore: 1800mm	m	0.63	21.17	12.88	40.31	**74.36**	*139.50*

L4 Haunches

		Unit	Labour Hours	Labour Net £	Plant Net £	Materials Net £	Unit Net £	CO_2 Kg
L4.4	**Mass Concrete**							
L4.4.1	Nominal bore: not exceeding 200mm							
L4.4.1.01	Including beds; grade 15, 20mm aggregate; Depth 100mm; Nominal bore: 100mm	m	0.12	4.03	2.45	8.36	**14.84**	*29.49*
L4.4.1.02	Including beds; grade 15, 20mm aggregate; Depth 100mm; Nominal bore: 150mm	m	0.15	5.04	3.07	9.20	**17.31**	*32.57*
L4.4.1.03	Including beds; grade 15, 20mm aggregate; Depth 150mm; Nominal bore: 100mm	m	0.15	5.04	3.07	10.87	**18.98**	*38.29*
L4.4.1.04	Including beds; grade 15, 20mm aggregate; Depth 150mm; Nominal bore: 150mm	m	0.19	6.39	3.88	11.96	**22.23**	*42.31*
L4.4.2	Nominal bore: 200 - 300mm							
L4.4.2.01	Including beds; grade 15, 20mm aggregate; Depth 100mm; Nominal bore: 225mm	m	0.18	6.05	3.68	10.45	**20.18**	*37.09*

L4 Haunches continued...

		Unit	Labour Hours	Labour Net £	Plant Net £	Materials Net £	Unit Net £	CO_2 Kg
L4.4	**Mass Concrete**							
L4.4.2	Nominal bore: 200 - 300mm							
L4.4.2.02	Including beds; grade 15, 20mm aggregate; Depth 100mm; Nominal bore: 300mm	m	0.22	7.39	4.50	12.12	24.01	*43.10*
L4.4.2.03	Including beds; grade 15, 20mm aggregate; Depth 150mm; Nominal bore: 225mm	m	0.22	7.39	4.50	14.22	26.11	*50.25*
L4.4.2.04	Including beds; grade 15, 20mm aggregate; Depth 150mm; Nominal bore: 300mm	m	0.27	9.07	5.52	15.47	30.06	*54.91*
L4.4.3	Nominal bore: 300 - 600mm							
L4.4.3.01	Including beds; grade 15, 20mm aggregate; Depth 100mm; Nominal bore: 375mm	m	0.27	9.07	5.52	15.05	29.64	*53.48*
L4.4.3.02	Including beds; grade 15, 20mm aggregate; Depth 100mm; Nominal bore: 450mm	m	0.32	10.76	6.54	18.40	35.70	*65.30*
L4.4.3.03	Including beds; grade 15, 20mm aggregate; Depth 100mm; Nominal bore: 600mm	m	0.40	13.44	8.18	29.27	50.89	*103.07*
L4.4.3.04	Including beds; grade 15, 20mm aggregate; Depth 150mm; Nominal bore: 375mm	m	0.33	11.09	6.75	18.73	36.57	*66.51*
L4.4.3.05	Including beds; grade 15, 20mm aggregate; Depth 150mm; Nominal bore: 450mm	m	0.38	12.77	7.77	22.41	42.95	*79.47*
L4.4.3.06	Including beds; grade 15, 20mm aggregate; Depth 150mm; Nominal bore: 600mm	m	0.46	15.46	9.40	33.87	58.73	*119.24*
L4.4.4	Nominal bore: 600 - 900mm							
L4.4.4.01	Including beds; grade 15, 20mm aggregate; Depth 100mm; Nominal bore: 675mm	m	0.50	16.81	10.22	32.61	59.64	*115.25*
L4.4.4.02	Including beds; grade 15, 20mm aggregate; Depth 100mm; Nominal bore: 750mm	m	0.69	23.19	14.10	40.14	77.43	*142.40*
L4.4.4.03	Including beds; grade 15, 20mm aggregate; Depth 100mm; Nominal bore: 800mm	m	0.85	28.57	17.37	48.50	94.44	*172.19*
L4.4.4.04	Including beds; grade 15, 20mm aggregate; Depth 100mm; Nominal bore: 900mm	m	0.95	31.93	19.42	52.68	104.03	*187.23*
L4.4.4.05	Including beds; grade 15, 20mm aggregate; Depth 150mm; Nominal bore: 675mm	m	0.57	19.16	11.65	38.05	68.86	*134.36*
L4.4.4.06	Including beds; grade 15, 20mm aggregate; Depth 150mm; Nominal bore: 750mm	m	0.77	25.88	15.74	45.41	87.03	*161.01*
L4.4.4.07	Including beds; grade 15, 20mm aggregate; Depth 150mm; Nominal bore: 800mm	m	0.95	31.93	19.42	53.93	105.28	*191.52*
L4.4.4.08	Including beds; grade 15, 20mm aggregate; Depth 150mm; Nominal bore: 900mm	m	1.05	35.29	21.46	58.53	115.28	*207.99*

L4 Haunches continued...

		Unit	Labour Hours	Labour Net £	Plant Net £	Materials Net £	Unit Net £	*CO_2 Kg*
L4.4	**Mass Concrete**							
L4.4.5	Nominal bore: 900 - 1200mm							
L4.4.5.01	Including beds; grade 15, 20mm aggregate; Depth 100mm; Nominal bore: 1200mm	m	1.15	38.65	23.51	75.26	**137.42**	*265.94*
L4.4.5.02	Including beds; grade 15, 20mm aggregate; Depth 150mm; Nominal bore: 1200mm	m	1.28	43.02	26.16	83.62	**152.80**	*295.50*
L4.4.6	Nominal bore: 1200 - 1500mm							
L4.4.6.01	Including beds; grade 15, 20mm aggregate; Depth 100mm; Nominal bore: 1500mm	m	1.38	46.38	28.21	89.47	**164.06**	*316.26*
L4.4.6.02	Including beds; grade 15, 20mm aggregate; Depth 150mm; Nominal bore: 1500mm	m	1.42	47.73	29.02	98.92	**175.67**	*348.88*
L4.4.7	Nominal bore: 1500 - 1800mm							
L4.4.7.01	Including beds; grade 15, 20mm aggregate; Depth 100mm; Nominal bore: 1800mm	m	1.60	53.78	32.70	108.71	**195.19**	*383.68*
L4.4.7.02	Including beds; grade 15, 20mm aggregate; Depth 150mm; Nominal bore: 1800mm	m	1.76	59.15	35.97	119.41	**214.53**	*421.47*
L4.5	**Reinforced concrete**							
L4.5.1	Nominal bore: not exceeding 200mm							
L4.5.1.01	Including beds; grade 25, 20mm aggregate; 1 layer A252 mesh reinforcement; Depth 100mm; Nominal bore: 100mm	m	0.15	5.04	3.07	10.35	**18.46**	*35.66*
L4.5.1.02	Including beds; grade 25, 20mm aggregate; 1 layer A252 mesh reinforcement; Depth 100mm; Nominal bore: 150mm	m	0.18	6.05	3.68	11.36	**21.09**	*39.24*
L4.5.1.03	Including beds; grade 25, 20mm aggregate; 1 layer A252 mesh reinforcement; Depth 150mm; Nominal bore: 100mm	m	0.18	6.05	3.68	12.99	**22.72**	*44.47*
L4.5.1.04	Including beds; grade 25, 20mm aggregate; 1 layer A252 mesh reinforcement; Depth 150mm; Nominal bore: 150mm	m	0.22	7.39	4.50	12.57	**24.46**	*42.53*
L4.5.2	Nominal bore: 200 - 300mm							
L4.5.2.01	Including beds; grade 25, 20mm aggregate; 1 layer A252 mesh reinforcement; Depth 100mm; Nominal bore: 225mm	m	0.22	7.39	4.50	13.59	**25.48**	*46.91*
L4.5.2.02	Including beds; grade 25, 20mm aggregate; 1 layer A252 mesh reinforcement; Depth 100mm; Nominal bore: 300mm	m	0.26	8.74	5.31	14.83	**28.88**	*51.33*
L4.5.2.03	Including beds; grade 25, 20mm aggregate; 1 layer A252 mesh reinforcement; Depth 150mm; Nominal bore: 225mm	m	0.26	8.74	5.31	16.84	**30.89**	*57.79*
L4.5.2.04	Including beds; grade 25, 20mm aggregate; 1 layer A252 mesh reinforcement; Depth 150mm; Nominal bore: 300mm	m	0.31	10.42	6.34	18.35	**35.11**	*63.14*

L4 Haunches continued...

		Unit	Labour Hours	Labour Net £	Plant Net £	Materials Net £	Unit Net £	CO_2 Kg
L4.5	**Reinforced concrete**							
L4.5.3	Nominal bore: 300 - 600mm							
L4.5.3.01	Including beds; grade 25, 20mm aggregate; 1 layer A252 mesh reinforcement; Depth 100mm; Nominal bore: 375mm	m	0.31	10.42	6.34	18.12	34.88	*62.51*
L4.5.3.02	Including beds; grade 25, 20mm aggregate; 1 layer A252 mesh reinforcement; Depth 100mm; Nominal bore: 450mm	m	0.37	12.44	7.56	21.81	41.81	*75.09*
L4.5.3.03	Including beds; grade 25, 20mm aggregate; 1 layer A252 mesh reinforcement; Depth 100mm; Nominal bore: 600mm	m	0.46	15.46	9.40	33.63	58.49	*114.42*
L4.5.3.04	Including beds; grade 25, 20mm aggregate; 1 layer A252 mesh reinforcement; Depth 150mm; Nominal bore: 375mm	m	0.37	12.44	7.56	21.98	41.98	*75.54*
L4.5.3.05	Including beds; grade 25, 20mm aggregate; 1 layer A252 mesh reinforcement; Depth 150mm; Nominal bore: 450mm	m	0.43	14.45	8.79	26.03	49.27	*89.26*
L4.5.3.06	Including beds; grade 25, 20mm aggregate; 1 layer A252 mesh reinforcement; Depth 150mm; Nominal bore: 600mm	m	0.52	17.48	10.63	38.46	66.57	*130.60*
L4.5.4	Nominal bore: 600 - 900mm							
L4.5.4.01	Including beds; grade 25, 20mm aggregate; 1 layer A252 mesh reinforcement; Depth 100mm; Nominal bore: 675mm	m	0.56	18.82	11.45	37.35	67.62	*127.40*
L4.5.4.02	Including beds; grade 25, 20mm aggregate; 1 layer A252 mesh reinforcement; Depth 100mm; Nominal bore: 750mm	m	0.75	25.21	15.33	45.44	85.98	*155.24*
L4.5.4.03	Including beds; grade 25, 20mm aggregate; 1 layer A252 mesh reinforcement; Depth 100mm; Nominal bore: 800mm	m	0.92	30.92	18.80	54.36	104.08	*185.60*
L4.5.4.04	Including beds; grade 25, 20mm aggregate; 1 layer A252 mesh reinforcement; Depth 100mm; Nominal bore: 900mm	m	1.02	34.28	20.85	59.02	114.15	*201.63*
L4.5.4.05	Including beds; grade 25, 20mm aggregate; 1 layer A252 mesh reinforcement; Depth 150mm; Nominal bore: 675mm	m	0.63	21.17	12.88	42.54	76.59	*144.79*
L4.5.4.06	Including beds; grade 25, 20mm aggregate; 1 layer A252 mesh reinforcement; Depth 150mm; Nominal bore: 750mm	m	0.83	27.90	16.97	50.98	95.85	*173.85*
L4.5.4.07	Including beds; grade 25, 20mm aggregate; 1 layer A252 mesh reinforcement; Depth 150mm; Nominal bore: 800mm	m	1.02	34.28	20.85	60.08	115.21	*204.93*
L4.5.4.08	Including beds; grade 25, 20mm aggregate; 1 layer A252 mesh reinforcement; Depth 150mm; Nominal bore: 900mm	m	1.12	37.64	22.89	65.17	125.70	*222.39*

L4 Haunches continued...

		Unit	Labour Hours	Labour Net £	Plant Net £	Materials Net £	Unit Net £	CO_2 Kg
L4.5	**Reinforced concrete**							
L4.5.5	Nominal bore: 900 - 1200mm							
L4.5.5.01	Including beds; grade 25, 20mm aggregate; 1 layer A252 mesh reinforcement; Depth 100mm; Nominal bore: 1200mm	m	1.25	42.01	25.55	84.18	**151.74**	*286.01*
L4.5.5.02	Including beds; grade 25, 20mm aggregate; 1 layer A252 mesh reinforcement; Depth 150mm; Nominal bore: 1200mm	m	1.38	46.38	28.21	92.97	**167.56**	*315.58*
L4.5.6	Nominal bore: 1200 - 1500mm							
L4.5.6.01	Including beds; grade 25, 20mm aggregate; 1 layer A252 mesh reinforcement; Depth 100mm; Nominal bore: 1500mm	m	1.49	50.08	30.46	99.90	**180.44**	*339.39*
L4.5.6.02	Including beds; grade 25, 20mm aggregate; 1 layer A252 mesh reinforcement; Depth 150mm; Nominal bore: 1500mm	m	1.53	51.42	31.27	109.83	**192.52**	*372.00*
L4.5.7	Nominal bore: 1500 - 1800mm							
L4.5.7.01	Including beds; grade 25, 20mm aggregate; 1 layer A252 mesh reinforcement; Depth 100mm; Nominal bore: 1800mm	m	1.73	58.15	35.36	107.38	**200.89**	*365.74*
L4.5.7.02	Including beds; grade 25, 20mm aggregate; 1 layer A252 mesh reinforcement; Depth 150mm; Nominal bore: 1800mm	m	1.89	63.52	38.63	132.15	**234.30**	*447.72*

L5 Surrounds

		Unit	Labour Hours	Labour Net £	Plant Net £	Materials Net £	Unit Net £	CO_2 Kg
L5.1	**Sand**							
L5.1.1	Nominal bore: not exceeding 200mm							
L5.1.1.01	Including beds; Thickness 100mm; Depth 100mm; Nominal bore: 100mm	m	0.15	5.04	3.07	7.34	**15.45**	*2.94*
L5.1.1.02	Including beds; Thickness 100mm; Depth 100mm; Nominal bore: 150mm	m	0.18	6.05	3.68	9.07	**18.80**	*3.59*
L5.1.1.03	Including beds; Thickness 100mm; Depth 150mm; Nominal bore: 100mm	m	0.19	6.39	3.88	9.93	**20.20**	*3.88*
L5.1.1.04	Including beds; Thickness 100mm; Depth 150mm; Nominal bore: 150mm	m	0.23	7.73	4.70	11.88	**24.31**	*4.66*
L5.1.2	Nominal bore: 200 - 300mm							
L5.1.2.01	Including beds; Thickness 100mm; Depth 100mm; Nominal bore: 225mm	m	0.20	6.72	4.09	11.62	**22.43**	*4.37*
L5.1.2.02	Including beds; Thickness 100mm; Depth 100mm; Nominal bore: 300mm	m	0.23	7.73	4.70	14.07	**26.50**	*5.21*
L5.1.2.03	Including beds; Thickness 100mm; Depth 150mm; Nominal bore: 225mm	m	0.25	8.40	5.11	14.75	**28.26**	*5.53*

L5 Surrounds continued...

		Unit	Labour Hours	Labour Net £	Plant Net £	Materials Net £	Unit Net £	CO_2 *Kg*
L5.1	**Sand**							
L5.1.2	Nominal bore: 200 - 300mm							
L5.1.2.04	Including beds; Thickness 100mm; Depth 150mm; Nominal bore: 300mm	m	0.28	9.41	5.72	17.53	32.66	*6.44*
L5.1.3	Nominal bore: 300 - 600mm							
L5.1.3.01	Including beds; Thickness 100mm; Depth 100mm; Nominal bore: 375mm	m	0.25	8.40	5.11	16.96	30.47	*6.08*
L5.1.3.02	Including beds; Thickness 100mm; Depth 100mm; Nominal bore: 450mm	m	0.27	9.07	5.52	19.82	34.41	*6.93*
L5.1.3.03	Including beds; Thickness 100mm; Depth 100mm; Nominal bore: 600mm	m	0.33	11.09	6.75	24.12	41.96	*8.45*
L5.1.3.04	Including beds; Thickness 100mm; Depth 150mm; Nominal bore: 375mm	m	0.31	10.42	6.34	20.74	37.50	*7.46*
L5.1.3.05	Including beds; Thickness 100mm; Depth 150mm; Nominal bore: 450mm	m	0.33	11.09	6.75	23.92	41.76	*8.40*
L5.1.3.06	Including beds; Thickness 100mm; Depth 150mm; Nominal bore: 600mm	m	0.38	12.77	7.77	30.69	51.23	*10.46*
L5.1.4	Nominal bore: 600 - 900mm							
L5.1.4.01	Including beds; Thickness 100mm; Depth 100mm; Nominal bore: 675mm	m	0.35	11.76	7.15	29.00	47.91	*9.81*
L5.1.4.02	Including beds; Thickness 100mm; Depth 100mm; Nominal bore: 750mm	m	0.38	12.77	7.77	32.22	52.76	*10.84*
L5.1.4.03	Including beds; Thickness 100mm; Depth 100mm; Nominal bore: 800mm	m	0.40	13.44	8.18	34.57	56.19	*11.57*
L5.1.4.04	Including beds; Thickness 100mm; Depth 100mm; Nominal bore: 900mm	m	0.43	14.45	8.79	38.79	62.03	*12.84*
L5.1.4.05	Including beds; Thickness 100mm; Depth 150mm; Nominal bore: 675mm	m	0.40	13.44	8.18	34.09	55.71	*11.45*
L5.1.4.06	Including beds; Thickness 100mm; Depth 150mm; Nominal bore: 750mm	m	0.43	14.45	8.79	37.63	60.87	*12.55*
L5.1.4.07	Including beds; Thickness 100mm; Depth 150mm; Nominal bore: 800mm	m	0.46	15.46	9.40	40.20	65.06	*13.41*
L5.1.4.08	Including beds; Thickness 100mm; Depth 150mm; Nominal bore: 900mm	m	0.49	16.47	10.02	44.82	71.31	*14.79*
L5.1.5	Nominal bore: 900 - 1200mm							
L5.1.5.01	Including beds; Thickness 100mm; Depth 100mm; Nominal bore: 1200mm	m	0.50	16.81	10.22	69.14	96.17	*20.91*
L5.1.5.02	Including beds; Thickness 100mm; Depth 150mm; Nominal bore: 1200mm	m	0.56	18.82	11.45	77.57	107.84	*23.45*

L5 Surrounds continued...

		Unit	Labour Hours	Labour Net £	Plant Net £	Materials Net £	Unit Net £	CO_2 Kg
L5.1	**Sand**							
L5.1.6	Nominal bore: 1200 - 1500mm							
L5.1.6.01	Including beds; Thickness 100mm; Depth 100mm; Nominal bore: 1500mm	m	0.58	19.49	11.86	89.45	**120.80**	*26.56*
L5.1.6.02	Including beds; Thickness 100mm; Depth 150mm; Nominal bore: 1500mm	m	0.63	21.17	12.88	108.22	**142.27**	*31.60*
L5.1.7	Nominal bore: 1500 - 1800mm							
L5.1.7.01	Including beds; Thickness 100mm; Depth 100mm; Nominal bore: 1800mm	m	0.65	21.85	13.29	110.55	**145.69**	*32.32*
L5.1.7.02	Including beds; Thickness 100mm; Depth 150mm; Nominal bore: 1800mm	m	0.72	24.20	14.72	121.56	**160.48**	*35.58*
L5.2	**Selected excavated granular material**							
L5.2.1	Nominal bore: not exceeding 200mm							
L5.2.1.01	Including beds; thickness 100mm; Depth 100mm; Nominal bore: 100mm	m	0.22	7.39	4.50	-	**11.89**	*1.63*
L5.2.1.02	Including beds; thickness 100mm; Depth 100mm; Nominal bore: 150mm	m	0.27	9.07	5.52	-	**14.59**	*2.00*
L5.2.1.03	Including beds; thickness 100mm; Depth 150mm; Nominal bore: 100mm	m	0.29	9.75	5.93	-	**15.68**	*2.15*
L5.2.1.04	Including beds; thickness 100mm; Depth 150mm; Nominal bore: 150mm	m	0.35	11.76	7.15	-	**18.91**	*2.60*
L5.2.2	Nominal bore: 200 - 300mm							
L5.2.2.01	Including beds; thickness 100mm; Depth 100mm; Nominal bore: 225mm	m	0.30	10.08	6.13	-	**16.21**	*2.23*
L5.2.2.02	Including beds; thickness 100mm; Depth 100mm; Nominal bore: 300mm	m	0.35	11.76	7.15	-	**18.91**	*2.60*
L5.2.2.03	Including beds; thickness 100mm; Depth 150mm; Nominal bore: 225mm	m	0.38	12.77	7.77	-	**20.54**	*2.82*
L5.2.2.04	Including beds; thickness 100mm; Depth 150mm; Nominal bore: 300mm	m	0.42	14.12	8.58	-	**22.70**	*3.12*
L5.2.3	Nominal bore: 300 - 600mm							
L5.2.3.01	Including beds; thickness 100mm; Depth 100mm; Nominal bore: 375mm	m	0.38	12.77	7.77	-	**20.54**	*2.82*
L5.2.3.02	Including beds; thickness 100mm; Depth 100mm; Nominal bore: 450mm	m	0.40	13.44	8.18	-	**21.62**	*2.97*
L5.2.3.03	Including beds; thickness 100mm; Depth 100mm; Nominal bore: 600mm	m	0.50	16.81	10.22	-	**27.03**	*3.71*
L5.2.3.04	Including beds; thickness 100mm; Depth 150mm; Nominal bore: 375mm	m	0.47	15.80	9.61	-	**25.41**	*3.49*

L5 Surrounds continued...

		Unit	Labour Hours	Labour Net £	Plant Net £	Materials Net £	Unit Net £	CO_2 Kg
L5.2	**Selected excavated granular material**							
L5.2.3	Nominal bore: 300 - 600mm							
L5.2.3.05	Including beds; thickness 100mm; Depth 150mm; Nominal bore: 450mm	m	0.50	16.81	10.22	-	27.03	*3.71*
L5.2.3.06	Including beds; thickness 100mm; Depth 150mm; Nominal bore: 600mm	m	0.57	19.16	11.65	-	30.81	*4.23*
L5.2.4	Nominal bore: 600 - 900mm							
L5.2.4.01	Including beds; thickness 100mm; Depth 100mm; Nominal bore: 675mm	m	0.53	17.81	10.83	-	28.64	*3.93*
L5.2.4.02	Including beds; thickness 100mm; Depth 100mm; Nominal bore: 750mm	m	0.57	19.16	11.65	-	30.81	*4.23*
L5.2.4.03	Including beds; thickness 100mm; Depth 100mm; Nominal bore: 800mm	m	0.60	20.17	12.26	-	32.43	*4.45*
L5.2.4.04	Including beds; thickness 100mm; Depth 100mm; Nominal bore: 900mm	m	0.65	21.85	13.29	-	35.14	*4.82*
L5.2.4.05	Including beds; thickness 100mm; Depth 150mm; Nominal bore: 675mm	m	0.60	20.17	12.26	-	32.43	*4.45*
L5.2.4.06	Including beds; thickness 100mm; Depth 150mm; Nominal bore: 750mm	m	0.65	21.85	13.29	-	35.14	*4.82*
L5.2.4.07	Including beds; thickness 100mm; Depth 150mm; Nominal bore: 800mm	m	0.69	23.19	14.10	-	37.29	*5.12*
L5.2.4.08	Including beds; thickness 100mm; Depth 150mm; Nominal bore: 900mm	m	0.74	24.87	15.13	-	40.00	*5.49*
L5.2.5	Nominal bore: 900 - 1200mm							
L5.2.5.01	Including beds; thickness 100mm; Depth 100mm; Nominal bore: 1200mm	m	0.75	25.21	15.33	-	40.54	*5.57*
L5.2.5.02	Including beds; thickness 100mm; Depth 150mm; Nominal bore: 1200mm	m	0.84	28.23	17.17	-	45.40	*6.24*
L5.2.6	Nominal bore: 1200 - 1500mm							
L5.2.6.01	Including beds; thickness 100mm; Depth 100mm; Nominal bore: 1500mm	m	0.87	29.24	17.78	-	47.02	*6.46*
L5.2.6.02	Including beds; thickness 100mm; Depth 150mm; Nominal bore: 1500mm	m	0.95	31.93	19.42	-	51.35	*7.05*
L5.2.7	Nominal bore: 1500 - 1800mm							
L5.2.7.01	Including beds; thickness 100mm; Depth 100mm; Nominal bore: 1800mm	m	0.98	32.94	20.03	-	52.97	*7.27*
L5.2.7.02	Including beds; thickness 100mm; Depth 150mm; Nominal bore: 1800mm	m	1.08	36.30	22.08	-	58.38	*8.02*

L5 Surrounds continued...

		Unit	Labour Hours	Labour Net £	Plant Net £	Materials Net £	Unit Net £	CO_2 Kg
L5.3	**Imported granular material**							
L5.3.1	Nominal bore: not exceeding 200mm							
L5.3.1.01	Including beds; DTp clause nr. 503; thickness 100mm; Depth 100mm; Nominal bore: 100mm	m	0.15	5.04	3.07	6.58	**14.69**	*2.94*
L5.3.1.02	Including beds; DTp clause nr. 503; thickness 100mm; Depth 100mm; Nominal bore: 150mm	m	0.18	6.05	3.68	8.13	**17.86**	*3.59*
L5.3.1.03	Including beds; DTp clause nr. 503; thickness 100mm; Depth 150mm; Nominal bore: 100mm	m	0.19	6.39	3.88	8.91	**19.18**	*3.88*
L5.3.1.04	Including beds; DTp clause nr. 503; thickness 100mm; Depth 150mm; Nominal bore: 150mm	m	0.23	7.73	4.70	11.09	**23.52**	*4.78*
L5.3.2	Nominal bore: 200 - 300mm							
L5.3.2.01	Including beds; DTp clause nr. 503; thickness 100mm; Depth 100mm; Nominal bore: 225mm	m	0.20	6.72	4.09	10.42	**21.23**	*4.37*
L5.3.2.02	Including beds; DTp clause nr. 503; thickness 100mm; Depth 100mm; Nominal bore: 300mm	m	0.23	7.73	4.70	12.62	**25.05**	*5.21*
L5.3.2.03	Including beds; DTp clause nr. 503; thickness 100mm; Depth 150mm; Nominal bore: 225mm	m	0.25	8.40	5.11	13.23	**26.74**	*5.53*
L5.3.2.04	Including beds; DTp clause nr. 503; thickness 100mm; Depth 150mm; Nominal bore: 300mm	m	0.28	9.41	5.72	15.72	**30.85**	*6.44*
L5.3.2.05	Including beds; DTp clause nr. 503; thickness 100mm; Depth 100mm; Nominal bore: 375mm	m	0.25	8.40	5.11	15.22	**28.73**	*6.08*
L5.3.3	Nominal bore: 300 - 600mm							
L5.3.3.01	Including beds; DTp clause nr. 503; thickness 100mm; Depth 100mm; Nominal bore: 450mm	m	0.27	9.07	5.52	17.78	**32.37**	*6.93*
L5.3.3.02	Including beds; DTp clause nr. 503; thickness 100mm; Depth 100mm; Nominal bore: 600mm	m	0.33	11.09	6.75	23.26	**41.10**	*8.90*
L5.3.3.03	Including beds; DTp clause nr. 503; thickness 100mm; Depth 150mm; Nominal bore: 375mm	m	0.31	10.42	6.34	18.61	**35.37**	*7.46*
L5.3.3.04	Including beds; DTp clause nr. 503; thickness 100mm; Depth 150mm; Nominal bore: 450mm	m	0.33	11.09	6.75	21.46	**39.30**	*8.40*
L5.3.3.05	Including beds; DTp clause nr. 503; thickness 100mm; Depth 150mm; Nominal bore: 600mm	m	0.38	12.77	7.77	27.53	**48.07**	*10.46*
L5.3.4	Nominal bore: 600 - 900mm							
L5.3.4.01	Including beds; DTp clause nr. 503; thickness 100mm; Depth 100mm; Nominal bore: 675mm	m	0.35	11.76	7.15	26.02	**44.93**	*9.81*
L5.3.4.02	Including beds; DTp clause nr. 503; thickness 100mm; Depth 100mm; Nominal bore: 750mm	m	0.38	12.77	7.77	28.90	**49.44**	*10.84*
L5.3.4.03	Including beds; DTp clause nr. 503; thickness 100mm; Depth 100mm; Nominal bore: 800mm	m	0.40	13.44	8.18	31.01	**52.63**	*11.57*
L5.3.4.04	Including beds; DTp clause nr. 503; thickness 100mm; Depth 100mm; Nominal bore: 900mm	m	0.43	14.45	8.79	41.47	**64.71**	*14.69*

L5 Surrounds continued...

		Unit	Labour Hours	Labour Net £	Plant Net £	Materials Net £	Unit Net £	CO_2 Kg
L5.3	**Imported granular material**							
L5.3.4	Nominal bore: 600 - 900mm							
L5.3.4.05	Including beds; DTp clause nr. 503; thickness 100mm; Depth 150mm; Nominal bore: 675mm	m	0.40	13.44	8.18	30.58	**52.20**	*11.45*
L5.3.4.06	Including beds; DTp clause nr. 503; thickness 100mm; Depth 150mm; Nominal bore: 750mm	m	0.43	14.45	8.79	33.75	**56.99**	*12.55*
L5.3.4.07	Including beds; DTp clause nr. 503; thickness 100mm; Depth 150mm; Nominal bore: 800mm	m	0.46	15.46	9.40	36.06	**60.92**	*13.41*
L5.3.4.08	Including beds; DTp clause nr. 503; thickness 100mm; Depth 150mm; Nominal bore: 900mm	m	0.49	16.47	10.02	40.21	**66.70**	*14.79*
L5.3.5	Nominal bore: 900 - 1200mm							
L5.3.5.01	Including beds; DTp clause nr. 503; thickness 100mm; Depth 100mm; Nominal bore: 1200mm	m	0.50	16.81	10.22	62.02	**89.05**	*20.91*
L5.3.5.02	Including beds; DTp clause nr. 503; thickness 100mm; Depth 150mm; Nominal bore: 1200mm	m	0.56	18.82	11.45	69.58	**99.85**	*23.45*
L5.3.6	Nominal bore: 1200 - 1500mm							
L5.3.6.01	Including beds; DTp clause nr. 503; thickness 100mm; Depth 100mm; Nominal bore: 1500mm	m	0.58	19.49	11.86	88.35	**119.70**	*28.81*
L5.3.6.02	Including beds; DTp clause nr. 503; thickness 100mm; Depth 150mm; Nominal bore: 1500mm	m	0.63	21.17	12.88	97.07	**131.12**	*31.60*
L5.3.7	Nominal bore: 1500 - 1800mm							
L5.3.7.01	Including beds; DTp clause nr. 503; thickness 100mm; Depth 100mm; Nominal bore: 1800mm	m	0.65	21.85	13.29	99.17	**134.31**	*32.32*
L5.3.7.02	Including beds; DTp clause nr. 503; thickness 100mm; Depth 150mm; Nominal bore: 1800mm	m	0.72	24.20	14.72	109.05	**147.97**	*35.58*
L5.4	**Mass Concrete**							
L5.4.1	Nominal bore: not exceeding 200mm							
L5.4.1.01	Including beds; grade 15, 20mm aggregate; thickness 100mm; Depth 100mm; Nominal bore: 100mm	m	0.12	4.03	2.45	14.22	**20.70**	*49.51*
L5.4.1.02	Including beds; grade 15, 20mm aggregate; thickness 100mm; Depth 100mm; Nominal bore: 150mm	m	0.15	5.04	3.07	17.56	**25.67**	*61.17*
L5.4.1.03	Including beds; grade 15, 20mm aggregate; thickness 100mm; Depth 150mm; Nominal bore: 100mm	m	0.15	5.04	3.07	19.23	**27.34**	*66.89*
L5.4.1.04	Including beds; grade 15, 20mm aggregate; thickness 100mm; Depth 150mm; Nominal bore: 150mm	m	0.19	6.39	3.88	23.00	**33.27**	*80.06*

L5 Surrounds continued...

		Unit	Labour Hours	Labour Net £	Plant Net £	Materials Net £	Unit Net £	CO_2 *Kg*
L5.4	**Mass Concrete**							
L5.4.2	Nominal bore: 200 - 300mm							
L5.4.2.01	Including beds; grade 15, 20mm aggregate; thickness 100mm; Depth 100mm; Nominal bore: 225mm	m	0.18	6.05	3.68	22.49	32.22	*78.27*
L5.4.2.02	Including beds; grade 15, 20mm aggregate; thickness 100mm; Depth 100mm; Nominal bore: 300mm	m	0.22	7.39	4.50	27.26	39.15	*94.87*
L5.4.2.03	Including beds; grade 15, 20mm aggregate; thickness 100mm; Depth 150mm; Nominal bore: 225mm	m	0.22	7.39	4.50	28.51	40.40	*99.16*
L5.4.2.04	Including beds; grade 15, 20mm aggregate; thickness 100mm; Depth 150mm; Nominal bore: 300mm	m	0.27	9.07	5.52	33.95	48.54	*118.12*
L5.4.3	Nominal bore: 300 - 600mm							
L5.4.3.01	Including beds; grade 15, 20mm aggregate; thickness 100mm; Depth 100mm; Nominal bore: 375mm	m	0.27	9.07	5.52	32.86	47.45	*114.40*
L5.4.3.02	Including beds; grade 15, 20mm aggregate; thickness 100mm; Depth 100mm; Nominal bore: 450mm	m	0.32	10.76	6.54	38.38	55.68	*133.65*
L5.4.3.03	Including beds; grade 15, 20mm aggregate; thickness 100mm; Depth 100mm; Nominal bore: 600mm	m	0.40	13.44	8.18	50.17	71.79	*174.57*
L5.4.3.04	Including beds; grade 15, 20mm aggregate; thickness 100mm; Depth 150mm; Nominal bore: 375mm	m	0.33	11.09	6.75	40.14	57.98	*139.73*
L5.4.3.05	Including beds; grade 15, 20mm aggregate; thickness 100mm; Depth 150mm; Nominal bore: 450mm	m	0.38	12.77	7.77	46.24	66.78	*160.98*
L5.4.3.06	Including beds; grade 15, 20mm aggregate; thickness 100mm; Depth 150mm; Nominal bore: 600mm	m	0.46	15.46	9.40	59.37	84.23	*206.47*
L5.4.4	Nominal bore: 600 - 900mm							
L5.4.4.01	Including beds; grade 15, 20mm aggregate; thickness 100mm; Depth 100mm; Nominal bore: 675mm	m	0.50	16.81	10.22	56.03	83.06	*195.33*
L5.4.4.02	Including beds; grade 15, 20mm aggregate; thickness 100mm; Depth 100mm; Nominal bore: 750mm	m	0.69	23.19	14.10	62.72	100.01	*219.62*
L5.4.4.03	Including beds; grade 15, 20mm aggregate; thickness 100mm; Depth 100mm; Nominal bore: 800mm	m	0.85	28.57	17.37	66.90	112.84	*235.11*
L5.4.4.04	Including beds; grade 15, 20mm aggregate; thickness 100mm; Depth 100mm; Nominal bore: 900mm	m	0.95	31.93	19.42	91.98	143.33	*321.65*

L5 Surrounds continued...

		Unit	Labour Hours	Labour Net £	Plant Net £	Materials Net £	Unit Net £	CO_2 Kg
L5.4	**Mass Concrete**							
L5.4.4	Nominal bore: 600 - 900mm							
L5.4.4.05	Including beds; grade 15, 20mm aggregate; thickness 100mm; Depth 150mm; Nominal bore: 675mm	m	0.57	19.16	11.65	65.98	**96.79**	*229.89*
L5.4.4.06	Including beds; grade 15, 20mm aggregate; thickness 100mm; Depth 150mm; Nominal bore: 750mm	m	0.77	25.88	15.74	72.83	**114.45**	*254.82*
L5.4.4.07	Including beds; grade 15, 20mm aggregate; thickness 100mm; Depth 150mm; Nominal bore: 800mm	m	0.95	31.93	19.42	77.77	**129.12**	*273.03*
L5.4.4.08	Including beds; grade 15, 20mm aggregate; thickness 100mm; Depth 150mm; Nominal bore: 900mm	m	1.05	35.29	21.46	86.71	**143.46**	*304.38*
L5.4.5	Nominal bore: 900 - 1200mm							
L5.4.5.01	Including beds; grade 15, 20mm aggregate; thickness 100mm; Depth 100mm; Nominal bore: 1200mm	m	1.15	38.65	23.51	133.79	**195.95**	*466.14*
L5.4.5.02	Including beds; grade 15, 20mm aggregate; thickness 100mm; Depth 150mm; Nominal bore: 1200mm	m	1.28	43.02	26.16	150.10	**219.28**	*522.87*
L5.4.6	Nominal bore: 1200 - 1500mm							
L5.4.6.01	Including beds; grade 15, 20mm aggregate; thickness 100mm; Depth 100mm; Nominal bore: 1500mm	m	1.38	46.38	28.21	190.65	**265.24**	*662.32*
L5.4.6.02	Including beds; grade 15, 20mm aggregate; thickness 100mm; Depth 150mm; Nominal bore: 1500mm	m	1.42	47.73	29.02	209.38	**286.13**	*726.68*
L5.4.7	Nominal bore: 1500 - 1800mm							
L5.4.7.01	Including beds; grade 15, 20mm aggregate; thickness 100mm; Depth 100mm; Nominal bore: 1800mm	m	1.60	53.78	32.70	214.07	**300.55**	*744.04*
L5.4.7.02	Including beds; grade 15, 20mm aggregate; thickness 100mm; Depth 150mm; Nominal bore: 1800mm	m	1.76	59.15	35.97	235.22	**330.34**	*817.58*
L5.5	**Reinforced concrete**							
L5.5.1	Nominal bore: not exceeding 200mm							
L5.5.1.01	Including beds; grade 25, 20mm aggregate; 1 layer A252 mesh reinforcement; thickness 100mm; Depth 100mm; Nominal bore: 100mm	m	0.15	5.04	3.07	16.51	**24.62**	*55.68*
L5.5.1.02	Including beds; grade 25, 20mm aggregate; 1 layer A252 mesh reinforcement; thickness 100mm; Depth 100mm; Nominal bore: 150mm	m	0.18	6.05	3.68	20.15	**29.88**	*67.84*

L5 Surrounds continued...

		Unit	Labour Hours	Labour Net £	Plant Net £	Materials Net £	Unit Net £	CO_2 Kg
L5.5	**Reinforced concrete**							
L5.5.1	Nominal bore: not exceeding 200mm							
L5.5.1.03	Including beds; grade 25, 20mm aggregate; 1 layer A252 mesh reinforcement; thickness 100mm; Depth 150mm; Nominal bore: 100mm	m	0.18	6.05	3.68	21.78	**31.51**	*73.07*
L5.5.1.04	Including beds; grade 25, 20mm aggregate; 1 layer A252 mesh reinforcement; thickness 100mm; Depth 150mm; Nominal bore: 150mm	m	0.22	7.39	4.50	25.86	**37.75**	*86.73*
L5.5.2	Nominal bore: 200 - 300mm							
L5.5.2.01	Including beds; grade 25, 20mm aggregate; 1 layer A252 mesh reinforcement; thickness 100mm; Depth 100mm; Nominal bore: 225mm	m	0.22	7.39	4.50	25.55	**37.44**	*85.81*
L5.5.2.02	Including beds; grade 25, 20mm aggregate; 1 layer A252 mesh reinforcement; thickness 100mm; Depth 100mm; Nominal bore: 300mm	m	0.26	8.74	5.31	30.74	**44.79**	*103.10*
L5.5.2.03	Including beds; grade 25, 20mm aggregate; 1 layer A252 mesh reinforcement; thickness 100mm; Depth 150mm; Nominal bore: 225mm	m	0.26	8.74	5.31	31.87	**45.92**	*106.69*
L5.5.2.04	Including beds; grade 25, 20mm aggregate; 1 layer A252 mesh reinforcement; thickness 100mm; Depth 150mm; Nominal bore: 300mm	m	0.31	10.42	6.34	37.77	**54.53**	*126.35*
L5.5.3	Nominal bore: 300 - 600mm							
L5.5.3.01	Including beds; grade 25, 20mm aggregate; 1 layer A252 mesh reinforcement; thickness 100mm; Depth 100mm; Nominal bore: 375mm	m	0.31	10.42	6.34	36.83	**53.59**	*123.42*
L5.5.3.02	Including beds; grade 25, 20mm aggregate; 1 layer A252 mesh reinforcement; thickness 100mm; Depth 100mm; Nominal bore: 450mm	m	0.37	12.44	7.56	42.82	**62.82**	*143.44*
L5.5.3.03	Including beds; grade 25, 20mm aggregate; 1 layer A252 mesh reinforcement; thickness 100mm; Depth 100mm; Nominal bore: 600mm	m	0.46	15.46	9.40	55.60	**80.46**	*185.92*
L5.5.3.04	Including beds; grade 25, 20mm aggregate; 1 layer A252 mesh reinforcement; thickness 100mm; Depth 150mm; Nominal bore: 375mm	m	0.37	12.44	7.56	44.48	**64.48**	*148.75*
L5.5.3.05	Including beds; grade 25, 20mm aggregate; 1 layer A252 mesh reinforcement; thickness 100mm; Depth 150mm; Nominal bore: 450mm	m	0.43	14.45	8.79	51.08	**74.32**	*170.77*

L5 Surrounds continued...

		Unit	Labour Hours	Labour Net £	Plant Net £	Materials Net £	Unit Net £	CO_2 Kg
L5.5	**Reinforced concrete**							
L5.5.3	Nominal bore: 300 - 600mm							
L5.5.3.06	Including beds; grade 25, 20mm aggregate; 1 layer A252 mesh reinforcement; thickness 100mm; Depth 150mm; Nominal bore: 600mm	m	0.52	17.48	10.63	65.27	**93.38**	*217.83*
L5.5.4	Nominal bore: 600 - 900mm							
L5.5.4.01	Including beds; grade 25, 20mm aggregate; 1 layer A252 mesh reinforcement; thickness 100mm; Depth 100mm; Nominal bore: 675mm	m	0.56	18.82	11.45	62.35	**92.62**	*208.71*
L5.5.4.02	Including beds; grade 25, 20mm aggregate; 1 layer A252 mesh reinforcement; thickness 100mm; Depth 100mm; Nominal bore: 750mm	m	0.77	25.88	15.74	69.17	**110.79**	*232.61*
L5.5.4.03	Including beds; grade 25, 20mm aggregate; 1 layer A252 mesh reinforcement; thickness 100mm; Depth 100mm; Nominal bore: 800mm	m	0.92	30.92	18.80	73.70	**123.42**	*248.52*
L5.5.4.04	Including beds; grade 25, 20mm aggregate; 1 layer A252 mesh reinforcement; thickness 100mm; Depth 100mm; Nominal bore: 900mm	m	1.02	34.28	20.85	82.75	**137.88**	*278.85*
L5.5.4.05	Including beds; grade 25, 20mm aggregate; 1 layer A252 mesh reinforcement; thickness 100mm; Depth 150mm; Nominal bore: 675mm	m	0.63	21.17	12.88	72.42	**106.47**	*242.03*
L5.5.4.06	Including beds; grade 25, 20mm aggregate; 1 layer A252 mesh reinforcement; thickness 100mm; Depth 150mm; Nominal bore: 750mm	m	0.83	27.90	16.97	79.81	**124.68**	*267.66*
L5.5.4.07	Including beds; grade 25, 20mm aggregate; 1 layer A252 mesh reinforcement; thickness 100mm; Depth 150mm; Nominal bore: 800mm	m	1.02	34.28	20.85	85.12	**140.25**	*286.44*
L5.5.4.08	Including beds; grade 25, 20mm aggregate; 1 layer A252 mesh reinforcement; thickness 100mm; Depth 150mm; Nominal bore: 900mm	m	1.12	37.64	22.89	94.79	**155.32**	*318.78*
L5.5.5	Nominal bore: 900 - 1200mm							
L5.5.5.01	Including beds; grade 25, 20mm aggregate; 1 layer A252 mesh reinforcement; thickness 100mm; Depth 100mm; Nominal bore: 1200mm	m	1.25	42.01	25.55	145.70	**213.26**	*486.21*
L5.5.5.02	Including beds; grade 25, 20mm aggregate; 1 layer A252 mesh reinforcement; thickness 100mm; Depth 150mm; Nominal bore: 1200mm	m	1.38	46.38	28.21	162.83	**237.42**	*542.95*

L5 Surrounds continued...

		Unit	Labour Hours	Labour Net £	Plant Net £	Materials Net £	Unit Net £	CO_2 Kg
L5.5	**Reinforced concrete**							
L5.5.6	Nominal bore: 1200 - 1500mm							
L5.5.6.01	Including beds; grade 25, 20mm aggregate; 1 layer A252 mesh reinforcement; thickness 100mm; Depth 100mm; Nominal bore: 1500mm	m	1.49	50.08	30.46	206.24	**286.78**	*685.45*
L5.5.6.02	Including beds; grade 25, 20mm aggregate; 1 layer A252 mesh reinforcement; thickness 100mm; Depth 150mm; Nominal bore: 1500mm	m	1.53	51.42	31.27	201.41	**284.10**	*670.02*
L5.5.7	Nominal bore: 1500 - 1800mm							
L5.5.7.01	Including beds; grade 25, 20mm aggregate; 1 layer A252 mesh reinforcement; thickness 100mm; Depth 100mm; Nominal bore: 1800mm	m	1.73	58.15	35.36	231.63	**325.14**	*770.29*
L5.5.7.02	Including beds; grade 25, 20mm aggregate; 1 layer A252 mesh reinforcement; thickness 100mm; Depth 150mm; Nominal bore: 1800mm	m	1.89	63.52	38.63	253.86	**356.01**	*843.83*

L7 Concrete Stools and Thrust Blocks

		Unit	Labour Hours	Labour Net £	Plant Net £	Materials Net £	Unit Net £	CO_2 Kg
L7.1	**Volume: not exceeding 0.1m³**							
L7.1.1	Concrete grade 25, 20mm aggregate							
L7.1.1.01	Generally	Nr	0.25	8.40	5.11	8.79	**22.30**	*30.46*
L7.1.2	Concrete grade 25, 20mm aggregate; Sulphate Resistant Cement, BS 4027							
L7.1.2.01	Generally	Nr	0.25	8.40	5.11	9.67	**23.18**	*30.46*
L7.2	**Volume: 0.1 – 0.2m³**							
L7.2.1	Concrete grade 25, 20mm aggregate							
L7.2.1.01	Generally	Nr	0.40	13.44	8.18	17.58	**39.20**	*60.17*
L7.2.2	Concrete grade 25, 20mm aggregate; Sulphate Resistant Cement, BS 4027							
L7.2.2.01	Generally	Nr	0.40	13.44	8.18	19.34	**40.96**	*60.17*
L7.3	**Volume: 0.2 – 0.5m³**							
L7.3.1	Concrete grade 25, 20mm aggregate							
L7.3.1.01	Generally	Nr	0.70	23.53	14.31	43.94	**81.78**	*148.20*
L7.3.2	Concrete grade 25, 20mm aggregate; Sulphate Resistant Cement, BS 4027							
L7.3.2.01	Generally	Nr	0.70	23.53	14.31	48.34	**86.18**	*148.20*
L7.4	**Volume: 0.5 – 1m³**							
L7.4.1	Concrete grade 25, 20mm aggregate							
L7.4.1.01	Generally	Nr	1.00	33.61	20.44	87.88	**141.93**	*293.42*
L7.4.2	Concrete grade 25, 20mm aggregate; Sulphate Resistant Cement, BS 4027							
L7.4.2.01	Generally	Nr	1.00	33.61	20.44	96.68	**150.73**	*293.42*

L7 Concrete Stools and Thrust Blocks continued...

		Unit	Labour Hours	Labour Net £	Plant Net £	Materials Net £	Unit Net £	CO_2 Kg
L7.5	**Volume: 1 – 2m³**							
L7.5.1	Concrete grade 25, 20mm aggregate							
L7.5.1.01	Generally	Nr	2.00	67.22	40.88	175.76	**283.86**	*586.85*
L7.5.2	Concrete grade 25, 20mm aggregate; Sulphate Resistant Cement, BS 4027							
L7.5.2.01	Generally	Nr	2.00	67.22	40.88	193.36	**301.46**	*586.85*
L7.6	**Volume: 2 – 4m³**							
L7.6.1	Concrete grade 25, 20mm aggregate							
L7.6.1.01	Generally	Nr	3.50	117.63	71.54	351.52	**540.69**	*1,169.98*
L7.6.2	Concrete grade 25, 20mm aggregate; Sulphate Resistant Cement, BS 4027							
L7.6.2.01	Generally	Nr	3.50	117.63	71.54	386.72	**575.89**	*1,169.98*
L7.8	**Volume: stated exceeding 6m**							
L7.8.1	Concrete grade 25, 20mm aggregate							
L7.8.1.01	Volume: 8m3	Nr	6.00	201.66	122.64	703.04	**1,027.34**	*2,332.54*
L7.8.1.02	Volume: 25m3	Nr	15.00	504.15	306.60	2,197.00	**3,007.75**	*7,261.35*
L7.8.2	Concrete grade 25, 20mm aggregate; Sulphate Resistant Cement, BS 4027							
L7.8.2.01	Volume: 8m3	Nr	6.00	201.66	122.64	773.44	**1,097.74**	*2,332.54*
L7.8.2.02	Volume: 25m3	Nr	15.00	504.15	306.60	2,417.00	**3,227.75**	*7,261.35*

CLASS M:
STRUCTURAL METALWORK

Calculations used throughout Class M - Structural Metalwork

Labour

		Qty		Rate		Total
L A0315ICE	**Paint Spray Labour Gang**					
	Spray painter	1	x	16.68	=	£16.68
	Total hourly cost of gang				**=**	**£16.68**
L M0001ICE	**Shot Blasting Labour Gang**					
	Ganger	1	x	16.99	=	£16.99
	Labourer (General Operative)	2	x	12.56	=	£25.12
	Total hourly cost of gang				**=**	**£42.11**
L M0002ICE	**Structural Steel Erection Labour Gang**					
	Labourer (Skill Rate 3)	1	x	14.34	=	£14.34
	Fitters and Welders	2	x	16.68	=	£33.37
	Total hourly cost of gang				**=**	**£47.71**
L M0003ICE	**Structural Steel Fabrication Labour Gang**					
	Labourer (Skill Rate 3)	1	x	14.34	=	£14.34
	Fitters and Welders	2	x	16.68	=	£33.37
	Total hourly cost of gang				**=**	**£47.71**

Plant

		Qty		Rate		Total
P M0004ICE	**Shot Blasting Plant Gang**					
	Shotblast Equipment (3.0 Bag Pot) with 250 cfm Compressor	1	x	3.35	=	£3.35
	Total hourly cost of gang				**=**	**£3.35**
P M0005ICE	**Structural Steel Erection Plant Gang**					
	Welding Set - 300 amp Diesel Electric Start Sil	1	x	4.18	=	£4.18
	Cutting and Burning Gear	1	x	3.52	=	£3.52
	Fork Lift Truck - 2.5t 4WD	1	x	26.80	=	£26.80
	Cranes Transit - 25t	1	x	56.27	=	£56.27
	Total hourly cost of gang				**=**	**£90.77**

Class M - Structural Metalwork

Note(s): The following prices are guide prices for approximate estimating.

M3 Fabrication of Members for Frames

		Unit	Labour Hours	Labour Net £	Plant Net £	Materials Net £	Unit Net £	CO_2 Kg
M3.1	**Columns**							
M3.1.1	Straight on plan							
M3.1.1.01	Universal Column section; 254 UC to 305 UC	Tonne	6.00	286.26	560.09	575.37	1,421.72	*2,106.56*
M3.2	**Beams**							
M3.2.1	Straight on plan							
M3.2.1.01	Universal Beam section; 356 UB to 533 UB; not exceeding 7m long	Tonne	6.00	286.26	560.09	575.37	1,421.72	*2,106.56*
M3.3	**Portal Frames**							
M3.3.1	Straight on plan							
M3.3.1.01	Span: 15m; 203 UB to 254 UB	Tonne	8.00	381.68	741.65	575.37	1,698.70	*2,216.22*
M3.3.1.02	Span: 20m; 406 UB to 457 UB	Tonne	7.00	333.97	650.87	575.37	1,560.21	*2,161.39*
M3.3.1.03	Span: 30m; 533 UB to 610 UB	Tonne	6.00	286.26	560.09	575.37	1,421.72	*2,106.56*
M3.4	**Trestles, towers and built-up columns**							
M3.4.1	Straight on plan							
M3.4.1.01	bolted angle construction, piece small	Tonne	9.00	429.39	832.43	575.37	1,837.19	*2,271.05*
M3.5	**Trusses and built-up girders**							
M3.5.1	Straight on plan; span							
M3.5.1.01	15m bolted angle construction	Tonne	10.00	477.10	923.21	575.37	1,975.68	*2,325.89*
M3.5.1.02	20m structural tee beam internal angles welded	Tonne	9.00	429.39	832.43	575.37	1,837.19	*2,271.05*
M3.5.1.03	30m structural tee beam internal angles welded	Tonne	9.00	429.39	832.43	575.37	1,837.19	*2,271.05*
M3.6	**Bracings, purlins and cladding rails**							
M3.6.1	Straight on plan							
M3.6.1.01	Generally	Tonne	10.00	477.10	923.21	575.37	1,975.68	*2,325.89*
M3.8	**Anchorages and holding down bolt assemblies**							
M3.8.1	Holding down bolts and plates (per tonne of base)							
M3.8.1.01	Generally	Tonne	12.00	572.52	1,104.77	575.37	2,252.66	*2,435.55*

M4 Fabrication of Other Members

M4.1	**Columns**							
M4.1.1	Straight on plan							
M4.1.1.01	Universal Column section; 254 UC to 305 UC	Tonne	6.00	286.26	560.09	575.37	1,421.72	*2,106.56*

M4 Fabrication of Other Members continued...

		Unit	Labour Hours	Labour Net £	Plant Net £	Materials Net £	Unit Net £	CO_2 Kg
M4.2	**Beams**							
M4.2.1	Straight on plan							
M4.2.1.01	Universal Beam section; 356 UB to 533 UB; not exceeding 7m long	Tonne	6.00	286.26	560.09	575.37	**1,421.72**	*2,106.56*
M4.3	**Portal frames**							
M4.3.1	Straight on plan							
M4.3.1.01	Universal Beam section; minimum section 457 UB	Tonne	7.00	333.97	650.87	575.37	**1,560.21**	*2,161.39*
M4.4	**Trestles, towers and built-up columns**							
M4.4.1	Straight on plan							
M4.4.1.01	bolted angle construction, piece small	Tonne	9.00	429.39	832.43	575.37	**1,837.19**	*2,271.05*
M4.5	**Trusses and built-up girders**							
M4.5.1	Straight on plan							
M4.5.1.01	not exceeding 20m long	Tonne	9.00	429.39	832.43	575.37	**1,837.19**	*2,271.05*
M4.6	**Bracings, purlins and cladding rails**							
M4.6.1	Straight on plan							
M4.6.1.01	Generally	Tonne	10.00	477.10	923.21	575.37	**1,975.68**	*2,325.89*
M4.8	**Anchorages and holding down bolt assemblies**							
M4.8.1	Holding down bolts and plates (per tonne of base)							
M4.8.1.01	Generally	Tonne	12.00	572.52	1,104.77	575.37	**2,252.66**	*2,435.55*

M6 Erection of Members for Frames

		Unit	Labour Hours	Labour Net £	Plant Net £	Materials Net £	Unit Net £	CO_2 Kg
M6.2	**Permanent erection**							
M6.2.1	Steel members							
M6.2.1.01	Generally	Tonne	2.00	95.42	181.56	-	**276.98**	*109.67*

M7 Erection of Other Members

		Unit	Labour Hours	Labour Net £	Plant Net £	Materials Net £	Unit Net £	CO_2 Kg
M7.2	**Permanent erection**							
M7.2.1	Steel members							
M7.2.1.01	Generally	Tonne	2.00	95.42	181.56	-	**276.98**	*109.67*
M7.3	**Site bolts: black**							
M7.3.1	Diameter: 20 - 24mm							
M7.3.1.01	Generally; 24mm diameter	Nr	0.01	0.24	0.45	3.00	**3.69**	*1.09*
M7.4	**HSFG general grade**							
M7.4.1	Diameter: 20 - 24mm							
M7.4.1.01	Generally; 24mm diameter	Nr	0.01	0.33	0.64	3.35	**4.32**	*1.26*

M7 Erection of Other Members continued...

		Unit	Labour Hours	Labour Net £	Plant Net £	Materials Net £	Unit Net £	CO_2 Kg
M7.5	**HSFG higher grade**							
M7.5.1	Diameter: 20 - 24mm							
M7.5.1.01	Generally; 24mm diameter	Nr	0.01	0.38	0.73	3.35	**4.46**	*1.31*
M7.6	**HSFG load indicating or load limit types, general grade**							
M7.6.1	Diameter: 20 - 24mm							
M7.6.1.01	Generally; 24mm diameter	Nr	0.01	0.62	1.18	4.21	**6.01**	*1.56*
M7.7	**HSFG load indicating or load limit types, higher grade**							
M7.7.1	Diameter: 20 - 24mm							
M7.7.1.01	Generally; 24mm diameter	Nr	0.01	0.62	1.18	4.21	**6.01**	*1.56*

M8 Off Site Surface Treatment

		Unit	Labour Hours	Labour Net £	Plant Net £	Materials Net £	Unit Net £	CO_2 Kg
M8.1	**Blast cleaning**							
M8.1.1	SA 2.5							
M8.1.1.01	Generally	m^2	0.05	2.11	0.17	2.04	**4.32**	*0.71*
M8.6	**Galvanising**							
M8.6.1	BS 729: 600g/m2; Average: 20m2/tonne							
M8.6.1.01	Generally	m^2	-	-	-	-	**26.62**	*52.50*
M8.7	**Painting**							
M8.7.1	High build Epoxy zinc phosphate							
M8.7.1.01	Generally	m^2	0.17	2.79	0.48	1.66	**4.93**	*0.60*

CLASS N:

MISCELLANEOUS METALWORK

Calculations used throughout Class N - Miscellaneous Metalwork

Labour

		Qty		Rate		Total
L M0003ICE	**Structural Steel Fabrication Labour Gang**					
	Labourer (Skill Rate 3)	1	x	14.34	=	£14.34
	Fitters and Welders	2	x	16.68	=	£33.37
	Total hourly cost of gang				**=**	**£47.71**
L N0001ICE	**Motorway Barrier Install Labour Gang**					
	Ganger	2	x	16.99	=	£33.97
	Labourer (Skill Rate 4)	2	x	13.53	=	£27.06
	Labourer (General Operative)	4	x	12.56	=	£50.24
	Plant Operator (Class 4)	2	x	14.75	=	£29.50
	Total hourly cost of gang				**=**	**£140.77**

Plant

		Qty		Rate		Total
P M0006ICE	**Structural Steel Fabrication Plant Gang**					
	Welding Set - 300 amp Diesel Electric Start Sil	1	x	4.18	=	£4.18
	Cutting and Burning Gear	1	x	3.52	=	£3.52
	Fork Lift Truck - 2.5t 4WD	1	x	26.80	=	£26.80
	Cranes Transit - 25t	1	x	56.27	=	£56.27
	Total hourly cost of gang				**=**	**£90.77**
P N0002ICE	**Motorway Barrier Install Plant Gang**					
	Tipping Waggon - 10t 4-Wheel (16t Gr)	1	x	41.94	=	£41.94
	Agricultural Tractor: Fencing Auger	1	x	23.44	=	£23.44
	Compressor - 2-Tool (Complete)	1	x	4.86	=	£4.86
	Hose & Breaker & 3 Steels	1	x	0.35	=	£0.35
	Dumper - 2.0t 4WD Swivel Skip	1	x	21.08	=	£21.08
	Generator - 3kvA Petrol	1	x	1.56	=	£1.56
	Generator - 3kvA Petrol	1	x	1.56	=	£1.56
	Total hourly cost of gang				**=**	**£94.79**

Class N - Miscellaneous Metalwork

Note(s): The following prices are guide prices for approximate estimating. All materials are mild steel unless stated otherwise.

N1 Miscellaneous Metalwork

		Unit	Labour Hours	Labour Net £	Plant Net £	Materials Net £	Unit Net £	CO_2 Kg
N1.1	**Stairways and landings**							
N1.1.1	Mild steel fabrication, fixings included							
N1.1.1.01	Generally	Tonne	12.00	572.52	1,104.77	1,341.01	**3,018.30**	*3,580.92*
N1.2	**Walkways and platforms**							
N1.2.1	Mild steel fabrication, fixings included							
N1.2.1.01	Generally	Tonne	12.00	572.52	1,104.77	1,341.01	**3,018.30**	*3,580.92*
N1.3	**Ladders**							
N1.3.1	Ladders; 400mm wide; 65 x 10mm stringers; 20mm diameter rungs							
N1.3.1.01	Generally	m	2.00	95.42	196.97	56.27	**348.66**	*245.50*
N1.5	**Bridge parapets**							
N1.5.1	Mild steel fabrication, fixing included; DTp specification for railings							
N1.5.1.01	Type P1; 3 rails; posts at 3m centres	m	0.63	87.98	59.25	67.90	**215.13**	*153.85*
N1.5.1.02	Type P4; pedestrian guard railing; posts at 2m centres	m	0.63	87.98	59.25	67.90	**215.13**	*153.85*
N1.5.1.03	Type P6; sound screen; solid infill; 2m high	m	0.67	93.89	63.23	137.90	**295.02**	*160.25*
N1.6	**Miscellaneous Framing**							
N1.6.1	Angle section							
N1.6.1.01	76 x 64mm x 9.68kg/m; galvanised steel walkway supports	m	0.08	3.96	22.95	13.39	**40.30**	*41.23*
N1.6.1.02	102 x 65mm x 13.4kg/m; galvanised steel toe plate	m	0.17	7.97	30.57	17.46	**56.00**	*54.65*
N1.6.2	Channel section							
N1.6.2.01	Galvanised walkway supports; Fixing 3m above ground level; 102 x 51mm x 10.42kg/m	m	0.08	3.96	22.95	13.43	**40.34**	*41.30*
N1.6.2.02	as above; 152 x 76mm x 17.88kg/m	m	0.17	7.97	30.57	24.13	**62.67**	*69.18*
N1.6.2.03	as above; 178 x 89mm x 26.81kg/m	m	0.25	11.93	38.11	36.20	**86.24**	*99.96*
N1.6.2.04	as above; 203 x 89mm x 29.78kg/m	m	0.33	15.89	45.64	40.22	**101.75**	*113.26*
N1.6.2.05	as above; 254 x 76mm x 28.29kg/m	m	0.33	15.89	45.64	37.56	**99.09**	*107.48*
N1.6.2.06	Galvanised walkway supports; Fixing 6m above ground level; 102 x 51mm x 10.42kg/m	m	0.17	7.97	30.57	13.43	**51.97**	*45.91*
N1.6.2.07	as above; 152 x 76mm x 17.88kg/m	m	0.33	15.89	45.64	24.13	**85.66**	*78.28*
N1.6.2.08	as above; 178 x 89mm x 26.81kg/m	m	0.50	23.86	60.80	36.20	**120.86**	*113.67*
N1.6.2.09	as above; 203 x 89mm x 29.78kg/m	m	0.67	31.82	75.96	40.22	**148.00**	*131.57*

N1 Miscellaneous Metalwork continued...

		Unit	Labour Hours	Labour Net £	Plant Net £	Materials Net £	Unit Net £	CO_2 Kg
N1.6	**Miscellaneous Framing**							
N1.6.2	Channel section							
N1.6.2.10	as above; 254 x 76mm x 28.29kg/m	m	0.67	31.82	75.96	37.56	**145.34**	*125.79*
N1.6.2.11	Galvanised steel cable tray supports; Section size: 305 x 89mm x 41.69kg/m	m	1.00	47.71	106.19	56.31	**210.21**	*184.81*

CLASS O:
TIMBER

Calculations used throughout Class O - Timber

Labour

		Qty		Rate		Total
L A0240ICE	**Timber Labour Gang**					
	Timberman	1	x	14.34	=	£14.34
	Labourer (Skill Rate 3)	1	x	14.34	=	£14.34
	Labourer (General Operative)	1	x	12.56	=	£12.56
	Total hourly cost of gang				**=**	**£41.24**

Plant

		Qty		Rate		Total
P A1240ICE	**Timber Plant Gang**					
	Compressor - 2-Tool (Complete)	1	x	4.86	=	£4.86
	Kango Type Tool - Electric Power Drill 19mm	2	x	1.04	=	£2.09
	Kango Type Tool - Electric Screwdriver	1	x	0.48	=	£0.48
	Kango Type Tool - Electric Nut Runner	1	x	0.48	=	£0.48
	Cranes Crawler - NCK 305B - 20t	0.5	x	45.36	=	£22.68
	Total hourly cost of gang				**=**	**£30.59**

Class O - Timber

Note(s): 1) The hardness and toughness of species of timber varies considerably. The labour rates shown are based on working an average timber of grade 4 such as Douglas Fir. As the grades go as high as grade 9 for Greenheart it follows that more time is required to work the high grades. For example, boring Greenheart would take three times as long as boring pine.

2) The very hard woods are difficult to shape truly, this makes it difficult to marry up bolt holes so it is recommeneded that structural members are constructed as modules with a minimum of in-place boring.

3) Most timber is imported into this country; thus the price is largely influenced by the currency rates of exchange, so it is essential to get up to date quotations for timber particularly the hardwoods, much of which comes from the Amercias and Canada.

O1 Hardwood Components

		Unit	Labour Hours	Labour Net £	Plant Net £	Materials Net £	Unit Net £	*CO_2 Kg*
O1.1	**Cross sectional area: not exceeding 0.01m²**							
O1.1.1	Length: not exceeding 1.5m							
O1.1.1.01	Sawn finish; Greenheart; 100 x 75mm	m	0.33	13.61	10.09	8.32	32.02	*5.95*
O1.1.2	Length: 1.5 - 3m							
O1.1.2.01	Sawn finish; Greenheart; 100 x 75mm	m	0.33	13.61	10.09	5.82	29.52	*5.20*
O1.1.3	Length: 3 - 5m							
O1.1.3.01	Sawn finish; Greenheart; 100 x 75mm	m	0.29	11.96	8.87	5.82	26.65	*4.78*
O1.2	**Cross sectional area: 0.01 - 0.02m²**							
O1.2.2	Length: 1.5 - 3m							
O1.2.2.01	Sawn finish; Greenheart; 150 x 75mm; runners in marine work	m	0.37	15.26	11.32	8.32	34.90	*6.37*
O1.2.2.02	Sawn finish; Greenheart; 75 x 225mm; runners in marine work	m	0.45	18.56	13.77	14.14	46.47	*8.94*
O1.2.3	Length: 3 - 5m							
O1.2.3.01	Sawn finish; Greenheart; 150 x 75mm; runners in marine work	m	0.33	13.61	10.09	8.32	32.02	*5.95*
O1.2.3.02	Sawn finish; Greenheart; 75 x 225mm; runners in marine work	m	0.41	16.91	12.54	14.14	43.59	*8.52*
O1.3	**Cross sectional area: 0.02 - 0.04m²**							
O1.3.2	Length: 1.5 - 3m							
O1.3.2.01	Sawn finish; Greenheart; 200 x 200mm; braces in marine work	m	1.48	61.04	45.27	33.28	139.59	*25.47*
O1.3.3	Length: 3 - 5m							
O1.3.3.01	Sawn finish; Greenheart; 200 x 200mm; braces in marine work	m	1.36	56.09	41.60	33.28	130.97	*24.20*
O1.4	**Cross sectional area: 0.04 - 0.1m²**							
O1.4.2	Length: 1.5 - 3m							
O1.4.2.01	Sawn finish; Greenheart; 300 x 150mm; braces between piles in marine work	m	1.49	61.45	45.58	37.44	144.47	*26.81*
O1.4.2.02	Sawn finish; Greenheart; 200 x 300mm; fenders in marine work	m	1.13	46.60	34.57	49.92	131.09	*26.74*
O1.4.2.03	Sawn finish; Greenheart; 300 x 300mm; fenders in marine work	m	1.41	58.15	43.13	74.87	176.15	*37.11*

O1 Hardwood Components continued...

		Unit	Labour Hours	Labour Net £	Plant Net £	Materials Net £	Unit Net £	CO_2 Kg
O1.4	**Cross sectional area: 0.04 - 0.1m²**							
O1.4.3	Length: 3 - 5m							
O1.4.3.01	Sawn finish; Greenheart; 300 x 150mm; braces between piles in marine work	m	1.37	56.50	41.91	37.44	135.85	*25.55*
O1.4.3.02	Sawn finish; Greenheart; 200 x 300mm; fenders in marine work	m	1.00	41.24	30.59	49.92	121.75	*25.37*
O1.4.3.03	Sawn finish; Greenheart; 300 x 300mm; fenders in marine work	m	1.21	49.90	37.01	74.87	161.78	*35.00*
O1.4.4	Length: 5 - 8m							
O1.4.4.01	Sawn finish; Greenheart; 300 x 150mm; braces between piles in marine work	m	1.29	53.20	39.46	37.44	130.10	*24.71*
O1.4.4.02	Sawn finish; Greenheart; 300 x 150mm; braces between piles in marine work; fixed between high water level ordinary spring tides (assumed 8m above ordnance datum) and low water level ordinary spring tides (assumed 3.5m above ordnance datum)	m	2.12	87.43	64.85	37.44	189.72	*33.44*
O1.4.4.03	Sawn finish; Greenheart; 200 x 300mm; fenders in marine work	m	0.95	39.18	29.06	49.92	118.16	*24.84*
O1.4.4.04	Sawn finish; Greenheart; 300 x 300mm; fenders in marine work	m	1.13	46.60	34.57	74.87	156.04	*34.16*
O1.5	**Cross sectional area: 0.1 - 0.2m²**							
O1.5.3	Length: 3 - 5m							
O1.5.3.01	Sawn finish; Greenheart; 600 x 300mm; baulk in marine work	m	1.61	66.40	49.25	149.75	265.40	*61.48*
O1.5.4	Length: 5 - 8m							
O1.5.4.01	Sawn finish; Greenheart; 600 x 300mm; baulk in marine work	m	1.41	58.15	43.13	149.75	251.03	*59.38*
O1.6	**Cross sectional area: 0.2 - 0.4m²**							
O1.6.3	Length: 3 - 5m							
O1.6.3.01	Sawn finish; Greenheart; 600 x 600mm; baulk in marine work	m	2.01	82.89	61.49	299.50	443.88	*110.24*
O1.6.4	Length: 5 - 8m							
O1.6.4.01	Sawn finish; Greenheart; 600 x 600mm; baulk in marine work	m	1.21	49.90	37.01	299.50	386.41	*101.83*
O1.7	**Cross sectional area: exceeding 0.4m²**							
O1.7.3	Length: 3 - 5m							
O1.7.3.01	Sawn finish; Greenheart; 750 x 600mm; baulk in marine work	m	2.01	82.89	61.49	374.37	518.75	*132.52*
O1.7.4	Length: 5 - 8m							
O1.7.4.01	Sawn finish; Greenheart; 750 x 600mm; baulk in marine work	m	1.21	49.90	37.01	374.37	461.28	*124.10*

O2 Softwood Components

		Unit	Labour Hours	Labour Net £	Plant Net £	Materials Net £	Unit Net £	CO_2 Kg
O2.1	**Cross sectional area: not exceeding 0.01m²**							
O2.1.1	Length: not exceeding 1.5m							
O2.1.1.01	Wrot finish; Douglas fir; 100 x 75mm	m	0.27	11.13	8.26	3.90	**23.29**	*4.57*
O2.1.2	Length: 1.5 - 3m							
O2.1.2.01	Wrot finish; Douglas fir; 100 x 75mm	m	0.27	11.13	8.26	3.90	**23.29**	*4.57*
O2.1.3	Length: 3 - 5m							
O2.1.3.01	Wrot finish; Douglas fir; 100 x 75mm	m	0.23	9.49	7.04	3.90	**20.43**	*4.15*
O2.2	**Cross sectional area: 0.01 - 0.02m²**							
O2.2.2	Length: 1.5 - 3m							
O2.2.2.01	Wrot finish; Douglas fir; 150 x 75mm; runners in marine work	m	0.25	10.31	7.65	6.12	**24.08**	*5.35*
O2.2.2.02	Wrot finish; Douglas fir; 75 x 225mm; runners in marine work	m	0.25	10.31	7.65	9.46	**27.42**	*6.84*
O2.2.3	Length: 3 - 5m							
O2.2.3.01	Wrot finish; Douglas fir; 150 x 75mm; runners in marine work	m	0.20	8.25	6.12	6.12	**20.49**	*4.83*
O2.2.3.02	Wrot finish; Douglas fir; 75 x 225mm; runners in marine work	m	0.21	8.66	6.42	9.46	**24.54**	*6.42*
O2.3	**Cross sectional area: 0.02 - 0.04m²**							
O2.3.2	Length: 1.5 - 3m							
O2.3.2.01	Wrot finish; Douglas fir; 200 x 200mm; braces in marine work	m	1.00	41.24	30.59	22.26	**94.09**	*20.42*
O2.3.3	Length: 3 - 5m							
O2.3.3.01	Wrot finish; Douglas fir; 200 x 200mm; braces in marine work	m	0.93	38.27	28.39	22.26	**88.92**	*19.66*
O2.4	**Cross sectional area: 0.04 - 0.1m²**							
O2.4.2	Length: 1.5 - 3m							
O2.4.2.01	Wrot finish; Douglas fir; 300 x 150mm; braces between piles in marine work	m	1.04	42.72	31.69	25.04	**99.45**	*22.03*
O2.4.2.02	Wrot finish; Douglas fir; 200 x 300mm; fenders in marine work	m	0.78	32.25	23.92	33.39	**89.56**	*23.08*
O2.4.2.03	Wrot finish; Douglas fir; 300 x 300mm; fenders in marine work	m	0.99	40.83	30.28	50.09	**121.20**	*32.69*
O2.4.3	Length: 3 - 5m							
O2.4.3.01	Wrot finish; Douglas fir; 300 x 150mm; braces between piles in marine work	m	0.96	39.43	29.24	25.04	**93.71**	*21.19*
O2.4.3.02	Wrot finish; Douglas fir; 200 x 300mm; fenders in marine work	m	0.65	26.72	19.82	33.39	**79.93**	*21.67*
O2.4.3.03	Wrot finish; Douglas fir; 300 x 300mm; fenders in marine work	m	0.90	37.12	27.84	50.09	**115.05**	*31.85*
O2.4.4	Length: 5 - 8m							
O2.4.4.01	Wrot finish; Douglas fir; 300 x 150mm; braces between piles in marine work	m	0.88	36.13	26.80	25.04	**87.97**	*20.35*

O2 Softwood Components continued...

		Unit	Labour Hours	Labour Net £	Plant Net £	Materials Net £	Unit Net £	CO_2 Kg
O2.4	**Cross sectional area: 0.04 - 0.1m²**							
O2.4.4	Length: 5 - 8m							
O2.4.4.02	Wrot finish; Douglas fir; 300 x 150mm; braces between piles in marine work; fixed between high water level ordinary spring tides (assumed 8m above ordnance datum) and low water level ordinary spring tides (assumed 3.5m above ordnance datum)	m	1.52	62.68	46.50	25.04	134.22	*27.12*
O2.4.4.03	Wrot finish; Douglas fir; 200 x 300mm; fenders in marine work	m	0.60	24.83	18.42	33.39	76.64	*21.18*
O2.4.4.04	Wrot finish; Douglas fir; 300 x 300mm; fenders in marine work	m	0.87	35.88	26.61	50.09	112.58	*31.43*
O2.5	**Cross sectional area: 0.1 - 0.2m²**							
O2.5.3	Length: 3 - 5m							
O2.5.3.01	Wrot finish; Douglas fir; 600 x 300mm; baulk in marine work	m	1.08	44.54	33.04	100.17	177.75	*55.91*
O2.5.4	Length: 5 - 8m							
O2.5.4.01	Wrot finish; Douglas fir; 600 x 300mm; baulk in marine work	m	1.02	42.06	31.20	100.17	173.43	*55.28*
O2.6	**Cross sectional area: 0.2 - 0.4m²**							
O2.6.3	Length: 3 - 5m							
O2.6.3.01	Wrot finish; Douglas fir; 600 x 600mm; baulk in marine work	m	1.41	58.15	43.13	200.35	301.63	*103.93*
O2.6.4	Length: 5 - 8m							
O2.6.4.01	Wrot finish; Douglas fir; 600 x 600mm; baulk in marine work	m	1.00	41.24	30.59	200.35	272.18	*99.62*
O2.7	**Cross sectional area: exceeding 0.4m²**							
O2.7.3	Length: 3 - 5m							
O2.7.3.01	Wrot finish; Douglas fir; 750 x 600mm; baulk in marine work	m	1.44	59.39	44.05	250.43	353.87	*126.52*
O2.7.4	Length: 5 - 8m							
O2.7.4.01	Wrot finish; Douglas fir; 750 x 600mm; baulk in marine work	m	1.00	41.24	30.59	250.43	322.26	*121.89*

O3 Hardwood Decking

		Unit	Labour Hours	Labour Net £	Plant Net £	Materials Net £	Unit Net £	CO_2 Kg
O3.2	**Thickness: 25 - 50mm**							
O3.2.1	Sawn finish; Greenheart; in marine work							
O3.2.1.01	Generally	m^2	0.60	24.74	18.35	41.60	84.69	*18.69*
O3.3	**Thickness: 50 - 75mm**							
O3.3.1	Sawn finish; Greenheart; in marine work							
O3.3.1.01	Generally	m^2	0.90	37.12	27.53	62.40	127.05	*28.03*

O3 Hardwood Decking continued...

		Unit	Labour Hours	Labour Net £	Plant Net £	Materials Net £	Unit Net £	*CO_2 Kg*
O3.4	**Thickness: 75 - 100mm**							
O3.4.1	Sawn finish; Greenheart; in marine work							
O3.4.1.01	Generally	m^2	1.20	49.49	36.71	83.19	169.39	*37.37*
O3.5	**Thickness: 100 - 125mm**							
O3.5.1	Sawn finish; Greenheart; in marine work							
O3.5.1.01	Generally	m^2	1.50	61.86	45.88	103.99	211.73	*46.71*
O3.6	**Thickness: 125 - 150mm**							
O3.6.1	Sawn finish; Greenheart; in marine work							
O3.6.1.01	Generally	m^2	1.80	74.23	55.06	124.79	254.08	*56.06*
O3.7	**Thickness: exceeding 150mm**							
O3.7.1	Sawn finish; Greenheart; in marine work							
O3.7.1.01	Generally	m^2	2.20	90.73	67.30	145.59	303.62	*66.45*

O4 Softwood Decking

		Unit	Labour Hours	Labour Net £	Plant Net £	Materials Net £	Unit Net £	*CO_2 Kg*
O4.2	**Thickness: 25 - 50mm**							
O4.2.1	Wrot finish; Douglas Fir; in marine work							
O4.2.1.01	Generally	m^2	0.50	20.62	15.30	27.83	63.75	*17.63*
O4.3	**Thickness: 50 - 75mm**							
O4.3.1	Wrot finish; Douglas Fir; in marine work							
O4.3.1.01	Generally	m^2	0.60	24.74	18.35	41.74	84.83	*24.87*
O4.4	**Thickness: 75 - 100mm**							
O4.4.1	Wrot finish; Douglas Fir; in marine work							
O4.4.1.01	Generally	m^2	0.90	37.12	27.53	55.65	120.30	*34.22*
O4.5	**Thickness: 100 - 125mm**							
O4.5.1	Wrot finish; Douglas Fir; in marine work							
O4.5.1.01	Generally	m^2	1.20	49.49	36.71	69.56	155.76	*43.56*
O4.6	**Thickness: 125 - 150mm**							
O4.6.1	Wrot finish; Douglas Fir; in marine work							
O4.6.1.01	Generally	m^2	1.50	61.86	45.88	83.48	191.22	*52.90*
O4.7	**Thickness: exceeding 150mm**							
O4.7.1	Wrot finish; Douglas Fir; in marine work							
O4.7.1.01	Generally	m^2	1.80	74.23	55.06	97.39	226.68	*62.24*

O5 Fittings and Fastenings

Note(s): 1) Electric power drill and attachments are deemed to have been included in the general items

2) It has been assumed that the timber is no harder than Douglas Fir

		Unit	Labour Hours	Labour Net £	Plant Net £	Materials Net £	Unit Net £	CO_2 Kg
O5.1	**Straps**							
O5.1.1	Galvanised mild steel straps; fixing with screws							
O5.1.1.01	30 x 2.5 x 400mm girth	Nr	0.32	13.20	-	0.30	13.50	*0.65*
O5.1.1.02	30 x 2.5 x 600mm girth	Nr	0.35	14.43	-	0.48	14.91	*0.98*
O5.1.1.03	30 x 2.5 x 800mm girth	Nr	0.38	15.67	-	0.65	16.32	*1.30*
O5.1.1.04	30 x 2.5 x 1000mm girth	Nr	0.47	19.38	-	0.80	20.18	*1.62*
O5.1.1.05	30 x 2.5 x 1200mm girth	Nr	0.50	20.62	-	1.20	21.82	*2.44*
O5.2	**Spikes**							
O5.2.1	Mild steel Rosehead spikes, including drilling holes							
O5.2.1.01	12.5 x 12.5 x 100mm girth	Nr	0.17	7.01	-	1.48	8.49	*0.09*
O5.2.1.02	14 x 14 x 275mm girth	Nr	0.25	10.31	-	2.66	12.97	*0.17*
O5.2.2	Mild steel dogs, including drilling holes							
O5.2.2.01	12.5 x 12.5 x 250mm long with 12.5 x 12.5 x 75mm spikes each end	Nr	0.30	12.37	-	3.03	15.40	*0.17*
O5.3	**Coach Screws**							
O5.3.1	Steel square head coach screws							
O5.3.1.01	6mm diameter; 50mm long	Nr	0.03	1.36	-	0.06	1.42	*0.02*
O5.3.1.02	as above; 75mm long	Nr	0.03	1.36	-	0.13	1.49	*0.03*
O5.3.1.03	as above; 100mm long	Nr	0.04	1.53	-	0.15	1.68	*0.04*
O5.3.1.04	as above; 125mm long	Nr	0.04	1.53	-	0.19	1.72	*0.05*
O5.3.1.05	8mm diameter; 50mm long	Nr	0.03	1.36	-	0.18	1.54	*0.03*
O5.3.1.06	as above; 75mm long	Nr	0.03	1.36	-	0.27	1.63	*0.05*
O5.3.1.07	as above; 100mm long	Nr	0.04	1.53	-	0.32	1.85	*0.07*
O5.3.1.08	8mm diameter; 125mm long	Nr	0.04	1.53	-	0.42	1.95	*0.08*
O5.3.1.09	as above; 150mm long	Nr	0.04	1.77	-	0.58	2.35	*0.10*
O5.3.1.10	9.5mm diameter; 50mm long	Nr	0.04	1.53	-	0.33	1.86	*0.05*
O5.3.1.11	as above; 75mm long	Nr	0.04	1.53	-	0.47	2.00	*0.07*
O5.3.1.12	as above; 100mm long	Nr	0.04	1.77	-	0.56	2.33	*0.09*
O5.3.1.13	as above; 125mm long	Nr	0.04	1.77	-	0.72	2.49	*0.12*
O5.3.1.14	as above; 150mm long	Nr	0.05	2.14	-	1.00	3.14	*0.14*
O5.3.1.15	12.5mm diameter; 50mm long	Nr	0.04	1.77	-	0.49	2.26	*0.08*

O5 Fittings and Fastenings continued...

		Unit	Labour Hours	Labour Net £	Plant Net £	Materials Net £	Unit Net £	CO_2 Kg
O5.3	**Coach Screws**							
O5.3.1	Steel square head coach screws							
O5.3.1.16	as previous item; 75mm long	Nr	0.04	1.77	-	0.71	**2.48**	*0.12*
O5.3.1.17	as above; 100mm long	Nr	0.05	2.14	-	0.80	**2.94**	*0.17*
O5.3.1.18	as above; 125mm long	Nr	0.05	2.14	-	1.07	**3.21**	*0.21*
O5.3.1.19	as above; 150mm long	Nr	0.07	2.76	-	1.30	**4.06**	*0.25*
O5.4	**Bolts**							
O5.4.1	Black hexagonal head bolts and nuts grade 4.6, BS 4190 including one nut and one washer; drilling holes							
O5.4.1.01	M6; 25mm long	Nr	0.10	4.12	-	0.06	**4.18**	*0.01*
O5.4.1.02	as above; 50mm long	Nr	0.10	4.12	-	0.07	**4.19**	*0.02*
O5.4.1.03	as above; 80mm long	Nr	0.10	4.12	-	0.10	**4.22**	*0.03*
O5.4.1.04	as above; 100mm long	Nr	0.10	4.12	-	0.12	**4.24**	*0.04*
O5.4.1.05	M8; 25mm long	Nr	0.10	4.12	-	0.08	**4.20**	*0.02*
O5.4.1.06	as above; 50mm long	Nr	0.10	4.12	-	0.10	**4.22**	*0.03*
O5.4.1.07	M10; 50mm	Nr	0.10	4.12	-	0.17	**4.29**	*0.05*
O5.4.1.08	as above; 80mm long	Nr	0.12	4.95	-	0.23	**5.18**	*0.08*
O5.4.1.09	as above; 100mm long	Nr	0.14	5.77	-	0.27	**6.04**	*0.11*
O5.4.1.10	as above; 140mm long	Nr	0.14	5.77	-	0.35	**6.12**	*0.15*
O5.4.1.11	M12; 50mm long	Nr	0.10	4.12	-	0.23	**4.35**	*0.08*
O5.4.1.12	as above; 80mm long	Nr	0.10	4.12	-	0.27	**4.39**	*0.12*
O5.4.1.13	as above; 100mm long	Nr	0.12	4.95	-	0.31	**5.26**	*0.15*
O5.4.1.14	as above; 140mm long	Nr	0.14	5.77	-	0.45	**6.22**	*0.21*
O5.4.1.15	as above; 200mm long	Nr	0.15	6.19	-	0.86	**7.05**	*0.30*
O5.4.1.16	as above; 260mm long	Nr	0.16	6.60	-	0.98	**7.58**	*0.39*
O5.4.1.17	as above; 300mm long	Nr	0.16	6.60	-	1.32	**7.92**	*0.45*
O5.4.1.18	M16; 50mm long	Nr	0.12	4.95	-	0.41	**5.36**	*0.13*
O5.4.1.19	as above; 80mm long	Nr	0.12	4.95	-	0.49	**5.44**	*0.21*
O5.4.1.20	as above; 100mm long	Nr	0.12	4.95	-	0.55	**5.50**	*0.27*
O5.4.1.21	M20; 50mm long	Nr	0.14	5.77	-	0.58	**6.35**	*0.21*
O5.4.1.22	as above; 100mm long	Nr	0.14	5.77	-	0.87	**6.64**	*0.42*

O5 Fittings and Fastenings continued...

		Unit	Labour Hours	Labour Net £	Plant Net £	Materials Net £	Unit Net £	CO_2 Kg
O5.4	**Bolts**							
O5.4.2	Black cup square hexagon carriage bolts and nuts, grade 4.6, BS 4933 including one nut and one washer; drilling holes							
O5.4.2.01	M12; 75mm long	Nr	0.10	4.12	-	0.37	4.49	*0.11*
O5.4.2.02	as above; 100mm long	Nr	0.12	4.95	-	0.43	5.38	*0.15*
O5.4.2.03	as above; 150mm long	Nr	0.14	5.77	-	0.61	6.38	*0.23*
O5.5	**Plates**							
O5.5.1	Galvanised mild steel single sided round toothed plate connectors, BS EN 912							
O5.5.1.01	38mm diameter for 9mm bolt	Nr	0.05	2.06	-	0.16	2.22	*0.04*
O5.5.1.02	57mm diameter for 12mm bolt	Nr	0.05	2.06	-	0.20	2.26	*0.04*
O5.5.1.03	63mm diameter for 12mm bolt	Nr	0.06	2.47	-	0.28	2.75	*0.04*
O5.5.1.04	75mm diameter for 12mm bolt	Nr	0.06	2.47	-	0.30	2.77	*0.04*
O5.5.2	Galvanised mild steel double sided round toothed plate connectors, BS EN 912							
O5.5.2.01	38mm diameter for 9mm bolt	Nr	0.07	2.89	-	0.18	3.07	*0.04*
O5.5.2.02	50mm diameter for 12mm bolt	Nr	0.07	2.89	-	0.19	3.08	*0.04*
O5.5.2.03	63mm diameter for 12mm bolt	Nr	0.08	3.30	-	0.30	3.60	*0.04*
O5.5.2.04	75mm diameter for 12mm bolt	Nr	0.08	3.30	-	0.32	3.62	*0.04*
O5.5.3	Galvanised mild steel split ring connectors, BS EN 912							
O5.5.3.01	50mm diameter; parallel sides	Nr	0.17	7.01	-	0.64	7.65	*0.07*
O5.5.3.02	64mm diameter; parallel sides	Nr	0.19	7.84	-	0.68	8.52	*0.08*
O5.5.4	Galvanised mild steel shear plate connectors, BS EN 912							
O5.5.4.01	67mm diameter pressed steel	Nr	0.17	7.01	-	1.07	8.08	*0.08*
O5.5.4.02	102mm diameter malleable cast iron	Nr	0.19	7.84	-	15.65	23.49	*4.45*

CLASS P: PILES

Calculations used throughout Class P - Piles

Labour

		Qty		Rate		Total
L C0002ICE	**Bored Piling Labour Gang**					
	Ganger	2	x	16.99	=	£33.97
	Labourer (General Operative)	2	x	12.56	=	£25.12
	Craftsman WRA	2	x	16.68	=	£33.37
	Total hourly cost of gang				**=**	**£92.46**
L C0012ICE	**Piling Labour Gang (Mobilise / Demobilise / Move)**					
	Ganger	16	x	16.99	=	£271.78
	Labourer (General Operative)	24	x	12.56	=	£301.45
	Total hourly cost of gang				**=**	**£573.23**
L P0001ICE	**Driven Cast in Place Piling Labour Gang**					
	Ganger	2	x	16.99	=	£33.97
	Labourer (General Operative)	2	x	12.56	=	£25.12
	Craftsman WRA	3	x	16.68	=	£50.05
	Total hourly cost of gang				**=**	**£109.14**
L P0002ICE	**Driven Piling Labour Gang**					
	Ganger	1	x	16.99	=	£16.99
	Labourer (General Operative)	1	x	12.56	=	£12.56
	Craftsman WRA	1	x	16.68	=	£16.68
	Total hourly cost of gang				**=**	**£46.23**

Plant

P C0002ICE	**Bored Piling (Medium Rig) Plant Gang**					
	Bored Piling Rig Medium	1	x	154.27	=	£154.27
	Concrete Mixer - Schwing BP1000R					
	Concrete Pumps	1	x	43.29	=	£43.29
	Total hourly cost of gang				**=**	**£197.56**
P C0003ICE	**Bored Piling (Medium) Plant Gang (Mobilise / Demobilise / Move)**					
	Bored Piling Rig Medium	8	x	154.27	=	£1,234.19
	Concrete Mixer - Schwing BP1000R					
	Concrete Pumps	8	x	43.29	=	£346.31
	Articulated Lorry	8	x	64.02	=	£512.14
	Low Loader Trailer	8	x	13.05	=	£104.37
	Bored Piling Rig Medium	10	x	154.27	=	£1,542.74
	Concrete Mixer - Schwing BP1000R					
	Concrete Pumps	10	x	43.29	=	£432.88
	Total hourly cost of gang				**=**	**£4,172.63**
P N0001ICE	**Sheet Piling Plant Gang Large (Mobilise / Demobilse / Move)**					
	Sheet Piling Rig Large	10	x	205.32	=	£2,053.21
	Compressor - 480 cfm	10	x	18.85	=	£188.49
	Articulated Lorry	10	x	64.02	=	£640.17
	Low Loader Trailer	10	x	13.05	=	£130.46
	Compressor - 480 cfm	10	x	18.85	=	£188.49
	Welding Set - 250 amp Diesel Electric Start Sil	10	x	3.52	=	£35.16
	Cutting and Burning Gear	10	x	3.52	=	£35.23
	Total hourly cost of gang				**=**	**£3,271.21**

P P0001ICE	**Bored Piling (Large Rig) Plant Gang**					
	Bored Piling Rig Large	1	x	205.32	=	£205.32
	Concrete Mixer - Schwing BP1000R					
	Concrete Pumps	1	x	43.29	=	£43.29
	Total hourly cost of gang				**=**	**£248.61**
P P0002ICE	**Bored Piling (Large) Plant Gang (Mobilise / Demobilise / Move)**					
	Bored Piling Rig Large	10	x	205.32	=	£2,053.21
	Concrete Mixer - Schwing BP1000R					
	Concrete Pumps	10	x	43.29	=	£432.88
	Articulated Lorry	10	x	64.02	=	£640.17
	Low Loader Trailer	10	x	13.05	=	£130.46
	Bored Piling Rig Medium	10	x	154.27	=	£1,542.74
	Concrete Mixer - Schwing BP1000R					
	Concrete Pumps	10	x	43.29	=	£432.88
	Total hourly cost of gang				**=**	**£5,232.34**
P P0003ICE	**Driven Cast in Place Piling (Large) Plant Gang (Mobilise / Demobilise / Move)**					
	Driven Piling Rig Large	10	x	205.32	=	£2,053.21
	Concrete Mixer - Schwing BP1000R					
	Concrete Pumps	10	x	43.29	=	£432.88
	Articulated Lorry	10	x	64.02	=	£640.17
	Low Loader Trailer	10	x	13.05	=	£130.46
	Driven Piling Rig Large	10	x	205.32	=	£2,053.21
	Concrete Mixer - Schwing BP1000R					
	Concrete Pumps	10	x	43.29	=	£432.88
	Welding Set - 250 amp Diesel Electric Start Sil	10	x	3.52	=	£35.16
	Cutting and Burning Gear	10	x	3.52	=	£35.23
	Total hourly cost of gang				**=**	**£5,813.20**
P P0004ICE	**Driven Cast in Place Piling (Medium) Plant Gang (Mobilise / Demobilise / Move)**					
	Driven Piling Rig Medium	8	x	154.27	=	£1,234.19
	Concrete Mixer - Schwing BP1000R					
	Concrete Pumps	1	x	43.29	=	£43.29
	Articulated Lorry	8	x	64.02	=	£512.14
	Low Loader Trailer	8	x	13.05	=	£104.37
	Bored Piling Rig Medium	10	x	154.27	=	£1,542.74
	Concrete Mixer - Schwing BP1000R					
	Concrete Pumps	10	x	43.29	=	£432.88
	Welding Set - 250 amp Diesel Electric Start Sil	10	x	3.52	=	£35.16
	Cutting and Burning Gear	10	x	3.52	=	£35.23
	Total hourly cost of gang				**=**	**£3,940.00**
P P0005ICE	**Driven Piling (Large) Plant Gang**					
	Driven Piling Rig Large	1	x	205.32	=	£205.32
	Total hourly cost of gang				**=**	**£205.32**
P P0006ICE	**Driven Piling (Large) Plant Gang (Mobilise / Demobilise / Move)**					
	Driven Piling Rig Large	10	x	205.32	=	£2,053.21
	Articulated Lorry	10	x	64.02	=	£640.17
	Low Loader Trailer	10	x	13.05	=	£130.46
	Driven Piling Rig Large	10	x	205.32	=	£2,053.21
	Total hourly cost of gang				**=**	**£4,877.05**
P P0007ICE	**Driven Piling (Medium) Plant Gang**					
	Bored Piling Rig Medium	1	x	154.27	=	£154.27
	Total hourly cost of gang				**=**	**£154.27**
P P0008ICE	**Driven Piling (Medium) Plant Gang (Mobilise / Demobilise / Move)**					
	Driven Piling Rig Medium	8	x	154.27	=	£1,234.19
	Articulated Lorry	8	x	64.02	=	£512.14
	Low Loader Trailer	8	x	13.05	=	£104.37
	Bored Piling Rig Medium	10	x	154.27	=	£1,542.74
	Total hourly cost of gang				**=**	**£3,393.44**

P P0009ICE	**Driven Cast in place Piling Plant Gang Medium**					
	Bored Piling Rig Medium	1	x	154.27	=	£154.27
	Concrete Mixer - Schwing BP1000R					
	Concrete Pumps	1	x	43.29	=	£43.29
	Welding Set - 250 amp Diesel Electric Start Sil	1	x	3.52	=	£3.52
	Cutting and Burning Gear	1	x	3.52	=	£3.52
	Total hourly cost of gang				**=**	**£204.60**
P P0011ICE	**Sheet Piling (Large) Plant Gang**					
	Sheet Piling Rig Large	1	x	205.32	=	£205.32
	Compressor - 480 cfm	1	x	18.85	=	£18.85
	Welding Set - 250 amp Diesel Electric Start Sil	1	x	3.52	=	£3.52
	Cutting and Burning Gear	1	x	3.52	=	£3.52
	Total hourly cost of gang				**=**	**£231.21**
P P0012ICE	**Sheet Piling (Medium) Plant Gang**					
	Sheet Piling Rig Medium	1	x	154.27	=	£154.27
	Compressor - 480 cfm	1	x	18.85	=	£18.85
	Welding Set - 250 amp Diesel Electric Start Sil	1	x	3.52	=	£3.52
	Cutting and Burning Gear	1	x	3.52	=	£3.52
	Total hourly cost of gang				**=**	**£180.16**
P P0013ICE	**Sheet Piling (Medium) Plant Gang (Mobilise / Demobilise / Move)**					
	Sheet Piling Rig Medium	8	x	154.27	=	£1,234.19
	Compressor - 480 cfm	8	x	18.85	=	£150.79
	Articulated Lorry	8	x	64.02	=	£512.14
	Low Loader Trailer	8	x	13.05	=	£104.37
	Compressor - 480 cfm	8	x	18.85	=	£150.79
	Welding Set - 250 amp Diesel Electric Start Sil	8	x	3.52	=	£28.13
	Cutting and Burning Gear	8	x	3.52	=	£28.18
	Total hourly cost of gang				**=**	**£2,208.59**

Class P - Piles

Note(s): The following prices are sub-contractor guide prices for approximate estimating only and assume not less than 50 piles will be cast on a level site. The cost of bringing to and from site the plant equipment and labour required including setting up and removal of the piling rig over each pile position is included in the items for 'number of piles'.

P1 Bored Cast in Place Concrete Piles

		Unit	Labour Hours	Labour Net £	Plant Net £	Materials Net £	Unit Net £	CO_2 Kg
P1.1	**Diameter: 300mm or 350mm**							
P1.1.1	Number of piles							
P1.1.1.01	Reinforced in situ concrete, BS EN 206 prescribed mix, grade 25, 20mm aggregate; Diameter: 300mm	Nr	0.02	11.46	83.45	-	94.91	*73.67*
P1.1.2	Concreted length							
P1.1.2.01	Reinforced in situ concrete, BS EN 206 prescribed mix, grade 25, 20mm aggregate; Diameter: 300mm	m	-	-	-	5.26	5.26	*21.84*
P1.1.3	Depth bored or driven to stated maximum depth							
P1.1.3.01	Reinforced in situ concrete, BS EN 206 prescribed mix, grade 25, 20mm aggregate; Diameter: 300mm; Depth bored: 10m	m	0.10	9.25	19.76	6.74	35.75	*37.60*
P1.1.3.02	as above; Depth bored: 15m	m	0.15	13.87	29.63	6.74	50.24	*46.99*
P1.1.3.03	as above; Depth bored: 20m	m	0.15	13.87	37.29	6.74	57.90	*46.99*
P1.4	**Diameter: 600mm or 750mm**							
P1.4.1	Number of piles							
P1.4.1.01	Reinforced in situ concrete, BS EN 206 prescribed mix, grade 25, 20mm aggregate; Diameter: 600mm	Nr	0.02	11.46	83.45	-	94.91	*73.67*
P1.4.2	Concreted length							
P1.4.2.01	Reinforced in situ concrete, BS EN 206 prescribed mix, grade 25, 20mm aggregate; Diameter: 600mm	m	-	-	-	21.27	21.27	*88.30*
P1.4.3	Depth bored or driven to stated maximum depth							
P1.4.3.01	Reinforced in situ concrete, BS EN 206 prescribed mix, grade 25, 20mm aggregate; Diameter: 600mm; Depth bored: 10m	m	0.05	4.62	9.88	25.73	40.23	*81.21*
P1.4.3.02	as above; Depth bored: 15m	m	0.10	9.25	19.76	25.73	54.74	*90.61*
P1.4.3.03	as above; Depth bored: 20m	m	0.15	13.87	37.29	25.73	76.89	*100.00*
P1.5	**Diameter: 900mm or 1050mm**							
P1.5.1	Number of piles							
P1.5.1.01	Reinforced in situ concrete, BS EN 206 prescribed mix, grade 25, 20mm aggregate; Diameter: 900mm	Nr	0.02	11.46	104.65	-	116.11	*82.70*

P1 Bored Cast in Place Concrete Piles continued...

		Unit	Labour Hours	Labour Net £	Plant Net £	Materials Net £	Unit Net £	CO_2 Kg
P1.5	**Diameter: 900mm or 1050mm**							
P1.5.2	Concreted length							
P1.5.2.01	Reinforced in situ concrete, BS EN 206 prescribed mix, grade 25, 20mm aggregate; Diameter: 900mm	m	-	-	-	48.10	48.10	*199.68*
P1.5.3	Depth bored or driven to stated maximum depth							
P1.5.3.01	Reinforced in situ concrete, BS EN 206 prescribed mix, grade 25, 20mm aggregate; Diameter: 900mm; Depth bored: 10m	m	0.05	4.62	12.43	61.27	78.32	*180.39*
P1.5.3.02	as above; Depth bored: 15m	m	0.10	9.25	24.86	61.27	95.38	*189.79*
P1.5.3.03	as above; Depth bored: 20m	m	0.15	13.87	37.29	61.27	112.43	*199.18*
P1.6	**Diameter: 1200mm or 1350mm**							
P1.6.1	Number of piles							
P1.6.1.01	Reinforced in situ concrete, BS EN 206 prescribed mix, grade 25, 20mm aggregate; Diameter: 1200mm	Nr	0.02	11.46	104.65	-	116.11	*82.70*
P1.6.2	Concreted length							
P1.6.2.01	Reinforced in situ concrete, BS EN 206 prescribed mix, grade 25, 20mm aggregate; Diameter: 1200mm	m	-	-	-	84.93	84.93	*352.56*
P1.6.3	Depth bored or driven to stated maximum depth							
P1.6.3.01	Reinforced in situ concrete, BS EN 206 prescribed mix, grade 25, 20mm aggregate; Diameter: 1200mm; Depth bored: 10m	m	0.30	27.74	74.58	104.15	206.47	*347.06*
P1.6.3.02	as above; Depth bored: 15m	m	0.35	32.36	87.01	104.15	223.52	*356.45*
P1.6.3.03	as above; Depth bored: 20m	m	0.40	36.98	99.44	104.15	240.57	*365.84*

P2 Driven Cast in Place Concrete Piles

		Unit	Labour Hours	Labour Net £	Plant Net £	Materials Net £	Unit Net £	CO_2 Kg
P2.1	**Diameter: 300mm or 350mm**							
P2.1.1	Number of piles							
P2.1.1.01	Diameter: 300mm; Design load 30t	Nr	0.02	11.46	78.80	-	90.26	*73.39*
P2.1.2	Concreted length							
P2.1.2.01	Diameter: 300mm; Design load 30t	m	0.08	8.73	-	37.16	45.89	*120.30*
P2.1.3	Depth bored or driven to stated maximum depth							
P2.1.3.01	Diameter: 300mm; Design load 30t; Depth bored: 10m	m	0.05	5.78	10.84	-	16.62	*10.07*
P2.1.3.02	as above; Depth bored: 15m	m	0.08	8.73	16.37	-	25.10	*15.20*
P2.1.3.03	as above; Depth bored: 20m	m	0.10	10.91	20.46	-	31.37	*19.00*
P2.4	**Diameter: 600mm or 750mm**							
P2.4.1	Number of piles							
P2.4.1.01	Diameter: 600mm; Design load 60t	Nr	0.02	11.46	78.80	-	90.26	*73.39*

P2 Driven Cast in Place Concrete Piles continued...

		Unit	Labour Hours	Labour Net £	Plant Net £	Materials Net £	Unit Net £	CO_2 Kg
P2.4	**Diameter: 600mm or 750mm**							
P2.4.2	Concreted length							
P2.4.2.01	Diameter: 600mm; Design load 60 t	m	0.08	8.73	-	98.21	106.94	*322.02*
P2.4.3	Depth bored or driven to stated maximum depth							
P2.4.3.01	Diameter: 600mm; Design load 60 t; Depth bored: 10m	m	0.07	7.31	13.71	-	21.02	*12.73*
P2.4.3.02	as above; Depth bored: 15m	m	0.08	8.73	16.37	-	25.10	*15.20*
P2.4.3.03	as above; Depth bored: 20m	m	0.10	10.91	20.46	-	31.37	*19.00*
P2.5	**Diameter: 900mm or 1050mm**							
P2.5.1	Number of piles							
P2.5.1.01	Diameter: 900mm; Design load 90 t	Nr	0.02	11.46	116.26	-	127.72	*83.13*
P2.5.2	Concreted length							
P2.5.2.01	Diameter: 900mm; Design load 90 t	m	0.08	8.73	-	205.30	214.03	*675.36*
P2.5.3	Depth bored or driven to stated maximum depth							
P2.5.3.01	Diameter: 900mm; Design load 90 t; Depth bored: 10m	m	0.05	5.78	13.55	-	19.33	*10.07*
P2.5.3.02	as above; Depth bored: 15m	m	0.08	8.73	20.45	-	29.18	*15.20*
P2.5.3.03	as above; Depth bored: 20m	m	0.10	10.91	25.57	-	36.48	*19.00*
P2.6	**Diameter: 1200mm or 1350mm**							
P2.6.1	Number of piles							
P2.6.1.01	Diameter: 1200mm; Design load 120 t	Nr	0.02	11.46	116.26	-	127.72	*83.13*
P2.6.2	Concreted length							
P2.6.2.01	Diameter: 1200mm; Design load 120 t	m	0.08	8.73	-	320.45	329.18	*1,059.21*
P2.6.3	Depth bored or driven to stated maximum depth							
P2.6.3.01	Diameter: 1200mm; Design load 120t; Depth bored: 10m	m	0.05	5.78	13.55	-	19.33	*10.07*
P2.6.3.02	as above; Depth bored: 15m	m	0.08	8.73	20.45	-	29.18	*15.20*
P2.6.3.03	as above; Depth bored: 20m	m	0.10	10.91	25.57	-	36.48	*19.00*

P3 Pre-formed Concrete Piles

		Unit	Labour Hours	Labour Net £	Plant Net £	Materials Net £	Unit Net £	CO_2 Kg
P3.2	**Cross-sectional area: 0.025 - 0.05m²**							
P3.2.1	Number of piles of stated length							
P3.2.1.01	Cross sectional area: 0.05m²; Length 10m	Nr	0.82	48.45	191.28	100.00	339.73	*454.55*
P3.2.1.02	as above; Length 15m	Nr	1.02	57.69	222.14	150.00	429.83	*609.35*
P3.2.1.03	as above; Length 20m	Nr	1.52	80.81	299.27	200.00	580.08	*818.99*
P3.2.2	Depth driven							
P3.2.2.01	Cross sectional area: 0.05m²	m	0.04	1.85	6.17	-	8.02	*7.31*
P3.3	**Cross-sectional area: 0.05 - 0.1m²**							
P3.3.1	Number of piles of stated length							
P3.3.1.01	Cross-sectional area: 0.075m²; Length 10m	Nr	0.82	48.45	261.80	150.00	460.25	*581.62*

P3 Pre-formed Concrete Piles continued...

		Unit	Labour Hours	Labour Net £	Plant Net £	Materials Net £	Unit Net £	CO_2 Kg
P3.3	**Cross-sectional area: 0.05 - 0.1m²**							
P3.3.1	Number of piles of stated length							
P3.3.1.02	as above; Length 15m	Nr	1.02	57.69	302.86	225.00	**585.55**	*795.55*
P3.3.1.03	as above; Length 20m	Nr	1.52	80.81	405.52	300.00	**786.33**	*1,064.31*
P3.3.2	Depth driven							
P3.3.2.01	Cross-sectional area: 0.075m²	m	0.04	1.85	8.21	-	**10.06**	*7.31*

P7 Isolated Steel Piles

		Unit	Labour Hours	Labour Net £	Plant Net £	Materials Net £	Unit Net £	CO_2 Kg
P7.2	**Mass: 15 - 30Kg/m**							
P7.2.1	Number of piles of stated length							
P7.2.1.01	I Sections; Mass: 25kg/m; Length 10m	Nr	1.02	57.69	222.14	230.22	**510.05**	*720.58*
P7.2.1.02	as above; Length 15m	Nr	1.52	80.81	299.27	344.90	**724.98**	*1,044.06*
P7.2.1.03	as above; Length 20m	Nr	2.02	103.92	376.41	459.57	**939.90**	*1,367.55*
P7.2.2	Depth driven							
P7.2.2.01	I Sections; Mass: 25kg/m	m	0.04	1.85	6.17	-	**8.02**	*7.31*
P7.3	**Mass: 30 - 60Kg/m**							
P7.3.1	Number of piles of stated length							
P7.3.1.01	I Sections; Mass: 50Kg/m; Length 10m	Nr	1.02	57.69	222.14	459.57	**739.40**	*1,184.78*
P7.3.1.02	as above; Length 15m	Nr	1.52	80.81	299.27	689.79	**1,069.87**	*1,742.14*
P7.3.1.03	as above; Length 20m	Nr	2.02	103.92	376.41	919.14	**1,399.47**	*2,297.73*
P7.3.2	Depth driven							
P7.3.2.01	I Sections; Mass: 50Kg/m	m	0.04	1.85	6.17	-	**8.02**	*7.31*
P7.4	**Mass: 60 - 120Kg/m**							
P7.4.1	Number of piles of stated length							
P7.4.1.01	I Sections; Mass: 100Kg/m; Length 10m	Nr	1.52	80.81	299.27	919.14	**1,299.22**	*2,206.34*
P7.4.1.02	as above; Length 15m	Nr	2.02	103.92	376.41	1,378.71	**1,859.04**	*3,227.90*
P7.4.1.03	as above; Length 20m	Nr	2.52	127.04	483.22	1,838.28	**2,448.54**	*4,258.29*
P7.4.2	Depth driven							
P7.4.2.01	I Sections; Mass: 100Kg/m	m	0.04	1.85	6.17	-	**8.02**	*7.31*
P7.5	**Mass: 120 - 250Kg/m**							
P7.5.1	Number of piles of stated length							
P7.5.1.01	I Sections; Mass: 250Kg/m; Length 10m	Nr	2.52	127.04	610.84	2,297.85	**3,035.73**	*5,188.47*
P7.5.1.02	as above; Length 15m	Nr	3.52	173.27	637.49	3,447.21	**4,257.97**	*7,697.56*
P7.5.1.03	as above; Length 20m	Nr	4.52	219.50	791.76	4,595.69	**5,606.95**	*10,204.89*
P7.5.2	Depth driven							
P7.5.2.01	I Sections; Mass: 250Kg/m	m	0.04	1.85	6.17	-	**8.02**	*7.31*

P8 Interlocking Steel Piles

		Unit	Labour Hours	Labour Net £	Plant Net £	Materials Net £	Unit Net £	CO_2 Kg
P8.2	**Section modulus: 500 - 800cm³/m**							
P8.2.1	Length of special piles							
P8.2.1.02	as previous items; Length of closure piles	m	0.15	10.85	27.02	48.80	**86.67**	*42.75*
P8.2.1.03	as above; Length of taper piles	m	0.25	18.08	45.04	48.80	**111.92**	*55.61*
P8.2.2	Driven area							
P8.2.2.01	Piles weldable structural steel, BS EN 10248; Section modulus: 601 cm³/m	m^2	0.10	7.23	18.02	-	**25.25**	*20.83*
P8.2.3	Area of piles of length: not exceeding 14m							
P8.2.3.01	Piles weldable structural steel, BS EN 10248; Section modulus: 601 cm³/m; Area of piles of length: 10m	m^2	0.02	11.46	44.17	76.93	**132.56**	*193.56*
P8.3	**Section modulus: 800 - 1200cm³/m**							
P8.3.1	Length of special piles							
P8.3.1.01	Piles weldable structural steel, BS EN 10248; Section modulus: 1199cm³/m; Length of corners	m	0.15	10.85	27.02	48.80	**86.67**	*42.75*
P8.3.1.02	as above; Length of closure piles	m	0.20	14.46	36.03	48.80	**99.29**	*53.16*
P8.3.1.03	as above; Length of taper piles	m	0.25	18.08	45.04	48.80	**111.92**	*55.61*
P8.3.2	Driven area							
P8.3.2.01	Piles weldable structural steel, BS EN 10248; Section modulus: 1199cm³/m	m^2	0.10	7.23	18.02	-	**25.25**	*20.83*
P8.3.3	Area of piles of length: not exceeding 14m							
P8.3.3.01	Piles weldable structural steel, BS EN 10248; Section modulus: 1199cm³/m; Area of piles of length: 10m	m^2	0.02	11.46	44.17	104.08	**159.71**	*246.66*
P8.3.4	Area of piles of length: 14 - 24m							
P8.3.4.01	Piles weldable structural steel, BS EN 10248; Section modulus: 1199cm³/m; Area of piles of length: 20m	m^2	0.02	11.46	44.17	104.08	**159.71**	*246.66*
P8.5	**Section modulus: 2000 - 3000cm³/m**							
P8.5.1	Length of special piles							
P8.5.1.01	Piles weldable structural steel, BS EN 10248; Section modulus: 2009cm³/m; Length of corners	m	0.20	14.46	36.03	48.80	**99.29**	*53.16*
P8.5.1.02	as above; Length of closure piles	m	0.25	18.08	45.04	48.80	**111.92**	*63.57*
P8.5.1.03	as above; Length of taper piles	m	0.30	21.70	54.05	48.80	**124.55**	*66.02*
P8.5.2	Driven area							
P8.5.2.01	Piles weldable structural steel, BS EN 10248; Section modulus: 2009cm³/m	m^2	0.15	10.85	27.02	-	**37.87**	*31.24*
P8.5.3	Area of piles of length: not exceeding 14m							
P8.5.3.01	Piles weldable structural steel, BS EN 10248; Section modulus: 2009cm³/m; Area of piles of length: 10m	m^2	0.02	11.46	44.17	133.05	**188.68**	*303.30*

P8 Interlocking Steel Piles continued...

		Unit	Labour Hours	Labour Net £	Plant Net £	Materials Net £	Unit Net £	CO_2 Kg
P8.5	**Section modulus: 2000 - 3000cm³/m**							
P8.5.4	Area of piles of length: 14 - 24m							
P8.5.4.01	Piles weldable structural steel, BS EN 10248; Section modulus: 2009cm³/m; Area of piles of length: 20m	m²	0.02	11.46	44.17	133.05	188.68	*303.30*
P8.5.5	Area of piles of length: exceeding 24m							
P8.5.5.01	Piles weldable structural steel, BS EN 10248; Section modulus: 2009cm³/m; Area of piles of length: 30m	m²	0.02	11.46	44.17	133.05	188.68	*303.30*
P8.7	**Section modulus: 4000 - 5000cm³/m**							
P8.7.1	Length of special piles							
P8.7.1.01	Piles weldable structural steel, BS EN 10248; Section modulus: 4200cm³/m; Length of corners	m	0.10	7.23	23.12	48.80	79.15	*32.33*
P8.7.1.02	as above; Length of closure piles	m	0.15	10.85	34.68	48.80	94.33	*42.75*
P8.7.1.03	as above; Length of taper piles	m	0.20	14.46	46.24	48.80	109.50	*45.20*
P8.7.2	Driven area							
P8.7.2.01	Piles weldable structural steel, BS EN 10248; Section modulus: 4200cm³/m	m²	0.10	7.23	23.12	-	30.35	*20.83*
P8.7.3	Area of piles of length: not exceeding 14m							
P8.7.3.01	Piles weldable structural steel, BS EN 10248; Section modulus: 4200cm³/m; Area of piles of length: 10m	m²	0.02	11.46	65.42	262.47	339.35	*567.19*
P8.7.4	Area of piles of length: 14 - 24m							
P8.7.4.01	Piles weldable structural steel, BS EN 10248; Section modulus: 4200cm³/m; Area of piles of length: 20m	m²	0.02	11.46	65.42	262.47	339.35	*567.19*
P8.7.5	Area of piles of length: exceeding 24m							
P8.7.5.01	Piles weldable structural steel, BS EN 10248; Section modulus: 4200cm³/m; Area of piles of length: 30m	m²	0.02	11.46	65.42	262.47	339.35	*567.19*

CLASS Q:

PILING ANCILLARIES

Calculations used throughout Class Q - Piling Ancillaries

Labour

		Qty		Rate		Total
L A0140ICE	**Steel fixing Labour Gang**					
	Craftsman WRA	2	x	16.68	=	£33.37
	Labourer (General Operative)	1	x	12.56	=	£12.56
	Total hourly cost of gang				=	**£45.93**
L A0145ICE	**Welding Labour Gang**					
	Labourer (Skill Rate 3)	1	x	14.34	=	£14.34
	Fitters and Welders	2	x	16.68	=	£33.37
	Total hourly cost of gang				=	**£47.71**
L C0012ICE	**Piling Labour Gang (Mobilise / Demobilise / Move)**					
	Ganger	16	x	16.99	=	£271.78
	Labourer (General Operative)	24	x	12.56	=	£301.45
	Total hourly cost of gang				=	**£573.23**
L P0001ICE	**Driven Cast in Place Piling Labour Gang**					
	Ganger	2	x	16.99	=	£33.97
	Labourer (General Operative)	2	x	12.56	=	£25.12
	Craftsman WRA	3	x	16.68	=	£50.05
	Total hourly cost of gang				=	**£109.14**
L P0002ICE	**Driven Piling Labour Gang**					
	Ganger	1	x	16.99	=	£16.99
	Labourer (General Operative)	1	x	12.56	=	£12.56
	Craftsman WRA	1	x	16.68	=	£16.68
	Total hourly cost of gang				=	**£46.23**
L P0003ICE	**Sheet Piling Labour Gang**					
	Ganger	1	x	16.99	=	£16.99
	Labourer (General Operative)	2	x	12.56	=	£25.12
	Craftsman WRA	1	x	16.68	=	£16.68
	Banksman	1	x	13.53	=	£13.53
	Total hourly cost of gang				=	**£72.32**
L Q0001ICE	**Pile Testing Labour Gang**					
	Ganger	1	x	16.99	=	£16.99
	Labourer (General Operative)	2	x	12.56	=	£25.12
	Total hourly cost of gang				=	**£42.11**
L Q0002ICE	**Piling - Head Works Labour Gang**					
	Labourer (Skill Rate 3)	2	x	14.34	=	£28.68
	Total hourly cost of gang				=	**£28.68**
L Q0003ICE	**Piling Backfilling Labour Gang**					
	Ganger	1	x	16.99	=	£16.99
	Labourer (General Operative)	1	x	12.56	=	£12.56
	Banksman	1	x	13.53	=	£13.53
	Total hourly cost of gang				=	**£43.08**

Plant

P A1000ICE	**Pile Testing Rig Plant Gang (Mobilise / Demobilise / Move)**					
	Pile Testing Rig and Equipment	10	x	219.32	=	£2,193.16
	Articulated Lorry	10	x	64.02	=	£640.17
	Low Loader Trailer	10	x	13.05	=	£130.46
	Pile Testing Rig and Equipment	5	x	219.32	=	£1,096.58
	Total hourly cost of gang				=	**£4,060.37**

P P0007ICE	**Driven Piling (Medium) Plant Gang**					
	Bored Piling Rig Medium	1	x	154.27	=	£154.27
	Total hourly cost of gang				**=**	**£154.27**
P P0011ICE	**Sheet Piling (Large) Plant Gang**					
	Sheet Piling Rig Large	1	x	205.32	=	£205.32
	Compressor - 480 cfm	1	x	18.85	=	£18.85
	Welding Set - 250 amp Diesel Electric Start Sil	1	x	3.52	=	£3.52
	Cutting and Burning Gear	1	x	3.52	=	£3.52
	Total hourly cost of gang				**=**	**£231.21**
P Q0005ICE	**Piling - Head Works Plant Gang**					
	Compressor - 2-Tool (Complete)	1	x	4.86	=	£4.86
	CP9 Air Breaker Drill	2	x	0.42	=	£0.85
	Hydraulic Excavator - Komatsu PC130	1	x	42.86	=	£42.86
	Dumper - 3.0t 4WD	1	x	23.77	=	£23.77
	Total hourly cost of gang				**=**	**£72.34**
P Q0006ICE	**Piling Backfilling Plant Gang**					
	Hydraulic Excavator - Komatsu PC130	1	x	42.86	=	£42.86
	Dumper - 3.0t 4WD	1	x	23.77	=	£23.77
	Total hourly cost of gang				**=**	**£66.63**

Class Q - Piling Ancillaries

Note(s): The following prices are Specialist sub-contractor guide prices for approximate estimating only.

Q1 Cast in Place Concrete Piles

		Unit	Labour Hours	Labour Net £	Plant Net £	Materials Net £	Unit Net £	CO_2 Kg
Q1.2	**Backfilling empty bore with stated material**							
Q1.2.1	Diameter: 300mm or 350mm							
Q1.2.1.01	Material arising from excavations; Diameter: 300mm	m	0.01	0.60	0.93	-	1.53	*0.37*
Q1.2.1.02	Sand; Diameter: 300mm	m	0.01	0.60	0.93	1.90	3.43	*0.96*
Q1.2.4	Diameter: 600mm or 750mm							
Q1.2.4.01	Material arising from excavations; Diameter: 600mm	m	0.05	2.02	3.13	-	5.15	*1.23*
Q1.2.4.02	Sand; Diameter: 600mm	m	0.05	2.02	3.13	7.57	12.72	*3.58*
Q1.2.5	Diameter: 900 - 1050mm							
Q1.2.5.01	Material arising from excavations; Diameter: 900mm	m	0.07	3.02	4.66	-	7.68	*1.83*
Q1.2.5.02	Sand; Diameter: 900mm	m	0.07	3.02	4.66	17.03	24.71	*7.12*
Q1.2.6	Diameter: 1200 - 1350mm							
Q1.2.6.01	Material arising from excavations; Diameter: 1200mm	m	0.09	4.05	6.26	-	10.31	*2.46*
Q1.2.6.02	Sand; Diameter: 1200mm	m	0.09	4.05	6.26	30.56	40.87	*11.95*
Q1.3	**Permanent casings each length: not exceeding 13m**							
Q1.3.1	Diameter: 300mm or 350mm							
Q1.3.1.01	Permanent casings each length: 10m; Diameter: 300mm	m	0.10	4.62	15.43	25.16	45.21	*97.93*
Q1.3.4	Diameter: 600mm or 750mm							
Q1.3.4.01	Permanent casings each length: 10m; Diameter: 600mm	m	0.10	4.62	15.43	51.43	71.48	*181.12*
Q1.3.5	Diameter: 900 - 1050mm							
Q1.3.5.01	Permanent casings each length: 10m; Diameter: 900mm	m	0.25	11.56	38.57	98.39	148.52	*357.21*
Q1.3.6	Diameter: 1200 - 1350mm							
Q1.3.6.01	Permanent casings each length: 10m; Diameter: 1200mm	m	0.40	18.49	61.71	131.37	211.57	*489.06*
Q1.4	**Permanent casings each length: exceeding 13m**							
Q1.4.1	Diameter: 300mm or 350mm							
Q1.4.1.01	Permanent casings each length: 20m; Diameter: 300mm	m	0.10	10.91	15.43	25.16	51.50	*97.93*
Q1.4.4	Diameter: 600mm or 750mm							
Q1.4.4.01	Permanent casings each length: 20m; Diameter: 600mm	m	0.10	10.91	15.43	51.43	77.77	*181.12*
Q1.4.5	Diameter: 900 - 1050mm							
Q1.4.5.01	Permanent casings each length: 20m; Diameter: 900mm	m	0.25	27.29	38.57	98.39	164.25	*357.21*

Q1 Cast in Place Concrete Piles continued...

		Unit	Labour Hours	Labour Net £	Plant Net £	Materials Net £	Unit Net £	*CO_2 Kg*
Q1.4	**Permanent casings each length: exceeding 13m**							
Q1.4.6	Diameter: 1200 - 1350mm							
Q1.4.6.01	Permanent casings each length: 20m; Diameter: 1200mm	m	0.40	43.66	61.71	131.37	**236.74**	*489.06*
Q1.5	**Enlarged bases**							
Q1.5.1	Diameter: 300mm or 350mm							
Q1.5.1.01	Diameter: 300mm	Nr	1.00	46.23	154.27	17.71	**218.21**	*224.05*
Q1.5.4	Diameter: 600mm or 750mm							
Q1.5.4.01	Diameter: 600mm	Nr	1.50	69.34	231.41	83.16	**383.91**	*441.86*
Q1.5.5	Diameter: 900 - 1050mm							
Q1.5.5.01	Diameter: 900mm	Nr	2.25	104.02	461.97	162.40	**728.39**	*788.82*
Q1.5.6	Diameter: 1200 - 1350mm							
Q1.5.6.01	Diameter: 1200mm	Nr	4.00	184.92	821.28	286.78	**1,292.98**	*1,397.76*
Q1.7	**Cutting off surplus lengths**							
Q1.7.1	Diameter: 300mm or 350mm							
Q1.7.1.01	Diameter: 300mm	m	0.17	4.79	12.08	-	**16.87**	*5.93*
Q1.7.4	Diameter: 600mm or 750mm							
Q1.7.4.01	Diameter: 600mm	m	0.25	7.17	18.09	-	**25.26**	*8.88*
Q1.7.5	Diameter: 900 - 1050mm							
Q1.7.5.01	Diameter: 900mm	m	0.33	9.55	24.09	-	**33.64**	*11.83*
Q1.7.6	Diameter: 1200 - 1350mm							
Q1.7.6.01	Diameter: 1200mm	m	0.50	14.34	36.17	-	**50.51**	*17.76*
Q1.8	**Preparing heads**							
Q1.8.1	Diameter: 300mm or 350mm							
Q1.8.1.01	Diameter: 300mm	Nr	0.33	9.55	24.09	-	**33.64**	*11.83*
Q1.8.4	Diameter: 600mm or 750mm							
Q1.8.4.01	Diameter: 600mm	Nr	0.42	11.96	30.17	-	**42.13**	*14.81*
Q1.8.5	Diameter: 900 - 1050mm							
Q1.8.5.01	Diameter: 900mm	Nr	0.50	14.34	36.17	-	**50.51**	*17.76*
Q1.8.6	Diameter: 1200 - 1350mm							
Q1.8.6.01	Diameter: 1200mm	Nr	0.75	21.51	54.26	-	**75.77**	*26.64*

Q2 Cast in Place Concrete Piles

		Unit	Labour Hours	Labour Net £	Plant Net £	Materials Net £	Unit Net £	CO_2 Kg
Q2.1	**Reinforcement**							
Q2.1.1	Straight bars, nominal size: not exceeding 25mm							
Q2.1.1.01	nominal size: 8mm	Tonne	10.00	459.30	-	692.11	1,151.41	*1,710.00*
Q2.1.1.02	nominal size: 12mm	Tonne	10.00	459.30	-	648.27	1,107.57	*1,710.00*
Q2.1.1.03	nominal size: 20mm	Tonne	8.00	367.44	-	612.65	980.09	*1,710.00*
Q2.1.1.04	nominal size: 25mm	Tonne	8.00	367.44	-	612.23	979.67	*1,710.00*

Q3 Preformed Concrete Piles

		Unit	Labour Hours	Labour Net £	Plant Net £	Materials Net £	Unit Net £	CO_2 Kg
Q3.1	**Pre-boring**							
Q3.1.2	Cross-sectional area: 0.025 - 0.05m²							
Q3.1.2.01	Cross sectional area: 0.05m²	m	0.05	2.31	7.71	-	10.02	*9.14*
Q3.1.3	Cross-sectional area: 0.05 - 0.1m²							
Q3.1.3.01	Cross sectional area: 0.10m²	m	0.05	2.31	7.71	-	10.02	*9.14*
Q3.1.4	Cross-sectional area: 0.1 - 0.15m²							
Q3.1.4.01	Cross sectional area: 0.15m²	m	0.08	3.47	11.57	-	15.04	*13.71*
Q3.1.5	Cross-sectional area: 0.15 - 0.25m²							
Q3.1.5.01	Cross sectional area: 0.20m²	m	0.10	4.62	15.43	-	20.05	*18.28*
Q3.2	**Jetting**							
Q3.2.2	Cross-sectional area: 0.025 - 0.05m²							
Q3.2.2.01	Cross sectional area: 0.05m²	m	0.05	2.31	9.41	-	11.72	*14.64*
Q3.2.3	Cross-sectional area: 0.05 - 0.1m²							
Q3.2.3.01	Cross sectional area: 0.10m²	m	0.05	2.31	9.41	-	11.72	*14.64*
Q3.2.4	Cross-sectional area: 0.1 - 0.15m²							
Q3.2.4.01	Cross sectional area: 0.15m²	m	0.10	4.62	18.83	-	23.45	*29.28*
Q3.2.5	Cross-sectional area: 0.15 - 0.25m²							
Q3.2.5.01	Cross sectional area: 0.20m²	m	0.15	6.93	28.24	-	35.17	*43.91*
Q3.3	**Filling hollow piles with concrete**							
Q3.3.2	Cross-sectional area: 0.025 - 0.05m²							
Q3.3.2.01	Cross sectional area: 0.05m²	m	0.10	4.62	4.33	3.76	12.71	*16.11*
Q3.3.3	Cross-sectional area: 0.05 - 0.1m²							
Q3.3.3.01	Cross sectional area: 0.10m²	m	0.15	6.93	6.49	7.52	20.94	*31.96*
Q3.3.4	Cross-sectional area: 0.1 - 0.15m²							
Q3.3.4.01	Cross sectional area: 0.15m²	m	0.20	9.25	8.66	11.27	29.18	*47.82*
Q3.3.5	Cross sectional area: 0.15 - 0.25m²							
Q3.3.5.01	Cross sectional area: 0.20m²	m	0.25	11.56	10.82	15.03	37.41	*63.67*

Q3 Preformed Concrete Piles continued...

		Unit	Labour Hours	Labour Net £	Plant Net £	Materials Net £	Unit Net £	CO_2 Kg
Q3.4	**Number of pile extensions**							
Q3.4.2	Cross-sectional area: 0.025 - 0.05m²							
Q3.4.2.01	Cross sectional area: 0.05m²	Nr	0.25	11.56	38.57	-	**50.13**	*45.69*
Q3.4.3	Cross-sectional area: 0.05 - 0.1m²							
Q3.4.3.01	Cross sectional area: 0.10m²	Nr	0.30	13.87	46.28	-	**60.15**	*54.83*
Q3.4.4	Cross-sectional area: 0.1 - 0.15m²							
Q3.4.4.01	Cross sectional area: 0.15m²	Nr	0.35	16.18	53.99	-	**70.17**	*63.97*
Q3.4.5	Cross-sectional area: 0.15 - 0.25m²							
Q3.4.5.01	Cross sectional area: 0.20m²	Nr	0.30	13.87	61.60	-	**75.47**	*54.83*
Q3.5	**Length of pile extensions, each length: 3m**							
Q3.5.2	Cross-sectional area: 0.025 - 0.05m²							
Q3.5.2.01	Each length 3m; Cross sectional area: 0.05m²	m	-	-	-	80.00	**80.00**	*165.55*
Q3.5.3	Cross-sectional area: 0.05 - 0.1m²							
Q3.5.3.01	Each length 3m; Cross sectional area: 0.10m²	m	-	-	-	90.00	**90.00**	*189.20*
Q3.5.4	Cross-sectional area: 0.1 - 0.15m²							
Q3.5.4.01	Each length 3m; Cross sectional area: 0.15m²	m	-	-	-	110.00	**110.00**	*354.75*
Q3.5.5	Cross-sectional area: 0.15 - 0.25m²							
Q3.5.5.01	Each length 3m; Cross sectional area: 0.20m²	m	-	-	-	130.00	**130.00**	*378.40*
Q3.6	**Length of pile extensions, each length: exceeding 3m**							
Q3.6.2	Cross-sectional area: 0.025 - 0.05m²							
Q3.6.2.01	Each length 5m; Cross sectional area: 0.05m²	m	-	-	-	100.00	**100.00**	*260.15*
Q3.6.3	Cross-sectional area: 0.05 - 0.1m²							
Q3.6.3.01	Each length 5m; Cross sectional area: 0.10m²	m	-	-	-	110.00	**110.00**	*283.80*
Q3.6.4	Cross-sectional area: 0.1 - 0.15m²							
Q3.6.4.01	Each length 5m; Cross sectional area: 0.15m²	m	-	-	-	120.00	**120.00**	*520.30*
Q3.6.5	Cross-sectional area: 0.15 - 0.25m²							
Q3.6.5.01	Each length 5m; Cross sectional area: 0.20m²	m	-	-	-	120.00	**120.00**	*520.30*

Q3 Preformed Concrete Piles continued...

		Unit	Labour Hours	Labour Net £	Plant Net £	Materials Net £	Unit Net £	CO_2 Kg
Q3.7	**Cutting off surplus lengths**							
Q3.7.2	Cross-sectional area: 0.025 - 0.05m^2							
Q3.7.2.01	Cross sectional area: 0.05m^2	m	0.25	7.17	18.09	-	25.26	*8.88*
Q3.7.3	Cross-sectional area: 0.05 - 0.1m^2							
Q3.7.3.01	Cross sectional area: 0.10m^2	m	0.33	9.55	24.09	-	33.64	*11.83*
Q3.7.4	Cross-sectional area: 0.1 - 0.15m^2							
Q3.7.4.01	Cross sectional area: 0.15m^2	m	0.42	11.96	30.17	-	42.13	*14.81*
Q3.7.5	Cross-sectional area: 0.15 - 0.25m^2							
Q3.7.5.01	Cross sectional area: 0.20m^2	m	0.50	14.34	36.17	-	50.51	*17.76*
Q3.8	**Preparing heads**							
Q3.8.2	Cross-sectional area: 0.025 - 0.05m^2							
Q3.8.2.01	Cross sectional area: 0.05m^2	Nr	0.25	7.17	18.09	-	25.26	*8.88*
Q3.8.3	Cross-sectional area: 0.05 - 0.1m^2							
Q3.8.3.01	Cross sectional area: 0.10m^2	Nr	0.33	9.55	24.09	-	33.64	*11.83*
Q3.8.4	Cross-sectional area: 0.1 - 0.15m^2							
Q3.8.4.01	Cross sectional area: 0.15m^2	Nr	0.42	11.96	30.17	-	42.13	*14.81*
Q3.8.5	Cross-sectional area: 0.15 - 0.25m^2							
Q3.8.5.01	Cross sectional area: 0.20m^2	Nr	0.50	14.34	36.17	-	50.51	*17.76*

Q5 Isolated Steel Piles

		Unit	Labour Hours	Labour Net £	Plant Net £	Materials Net £	Unit Net £	CO_2 Kg
Q5.1	**Pre-boring**							
Q5.1.1	Cross-sectional area: not exceeding 0.025m^2							
Q5.1.1.01	Mass: 25kg/m	m	0.05	2.31	7.71	-	10.02	*9.14*
Q5.1.3	Cross-sectional area: 0.05 - 0.1m^2							
Q5.1.3.01	Mass: 50kg/m	m	0.05	2.31	7.71	-	10.02	*9.14*
Q5.1.5	Cross-sectional area: 0.15 - 0.25m^2							
Q5.1.5.01	Mass: 100kg/m	m	0.08	3.47	11.57	-	15.04	*13.71*
Q5.1.6	Cross-sectional area: 0.25 - 0.5m^2							
Q5.1.6.01	Mass: 250kg/m	m	0.10	4.62	15.43	-	20.05	*18.28*
Q5.2	**Jetting**							
Q5.2.1	Cross-sectional area: not exceeding 0.025m^2							
Q5.2.1.01	Mass: 25kg/m	m	0.05	2.31	9.41	-	11.72	*14.64*
Q5.2.3	Cross-sectional area: 0.05 - 0.1m^2							
Q5.2.3.01	Mass: 50kg/m	m	0.05	2.31	9.41	-	11.72	*14.64*

Q5 Isolated Steel Piles continued...

		Unit	Labour Hours	Labour Net £	Plant Net £	Materials Net £	Unit Net £	CO_2 Kg
Q5.2	**Jetting**							
Q5.2.5	Cross-sectional area: 0.15 - 0.25m^2							
Q5.2.5.01	Mass: 100kg/m	m	0.10	4.62	18.83	-	23.45	*29.28*
Q5.2.6	Cross-sectional area: 0.25 - 0.5m^2							
Q5.2.6.01	Mass: 250kg/m	m	0.15	6.93	28.24	-	35.17	*43.91*
Q5.4	**Number of pile extensions**							
Q5.4.1	Cross-sectional area: not exceeding 0.025m^2							
Q5.4.1.01	Mass: 25kg/m	Nr	0.50	23.48	39.61	-	63.09	*46.31*
Q5.4.3	Cross-sectional area: 0.05 - 0.1m^2							
Q5.4.3.01	Mass: 50kg/m	Nr	0.67	31.28	52.76	-	84.04	*61.68*
Q5.4.5	Cross-sectional area: 0.15 - 0.25m^2							
Q5.4.5.01	Mass: 100kg/m	Nr	1.00	46.97	79.23	-	126.20	*92.61*
Q5.4.6	Cross-sectional area: 0.25 - 0.5m^2							
Q5.4.6.01	Mass: 250kg/m	Nr	1.50	70.45	118.84	-	189.29	*138.92*
Q5.5	**Length of pile extensions, each length: not exceeding 3m**							
Q5.5.1	Cross-sectional area: not exceeding 0.025m^2							
Q5.5.1.01	Length of pile extensions, each length 3m; Mass: 25kg/m	m	-	-	-	14.38	14.38	*44.25*
Q5.5.3	Cross-sectional area: 0.05 - 0.1m^2							
Q5.5.3.01	Length of pile extensions, each length 3m; Mass: 50kg/m	m	-	-	-	28.77	28.77	*88.50*
Q5.5.5	Cross-sectional area: 0.15 - 0.25m^2							
Q5.5.5.01	Length of pile extensions, each length 3m; Mass: 100kg/m	m	-	-	-	57.54	57.54	*177.00*
Q5.5.6	Cross-sectional area: 0.25 - 0.5m^2							
Q5.5.6.01	Length of pile extensions, each length 3m; Mass: 250kg/m	m	-	-	-	143.84	143.84	*442.50*
Q5.7	**Cutting off surplus lengths**							
Q5.7.1	Cross-sectional area: not exceeding 0.025m^2							
Q5.7.1.01	Length of pile extensions, each length 3m; Mass: 25kg/m	m	0.20	9.49	5.68	-	15.17	*6.28*
Q5.7.3	Cross-sectional area: 0.05 - 0.1m^2							
Q5.7.3.01	Length of pile extensions, each length 3m; Mass: 50kg/m	m	0.28	13.45	5.97	-	19.42	*6.41*
Q5.7.5	Cross-sectional area: 0.15 - 0.25m^2							
Q5.7.5.01	Length of pile extensions, each length 3m; Mass: 100kg/m	m	0.38	18.20	8.89	-	27.09	*9.64*
Q5.7.6	Cross-sectional area: 0.25 - 0.5m^2							
Q5.7.6.01	Length of pile extensions, each length 3m; Mass: 250kg/m	m	0.55	26.17	9.47	-	35.64	*9.89*

Q6 Interlocking Steel Piles

		Unit	Labour Hours	Labour Net £	Plant Net £	Materials Net £	Unit Net £	CO_2 Kg
Q6.1	**Pre-boring**							
Q6.1.1	Section modulus: not exceeding 500cm³ /m							
Q6.1.1.01	Section modulus: 500cm³/m	m	0.05	3.62	9.01	-	12.63	*10.41*
Q6.1.3	Section modulus: not exceeding 800 - 1200cm³ /m							
Q6.1.3.01	Section modulus: 1000cm³/m	m	0.05	3.62	9.01	-	12.63	*10.41*
Q6.1.4	Section modulus: not exceeding 1200 - 2000cm³ /m							
Q6.1.4.01	Section modulus: 2000cm³/m	m	0.08	6.00	14.95	-	20.95	*17.29*
Q6.1.6	Section modulus: not exceeding 3000 - 4000cm³ /m							
Q6.1.6.01	Section modulus: 4000cm³/m	m	0.10	7.23	18.02	-	25.25	*20.83*
Q6.2	**Jetting**							
Q6.2.1	Section modulus: not exceeding 500cm³ /m							
Q6.2.1.01	Section modulus: 500cm³/m	m	0.07	4.85	14.35	-	19.20	*21.32*
Q6.2.3	Section modulus: not exceeding 800 - 1200cm³ /m							
Q6.2.3.01	Section modulus: 1000cm³/m	m	0.07	4.85	14.35	-	19.20	*21.32*
Q6.2.4	Section modulus: not exceeding 1200 - 2000cm³ /m							
Q6.2.4.01	Section modulus: 2000cm³/m	m	0.10	7.23	21.42	-	28.65	*31.83*
Q6.2.6	Section modulus: not exceeding 3000 - 4000cm³ /m							
Q6.2.6.01	Section modulus: 4000cm³/m	m	0.17	12.08	35.77	-	47.85	*53.15*
Q6.4	**Number of pile extensions**							
Q6.4.1	Section modulus: not exceeding 500cm³ /m							
Q6.4.1.01	Full butt weld; Section modulus: 500cm³/m	Nr	1.67	108.25	212.34	-	320.59	*244.29*
Q6.4.3	Section modulus: not exceeding 800 - 1200cm³ /m							
Q6.4.3.01	Full butt weld; Section modulus: 1000cm³/m	Nr	2.17	138.26	258.42	-	396.68	*296.98*
Q6.4.4	Section modulus: not exceeding 1200 - 2000cm³ /m							
Q6.4.4.01	Full butt weld; Section modulus: 2000cm³/m	Nr	2.67	168.27	304.51	-	472.78	*349.66*
Q6.4.6	Section modulus: not exceeding 3000 - 4000cm³ /m							
Q6.4.6.01	Full butt weld; Section modulus: 4000cm³/m	Nr	4.67	288.30	625.00	-	913.30	*560.40*
Q6.5	**Length of pile extensions, each length: not exceeding 3m**							
Q6.5.1	Section modulus: not exceeding 500cm³ /m							
Q6.5.1.01	Each length 3m; Section modulus: 500cm³/m	m	0.17	12.08	30.09	40.73	82.90	*114.43*
Q6.5.3	Section modulus: not exceeding 800 - 1200cm³ /m							
Q6.5.3.01	Each length 3m; Section modulus: 1000cm³/m	m	0.17	12.08	30.09	57.92	100.09	*148.06*

Q6 Interlocking Steel Piles continued...

		Unit	Labour Hours	Labour Net £	Plant Net £	Materials Net £	Unit Net £	CO_2 Kg
Q6.5	**Length of pile extensions, each length: not exceeding 3m**							
Q6.5.4	Section modulus: not exceeding 1200 - 2000cm³ /m							
Q6.5.4.01	Each length 3m; Section modulus: 2000cm³/m	m	0.33	24.08	59.99	75.12	**159.19**	*216.27*
Q6.5.6	Section modulus: not exceeding 3000 - 4000cm³ /m							
Q6.5.6.01	Each length 3m; Section modulus: 4000cm³/m	m	0.50	36.16	115.61	131.24	**283.01**	*360.79*
Q6.6	**Length of pile extensions, each length: exceeding 3m**							
Q6.6.1	Section modulus: not exceeding 500cm³ /m							
Q6.6.1.01	Length of pile extensions, each length 5m; Section modulus: 500cm³/m	m	0.10	7.23	18.02	40.73	**65.98**	*100.48*
Q6.6.3	Section modulus: not exceeding 800 - 1200cm³ /m							
Q6.6.3.01	Length of pile extensions, each length 5m; Section modulus: 1000cm³/m	m	0.10	7.23	18.02	57.92	**83.17**	*134.11*
Q6.6.4	Section modulus: not exceeding 1200 - 2000cm³ /m							
Q6.6.4.01	Length of pile extensions, each length 5m; Section modulus: 2000cm³/m	m	0.30	21.70	54.05	57.92	**133.67**	*175.76*
Q6.6.6	Section modulus: not exceeding 3000 - 4000cm³ /m							
Q6.6.6.01	Length of pile extensions, each length 5m; Section modulus: 4000cm³/m	m	0.40	28.93	92.48	57.92	**179.33**	*196.59*
Q6.7	**Cutting off surplus lengths**							
Q6.7.1	Section modulus: not exceeding 500cm³ /m							
Q6.7.1.01	Section modulus: 500cm³/m	m	0.28	14.31	6.83	-	**21.14**	*7.25*
Q6.7.3	Section modulus: not exceeding 800 - 1200cm³ /m							
Q6.7.3.01	Section modulus: 1000cm³/m	m	0.53	26.24	7.71	-	**33.95**	*7.63*
Q6.7.4	Section modulus: not exceeding 1200 - 2000cm³ /m							
Q6.7.4.01	Section modulus: 2000cm³/m	m	0.70	34.21	8.29	-	**42.50**	*7.88*
Q6.7.6	Section modulus: not exceeding 3000 - 4000cm³ /m							
Q6.7.6.01	Section modulus: 4000cm³/m	m	1.03	50.10	11.15	-	**61.25**	*8.38*

Q7 Obstructions

		Unit	Labour Hours	Labour Net £	Plant Net £	Materials Net £	Unit Net £	CO_2 Kg
Q7.1	**Breaking out rock**							
Q7.1.1	Encountered above the founding stratum							
Q7.1.1.01	per rig	Hr	1.00	72.32	180.16	-	**252.48**	*208.28*

Q8 Pile Tests

		Unit	Labour Hours	Labour Net £	Plant Net £	Materials Net £	Unit Net £	CO_2 Kg
Q8.1	**Maintained loading with various reactions**							
Q8.1.1	Test load: not exceeding 100 t							
Q8.1.1.01	Tests by anchor piles, loads applied in 10 tonne increments at hourly intervals maintained for 24 hours; removed in equal increments over 6 hours; Test load: 50 t, establish equipment and carry out test	Nr	19.20	1,145.78	8,488.27	-	**9,634.05**	*7,020.57*
Q8.1.1.02	as above; Test load: 100t, establish equipment and carry out test	Nr	24.20	1,356.33	9,584.87	-	**10,941.20**	*7,934.38*
Q8.1.1.03	Tests by anchor piles, loads applied in 10 tonne increments at hourly intervals maintained for 24 hours; removed in equal increments over 6 hours; Test load: 50 t; excludes establish of equipment	Nr	15.20	861.82	3,224.59	-	**4,086.41**	*2,634.26*
Q8.1.1.04	as above; Test load: 100 t; excludes establish of equipment	Nr	20.20	1,072.37	4,321.19	-	**5,393.56**	*3,548.07*
Q8.1.2	Test load: not exceeding 100 - 200 t							
Q8.1.2.01	Tests by anchor piles, loads applied in 10 tonne increments at hourly intervals maintained for 24 hours; removed in equal increments over 6 hours; Test load: 150 t, establish equipment and carry out test	Nr	34.10	1,720.10	10,275.44	-	**11,995.54**	*8,536.27*
Q8.1.2.02	as above; Test load: 200 t, establish equipment and carry out test	Nr	34.10	1,720.10	11,372.04	-	**13,092.14**	*9,450.08*
Q8.1.2.03	Tests by anchor piles, loads applied in 10 tonne increments at hourly intervals maintained for 24 hours; removed in equal increments over 6 hours; Test load: 150 t; excludes establish of equipment	Nr	25.20	1,282.92	5,417.79	-	**6,700.71**	*4,461.89*
Q8.1.2.04	as above; Test load: 200 t; excludes establish of equipment	Nr	30.20	1,493.47	6,514.39	-	**8,007.86**	*5,375.70*
Q8.2	**Constant rate of penetration**							
Q8.2.1	Test load: not exceeding 100 t							
Q8.2.1.01	Test load: 50 t	Nr	14.20	819.71	3,005.27	-	**3,824.98**	*2,451.49*
Q8.2.1.02	Test load: 100 t	Nr	19.20	1,030.26	4,101.87	-	**5,132.13**	*3,365.31*
Q8.2.2	Test load: not exceeding 100 - 200 t							
Q8.2.2.01	Test load: 150 t	Nr	24.20	1,240.81	5,198.47	-	**6,439.28**	*4,279.12*
Q8.2.2.02	Test load: 200 t	Nr	29.20	1,451.36	6,295.07	-	**7,746.43**	*5,192.94*

CLASS R:

ROADS AND PAVINGS

Calculations used throughout Class R - Roads and Pavings

Labour

		Qty		Rate		Total
L A0140ICE	**Steel fixing Labour Gang**					
	Craftsman WRA	2	x	16.68	=	£33.37
	Labourer (General Operative)	1	x	12.56	=	£12.56
	Total hourly cost of gang				**=**	**£45.93**
L A0270ICE	**Road sub-base Labour Gang**					
	Ganger	1	x	16.99	=	£16.99
	Labourer (General Operative)	2	x	12.56	=	£25.12
	Total hourly cost of gang				**=**	**£42.11**
L A0271ICE	**Soil cement Labour Gang**					
	Banksman	1	x	13.53	=	£13.53
	Ganger	1	x	16.99	=	£16.99
	Labourer (General Operative)	2	x	12.56	=	£25.12
	Labourer (Skill Rate 3)	1	x	14.34	=	£14.34
	Total hourly cost of gang				**=**	**£69.98**
L A0274ICE	**Concrete pavement Labour Gang**					
	Craftsman WRA	1	x	16.68	=	£16.68
	Ganger	1	x	16.99	=	£16.99
	Labourer (General Operative)	2	x	12.56	=	£25.12
	Labourer (Skill Rate 3)	1	x	14.34	=	£14.34
	Banksman	1	x	13.53	=	£13.53
	Total hourly cost of gang				**=**	**£86.66**
L A0275ICE	**Concrete joints Labour Gang**					
	Craftsman WRA	2	x	16.68	=	£33.37
	Labourer (General Operative)	1	x	12.56	=	£12.56
	Total hourly cost of gang				**=**	**£45.93**
L A0276ICE	**Kerbs and paving Labour Gang**					
	Ganger	1	x	16.99	=	£16.99
	Labourer (General Operative)	2	x	12.56	=	£25.12
	Total hourly cost of gang				**=**	**£42.11**
L A0320ICE	**Waterproofing Labour Gang**					
	Ganger	1	x	16.99	=	£16.99
	Labourer (General Operative)	3	x	12.56	=	£37.68
	Total hourly cost of gang				=	£54.67

Plant

		Qty		Rate		Total
P A1140ICE	**Steel fixing Plant Gang**					
	Cranes crawler - NCK 305C 19t	0.25	x	43.26	=	£10.81
	Total hourly cost of gang				**=**	**£10.81**
P A1270ICE	**Road sub-base Plant Gang**					
	Crawler Tractor / Dozer - Cat D4C LGP 60kW	1	x	35.68	=	£35.68
	Roller - 800mm Ride on Roller	1	x	6.068	=	£6.07
	Total hourly cost of gang				**=**	**£41.75**
P A1271ICE	**Soil cement Plant Gang**					
	Hydraulic Excavator - Cat 320 96kW	1	x	33.98	=	£33.98
	Tipping Waggon - 16t 6-Wheel (24t Gr)	2	x	47.978	=	£95.95
	Concrete Mixer - Liner Rolpanit	1	x	37.368	=	£37.36
	Cement Silo 50t	1	x	2.47	=	£2.47
	Road Plant - Barber Greene BGP 200 Paver	1	x	51.45	=	£51.45
	Total hourly cost of gang				**=**	**£221.21**

P A1272ICE	**Cement bound granular material Plant Gang**					
	Tipping Waggon - 16t 6-Wheel (24t Gr)	2	x	47.97	=	£95.95
	Concrete Mixer - Liner Rolpanit	1	x	37.36	=	£37.36
	Cement Silo 50t	1	x	2.47	=	£2.47
	Road Plant - Barber Greene BGP 200 Paver	1	x	51.45	=	£51.45
	Total hourly cost of gang				**=**	**£187.23**
P A1274ICE	**Concrete pavement Plant Gang**					
	Road Plant - Barber Greene BGP 200 Paver	1	x	51.45	=	£51.45
	Compressor - 375 cfm	0.5	x	14.95	=	£7.48
	Air Vibrating Poker up to 75mm	2	x	1.25	=	£2.49
	Total hourly cost of gang				**=**	**£61.42**

Class R - Roads and Pavings

R1 Sub-bases, Flexible Road Bases and Surfacing

		Unit	Labour Hours	Labour Net £	Plant Net £	Materials Net £	Unit Net £	CO_2 Kg
R1.1	**Granular material DTp Specified type 1**							
R1.1.4	Depth: 100 - 150mm							
R1.1.4.01	DTp clause nr. 803; Levelling and compacting with a vibratory roller; depth: 100mm	m^2	0.01	0.38	0.38	3.14	3.90	*1.24*
R1.1.4.02	as above; depth: 150mm	m^2	0.01	0.55	0.54	4.70	5.79	*1.85*
R1.1.5	Depth: 150 - 200mm							
R1.1.5.01	DTp clause nr. 803; Levelling and compacting with a vibratory roller; depth: 200mm	m^2	0.02	0.76	0.75	6.27	7.78	*2.47*
R1.1.6	Depth: 200 - 250mm							
R1.1.6.01	DTp clause nr. 803; Levelling and compacting with a vibratory roller; depth: 250mm	m^2	0.02	0.93	0.92	7.84	9.69	*3.08*
R1.1.7	Depth: 250 - 300mm							
R1.1.7.01	DTp clause nr. 803; Levelling and compacting with a vibratory roller; depth: 300mm	m^2	0.03	1.09	1.09	9.41	11.59	*3.69*
R1.1.8	Depth: exceeding 300mm							
R1.1.8.01	DTp clause nr. 803; Levelling and compacting with a vibratory roller; depth: 400mm	m^2	0.04	1.47	1.46	12.54	15.47	*4.93*
R1.1.8.02	as above; depth: 500mm	m^2	0.04	1.85	1.84	15.68	19.37	*6.17*
R1.1.8.03	as above; depth: 1m	m^2	0.09	3.71	3.67	31.35	38.73	*12.33*
R1.2	**Granular material DTp Specified type 2**							
R1.2.4	Depth: 100 - 150mm							
R1.2.4.01	DTp clause nr. 804; Levelling and compacting with a vibratory roller; depth: 100mm	m^2	0.01	0.38	0.38	3.36	4.12	*1.24*
R1.2.4.02	as above; depth: 150mm	m^2	0.01	0.55	0.54	5.03	6.12	*1.85*
R1.2.5	Depth: 150 - 200mm							
R1.2.5.01	DTp clause nr. 804; Levelling and compacting with a vibratory roller; depth: 200mm	m^2	0.02	0.76	0.75	6.71	8.22	*2.47*
R1.2.6	Depth: 200 - 250mm							
R1.2.6.01	DTp clause nr. 804; Levelling and compacting with a vibratory roller; depth: 250mm	m^2	0.02	0.93	0.92	8.39	10.24	*3.08*
R1.2.7	Depth: 250 - 300mm							
R1.2.7.01	DTp clause nr. 804; Levelling and compacting with a vibratory roller; depth: 300mm	m^2	0.03	1.09	1.09	10.07	12.25	*3.69*
R1.2.8	Depth: exceeding 300mm							
R1.2.8.01	DTp clause nr. 804; Levelling and compacting with a vibratory roller; depth: 400mm	m^2	0.04	1.47	1.46	12.96	15.89	*4.78*
R1.2.8.02	as above; depth: 500mm	m^2	0.04	1.85	1.84	16.78	20.47	*6.17*
R1.2.8.03	as above; depth: 1m	m^2	0.09	3.71	3.67	33.55	40.93	*12.33*

R1 Sub-bases, Flexible Road Bases and Surfacing continued...

		Unit	Labour Hours	Labour Net £	Plant Net £	Materials Net £	Unit Net £	CO_2 Kg
R1.3	**Soil cement**							
R1.3.3	Depth: 60 - 100mm							
R1.3.3.01	DTp clause nr. 805; 100kg dry Ordinary Portland Cement per cubic metre of soil (supply of soil excluded); depth: 75mm	m^2	0.01	0.56	1.77	0.95	**3.28**	*7.33*
R1.3.3.02	as above; depth: 100mm	m^2	0.01	0.77	2.43	1.19	**4.39**	*9.24*
R1.3.4	Depth: 100 - 150mm							
R1.3.4.01	DTp clause nr. 805; 100kg dry Ordinary Portland Cement per cubic metre of soil (supply of soil excluded); depth: 150mm	m^2	0.02	1.19	3.76	1.78	**6.73**	*13.91*
R1.3.5	Depth: 150 - 200mm							
R1.3.5.01	DTp clause nr. 805; 100kg dry Ordinary Portland Cement per cubic metre of soil (supply of soil excluded); depth: 200mm	m^2	0.02	1.54	4.87	2.37	**8.78**	*18.48*
R1.4	**Cement bound granular material**							
R1.4.3	Depth: 60 - 100mm							
R1.4.3.01	DTp clause nr. 806; 100kg dry Ordinary Portland Cement per cubic metre of sub-base granular material; depth: 75mm	m^2	0.01	0.56	1.50	3.30	**5.36**	*8.03*
R1.4.3.02	as above; depth: 100mm	m^2	0.01	0.77	2.06	4.32	**7.15**	*10.18*
R1.4.4	Depth: 100 - 150mm							
R1.4.4.01	DTp clause nr. 806; 100kg dry Ordinary Portland Cement per cubic metre of sub-base granular material; depth: 150mm	m^2	0.02	1.19	3.18	6.48	**10.85**	*15.31*
R1.4.5	Depth: 150 - 200mm							
R1.4.5.01	DTp clause nr. 806; 100kg dry Ordinary Portland Cement per cubic metre of sub-base granular material; depth: 200mm	m^2	0.02	1.54	4.12	8.64	**14.30**	*20.36*
R1.5	**Lean concrete DTp Specified strength**							
R1.5.3	Depth: 60 - 100mm							
R1.5.3.01	DTp clause nr. 807; Concrete grade 10, 20mm aggregate; depth: 75mm	m^2	0.01	0.56	1.50	4.48	**6.54**	*16.33*
R1.5.3.02	as above; depth: 100mm	m^2	0.01	0.77	2.06	5.98	**8.81**	*21.80*
R1.5.4	Depth: 100 - 150mm							
R1.5.4.01	DTp clause nr. 807; Concrete grade 10, 20mm aggregate; depth: 150mm	m^2	0.02	1.19	3.18	8.97	**13.34**	*32.74*
R1.5.5	Depth: 150 - 200mm							
R1.5.5.01	DTp clause nr. 807; Concrete grade 10, 20mm aggregate; depth: 200mm	m^2	0.02	1.54	4.12	11.96	**17.62**	*43.60*

R1 Sub-bases, Flexible Road Bases and Surfacing continued...

		Unit	Labour Hours	Labour Net £	Plant Net £	Materials Net £	Unit Net £	CO_2 Kg
R1.6	**Hardcore**							
R1.6.4	Depth: 100 - 150mm							
R1.6.4.01	Clean imported filling; levelling and compacting with a vibratory roller; depth: 100mm	m^2	0.01	0.38	0.38	1.79	2.55	*0.74*
R1.6.4.02	as above; depth: 150mm	m^2	0.01	0.55	0.54	2.39	3.48	*1.00*
R1.6.5	Depth: 150 - 200mm							
R1.6.5.01	Clean imported filling; levelling and compacting with a vibratory roller; depth: 200mm	m^2	0.02	0.76	0.75	3.59	5.10	*1.47*
R1.6.6	Depth: 200 - 250mm							
R1.6.6.01	Clean imported filling; levelling and compacting with a vibratory roller; depth: 250mm	m^2	0.02	0.93	0.92	4.78	6.63	*1.93*
R1.6.7	Depth: 250 - 300mm							
R1.6.7.01	Clean imported filling; levelling and compacting with a vibratory roller; depth: 300mm	m^2	0.03	1.09	1.09	7.17	9.35	*2.79*
R1.6.8	Depth: exceeding 300mm							
R1.6.8.01	Clean imported filling; levelling and compacting with a vibratory roller; depth: 400mm	m^2	0.04	1.47	1.46	9.56	12.49	*3.73*
R1.6.8.02	as above; depth: 500mm	m^2	0.04	1.85	1.84	11.95	15.64	*4.67*
R1.6.8.03	as above; depth: 1m	m^2	0.09	3.71	3.67	23.90	31.28	*9.33*
R1.7	**Geotextiles**							
R1.7.1	Lotrak 10/7 ground stabilising matting; 150mm laps							
R1.7.1.01	horizontal	m^2	0.01	0.38	-	0.51	0.89	*0.55*

R2 Sub-bases, Flexible Road Bases and Surfacing

		Unit	Labour Hours	Labour Net £	Plant Net £	Materials Net £	Unit Net £	CO_2 Kg
R2.1	**Wet mix macadam**							
R2.1.3	Depth: 60 - 100mm							
R2.1.3.01	Single course (DTp clause nr. 808); depth: 75mm	m^2	0.01	0.38	0.38	2.35	3.11	*0.96*
R2.1.3.02	as above; depth: 100mm	m^2	0.01	0.55	0.42	3.33	4.30	*1.32*
R2.1.4	Depth: 100 - 150mm							
R2.1.4.01	Single course (DTp clause nr. 808); depth: 150mm	m^2	0.02	0.76	0.75	4.70	6.21	*1.92*
R2.1.5	Depth: 150 - 200mm							
R2.1.5.01	Single course (DTp clause nr. 808); depth: 200mm	m^2	0.02	0.93	0.92	6.27	8.12	*2.53*
R2.2	**Dry bound macadam**							
R2.2.3	Depth: 60 - 100mm							
R2.2.3.01	Single course (DTp clause nr. 809); depth: 75mm	m^2	0.01	0.38	0.38	2.35	3.11	*0.96*
R2.2.3.02	as above; depth: 100mm	m^2	0.01	0.55	0.54	3.14	4.23	*1.30*
R2.2.4	Depth: 100 - 150mm							
R2.2.4.01	Single course (DTp clause nr. 809); depth: 150mm	m^2	0.02	0.76	0.75	4.70	6.21	*1.92*

R2 Sub-bases, Flexible Road Bases and Surfacing continued...

		Unit	Labour Hours	Labour Net £	Plant Net £	Materials Net £	Unit Net £	CO_2 Kg
R2.2	**Dry bound macadam**							
R2.2.5	Depth: 150 - 200mm							
R2.2.5.01	Single course (DTp clause nr. 809); depth: 200mm	m²	0.02	0.93	0.92	6.27	**8.12**	*2.53*
R2.3	**Dense bitumen macadam**							
R2.3.2	Depth: 30 - 60mm							
R2.3.2.01	BS EN 13108, (DTp clause nr. 811 and 908); wearing course material; sub-clause 2.3.5; 10mm nominal size aggregate; depth: 30mm	m²	0.01	1.53	1.56	3.37	**6.46**	*9.96*
R2.3.2.02	as above; depth: 35mm	m²	0.01	1.53	1.56	3.95	**7.04**	*11.64*
R2.3.2.03	BS EN 13108, (DTp clause nr. 811 and 908); wearing course material; sub-clause 2.3.4; 14mm nominal size aggregate; depth: 30mm	m²	0.01	1.53	1.56	3.37	**6.46**	*9.96*
R2.3.2.04	as above; depth: 45mm	m²	0.01	1.53	1.56	5.08	**8.17**	*14.86*
R2.3.2.05	BS EN 13108, (DTp clause nr. 811 and 908); base course material; sub-clause 2.2.6; 20mm nominal size aggregate; depth: 35mm	m²	0.02	3.07	3.12	3.67	**9.86**	*11.93*
R2.3.2.06	as above; depth: 50mm	m²	0.02	3.07	3.12	5.20	**11.39**	*16.69*
R2.3.2.07	BS EN 13108, (DTp clause nr. 811 and 908); base course material; sub-clause 2.2.5; 28mm nominal size aggregate; depth: 50mm	m²	0.02	3.07	3.12	5.20	**11.39**	*16.69*
R2.3.2.08	as above; depth: 60mm	m²	0.02	3.07	3.12	6.25	**12.44**	*19.91*
R2.3.3	Depth: 60 - 100mm							
R2.3.3.01	BS EN 13108, (DTp clause nr. 811 and 908); wearing course material; single course; sub-clause 2.2.3; 40mm nominal size aggregate; depth: 65mm	m²	0.02	3.07	3.12	7.32	**13.51**	*21.59*
R2.3.3.02	as above; depth: 80mm	m²	0.02	3.07	3.12	8.98	**15.17**	*26.35*
R2.3.3.03	BS EN 13108, (DTp clause nr. 811 and 908); base course material; sub-clause 2.2.4; 40mm nominal size aggregate; depth: 60mm	m²	0.02	3.07	3.12	6.25	**12.44**	*19.91*
R2.3.3.04	as above; depth: 80mm	m²	0.02	3.07	3.12	8.33	**14.52**	*26.35*
R2.3.3.05	BS EN 13108, (DTp clause nr. 811 and 908); base course material; single course; sub-clause 2.2.3; 40mm nominal size aggregate; depth: 60mm	m²	0.02	3.07	3.12	6.25	**12.44**	*19.91*
R2.3.3.06	as above; depth: 80mm	m²	0.02	3.07	3.12	8.33	**14.52**	*26.35*
R2.3.3.07	BS EN 13108, (DTp clause nr. 811 and 908); road base material; sub-clause 2.1.1; 40mm nominal size aggregate; depth: 65mm	m²	0.03	4.60	4.67	6.39	**15.66**	*21.89*
R2.3.3.08	as above; depth: 100mm	m²	0.03	4.60	4.67	9.80	**19.07**	*33.09*

R2 Sub-bases, Flexible Road Bases and Surfacing continued...

		Unit	Labour Hours	Labour Net £	Plant Net £	Materials Net £	Unit Net £	CO_2 Kg
R2.4	**Open texture bitumen macadam**							
R2.4.1	Depth: not exceeding 30mm							
R2.4.1.01	BS EN 13108, (DTp clause nr. 912); Wearing course material; sub-clause 2.3.2; 10mm nominal size aggregate; depth: 20mm	m^2	0.01	1.53	1.56	2.24	5.33	*6.74*
R2.4.1.02	as above; depth: 25mm	m^2	0.01	1.53	1.56	2.83	5.92	*8.42*
R2.4.1.03	BS EN 13108, (DTp clause nr. 912); Medium texture wearing course material; sub-clause 2.3.3; 6mm nominal size aggregate; depth: 20mm	m^2	0.01	1.53	1.56	2.08	5.17	*6.74*
R2.4.2	Depth: 30 - 60mm							
R2.4.2.01	BS EN 13108, (DTp clause nr. 912); Wearing course material; sub-clause 2.3.1; 14mm nominal size aggregate; depth: 30mm	m^2	0.01	1.53	1.56	3.37	6.46	*9.96*
R2.4.2.02	as above; depth: 40mm	m^2	0.01	1.53	1.56	4.49	7.58	*13.18*
R2.4.2.03	BS EN 13108, (DTp clause nr. 912); Base course material; sub-clause 2.2.2; 20mm nominal size aggregate; depth: 35mm	m^2	0.01	1.53	1.56	3.67	6.76	*11.64*
R2.4.2.04	as above; depth: 50mm	m^2	0.02	3.07	3.12	5.20	11.39	*16.69*
R2.4.3	Depth: 60 - 100mm							
R2.4.3.01	BS EN 13108, (DTp clause nr. 912); Base course material; sub-clause 2.2.1; 40mm nominal size aggregate; depth: 60mm	m^2	0.02	3.07	3.12	6.25	12.44	*19.91*
R2.4.3.02	as above; depth: 80mm	m^2	0.02	3.07	3.12	8.33	14.52	*26.35*
R2.6	**Open texture tarmacadam**							
R2.6.1	Depth: not exceeding 30mm							
R2.6.1.01	BS EN 13108, (DTp clause nr. 913); Fine texture wearing course material; sub-clause 2.3.7; 6mm nominal size aggregate; depth: 15mm	m^2	0.01	1.53	1.56	1.58	4.67	*5.20*
R2.6.1.02	as above; depth: 25mm	m^2	0.01	1.53	1.56	2.63	5.72	*8.42*
R2.7	**Dense tar surfacing**							
R2.7.1	Depth: not exceeding 30mm							
R2.7.1.01	Wearing course material; 14mm nominal size; depth: 30mm	m^2	0.01	1.53	1.56	3.06	6.15	*9.96*

R3 Sub-bases, Flexible Road Bases and Surfacing

		Unit	Labour Hours	Labour Net £	Plant Net £	Materials Net £	Unit Net £	CO_2 Kg
R3.1	**Cold asphalt wearing course**							
R3.1.1	Depth: not exceeding 30mm							
R3.1.1.01	BS EN 13108, (DTp clause nr. 910); Fine cold asphalt (6mm fine-texture bitumen macadam); sub-clause 2.3.7; 6mm nominal size aggregate; depth: 15mm	m^2	0.01	1.53	1.56	1.65	4.74	*5.20*
R3.1.1.02	as above; depth: 25mm	m^2	0.01	1.53	1.56	2.73	5.82	*8.42*

R3 Sub-bases, Flexible Road Bases and Surfacing continued...

		Unit	Labour Hours	Labour Net £	Plant Net £	Materials Net £	Unit Net £	CO_2 Kg
R3.1	**Cold asphalt wearing course**							
R3.1.2	Depth: 30 - 60mm							
R3.1.2.01	BS EN 13108, (DTp clause nr. 910); Course cold asphalt (10mm medium-texture bitumen macadam); sub-clause 2.3.6; 10mm nominal size aggregate; depth: 30mm	m^2	0.02	3.07	3.12	3.15	9.34	*10.25*
R3.1.2.02	as above; depth: 35mm	m^2	0.02	3.07	3.12	3.70	9.89	*11.93*
R3.3	**Slurry sealing**							
R3.3.1	Depth: not exceeding 30mm							
R3.3.1.01	BS EN 13808 (DTp clause nr. 914); Bitumen emulsion, sand, cement composition (200 litres per tonne dry aggregate; 2% cement by mass of aggregate); spread by mechanical means; depth: 3mm	m^2	0.01	0.31	-	1.15	1.46	*5.04*
R3.4	**Surface dressing**							
R3.4.1	Depth: not exceeding 30mm							
R3.4.1.01	Coated chippings evenly applied to macadam surfaces; rolled or pressed into surface; nominal size 10mm; at the rate of 4kg per m2	m^2	0.01	0.57	0.51	0.53	1.61	*2.39*
R3.4.1.02	as above; nominal size 10mm; at the rate of 6kg per m2	m^2	0.01	0.57	0.51	0.56	1.64	*2.40*
R3.4.1.03	as above; nominal size 10mm; at the rate of 8kg per m2	m^2	0.01	0.57	0.51	0.59	1.67	*2.41*
R3.4.1.04	Coated chippings evenly applied to macadam surfaces; rolled or pressed into surface; nominal size 14mm; at the rate of 6kg per m2	m^2	0.01	0.57	0.51	0.55	1.63	*2.40*
R3.4.1.05	as above; nominal size 14mm; at the rate of 8kg per m2	m^2	0.01	0.57	0.51	0.58	1.66	*2.41*
R3.4.1.06	as above; nominal size 14mm; at the rate of 10kg per m2	m^2	0.01	0.57	0.51	0.61	1.69	*2.42*
R3.4.1.07	Uncoated chippings evenly applied to macadam surfaces; rolled or pressed into surface; nominal size 10mm; at the rate of 4kg per m2	m^2	0.01	0.57	0.51	0.06	1.14	*0.25*
R3.4.1.08	as above; nominal size 10mm; at the rate of 6kg per m2	m^2	0.01	0.57	0.51	0.09	1.17	*0.26*
R3.4.1.09	as above; nominal size 10mm; at the rate of 8kg per m2	m^2	0.01	0.57	0.51	0.12	1.20	*0.27*
R3.4.1.10	as above; nominal size 14mm; at the rate of 6kg per m2	m^2	0.01	0.57	0.51	0.08	1.16	*0.26*
R3.4.1.11	as above; nominal size 14mm; at the rate of 8kg per m2	m^2	0.01	0.57	0.51	0.11	1.19	*0.27*
R3.4.1.12	as above; nominal size 14mm; at the rate of 10kg per m2	m^2	0.01	0.57	0.51	0.14	1.22	*0.28*
R3.5	**Bituminous Spray**							
R3.5.1	Depth: not exceeding 30mm							
R3.5.1.01	Cationic bitumen emulsion tack coat applied to; new surfaces	m^2	0.02	0.29	0.02	0.31	0.62	*1.42*

R3 Sub-bases, Flexible Road Bases and Surfacing continued...

		Unit	Labour Hours	Labour Net £	Plant Net £	Materials Net £	Unit Net £	CO_2 Kg
R3.5	**Bituminous Spray**							
R3.5.1	Depth: not exceeding 30mm							
R3.5.1.02	as previous item; existing surfaces	m²	0.02	0.29	0.02	0.31	0.62	*1.42*
R3.6	**Removal of flexible surface**							
R3.6.1	Depth: not exceeding 30mm							
R3.6.1.01	Breaking up existing fine texture wearing course; 6mm nominal size aggregate; 15mm deep	m²	0.02	1.89	4.10	-	5.99	*6.20*
R3.6.2	Depth: 30 - 60mm							
R3.6.2.01	Breaking up existing dense bitumen macadam wearing course; 14mm nominal size aggregate; 30mm deep	m²	0.02	2.26	4.92	-	7.18	*7.44*
R3.6.2.02	as above; 45mm deep	m²	0.03	2.83	6.15	-	8.98	*9.29*
R3.6.3	Depth: 60 - 100mm							
R3.6.3.01	Breaking up existing dense bitumen macadam base course; 40mm nominal size aggregate; 65mm deep	m²	0.03	2.83	6.15	-	8.98	*9.29*
R3.6.3.02	as above; 100mm deep	m²	0.04	3.77	8.21	-	11.98	*12.39*
R3.6.3.03	Breaking up existing dense bitumen macadam base course 65mm deep, 40mm nominal size aggregate; wearing course 30mm deep, 14mm nominal size; 95mm deep overall	m²	0.05	5.09	11.08	-	16.17	*16.73*

R4 Concrete Pavements

		Unit	Labour Hours	Labour Net £	Plant Net £	Materials Net £	Unit Net £	CO_2 Kg
R4.1	**Carriageway slabs of DTp Specified paving quality concrete**							
R4.1.3	Depth: 60 - 100mm							
R4.1.3.01	Concrete grade 30, 20mm aggregate; depth: 100mm	m²	0.01	0.87	0.61	9.49	10.97	*31.91*
R4.1.4	Depth: 100 - 150mm							
R4.1.4.01	Concrete grade 30, 20mm aggregate; depth: 150mm	m²	0.02	1.30	0.92	14.24	16.46	*47.86*
R4.1.5	Depth: 150 - 200mm							
R4.1.5.01	Concrete grade 30, 20mm aggregate; depth: 200mm	m²	0.02	1.73	1.23	18.98	21.94	*63.82*
R4.1.6	Depth: 200 - 250mm							
R4.1.6.01	Concrete grade 30, 20mm aggregate; depth: 250mm	m²	0.03	2.17	1.54	23.73	27.44	*79.77*
R4.1.7	Depth: 250 - 300mm							
R4.1.7.01	Concrete grade 30, 20mm aggregate; depth: 300mm	m²	0.03	2.60	1.84	28.48	32.92	*95.73*
R4.1.8	Depth: exceeding 300mm							
R4.1.8.01	Concrete grade 30, 20mm aggregate; depth: 400mm	m²	0.04	3.47	2.46	37.97	43.90	*127.64*

R4 Concrete Pavements continued...

		Unit	Labour Hours	Labour Net £	Plant Net £	Materials Net £	Unit Net £	CO_2 Kg
R4.4	**Steel fabric reinforcement, BS 4483**							
R4.4.2	Nominal size: 8mm							
R4.4.2.01	nominal mass: 2.22kg/m²; A142	m²	0.06	2.76	-	1.43	4.19	*5.57*
R4.4.2.02	nominal mass: 2.61kg/m²; C283	m²	0.06	2.76	-	1.85	4.61	*6.55*
R4.4.3	Nominal size: 10mm							
R4.4.3.01	nominal mass: 3.02kg/m²; A193	m²	0.06	2.76	-	1.98	4.74	*7.58*
R4.4.3.02	nominal mass: 3.05kg/m²; B196	m²	0.07	3.22	-	3.62	6.84	*7.66*
R4.4.3.03	nominal mass: 3.41kg/m²; C385	m²	0.07	3.22	-	2.23	5.45	*8.56*
R4.4.3.04	nominal mass: 3.73kg/m²; B283	m²	0.07	3.22	-	2.42	5.64	*9.36*
R4.4.3.05	nominal mass: 3.95kg/m²; A252	m²	0.09	4.13	-	2.61	6.74	*9.92*
R4.4.4	Nominal size: 12mm							
R4.4.4.01	nominal mass: 4.34kg/m²; C503	m²	0.09	4.13	-	2.87	7.00	*10.89*
R4.4.4.02	nominal mass: 4.53kg/m²; B385	m²	0.10	4.59	-	2.94	7.53	*11.37*
R4.4.5	Nominal size: 16mm							
R4.4.5.01	nominal mass: 5.55kg/m²; C636	m²	0.10	4.59	-	3.67	8.26	*13.93*
R4.4.5.02	nominal mass: 5.93kg/m²; B503	m²	0.10	4.59	-	3.85	8.44	*14.88*
R4.6	**Plain round steel bar reinforcement to BS 4449**							
R4.6.1	Nominal size: 6mm							
R4.6.1.01	generally	Tonne	11.70	537.38	126.48	662.18	1,326.04	*1,732.89*
R4.6.2	Nominal size: 8mm							
R4.6.2.01	generally	Tonne	9.70	445.52	104.86	643.84	1,194.22	*1,728.97*
R4.6.3	Nominal size: 10mm							
R4.6.3.01	generally	Tonne	7.00	321.51	75.67	618.13	1,015.31	*1,723.69*
R4.6.4	Nominal size: 12mm							
R4.6.4.01	generally	Tonne	6.30	289.36	68.10	602.96	960.42	*1,722.32*
R4.6.5	Nominal size: 16mm							
R4.6.5.01	generally	Tonne	5.30	243.43	57.29	569.87	870.59	*1,720.37*
R4.6.6	Nominal size: 20mm							
R4.6.6.01	generally	Tonne	5.00	229.65	54.05	569.87	853.57	*1,719.78*
R4.7	**Deformed high yield steel bar reinforcement to BS 4449**							
R4.7.1	Nominal size: 6mm							
R4.7.1.01	generally	Tonne	11.70	537.38	126.48	662.18	1,326.04	*1,732.89*
R4.7.2	Nominal size: 8mm							
R4.7.2.01	generally	Tonne	9.70	445.52	104.86	643.84	1,194.22	*1,728.97*
R4.7.3	Nominal size: 10mm							
R4.7.3.01	generally	Tonne	7.00	321.51	75.67	618.13	1,015.31	*1,723.69*
R4.7.4	Nominal size: 12mm							
R4.7.4.01	generally	Tonne	6.30	289.36	68.10	602.96	960.42	*1,722.32*
R4.7.5	Nominal size: 16mm							
R4.7.5.01	generally	Tonne	5.30	243.43	57.29	569.87	870.59	*1,720.37*
R4.7.6	Nominal size: 20mm							
R4.7.6.01	generally	Tonne	5.00	229.65	54.05	569.87	853.57	*1,719.78*

R4 Concrete Pavements continued...

		Unit	Labour Hours	Labour Net £	Plant Net £	Materials Net £	Unit Net £	CO_2 Kg
R4.8	**Waterproof membranes below concrete pavements**							
R4.8.1	Impermeable plastic sheeting							
R4.8.1.01	1200 gauge	m^2	0.01	0.27	-	0.68	0.95	*0.55*
R4.8.1.02	4000 gauge	m^2	0.01	0.27	-	1.68	1.95	*0.55*

R5 Joints in concrete pavement

		Unit	Labour Hours	Labour Net £	Plant Net £	Materials Net £	Unit Net £	CO_2 Kg
R5.1	**Longitudinal joints**							
R5.1.4	Depth of joint: 100 - 150mm							
R5.1.4.01	DTp clause nr. 1010; 12mm diameter mild steel bars 1m long at 600mm centres; 5 x 15mm cold poured Expandite Colpor 200 joint sealing compound; forming groove; crack inducer; including formwork; 150mm deep	m	0.47	21.63	-	5.17	26.80	*7.23*
R5.1.5	Depth of joint: 150 - 200mm							
R5.1.5.01	DTp clause nr. 1010; 12mm diameter mild steel bars 1m long at 600mm centres; 5 x 15mm cold poured Expandite Colpor 200 joint sealing compound; forming groove; crack inducer; including formwork; 200mm deep	m	0.47	21.63	-	6.69	28.32	*10.00*
R5.1.6	Depth of joint: 200 - 250mm							
R5.1.6.01	DTp clause nr. 1010; 12mm diameter mild steel bars 1m long at 600mm centres; 5 x 15mm cold poured Expandite Colpor 200 joint sealing compound; forming groove; crack inducer; including formwork; 250mm deep	m	0.47	21.63	-	8.51	30.14	*13.30*
R5.1.7	Depth of joint: 250 - 300mm							
R5.1.7.01	DTp clause nr. 1010; 12mm diameter mild steel bars 1m long at 600mm centres; 5 x 15mm cold poured Expandite Colpor 200 joint sealing compound; forming groove; crack inducer; including formwork; 300mm deep	m	0.47	21.63	-	10.33	31.96	*16.60*
R5.2	**Expansion joints**							
R5.2.4	Depth of joint: 100 - 150mm							
R5.2.4.01	DTp clause nr. 1009/6; Korkpak joint filler; 12mm diameter mild steel bar 1m long at 400mm centres; cold pored Expandite Colpor 200 joint sealant compound; forming groove; casting bars into side of joint and debonding for a length of 500mm and capped with PVC dowel caps; 10 x 150mm deep; 13 x 25mm sealant	m	0.54	24.94	-	15.71	40.65	*8.92*
R5.2.4.02	as above; 13 x 150mm deep; 19 x 25mm sealant	m	0.54	24.94	-	17.10	42.04	*8.96*
R5.2.4.03	as above; 19 x 150mm deep; 25 x 25mm sealant	m	0.54	24.94	-	23.77	48.71	*9.74*

R5 Joints in concrete pavement continued...

		Unit	Labour Hours	Labour Net £	Plant Net £	Materials Net £	Unit Net £	CO_2 Kg
R5.2	**Expansion joints**							
R5.2.4	Depth of joint: 100 - 150mm							
R5.2.4.04	as previous item; 25 x 100mm deep; 30 x 25mm sealant	m	0.54	24.94	-	29.48	**54.42**	*10.73*
R5.2.5	Depth of joint: 150 - 200mm							
R5.2.5.01	DTp clause nr. 1009/6; Korkpak joint filler; 12mm diameter mild steel bar 1m long at 400mm centres; cold pored Expandite Colpor 200 joint sealant compound; forming groove; casting bars into side of joint and debonding for a length of 500mm and capped with PVC dowel caps	m	0.54	24.94	-	19.45	**44.39**	*12.21*
R5.2.6	Depth of joint: 200 - 250mm							
R5.2.6.01	DTp clause nr. 1009/6; Korkpak joint filler; 12mm diameter mild steel bar 1m long at 400mm centres; cold pored Expandite Colpor 200 joint sealant compound; forming groove; casting bars into side of joint and debonding for a length of 500mm and capped with PVC dowel caps	m	0.54	24.94	-	25.91	**50.85**	*16.59*
R5.2.7	Depth of joint: 250 - 300mm							
R5.2.7.01	DTp clause nr. 1009/6; Korkpak joint filler; 12mm diameter mild steel bar 1m long at 400mm centres; cold pored Expandite Colpor 200 joint sealant compound; forming groove; casting bars into side of joint and debonding for a length of 500mm and capped with PVC dowel caps	m	0.54	24.94	-	32.12	**57.06**	*20.92*
R5.3	**Contraction joints**							
R5.3.4	Depth of joint: 100 - 150mm							
R5.3.4.01	DTp clause nr. 1009/10; 12mm diameter mild steel bars 1m long at 600mm centres; cold poured Expandite Colpor 200 joint sealing compound; forming groove; crack inducer; including formwork; 150mm deep; 10 x 10mm sealant	m	0.51	23.42	-	5.17	**28.59**	*7.23*
R5.3.4.02	as above; 150mm deep; 15 x 15mm sealant	m	0.51	23.42	-	7.39	**30.81**	*7.29*
R5.3.4.03	as above; 150mm deep; 20 x 20mm sealant	m	0.51	23.42	-	9.62	**33.04**	*7.35*

R5 Joints in concrete pavement continued...

		Unit	Labour Hours	Labour Net £	Plant Net £	Materials Net £	Unit Net £	CO_2 Kg
R5.3	**Contraction joints**							
R5.3.5	Depth of joint: 150 - 200mm							
R5.3.5.01	DTp clause nr. 1009/10; 12mm diameter mild steel bars 1m long at 600mm centres; cold poured Expandite Colpor 200 joint sealing compound; forming groove; crack inducer; including formwork; 200mm deep; 10 x 10mm sealant	m	0.51	23.42	-	6.69	30.12	*10.00*
R5.3.6	Depth of joint: 200 - 250mm							
R5.3.6.01	DTp clause nr. 1009/10; 12mm diameter mild steel bars 1m long at 600mm centres; cold poured Expandite Colpor 200 joint sealing compound; forming groove; crack inducer; including formwork; 250mm deep; 10 x 10mm sealant	m	0.51	23.42	-	8.51	31.93	*13.30*
R5.3.7	Depth of joint: 250 - 300mm							
R5.3.7.01	DTp clause nr. 1009/10; 12mm diameter mild steel bars 1m long at 600mm centres; cold poured Expandite Colpor 200 joint sealing compound; forming groove; crack inducer; including formwork; 300mm deep; 10 x 10mm sealant	m	0.51	23.42	-	10.33	33.75	*16.60*
R5.4	**Warping joints**							
R5.4.4	Depth of joint: 100 - 150mm							
R5.4.4.01	DTp clause nr. 1009/11; 12mm diameter mild steel bars 1.2m long at 400mm centres; cold poured Expandite Colpor 200 joint sealing compound; forming groove; crack inducer; including formwork; 150mm deep; 10 x 10mm sealant	m	0.51	23.42	-	5.17	28.59	*7.23*
R5.4.5	Depth of joint: 150 - 200mm							
R5.4.5.01	DTp clause nr. 1009/11; 12mm diameter mild steel bars 1.2m long at 300mm centres; cold poured Expandite Colpor 200 joint sealing compound; forming groove; crack inducer; including formwork; 200mm deep; 10 x 10mm sealant	m	0.51	23.42	-	6.78	30.20	*10.50*
R5.4.6	Depth of joint: 200 - 250mm							
R5.4.6.01	DTp clause nr. 1009/11; 12mm diameter mild steel bars 1.2m long at 230mm centres; cold poured Expandite Colpor 200 joint sealing compound; forming groove; crack inducer; including formwork; 250mm deep; 10 x 10mm sealant	m	0.51	23.42	-	8.70	32.12	*14.42*
R5.4.7	Depth of joint: 250 - 300mm							
R5.4.7.01	DTp clause nr. 1009/11; 12mm diameter mild steel bars 1.2m long at 180mm centres; cold poured Expandite Colpor 200 joint sealing DTp clause nr. 1009/11; compound; forming groove; crack inducer; including formwork; 300mm deep; 10 x 10mm sealant	m	0.51	23.42	-	10.65	34.07	*18.44*

R5 Joints in concrete pavement continued...

		Unit	Labour Hours	Labour Net £	Plant Net £	Materials Net £	Unit Net £	CO_2 Kg
R5.6	**Construction joints**							
R5.6.4	Depth of joint: 100 - 150mm							
R5.6.4.01	DTp clause nr. 1009/14; 12mm diameter mild steel bars 1m long at 600mm centres; including formwork; 150mm deep	m	0.47	21.63	-	3.39	**25.02**	*7.18*
R5.6.5	Depth of joint: 150 - 200mm							
R5.6.5.01	DTp clause nr. 1009/14; 12mm diameter mild steel bars 1m long at 600mm centres; including formwork; 200mm deep	m	0.47	21.63	-	4.91	**26.54**	*9.95*
R5.6.6	Depth of joint: 200 - 250mm							
R5.6.6.01	DTp clause nr. 1009/14; 12mm diameter mild steel bars 1m long at 600mm centres; including formwork; 250mm deep	m	0.47	21.63	-	6.73	**28.36**	*13.25*
R5.6.7	Depth of joint: 250 - 300mm							
R5.6.7.01	DTp clause nr. 1009/14; 12mm diameter mild steel bars 1m long at 600mm centres; including formwork; 300mm deep	m	0.47	21.63	-	8.55	**30.18**	*16.55*

R6 Kerbs, Channels and Edgings

		Unit	Labour Hours	Labour Net £	Plant Net £	Materials Net £	Unit Net £	CO_2 Kg
R6.1	**Precast concrete kerbs, BS 7263; Part 1 figure 1(b), (c) and (d)**							
R6.1.1	Straight or curved to radius exceeding 12m							
R6.1.1.01	Including concrete bed and backing grade 7.5, 20mm aggregate; 125 x 255mm; (b)	m	0.16	6.74	-	9.82	**16.56**	*32.93*
R6.1.1.02	as above; 150 x 305mm; (c)	m	0.16	6.74	-	14.76	**21.50**	*47.61*
R6.1.1.03	as above; 125 x 255mm; (d)	m	0.13	5.47	-	7.05	**12.52**	*19.86*
R6.1.2	Curved to radius not exceeding 12m							
R6.1.2.01	Including concrete bed and backing grade 7.5, 20mm aggregate; 125 x 255mm; (b); 4m radius	m	0.26	10.95	-	15.54	**26.49**	*48.71*
R6.1.2.02	as above; 125 x 255mm; (b); 8m radius	m	0.21	8.84	-	15.54	**24.38**	*48.71*
R6.1.2.03	as above; 125 x 255mm; (b); 12m radius	m	0.16	6.74	-	15.54	**22.28**	*48.71*
R6.1.2.04	as above; 150 x 305mm; (c); 4m radius	m	0.26	10.95	-	10.43	**21.38**	*33.90*
R6.1.2.05	as above; 150 x 305mm; (c); 8m radius	m	0.21	8.84	-	10.43	**19.27**	*33.90*
R6.1.2.06	as above; 150 x 305mm; (c); 12m radius	m	0.16	6.74	-	10.43	**17.17**	*33.90*
R6.1.2.07	as above; 125 x 255mm; (d); 4m radius	m	0.23	9.69	-	8.15	**17.84**	*37.26*
R6.1.2.08	as above; 125 x 255mm; (d); 8m radius	m	0.18	7.58	-	8.15	**15.73**	*37.26*
R6.1.2.09	as above; 125 x 255mm; (d); 12m radius	m	0.13	5.47	-	8.15	**13.62**	*37.26*

R6 Kerbs, Channels and Edgings continued...

		Unit	Labour Hours	Labour Net £	Plant Net £	Materials Net £	Unit Net £	CO_2 Kg
R6.1	**Precast concrete kerbs, BS 7263; Part I figure I (b), (c) and (d)**							
R6.1.3	Quadrants							
R6.1.3.01	Including concrete bed and backing; grade7.5, 20mm aggregate; 455 x 455 x 255mm	Nr	0.16	6.74	-	16.86	**23.59**	*48.52*
R6.1.3.02	as above; 455 x 455 x 105mm	Nr	0.16	6.74	-	13.80	**20.54**	*38.36*
R6.1.3.03	as above; 305 x 305 x 255mm	Nr	0.14	5.90	-	14.99	**20.89**	*27.02*
R6.1.3.04	as above; 305 x 305 x 150mm	Nr	0.14	5.90	-	13.66	**19.56**	*22.32*
R6.1.4	Drops							
R6.1.4.01	Including concrete bed and backing grade 7.5, 20mm aggregate; 125 x 255mm	Nr	0.14	5.90	-	10.01	**15.91**	*27.83*
R6.1.4.02	as above; 125 x 175mm	Nr	0.14	5.90	-	9.92	**15.82**	*23.02*
R6.1.4.03	as above; 125 x 150mm	Nr	0.14	5.90	-	9.80	**15.70**	*21.51*
R6.2	**Precast concrete kerbs to, BS 7263; part I figure I (a) and (e)**							
R6.2.1	Straight or curved to radius exceeding 12m							
R6.2.1.01	Including concrete bed and backing grade 7.5, 20mm aggregate; 125 x 150mm; (a)	m	0.13	5.47	-	16.06	**21.53**	*34.61*
R6.2.1.02	as above; 125 x 150mm; (e)	m	0.16	6.74	-	9.93	**16.67**	*33.13*
R6.2.2	Curved to radius not exceeding 12m							
R6.2.2.01	Including concrete bed and backing grade 7.5, 20mm aggregate; 125 x 150mm; (a); 4m radius	m	0.26	10.95	-	15.54	**26.49**	*48.71*
R6.2.2.02	as above; 125 x 150mm; (a); 8m radius	m	0.21	8.84	-	15.54	**24.38**	*48.71*
R6.2.2.03	as above; 125 x 150mm; (a); 12m radius	m	0.16	6.74	-	15.54	**22.28**	*48.71*
R6.2.2.04	as above; 125 x 150mm; (e); 4m radius	m	0.26	10.95	-	10.43	**21.38**	*33.90*
R6.2.2.05	as above; 125 x 150mm; (e); 8m radius	m	0.21	8.84	-	10.43	**19.27**	*33.90*
R6.2.2.06	as above; 125 x 150mm; (e); 12m radius	m	0.16	6.74	-	10.43	**17.17**	*33.90*
R6.3	**Precast concrete channels, BS 7263; Part I figure I (f) and (g)**							
R6.3.1	Straight or curved to radius exceeding 12m							
R6.3.1.01	Including concrete bed and backing grade 7.5, 20mm aggregate; 255 x 125mm; (f)	m	0.16	6.74	-	14.76	**21.50**	*47.61*
R6.3.1.02	as above; 150 x 125mm; (g)	m	0.16	6.74	-	9.93	**16.67**	*33.13*
R6.3.2	Curved to radius not exceeding 12m							
R6.3.2.01	Including concrete bed and backing grade 7.5, 20mm aggregate; 255 x 125mm; (f); 4m radius	m	0.26	10.95	-	15.54	**26.49**	*48.71*
R6.3.2.02	as above; 255 x 125mm; (f); 8m radius	m	0.21	8.84	-	15.54	**24.38**	*48.71*
R6.3.2.03	as above; 255 x 125mm; (f); 12m radius	m	0.16	6.74	-	15.54	**22.28**	*48.71*
R6.3.2.04	as above; 150 x 125mm; (g); 4m radius	m	0.26	10.95	-	10.43	**21.38**	*33.90*
R6.3.2.05	as above; 150 x 125mm; (g); 8m radius	m	0.21	8.84	-	10.43	**19.27**	*33.90*
R6.3.2.06	as above; 150 x 125mm; (g); 12m radius	m	0.16	6.74	-	10.43	**17.17**	*33.90*

R6 Kerbs, Channels and Edgings continued...

		Unit	Labour Hours	Labour Net £	Plant Net £	Materials Net £	Unit Net £	CO_2 Kg
R6.4	**Precast concrete channels, BS 7263; Part 1 figure 1 (h)**							
R6.4.1	Straight or curved to radius exceeding 12m							
R6.4.1.01	Including concrete bed and backing grade 7.5, 20mm aggregate; 255 x 125mm; (h)	m	0.16	6.74	-	9.90	**16.64**	*33.95*
R6.4.2	Curved to radius not exceeding 12m							
R6.4.2.01	Including concrete bed and backing grade 7.5, 20mm aggregate; 255 x 125mm; (h); 4m radius	m	0.26	10.95	-	10.45	**21.40**	*34.79*
R6.4.2.02	as above; 255 x 125mm; (h); 8m radius	m	0.21	8.84	-	10.45	**19.29**	*34.79*
R6.4.2.03	as above; 255 x 125mm; (h); 12m radius	m	0.16	6.74	-	10.45	**17.19**	*34.79*
R6.5	**Precast concrete edgings, BS 7263; Part 1 figure 1 (m), (n) and (p)**							
R6.5.1	Straight or curved to radius exceeding 12m							
R6.5.1.01	Including concrete bed and backing grade 7.5, 20mm aggregate; 50 x 150mm; (m) and (p); shaped	m	0.09	3.71	-	5.01	**8.72**	*13.94*
R6.5.1.02	50 x 200mm; (m) and (p); shaped	m	0.09	3.87	-	5.55	**9.42**	*15.25*
R6.5.1.03	50 x 250mm; (m) and (p); shaped	m	0.10	4.08	-	6.04	**10.12**	*16.70*
R6.5.1.04	50 x 150mm; (n); flat top	m	0.09	3.71	-	5.01	**8.72**	*13.94*
R6.5.1.05	50 x 200mm; (n); flat top	m	0.09	3.87	-	6.43	**10.30**	*15.25*
R6.5.1.06	50 x 250mm; (n); flat top	m	0.10	4.08	-	5.70	**9.78**	*16.70*
R6.5.2	Curved to radius not exceeding 12m							
R6.5.2.01	Including concrete bed and backing grade 7.5, 20mm aggregate; 50 x 250mm; (n); flat top; 8m radius	m	0.10	4.21	-	5.60	**9.81**	*16.75*

R7 Light Duty Pavements

		Unit	Labour Hours	Labour Net £	Plant Net £	Materials Net £	Unit Net £	CO_2 Kg
R7.8	**Precast concrete flags to stated specification**							
R7.8.2	Depth: 30 - 60mm							
R7.8.2.01	BS 7263, natural finish; on mortar dabs in cement lime mortar (1:1:6); Close butt joints; 600 x 450 x 50mm thick	m^2	0.08	3.37	-	11.82	**15.19**	*23.95*
R7.8.2.02	as above; 600 x 600 x 50mm thick	m^2	0.10	4.21	-	9.76	**13.97**	*24.64*
R7.8.2.03	as above; 600 x 750 x 50mm thick	m^2	0.12	5.05	-	9.04	**14.09**	*24.06*
R7.8.2.04	as above; 600 x 900 x 50mm thick	m^2	0.17	7.16	-	8.31	**15.47**	*24.06*
R7.8.2.05	BS 7263, natural finish; on mortar dabs in cement lime mortar (1:1:6); Pointing 10mm joints in cement lime mortar (1:1:6); 600 x 450 x 50mm thick	m^2	0.10	4.21	-	12.11	**16.32**	*24.75*
R7.8.2.06	as above; 600 x 600 x 50mm thick	m^2	0.12	5.05	-	10.04	**15.09**	*25.44*
R7.8.2.07	as above; 600 x 750 x 50mm thick	m^2	0.14	5.90	-	9.52	**15.42**	*25.40*

R7 Light Duty Pavements continued...

		Unit	Labour Hours	Labour Net £	Plant Net £	Materials Net £	Unit Net £	CO_2 Kg
R7.8	**Precast concrete flags to stated specification**							
R7.8.2	Depth: 30 - 60mm							
R7.8.2.08	as previous item; 600 x 900 x 50mm thick	m²	0.18	7.58	-	8.79	16.37	*25.40*
R7.8.2.09	BS 7263, buff finish; on mortar dabs in cement lime mortar (1:1:6); Pointing 10mm joints in cement lime mortar (1:1:6); 600 x 450 x 50mm thick	m²	0.08	3.37	-	18.08	21.45	*24.75*
R7.8.2.10	as above; 600 x 600 x 50mm thick	m²	0.11	4.63	-	15.60	20.23	*25.44*
R7.8.2.11	as above; 600 x 750 x 50mm thick	m²	0.12	5.05	-	14.47	19.52	*25.40*
R7.8.2.12	as above; 600 x 900 x 50mm thick	m²	0.17	7.16	-	12.89	20.05	*25.40*
R7.8.3	Depth: 60 - 100mm							
R7.8.3.01	BS 7263, natural finish; on mortar dabs in cement lime mortar (1:1:6); Close butt joints; 600 x 450 x 63mm thick	m²	0.10	4.21	-	13.54	17.75	*29.49*
R7.8.3.02	as above; 600 x 600 x 63mm thick	m²	0.12	5.05	-	11.62	16.67	*30.90*
R7.8.3.03	as above; 600 x 750 x 63mm thick	m²	0.14	5.90	-	10.30	16.20	*30.31*
R7.8.3.04	as above; 600 x 900 x 63mm thick	m²	0.18	7.58	-	9.34	16.92	*30.31*
R7.8.3.05	BS 7263, natural finish; on mortar dabs in cement lime mortar (1:1:6); Pointing 10mm joints in cement lime mortar (1:1:6); 600 x 450 x 63mm thick	m²	0.12	5.05	-	14.11	19.16	*31.10*
R7.8.3.06	as above; 600 x 600 x 63mm thick	m²	0.14	5.90	-	12.00	17.90	*31.98*
R7.8.3.07	as above; 600 x 750 x 63mm thick	m²	0.16	6.74	-	10.88	17.62	*31.92*
R7.8.3.08	as above; 600 x 900 x 63mm thick	m²	0.20	8.42	-	9.92	18.34	*31.92*
R7.8.3.09	BS 7263, buff finish; on mortar dabs in cement lime mortar (1:1:6); Pointing 10mm joints in cement lime mortar (1:1:6); 600 x 450 x 63mm thick	m²	0.10	4.21	-	24.44	28.65	*31.10*
R7.8.3.10	as above; 600 x 600 x 63mm thick	m²	0.12	5.05	-	20.76	25.81	*30.90*
R7.8.3.11	as above; 600 x 750 x 63mm thick	m²	0.14	5.90	-	18.91	24.81	*31.92*
R7.8.3.12	as above; 600 x 900 x 63mm thick	m²	0.18	7.58	-	17.34	24.92	*31.92*

R8 Ancillaries

Note(s): The following rates have been based on those provided by a specialist sub-contractor and are supplied as guide prices ony.

		Unit	Labour Hours	Labour Net £	Plant Net £	Materials Net £	Unit Net £	CO_2 Kg
R8.2	**Surface markings**							
R8.2.2	Reflecting road studs							
R8.2.2.01	Cats-eyes; in preformed pockets	Nr	0.10	4.21	4.42	13.57	22.20	*8.18*

R8 Ancillaries continued...

		Unit	Labour Hours	Labour Net £	Plant Net £	Materials Net £	Unit Net £	CO_2 Kg
R8.2	**Surface markings**							
R8.2.3	Letters and shapes							
R8.2.3.01	Directional arrow 6.0m high; to tarmac; thermoplastic material, BS 3262	m	0.33	14.02	14.72	6.80	**35.54**	*39.04*
R8.2.3.02	Give Way triangle; to tarmac; thermoplastic material, BS 3262	m	0.17	7.03	7.38	4.08	**18.49**	*21.33*
R8.2.4	Continuous lines							
R8.2.4.01	To tarmac; 100mm wide	m	0.01	0.29	0.31	0.34	**0.94**	*1.34*
R8.2.4.02	as above; 200mm wide	m	0.01	0.34	0.35	0.74	**1.43**	*1.40*
R8.2.4.03	Continuous lines; to concrete; one coat bituminous tack coat; 100mm wide	m	0.01	0.29	0.31	0.34	**0.94**	*1.34*
R8.2.4.04	as above; 200mm wide	m	0.01	0.34	0.35	0.76	**1.45**	*1.49*
R8.2.5	Intermittent lines							
R8.2.5.01	To tarmac; 100mm wide	m	0.01	0.34	0.35	0.34	**1.03**	*1.40*
R8.2.5.02	as above; 200mm wide	m	0.01	0.42	0.44	0.74	**1.60**	*1.53*

CLASS S:
RAILTRACK

Calculations used throughout Class S - Railtrack

Labour

		Qty		Rate		Total
L A0120ICE	**General Earthworks Labour Gang**					
	Ganger	1	x	16.99	=	£16.99
	Labourer (General Operative)	1	x	12.56	=	£12.56
	Banksman	1	x	13.53	=	£13.53
	Total hourly cost of gang				**=**	**£43.08**
L A0130ICE	**Formwork (make, fix and strike) Labour Gang**					
	Craftsman WRA	1	x	16.68	=	£16.68
	Labourer (Skill Rate 3)	1	x	14.34	=	£14.34
	Carpenter (charge hand)	1	x	17.93	=	£17.93
	Total hourly cost of gang				**=**	**£48.95**
L A0150ICE	**Provision of concrete Labour Gang**					
	Labourer (Skill Rate 3)	1	x	14.34	=	£14.34
	Labourer (General Operative)	1	x	12.56	=	£12.56
	Banksman	0.5	x	13.53	=	£6.77
	Total hourly cost of gang				**=**	**£33.67**
L A0155ICE	**Placing of concrete Labour Gang**					
	Labourer (Skill Rate 3)	1	x	14.34	=	£14.34
	Labourer (General Operative)	4	x	12.56	=	£50.24
	Banksman	0.25	x	13.53	=	£3.38
	Ganger	1	x	16.99	=	£16.99
	Craftsman WRA	0.5	x	16.68	=	£8.34
	Total hourly cost of gang				**=**	**£93.29**
L A0184ICE	**Small bore pipes in shallow trenches Labour Gang**					
	Banksman	1	x	13.53	=	£13.53
	Ganger	1	x	16.99	=	£16.99
	Pipelayer (standard rate)	1	x	14.34	=	£14.34
	Labourer (General Operative)	5	x	12.56	=	£62.80
	Total hourly cost of gang				**=**	**£107.66**
L A0300ICE	**Brickwork Labour Gang**					
	Bricklayer (chargehand)	1	x	17.93	=	£17.93
	Bricklayer	4	x	16.68	=	£66.73
	Labourer (General Operative)	2	x	12.56	=	£25.12
	Total hourly cost of gang				**=**	**£109.78**
L A0320ICE	**Waterproofing Labour Gang**					
	Ganger	1	x	16.99	=	£16.99
	Labourer (General Operative)	3	x	12.56	=	£37.68
	Total hourly cost of gang				**=**	**£54.67**
L K0200ICE	**Manholes Labour Gang**					
	Ganger	1	x	16.99	=	£16.99
	Labourer (General Operative)	3	x	12.56	=	£37.68
	Craftsman WRA	1	x	16.68	=	£16.68
	Total hourly cost of gang				**=**	**£71.35**
L S2000ICE	**Bottom ballast Labour Gang**					
	Principal Track Officer	2	x	73.13	=	£146.26
	Chainman	2	x	33.03	=	£66.07
	Trackman	4	x	35.81	=	£143.23
	Total hourly cost of gang				**=**	**£355.56**

L S2005ICE	**Top ballast Labour Gang**					
	Track Chargeman	8	x	39.59	=	£316.72
	Leading Trackman	8	x	39.59	=	£316.72
	Trackman	32	x	35.81	=	£1,145.86
	Principal Track Officer	2	x	73.13	=	£146.26
	Chainman	2	x	33.03	=	£66.07
	Total hourly cost of gang				**=**	**£1,991.63**
L S2070ICE	**Brickwork cleaning Labour Gang**					
	Labourer (General Operative)	1	x	12.56	=	£12.56
	Labourer (Skill Rate 3)	2	x	14.34	=	£28.68
	Total hourly cost of gang				**=**	**£41.24**
L S2075ICE	**Brickwork remedial Labour Gang**					
	Labourer (General Operative)	1	x	12.56	=	£12.56
	Bricklayer	3	x	16.68	=	£50.05
	Total hourly cost of gang				**=**	**£62.61**

Plant

P A1124ICE	**General excavation Plant Gang**					
	Hydraulic Excavator - Cat 166kW	1	x	41.41	=	£41.41
	Crawler Tractor / Dozer - Cat D6 LGP 160 Hp	0.5	x	48.61	=	£24.30
	Total hourly cost of gang				**=**	**£65.71**
P A1126ICE	**General spoil haulage Plant Gang**					
	Dumper Truck - Volvo A25C 25t 6x6	3	x	56.35	=	£169.04
	Total hourly cost of gang				**=**	**£169.04**
P A1127ICE	**General compaction Plant Gang**					
	Roller - Bomag 90 900mm	1	x	3.27	=	£3.27
	Crawler Tractor / Dozer - Dresser 1004 48kW	1	x	28.68	=	£28.68
	Total hourly cost of gang				**=**	**£31.95**
P A1150ICE	**Provision of concrete Plant Gang**					
	Concrete Mixer - Liner Rolpanit	1	x	37.36	=	£37.36
	Cement Silo 50t	1	x	2.47	=	£2.47
	Concrete Mixer - Schwing BP1000R					
	Concrete Pumps	1	x	43.29	=	£43.29
	Crawler Tractor / Dozer - Dresser 1004 48kW	1	x	28.68	=	£28.68
	Compressor - 250 cfm	1	x	10.81	=	£10.81
	Air Hose - 1 inch - 15m length	1	x	0.35	=	£0.35
	Total hourly cost of gang				**=**	**£122.96**
P A1155ICE	**Placing of concrete Plant Gang**					
	Air Vibrating Poker up to 75mm	3	x	1.25	=	£3.74
	Concrete Skip	2	x	0.71	=	£1.41
	Scabbler - Floor - 3 Headed	1	x	2.47	=	£2.47
	Scabbler - Floor - 5 Headed	1	x	3.52	=	£3.52
	Excavators Cable - NCK 305A 0.67m3	0.25	x	41.78	=	£10.45
	Compressor - 375 cfm	1	x	14.95	=	£14.95
	Total hourly cost of gang				**=**	**£36.54**
P A1184ICE	**Small bore pipes in shallow trench Plant Gang**					
	Hydraulic Excavator - Cat 320 96kW	1	x	33.98	=	£33.98
	Pump - Godwin ET50 23m3/h 4 inches	1	x	2.74	=	£2.74
	Vibrating Plate Diesel 24kN	1	x	2.36	=	£2.36
	Trench Sheets	90	x	0.08	=	£7.15
	Acrow Props	70	x	0.08	=	£5.56
	Landrover 4WD	1	x	15.10	=	£15.10
	Total hourly cost of gang				**=**	**£66.89**

P A1332ICE	**Brickwork raking out Plant Gang**					
	Kango Type Tool - 950 Kango	1	x	1.24	=	£1.24
	Total hourly cost of gang				**=**	**£1.24**
P K1200ICE	**Precast concrete manholes (shallow) Plant Gang**					
	Hydraulic Excavator - Cat 320 96kW	1	x	33.98	=	£33.98
	Pump - Godwin ET50 23m3/h 4 inches	1	x	2.74	=	£2.74
	Wheeled Tractor / Grader - Ford 3190H	1	x	23.52	=	£23.52
	Trailer - Massey Tipping	1	x	1.69	=	£1.69
	Dumper - 1.50t 2WD	1	x	2.75	=	£2.75
	Trench Sheets	72	x	0.08	=	£5.72
	Acrow Props	50	x	0.08	=	£3.97
	Concrete Mixer - 4/3 Petrol	1	x	2.04	=	£2.04
	Total hourly cost of gang				**=**	**£76.41**
P S2025ICE	**Top ballast Plant Gang**					
	Dumper - 2.5t 4WD	2	x	21.48	=	£42.97
	Lighting Tower - Lighting the Works	20	x	4.96	=	£99.13
	Generator - 10kvA Diesel	5	x	3.55	=	£17.74
	Total hourly cost of gang				**=**	**£159.84**
P S2200ICE	**Bottom ballast Plant Gang**					
	Lighting Tower - Lighting the Works	20	x	4.96	=	£99.13
	Generator - 10kvA Diesel	5	x	3.55	=	£17.74
	Crawler Tractor / Dozer - Cat D6 LGP 160 Hp	4	x	48.61	=	£194.43
	Total hourly cost of gang				**=**	**£311.30**
P S2250ICE	**Power wash**					
	Air Hose - 1 inch - 15m length	1	x	0.35	=	£0.35
	Air Pump	1	x	1.03	=	£1.03
	Total hourly cost of gang				**=**	**£1.38**

Class S - Railtrack

Note(s): 1) The prices are applicable to sites based in an average UK location, where total track work involved exceeds 2000 linear metres.

2) The prices assume that the track to be railed is adjacent to an existing track that is under possession from which locomotives and other plant can operate.

3) The prices assume that the works will be carried out under a series of possession arrangements of a typical 29 hour duration Sunday 0001 to Monday 0500.

4) Excluded from the prices are any allowances for:-

- design of the works
- follow up tamping and removal of temporary speed restrictions
- forming access to the works and removal on completion
- site welfare and accommodation facilities
- non-working supervision staff e.g. site managers, Agents, contract manager etc.
- other items of costs normally allowed for in the General Items section of a Tender
- overheads and profit

5) Possession, protection and isolation costs have been separately identified and are not included inb other items of work.

6) Tipping charges have not been included in the disposal rates due to the wide variation in prices from tip to tip.

7) Landfill Tax has not been included in the disposal rates as this is dependent on the nature of the material and statutory adjustment.

S1 Track Foundations

		Unit	Labour Hours	Labour Net £	Plant Net £	Materials Net £	Unit Net £	CO_2 *Kg*
S1.1	**Bottom ballast**							
S1.1.1	Crushed and graded;							
S1.1.1.01	Limestone	m^3	0.01	3.91	8.09	24.34	**36.34**	*11.67*
S1.1.1.02	Granite	m^3	0.01	3.91	8.09	27.27	**39.27**	*11.67*
S1.2	**Top ballast**							
S1.2.1	Crushed and graded;							
S1.2.1.01	Limestone	m^3	0.01	21.91	4.32	24.34	**50.57**	*9.00*
S1.2.1.02	Granite	m^3	0.01	21.91	4.32	27.27	**53.50**	*9.00*
S1.4	**Blankets**							
S1.4.1	Imported material							
S1.4.1.01	Granular stone thickness: 100mm	m^2	0.00	0.36	2.49	2.73	**5.58**	*1.86*
S1.4.1.02	Granular stone thickness: 150mm	m^2	0.00	0.71	3.74	4.11	**8.56**	*2.79*
S1.4.1.03	Granular sand thickness: 100mm	m^2	0.00	0.36	2.49	2.65	**5.50**	*1.86*
S1.4.1.04	Granular sand thickness: 150mm	m^2	0.00	0.71	3.74	3.99	**8.44**	*2.79*
S1.5	**Waterproof and membranes**							
S1.5.1	Polythene sheet;							
S1.5.1.01	1200 gauge	m^3	0.02	0.82	-	0.68	**1.50**	*0.55*

S2 Taking Up

		Unit	Labour Hours	Labour Net £	Plant Net £	Materials Net £	Unit Net £	*CO_2 Kg*
S2.1	**Bullhead rails**							
S2.1.1	Plain track							
S2.1.1.01	Take up, strip into component parts and stack in designated area for subsequent disposal; Plain fishplated Bullhead rails on timber sleepers	m	0.10	11.12	14.26	-	25.38	*9.12*
S2.1.1.02	Take up, strip into component parts and stack in designated area for subsequent disposal; Plain fishplated Bullhead rails on concrete sleepers	m	0.11	12.23	15.68	-	27.91	*10.03*
S2.1.1.03	Take up, strip into component parts and stack in designated area for subsequent disposal; Design BB of Bullhead rails on timbers	Nr	10.00	1,112.10	1,425.60	-	2,537.70	*912.11*
S2.1.4	Turnouts							
S2.1.4.01	Take up; turnout design C20 of Bullhead on timbers, strip into component parts and stack in designated areas for disposal	Nr	20.00	2,224.20	2,851.20	-	5,075.40	*1,824.22*
S2.1.5	Diamond crossings							
S2.1.5.01	Take up, strip into component parts and stack in designated area for subsequent disposal; Diamond crossing of Bullhead rails on timbers	Nr	10.00	1,112.10	1,425.60	-	2,537.70	*912.11*
S2.8	**Sundries**							
S2.8.1	Buffer stops							
S2.8.1.01	Take up buffer stops of steel rail and timber construction, weight approx 2.5 tonnes and stack in designated areas for disposal	Nr	3.00	333.63	427.68	-	761.31	*273.63*

S4 Supplying

		Unit	Labour Hours	Labour Net £	Plant Net £	Materials Net £	Unit Net £	*CO_2 Kg*
S4.1	**Bullhead rails**							
S4.1.1	Mass: 40 - 50Kg/m							
S4.1.1.01	Rails for jointed or welded track; new perfect quality BS95R section Bullhead rail in main lengths of 18.288m manufactured in accordance with BS9, both ends to be drilled for fish bolts	Tonne	-	-	-	961.00	961.00	*1,780.00*
S4.1.1.02	Rails for jointed or welded track; new perfect quality BS95R section Bullhead Rail in main lengths of 18.288m manufactured in accordance with BS9, ends undrilled	Tonne	-	-	-	961.00	961.00	*1,780.00*

S4 Supplying continued...

		Unit	Labour Hours	Labour Net £	Plant Net £	Materials Net £	Unit Net £	CO_2 Kg
S4.2	**Flat bottom rails**							
S4.2.5	Mass: exceeding 50Kg/m							
S4.2.5.01	Rails for jointed or welded track; new perfect quality BS113 'A' section Flat bottom rail in main lengths of 18.288m manufactured in accordance with BS11, both ends drilled for fish bolts	Tonne	-	-	-	746.00	**746.00**	*1,780.00*
S4.2.5.02	Rails for jointed or welded track; new perfect quality BS113 'A' section Flat bottom rail in main lengths of 18.288m manufactured in accordance with BS11, ends undrilled	Tonne	-	-	-	746.00	**746.00**	*1,780.00*
S4.2.5.03	Guard rails: new perfect quality BS113 'A' section Flat bottom rail in main lengths of 18.288m manufactured in accordance with BS11, both ends drilled for fish bolts and flange planed to allow 50mm FWC	Tonne	-	-	-	746.00	**746.00**	*1,780.00*
S4.6	**Twist rails**							
S4.6.5	Mass: exceeding 50Kg/m							
S4.6.5.01	Twist rails for jointed track adjacent turnouts: new perfect quality BS113 'A' section Flat bottom rail in main lengths of 9.144m manufactured in accordance with BS11, both ends drilled for fish bolts	Tonne	-	-	-	746.00	**746.00**	*1,780.00*
S4.7	**Sleepers**							
S4.7.1	Timber							
S4.7.1.01	Softwood timber sleepers, new French Maritime Pine, 250 x 125 x 2600mm long	Nr	-	-	-	24.45	**24.45**	*18.65*
S4.7.1.02	Hardwood timber sleepers, new Western Australian Jarrah, 250 x 130 x 2600mm long	Nr	-	-	-	37.00	**37.00**	*25.82*
S4.7.2	Concrete							
S4.7.2.01	Concrete sleepers, type 'F27' including malleable iron cast in shoulders	Nr	-	-	-	33.00	**33.00**	*0.83*
S4.8	**Sundries**							
S4.8.1	Chairs							
S4.8.1.01	Cast iron chairs, new 'S1' pattern with 3nr. 25mm dia x 160mm long galvanised chairscrews, 3 nr. plastic ferrules and new spring steel key	Nr	-	-	-	30.00	**30.00**	*6.27*

S4 Supplying continued...

		Unit	Labour Hours	Labour Net £	Plant Net £	Materials Net £	Unit Net £	CO_2 Kg
S4.8	**Sundries**							
S4.8.1	Chairs							
S4.8.1.02	Cast iron chairs, new 'CC' pattern 50mm FWC with 4nr. 25mm dia x 160mm long galvanised chairscrews, 4 nr. plastic ferrules, new spring steel and new oak keys	Nr	-	-	-	55.00	55.00	*9.55*
S4.8.2	Baseplates							
S4.8.2.01	Cast iron baseplates, new 'Pan 6' pattern with 5mm thick resilient rail pad, 3nr. 25mm dia x 160mm long galvanised chairscrews, 3 nr. plastic ferrules, 2 nr. 'Pandrol' rail clips and nylon insulators	Nr	-	-	-	40.00	40.00	*8.12*
S4.8.2.02	Cast iron baseplates, new 'VN' pattern with 5mm thick resilient rail pad, 3nr. 25mm dia x 160mm long galvanised chairscrews, 3 nr. plastic ferrules, 2nr. 'Pandrol' rail clips and nylon insulators	Nr	-	-	-	42.00	42.00	*9.07*
S4.8.2.03	Cast iron baseplates, new 'C' pattern with 50mm thick resilient rail pad, 4nr. 25mm dia x 160mm long galvanised chairscrews, 4 nr. plastic ferrules, 2nr. 'Pandrol' rail clips and nylon insulators	Nr	-	-	-	56.50	56.50	*11.33*
S4.8.3	Panrol fishplates							
S4.8.3.01	New 'Pandrol' rail clips and nylon insulator for F27 concrete sleepers	Nr	-	-	-	43.00	43.00	*13.53*
S4.8.4	Plain fishplates							
S4.8.4.01	Set comprising 2nr. steel four hole skirted pattern fishplates for BS95R section rail and 4nr. standard pattern fishbolts with nuts and washers	Nr	-	-	-	45.00	45.00	*7.57*
S4.8.4.02	Set comprising 2nr. steel four hole shallow section fishplates for BS113 'A' section rail and 4nr. standard pattern fishbolts with nuts and washers	Nr	-	-	-	55.00	55.00	*8.90*
S4.8.4.03	Set comprising 2nr. steel four hole joggled pattern fishplates for jointing BS95R and BS113 'A' section rails and 4nr. standard pattern fishbolts with nuts and washers	Nr	-	-	-	115.00	115.00	*16.02*
S4.8.5	Insulated fishplates							
S4.8.5.01	Set comprising 2nr. four hole steel billet type insulated fishplates for jointing BS95R section rail with 4nr. 25mm dia. high tensile steel bolts with nuts and washers and 1nr. end post	Nr	-	-	-	155.00	155.00	*22.25*

S4 Supplying continued...

		Unit	Labour Hours	Labour Net £	Plant Net £	Materials Net £	Unit Net £	CO_2 Kg
S4.8	**Sundries**							
S4.8.5	Insulated fishplates							
S4.8.5.02	Set comprising 2nr. four hole steel billet type insulated fishplates for jointing BS113 'A' section rail with 4nr. 25mm dia. high tensile steel bolts with nuts and washers and 1nr. end post	Nr	-	-	-	140.00	140.00	*17.80*
S4.8.5.03	Set comprising 2nr. four hole steel billet type insulated fishplates for jointing BS95R and BS113 'A' section rails and 4nr. 25mm dia. high tensile steel bolts with nuts and washers and 1nr. end post	Nr	-	-	-	140.00	140.00	*17.80*

S5 Supplying

		Unit	Labour Hours	Labour Net £	Plant Net £	Materials Net £	Unit Net £	CO_2 Kg
S5.1	**Turnouts**							
S5.1.1	Plain Line Materials; Track Assemblies; Switches and Crossings; standard assemblies complete with all associated closure and check rails and all fittings							
S5.1.1.01	BR design, B8, manufactured from new perfect quality BS95R Bullhead rail, set on new 300 x 150mm section Douglas Fir softwood timbers	Nr	-	-	-	16,200.00	16,200.00	*2,937.00*
S5.1.1.02	BR design, C10, manufactured from new perfect quality BS95R Bullhead rail, set on new 300 x 150mm section Douglas Fir softwood timbers	Nr	-	-	-	18,100.00	18,100.00	*2,848.00*
S5.1.1.03	BR vertical design, Bv8, manufactured from new perfect quality BS113 'A' flat bottom rail, set on 300 x 130mm section Jarrah hardwood timbers	Nr	-	-	-	25,000.00	25,000.00	*3,560.00*
S5.1.1.04	BR vertical design, Cv9.25, manufactured from new perfect quality BS113 'A' flat bottom rail, set on 300 x 130mm section Jarrah hardwood timbers	Nr	-	-	-	27,500.00	27,500.00	*4,450.00*
S5.2	**Diamond crossings**							
S5.2.1	Plain Line Materials; Track Assemblies; Switches and Crossings; standard assemblies complete with all associated closure and check rails and all fittings							
S5.2.1.01	BR design, angle 1 in 4, manufactured from new perfect quality BS95R Bullhead rail, set on new 300 x 150mm section Douglas Fir softwood timbers	Nr	-	-	-	152,750.00	152,750.00	*14,685.00*
S5.2.1.02	BR Vertical design, angle 1 in 4 manufactured from new perfect quality BS113 'A' flat bottom rail, set on 300 x 130mm section Jarrah hardwood timbers	Nr	-	-	-	110,000.00	110,000.00	*10,324.00*

S6 Laying

		Unit	Labour Hours	Labour Net £	Plant Net £	Materials Net £	Unit Net £	CO_2 Kg
S6.1	**Bullhead rails**							
S6.1.1	Plain track							
S6.1.1.01	Plain fishplated track, type BS95R Bullhead rail on softwood timber sleepers	m	0.50	55.60	32.54	-	88.14	*26.03*
S6.1.1.02	Plain welded track, type BS95R Bullhead rail on softwood timber sleepers	m	0.75	83.41	48.81	-	132.22	*39.05*
S6.1.1.03	Guard rail, type BS95R Bullhead rail fixed to BS95R Bullhead track	m	0.33	36.70	21.48	-	58.18	*17.18*
S6.1.2	Form curve in plain track radius not exceeding 300m							
S6.1.2.01	Extra over straight track for curved plain fishplated track, type BS95R Bullhead rail on softwood timber sleepers	m	0.25	27.80	16.27	-	44.07	*13.02*
S6.1.2.02	Extra over straight track for curved plain welded track, type BS95R Bullhead rail on softwood timber sleepers	m	0.25	27.80	16.27	-	44.07	*13.02*
S6.1.4	Turnouts							
S6.1.4.01	Standard turnout, B8, type BS95R rail on softwood sleepers	Nr	20.00	2,224.20	1,301.60	-	3,525.80	*1,041.28*
S6.1.4.02	Standard turnout, C10, type BS95R rail on softwood sleepers	Nr	24.00	2,669.04	1,561.92	-	4,230.96	*1,249.54*
S6.1.5	Diamond crossings							
S6.1.5.01	Standard diamond crossing, type BS95R rail on softwood timbers	Nr	24.00	2,669.04	1,561.92	-	4,230.96	*1,249.54*
S6.1.5.02	Standard double slip, type BS95R rail on softwood timbers	Nr	24.00	2,669.04	1,561.92	-	4,230.96	*1,249.54*
S6.1	**Bullhead rails**							
S6.1.7	Welded joints							
S6.1.7.01	Thermit welds; by the SKV process BS95R Bullhead rail	Nr	-	-	-	-	250.00	-

S6 Laying continued...

		Unit	Labour Hours	Labour Net £	Plant Net £	Materials Net £	Unit Net £	CO_2 Kg
S6.2	**Flat bottom rails**							
S6.2.1	Plain track							
S6.2.1.01	Plain fishplated track, type BS113 'A' Flat bottom rail on hardwood timber sleepers	m	0.50	55.60	32.54	-	88.14	*26.03*
S6.2.1.02	Plain fishplated track, type BS113 'A' Flat bottom rail on concrete sleepers	m	0.50	55.60	32.54	-	88.14	*26.03*
S6.2.1.03	Plain welded track, type BS113 'A' Flat bottom rail on hardwood timber sleepers	m	0.75	83.41	48.81	-	132.22	*39.05*
S6.2.1.04	Plain welded track, type BS113 'A' Flat bottom rail on concrete sleepers	m	0.75	83.41	48.81	-	132.22	*39.05*
S6.2.1.05	Guard rail, type BS113 Flat bottom rail fixed to BS113 Flat bottom track	m	0.33	36.70	21.48	-	58.18	*17.18*
S6.2.2	Form curve in plain track radius not exceeding 300m							
S6.2.2.01	Extra over straight track for curved plain fishplated track, type BS113 'A' Flat bottom rail on hardwood timber or concrete sleepers	m	0.25	27.80	16.27	-	44.07	*13.02*
S6.2.2.02	Extra over straight track for curved plain welded track, type BS113 'A' Flat bottom rail on hardwood timber or concrete sleepers	m	0.25	27.80	16.27	-	44.07	*13.02*
S6.2.4	Turnouts							
S6.2.4.01	Standard turnout, Bv8, type BS113 'A' rail on hardwood timbers	Nr	24.00	2,669.04	1,561.92	-	4,230.96	*1,249.54*
S6.2.4.02	Standard turnout, Cv9.25, type BS113 'A' rail on hardwood timbers	Nr	32.00	3,558.72	2,082.56	-	5,641.28	*1,666.05*
S6.2.5	Diamond crossings							
S6.2.5.01	Standard diamond crossing, angle 1 in 4, type BS113 'A' rail on hardwood timbers	Nr	32.00	3,558.72	2,082.56	-	5,641.28	*1,666.05*
S6.2	**Flat bottom rails**							
S6.2.7	Welded joints							
S6.2.7.01	Thermit welds; by the SKV process BS113 'A' Flat bottom rail	Nr	-	-	-	-	250.00	-

CLASS T:
TUNNELS

Calculations used throughout Class T - Tunnels

Labour

		Qty		Rate		Total
L A0120ICE	**General Earthworks Labour Gang**					
	Ganger	1	x	16.99	=	£16.99
	Labourer (General Operative)	1	x	12.56	=	£12.56
	Banksman	1	x	13.53	=	£13.53
	Total hourly cost of gang				**=**	**£43.08**
L A0122ICE	**Drill and Blast Labour Gang**					
	Driller	1	x	14.34	=	£14.34
	Shot firer	0.5	x	14.34	=	£7.17
	Total hourly cost of gang				**=**	**£21.51**
L A0130ICE	**Formwork (Make, Fix and Strike) Labour Gang**					
	Craftsman WRA	1	x	16.68	=	£16.68
	Labourer (Skill Rate 3)	1	x	14.34	=	£14.34
	Carpenter (charge hand)	1	x	17.93	=	£17.93
	Total hourly cost of gang				**=**	**£48.95**
L A0155ICE	**Placing of concrete Labour Gang**					
	Labourer (Skill Rate 3)	1	x	14.34	=	£14.34
	Labourer (General Operative)	4	x	12.56	=	£50.24
	Banksman	0.25	x	13.53	=	£3.38
	Ganger	1	x	16.99	=	£16.99
	Craftsman WRA	0.5	x	16.68	=	£8.34
	Total hourly cost of gang				**=**	**£93.29**
L C0010ICE	**Grout Hole Labour Gang**					
	Ganger	1	x	16.99	=	£16.99
	Labourer (General Operative)	1	x	12.56	=	£12.56
	Craftsman WRA	1	x	16.68	=	£16.68
	Total hourly cost of gang				**=**	**£46.23**
L C0011ICE	**Grout Hole Labour Gang (Mobilise / Demobilise / Move)**					
	Ganger	20	x	16.99	=	£339.72
	Labourer (General Operative)	30	x	12.56	=	£376.81
	Total hourly cost of gang				**=**	**£716.53**
L M0003ICE	**Structural Steel Fabrication Labour Gang**					
	Labourer (Skill Rate 3)	1	x	14.34	=	£14.34
	Fitters and Welders	2	x	16.68	=	£33.37
	Total hourly cost of gang				**=**	**£47.71**
L T0001ICE	**Tunnelling Labour Gang**					
	Labourer (Skill Rate 3)	2	x	14.34	=	£28.68
	Ganger	1	x	16.99	=	£16.99
	Banksman	1	x	13.53	=	£13.53
	Miners	4	x	39.86	=	£159.45
	Fitters and Welders	1	x	16.68	=	£16.68
	Total hourly cost of gang				**=**	**£235.33**

Plant

P A1035ICE	**Formwork (Fix and Strike) Plant Gang**					
	Kango Type Tool - Electric Power Woodauger	1	x	0.57	=	£0.57
	Kango Type Tool - Electric Nut Runner	1	x	0.48	=	£0.48
	Cranes Crawler - NCK 305B - 20t	0.25	x	45.36	=	£11.34
	Total hourly cost of gang				**=**	**£12.39**
P A1040ICE	**Formwork (Make) Plant Gang**					
	Saw Bench - 24 inch Diesel / Electric	1	x	1.89	=	£1.89
	Kango Type Tool - Electric Power Woodauger	1	x	0.57	=	£0.57
	Kango Type Tool - Electric Nut Runner	1	x	0.48	=	£0.48
	Total hourly cost of gang				**=**	**£2.94**
P A1128ICE	**Drill and Blast Plant Gang**					
	Waggon Drill with Steel & bits	1	x	4.58	=	£4.58
	Compressor - 375 cfm	1	x	14.95	=	£14.95
	Exploder with Circuit Tester	1	x	2.47	=	£2.47
	Total hourly cost of gang				**=**	**£22.00**
P A1155ICE	**Placing of concrete Plant Gang**					
	Air Vibrating Poker up to 75mm	3	x	1.25	=	£3.74
	Concrete Skip	2	x	0.71	=	£1.41
	Scabbler - Floor - 3 Headed	1	x	2.47	=	£2.47
	Scabbler - Floor - 5 Headed	1	x	3.52	=	£3.52
	Excavators Cable - NCK 305A 0.67m3	0.25	x	41.78	=	£10.45
	Compressor - 375 cfm	1	x	14.95	=	£14.95
	Total hourly cost of gang				**=**	**£36.54**
P C0012ICE	**Grout Hole Plant Gang (Grouting rock or other artificial hard material)**					
	Anchor Drilling Rig (Rock)	1	x	79.67	=	£79.67
	Compressor - 480 cfm	1	x	18.85	=	£18.85
	Bowsers (250 gallon water / fuel)	1	x	0.88	=	£0.88
	Grouting Rig (Anchorage Items)	1	x	9.84	=	£9.84
	Total hourly cost of gang				**=**	**£109.24**
P C0014ICE	**Grout Hole Plant Gang (Grouting Soils)**					
	Anchor Drilling Rig (Soil)	1	x	73.74	=	£73.74
	Compressor - 480 cfm	1	x	18.85	=	£18.85
	Bowsers (250 gallon water / fuel)	1	x	0.88	=	£0.88
	Grouting Rig (Anchorage Items)	1	x	9.84	=	£9.84
	Total hourly cost of gang				**=**	**£103.31**
P M0005ICE	**Structural Steel Erection Plant Gang**					
	Welding Set - 300 amp Diesel Electric Start Sil	1	x	4.18	=	£4.18
	Cutting and Burning Gear	1	x	3.52	=	£3.52
	Fork Lift Truck - 2.5t 4WD	1	x	26.80	=	£26.80
	Cranes Transit - 25t	1	x	56.27	=	£56.27
	Total hourly cost of gang				**=**	**£90.77**
P M0006ICE	**Structural Steel Fabrication Plant Gang**					
	Welding Set - 300 amp Diesel Electric Start Sil	1	x	4.18	=	£4.18
	Cutting and Burning Gear	1	x	3.52	=	£3.52
	Fork Lift Truck - 2.5t 4WD	1	x	26.80	=	£26.80
	Cranes Transit - 25t	1	x	56.27	=	£56.27
	Total hourly cost of gang				**=**	**£90.77**

Class T - Tunnels

Note(s): The following prices are specialist guide prices only for use in preliminary approximate estimating. In accordance with common practice in tunnelling all diameters referred to are internal diameter of segments. Rates quoted are average rates only and can vary considerably according to conditions prevailing on particular contracts, e.g. ground conditions, hardness of rocks, lengths of tunnels, size of contract etc. Rates quoted are for either hand-working or machine working, with the use of tunnel shields where necessary. The following works are not priced separately, their costs are included in the rates:

1) Temporary supports to excavations.

2) Keeping excavations free from water

3) Working around and supporting services.

4) Any intermediate shafts required

5) Use of tunnel shield where necessary

6) Interruption of works required to carry out survey and inspection checks

7) Construction and removal of temporary shaft rings

8) Breaking through linings at shaft/tunnel or shaft/heading intersections.

The grouting up of tunnels and shafts is included in the items excavated surfaces. The rates quoted allow for a norminal £8.50 per m³ to cover the disposal of surplus excavated material off site. This figure excludes landfill tax which should be added at the relevant level.

Compressed air working will increase the rates quoted according to the project.

T1 Excavation

		Unit	Labour Hours	Labour Net £	Plant Net £	Materials Net £	Unit Net £	CO_2 Kg
T1.1	**Tunnels in rock**							
T1.1.1	Stated diameter: not exceeding 2m							
T1.1.1.01	Diameter: 1.2m	m^3	0.90	255.22	375.38	-	**630.60**	*84.67*
T1.1.1.02	Diameter: 1.5m	m^3	0.85	243.45	367.66	-	**611.11**	*109.50*
T1.1.1.03	Diameter: 1.8m	m^3	0.70	208.15	332.11	-	**540.26**	*125.40*
T1.1.2	Stated diameter: 2 - 3m							
T1.1.2.01	Diameter: 3m	m^3	0.50	161.09	330.97	-	**492.06**	*227.81*
T1.2	**Tunnels in other stated material**							
T1.2.1	Stated diameter: not exceeding 2m							
T1.2.1.01	In generally soft material; Diameter: 1.2m	m^3	0.45	149.32	213.69	-	**363.01**	*78.39*
T1.2.1.02	In generally soft material; Diameter: 1.5m	m^3	0.43	143.44	209.01	-	**352.45**	*101.46*
T1.2.1.03	In generally soft material; Diameter: 1.8m	m^3	0.35	125.79	192.24	-	**318.03**	*123.07*
T1.2.2	Stated diameter: 2 - 3m							
T1.2.2.01	In generally soft material; Diameter: 3m	m^3	0.25	102.26	201.63	-	**303.89**	*234.01*
T1.3	**Shafts in rock**							
T1.3.2	Stated diameter: 2 - 3m							
T1.3.2.01	Diameter: 3m	m^3	2.00	64.59	166.85	-	**231.44**	*125.42*

T1 Excavation continued...

		Unit	Labour Hours	Labour Net £	Plant Net £	Materials Net £	Unit Net £	CO_2 Kg
T1.3	**Shafts in rock**							
T1.3.3	Stated diameter: 3 - 4m							
T1.3.3.01	Diameter: 3.3m	m^3	1.80	58.13	150.17	-	**208.30**	*112.88*
T1.3.3.02	Diameter: 3.6m	m^3	1.60	51.67	133.48	-	**185.15**	*100.34*
T1.3.4	Stated diameter: 4 - 5m							
T1.3.4.01	Diameter: 4.5m	m^3	1.40	45.21	116.80	-	**162.01**	*87.79*
T1.4	**Shafts in other stated material**							
T1.4.2	Stated diameter: 2 - 3m							
T1.4.2.01	In generally soft material; Diameter: 3m	m^3	0.70	30.16	101.40	-	**131.56**	*72.56*
T1.4.3	Stated diameter: 3 - 4m							
T1.4.3.01	In generally soft material; Diameter: 3.3m	m^3	0.60	25.85	86.91	-	**112.76**	*62.20*
T1.4.3.02	In generally soft material; Diameter: 3.6m	m^3	0.60	25.85	86.91	-	**112.76**	*62.20*
T1.4.4	Stated diameter: 4 - 5m							
T1.4.4.01	In generally soft material; Diameter: 4.5m	m^3	0.50	21.54	72.43	-	**93.97**	*51.83*
T1.5	**Other cavities in rock**							
T1.5.1	Stated diameter: not exceeding 2m							
T1.5.1.01	Diameter: 1.2m	m^3	0.90	211.80	302.13	-	**513.93**	*21.67*
T1.5.4	Stated diameter: 4 - 5m							
T1.5.4.01	Diameter: 4.5m	m^3	6.50	150.60	295.09	-	**445.69**	*292.05*
T1.6	**Other cavities in other stated material**							
T1.6.1	Stated diameter: not exceeding 2m							
T1.6.1.01	In generally soft material; Diameter: 1.2m	m^3	0.45	105.90	134.79	-	**240.69**	*9.75*
T1.6.4	Stated diameter: 4 - 5m							
T1.6.4.01	In generally soft material; Diameter: 4.5m	m^3	1.00	43.08	129.75	-	**172.83**	*85.39*
T1.7	**Excavated surfaces in rock**							
T1.7.1	Grouting							
T1.7.1.01	Cement grout	m^2	0.05	2.31	5.46	13.50	**21.27**	*31.98*
T1.7.1.02	PFA/OPC (1:3) grout	m^2	0.05	2.31	5.46	10.00	**17.77**	*33.17*
T1.8	**Excavated surfaces in other stated material**							
T1.8.1	Grouting							
T1.8.1.01	In generally soft material; Cement grout	m^2	0.05	2.31	5.17	13.50	**20.98**	*31.98*
T1.8.1.02	In generally soft material; PFA/OPC (1:3) grout	m^2	0.05	2.31	5.17	10.00	**17.48**	*33.17*

T2 In Situ Linings to Tunnels

		Unit	Labour Hours	Labour Net £	Plant Net £	Materials Net £	Unit Net £	CO_2 Kg
T2.3	**Cast concrete primary**							
T2.3.1	Stated diameter: not exceeding 2m							
T2.3.1.01	Grade 25, 20mm aggregate; Diameter 2m	m^3	1.00	93.29	79.83	86.17	**259.29**	*345.18*
T2.4	**Cast concrete secondary**							
T2.4.1	Stated diameter: not exceeding 2m							
T2.4.1.01	Grade 25, 20mm aggregate; Diameter 2m	m^2	1.10	102.62	87.81	86.17	**276.60**	*348.50*
T2.5	**Formwork to stated finish**							
T2.5.1	Stated diameter: not exceeding 2m							
T2.5.1.01	Rough finish; Diameter: 2m	m^3	0.52	25.31	16.22	5.71	**47.24**	*5.77*
T2.5.1.02	Wrot finish; Diameter: 2m	m^2	0.58	28.54	18.33	8.56	**55.43**	*6.68*

T3 In Situ Linings to Shafts

		Unit	Labour Hours	Labour Net £	Plant Net £	Materials Net £	Unit Net £	CO_2 Kg
T3.3	**Cast concrete primary**							
T3.3.1	Stated diameter: not exceeding 2m							
T3.3.1.01	Grade 25, 20mm aggregate; Diameter 2m	m^3	0.90	83.96	71.85	86.17	**241.98**	*341.86*
T3.4	**Cast concrete secondary**							
T3.4.1	Stated diameter: not exceeding 2m							
T3.4.1.01	Grade 25, 20mm aggregate; Diameter 2m	m^3	0.90	83.96	71.85	86.17	**241.98**	*341.86*
T3.5	**Formwork to stated finish**							
T3.5.1	Stated diameter: not exceeding 2m							
T3.5.1.01	Rough finish; Diameter: 2m	m^2	0.75	36.72	23.56	5.71	**65.99**	*6.99*
T3.5.1.02	Wrot finish; Diameter: 2m	m^2	0.83	40.78	26.18	8.56	**75.52**	*7.99*

T4 In Situ Linings to Other Cavities

		Unit	Labour Hours	Labour Net £	Plant Net £	Materials Net £	Unit Net £	CO_2 Kg
T4.3	**Cast concrete primary**							
T4.3.1	Stated diameter: not exceeding 2m							
T4.3.1.01	Grade 25, 20mm aggregate; Diameter 2m	m^3	1.00	93.29	79.83	86.17	**259.29**	*345.18*
T4.4	**Cast concrete secondary**							
T4.4.1	Stated diameter: not exceeding 2m							
T4.4.1.01	Grade 25, 20mm aggregate; Diameter 2m	m^3	1.10	102.62	87.81	86.17	**276.60**	*348.50*
T4.5	**Formwork to stated finish**							
T4.5.1	Stated diameter: not exceeding 2m							
T4.5.1.01	Rough finish; Diameter: 2m	m^2	0.75	36.72	23.56	5.71	**65.99**	*6.99*
T4.5.1.02	Wrot finish; Diameter: 2m	m^2	0.83	40.78	26.18	8.56	**75.52**	*7.99*

T5 Preformed Segmental Lining to Tunnels

Note(s): Segment prices may vary considerably according to size of contract, location and other contracts in operation.

		Unit	Labour Hours	Labour Net £	Plant Net £	Materials Net £	Unit Net £	CO_2 Kg
T5.1	**Precast concrete bolted rings**							
T5.1.1	Stated diameter: not exceeding 2m							
T5.1.1.01	Standard Bolted Segments; Diameter: 1.52m	Nr	1.00	235.33	32.12	197.85	**465.30**	*154.76*
T5.1.1.02	Standard Bolted Segments; Diameter: 1.83m	Nr	1.00	235.33	32.12	238.22	**505.67**	*187.01*
T5.7	**Lining ancillaries**							
T5.7.1	Parallel circumferential packing							
T5.7.1.01	Generally	Nr	0.01	1.88	-	3.99	**5.87**	*9.32*
T5.7.2	Tapered circumferential packing							
T5.7.2.01	Generally	Nr	0.02	4.00	-	6.66	**10.66**	*15.54*
T5.7.4	Caulking of stated material							
T5.7.4.01	Caulking; PC4AF	Nr	0.02	4.00	-	4.74	**8.74**	*0.59*

T6 Preformed Segmental Lining to Shafts

		Unit	Labour Hours	Labour Net £	Plant Net £	Materials Net £	Unit Net £	CO_2 Kg
T6.1	**Precast concrete bolted rings**							
T6.1.3	Stated diameter: 3 - 4m							
T6.1.3.01	Standard Bolted Segments; Diameter: 3.05m	Nr	0.50	117.67	16.06	604.00	**737.73**	*322.48*
T6.1.3.02	Standard Bolted Segments; Diameter: 3.35m	Nr	0.75	176.50	24.09	635.50	**836.09**	*364.40*
T6.1.3.03	Standard Bolted Segments; Diameter: 3.66m	Nr	0.75	176.50	24.09	667.00	**867.59**	*390.20*
T6.1.4	Stated diameter: 4 - 5m							
T6.1.4.01	Standard Bolted Segments; Diameter: 4.57m	Nr	1.00	235.33	32.12	1,141.00	**1,408.45**	*625.61*

T7 Preformed Segmental Lining to Other Cavities

		Unit	Labour Hours	Labour Net £	Plant Net £	Materials Net £	Unit Net £	CO_2 Kg
T7.1	**Precast concrete bolted rings**							
T7.1.3	Stated diameter: 3 - 4m							
T7.1.3.01	Standard Bolted Segments; Diameter: 3.05m	Nr	0.75	176.50	24.09	604.00	**804.59**	*323.55*
T7.1.3.02	Standard Bolted Segments; Diameter: 3.35m	Nr	1.00	235.33	32.12	635.50	**902.95**	*365.46*
T7.1.3.03	Standard Bolted Segments; Diameter: 3.66m	Nr	1.25	294.16	40.15	667.00	**1,001.31**	*392.33*
T7.1.4	Stated diameter: 4 - 5m							
T7.1.4.01	Standard Bolted Segments; Diameter: 4.57m	Nr	1.50	353.00	48.18	1,141.00	**1,542.18**	*627.74*

T8 Support and Stabilisation

		Unit	Labour Hours	Labour Net £	Plant Net £	Materials Net £	Unit Net £	CO_2 Kg
T8.1	**Rock bolts**							
T8.1.1	Mechanical							
T8.1.1.01	Generally	m	0.05	11.77	0.29	20.00	**32.06**	*4.72*

T8 Support and Stabilisation continued...

		Unit	Labour Hours	Labour Net £	Plant Net £	Materials Net £	Unit Net £	CO_2 Kg
T8.1	**Rock bolts**							
T8.1.2	Mechanical grouted							
T8.1.2.01	Generally	m	0.05	11.77	0.29	28.81	**40.87**	*5.55*
T8.1.3	Pre-grouted impacted							
T8.1.3.01	Generally	m	0.05	11.77	0.29	35.00	**47.06**	*5.57*
T8.1.4	Chemical and anchor							
T8.1.4.01	Generally	m	0.05	11.77	0.29	30.90	**42.96**	*6.72*
T8.1.5	Chemical grouted							
T8.1.5.01	Generally	m	0.05	11.77	0.29	32.58	**44.64**	*7.39*
T8.1.6	Chemically filled							
T8.1.6.01	Generally	m	0.05	11.77	0.29	41.77	**53.83**	*8.28*
T8.2	**Internal support**							
T8.2.1	Steel arches: supply							
T8.2.1.01	Generally	Tonne	6.00	286.26	560.09	575.37	**1,421.72**	*2,106.56*
T8.2.2	Steel arches: erection							
T8.2.2.01	Generally	Tonne	1.50	353.00	136.17	-	**489.17**	*82.25*
T8.2.3	Timber supports: supply							
T8.2.3.01	Generally	m^3	-	-	-	306.17	**306.17**	*220.14*
T8.2.4	Timber supports: erection							
T8.2.4.01	Generally	m^3	2.00	284.29	15.35	-	**299.64**	*3.10*
T8.2.5	Lagging: Backsheets							
T8.2.5.01	Generally	m^2	0.05	11.77	-	8.97	**20.74**	*20.95*
T8.2.6	Sprayed concrete; 50mm thick							
T8.2.6.01	Generally	m^2	0.10	23.53	2.87	1.93	**28.33**	*15.27*
T8.2.7	Mesh or link							
T8.2.7.01	Generally	m^2	0.03	7.77	-	2.61	**10.38**	*9.92*
T8.3	**Pressure grouting**							
T8.3.1	Sets of drilling and grouting plant							
T8.3.1.01	Generally	Nr	0.22	23.58	185.21	815.45	**1,024.24**	*227.77*
T8.3.2	Face packers							
T8.3.2.01	Generally	Nr	2.22	146.25	-	3.86	**150.11**	*8.46*
T8.3.4	Drilling and flushing to stated diameter							
T8.3.4.01	40mm diameter; not exceeding 20m deep	m	0.17	7.72	16.60	-	**24.32**	*40.64*
T8.3.5	Re-drilling and flushing							
T8.3.5.01	Generally	m	0.17	7.72	16.60	-	**24.32**	*40.64*
T8.3.6	Injection of grout materials of stated composition							
T8.3.6.01	Injection of cement grout	Tonne	1.00	46.23	99.39	567.00	**712.62**	*1,075.35*
T8.4	**Forward probing**							
T8.4.1	Thickness: 40mm							
T8.4.1.01	Generally	m	0.20	9.25	19.88	-	**29.13**	*48.67*

CLASS U:

BRICKWORK, BLOCKWORK AND MASONRY

Calculations used throughout Class U - Brickwork, Blockwork and Masonry

Labour

		Qty		Rate		Total
L A0300ICE	**Brickwork Labour Gang**					
	Bricklayer (chargehand)	1	x	17.93	=	£17.93
	Bricklayer	4	x	16.68	=	£66.73
	Labourer (General Operative)	2	x	12.56	=	£25.12
	Total hourly cost of gang				**=**	**£109.78**
L A0301ICE	**Blockwork Labour Gang**					
	Bricklayer	4	x	16.68	=	£66.73
	Labourer (General Operative)	3	x	12.56	=	£37.68
	Total hourly cost of gang				**=**	**£104.41**

Class U - Brickwork, Blockwork and Masonry

Note(s): 1) The hire, erection and dismantling of access and working scaffolding has not been allowed for in the rates because it is usually included in the preliminaries as scaffolding is frequently used by more than one trade. However if the user wishes to include for scaffolding a sub-contract price for hire, erect and dismantle should be obtained as the cost varies with the shape and height of the structure as well as the length of time the scaffolding is required.

2) Rates for brickwork assume a height not in excess of 10 metres; heights in excess of this bear the following multiples of the labour element.

Height above ground metres	Labour hours multiple
0-10	1.00
10-15	1.10
15-20	1.25
20-25	1.50

3) Surface features are measured as part of the wall to which they belong, the voulme having been enhanced by the appropriate amount. The additional work entailed measured as a labour only item and should be added to the labour content of the wall.

4) Labour rates have been based on the following outputs. The reader will be able to increase or decrease the labour element of the rate in accordance with his knowledge of the circumstances applying.

Type of brickwork	Brick laid per hour
Common brickwork 102.5mm thick	45
Common brickwork 215mm thick	50
Common brickwork 317.5mm thick	60
Common brickwork 440mm thick	65
Common brickwork Mass	70
Brick facings pointed as	
Work proceeds - one face	40
both faces	35
Rake out joints and point	0.75 hours per m^2

5) It has been assumed that materials have been delivered to the point of placing and that water is freely available.

U1 Common Brickwork

		Unit	Labour Hours	Labour Net £	Plant Net £	Materials Net £	Unit Net £	CO_2 Kg
U1.1	**Thickness: not exceeding: 150mm**							
U1.1.1	vertical straight walls							
U1.1.1.01	BS 3921; PC £230 per 1000 in cement mortar (1:3); 102.5mm thick	m^2	0.26	28.33	-	15.42	**43.75**	*97.04*
U1.1.2	vertical curved walls							
U1.1.2.01	BS 3921; PC £230 per 1000 in cement mortar (1:3); 102.5mm thick; 5m mean radius	m^2	0.45	49.41	-	15.42	**64.83**	*97.04*
U1.1.2.02	as above; 10m mean radius	m^2	0.39	42.60	-	15.42	**58.02**	*97.04*
U1.2	**Thickness: 150 - 250mm**							
U1.2.1	vertical straight walls							
U1.2.1.01	BS 3921; PC £230 per 1000 in cement mortar (1:3); 215mm thick	m^2	0.46	50.94	-	30.49	**81.43**	*191.91*

U1 Common Brickwork continued...

		Unit	Labour Hours	Labour Net £	Plant Net £	Materials Net £	Unit Net £	CO_2 Kg
U1.2	**Thickness: 150 - 250mm**							
U1.2.2	vertical curved walls							
U1.2.2.01	BS 3921; PC £230 per 1000 in cement mortar (1:3); 215mm thick; 5m mean radius	m^2	0.81	88.93	-	30.49	119.42	*191.91*
U1.2.2.02	as above; 10m mean radius	m^2	0.70	76.85	-	30.49	107.34	*191.91*
U1.3	**Thickness: 250 - 500mm**							
U1.3.1	vertical straight walls							
U1.3.1.01	BS 3921; PC £230 per 1000 in cement mortar (1:3); 327.5mm thick	m^2	0.59	64.78	-	44.06	108.84	*278.05*
U1.3.1.02	as above; 440mm thick	m^2	0.79	86.73	-	61.45	148.18	*386.73*
U1.3.2	vertical curved walls							
U1.3.2.01	BS 3921; PC £230 per 1000 in cement mortar (1:3); 327.5mm thick; 5m mean radius	m^2	1.03	113.08	-	44.06	157.14	*278.05*
U1.3.2.02	as above; 10m mean radius	m^2	0.88	96.62	-	44.06	140.68	*278.05*
U1.3.2.03	BS 3921; PC £230 per 1000 in cement mortar (1:3); 440mm thick;	m^2	1.38	151.51	-	61.45	212.96	*386.73*
U1.3.2.04	as above; 10m mean radius	m^2	1.19	130.65	-	61.45	192.10	*386.73*
U1.3.5	vertical facing to concrete							
U1.3.5.01	BS 3921; PC £230 per 1000 in cement mortar (1:3); 440mm thick; building in 4nr wall ties/m^2; casting into concrete	m^2	0.79	86.73	-	44.57	131.30	*278.35*
U1.4	**Thickness: 500mm - 1m**							
U1.4.1	vertical straight walls							
U1.4.1.01	BS 3921; PC £230 per 1000 in cement mortar (1:3); 890mm thick	m^2	1.35	148.22	-	122.89	271.11	*773.47*
U1.4.2	vertical curved walls							
U1.4.2.01	BS 3921; PC £230 per 1000 in cement mortar (1:3); 890mm thick; 5m mean radius	m^2	2.36	259.10	-	122.89	381.99	*773.47*
U1.4.2.02	as above; 10m mean radius	m^2	2.02	221.78	-	122.89	344.67	*773.47*
U1.4.3	battered straight walls							
U1.4.3.01	BS 3921; PC £230 per 1000 in cement mortar (1:3); 890mm thick; one face battered at an angle of 1:20	m^2	2.41	264.59	-	122.89	387.48	*773.47*
U1.5	**Thickness: exceeding 1m**							
U1.5.1	vertical straight walls							
U1.5.1.01	BS 3921; PC £230 per 1000 in cement mortar (1:3)	m^2	1.31	143.61	-	142.16	285.77	*894.97*
U1.6	**Columns and piers of stated cross-sectional dimensions**							
U1.6.1	215 x 215mm							
U1.6.1.01	BS 3921; PC £230 per 1000 in cement mortar (1:3)	m	0.15	16.91	-	7.05	23.96	*44.34*

U1 Common Brickwork continued...

		Unit	Labour Hours	Labour Net £	Plant Net £	Materials Net £	Unit Net £	CO_2 Kg
U1.6	**Columns and piers of stated cross-sectional dimensions**							
U1.6.2	327.5 x 215mm							
U1.6.2.01	BS 3921; PC £230 per 1000 in cement mortar (1:3)	m	0.23	25.03	-	10.45	**35.48**	*65.78*
U1.6.3	327.5 x 327.5mm							
U1.6.3.01	BS 3921; PC £230 per 1000 in cement mortar (1:3)	m	0.34	37.55	-	15.71	**53.26**	*98.85*
U1.6.4	440 x 440mm							
U1.6.4.01	BS 3921; PC £230 per 1000 in cement mortar (1:3)	m	0.62	67.63	-	28.06	**95.69**	*176.66*
U1.6.5	890 x 890mm							
U1.6.5.01	BS 3921; PC £230 per 1000 in cement mortar (1:3)	m	1.13	124.50	-	110.75	**235.25**	*697.23*
U1.7	**Surface features**							
U1.7.1	Copings and sills, material stated							
U1.7.1.01	Brick on-edge-coping; flush pointing top and both sides; 225mm wide	m	0.06	6.59	-	2.43	**9.02**	*15.25*
U1.7.2	Rebates and chases							
U1.7.2.01	Forming fair chase 25 x 25mm wide	m	0.20	21.96	-	-	**21.96**	-
U1.7.4	Band courses							
U1.7.4.01	Projecting plain band set forward 25mm from wall face; 225mm high flush pointing one side and top and bottom of projection	m	0.03	3.29	-	-	**3.29**	-
U1.7.6	Pilasters							
U1.7.6.01	attached to wall face; 215 x 112.5mm; flush pointing all faces	m	0.03	3.29	-	3.83	**7.12**	*23.90*
U1.7.6.02	attached to wall face; 890 x 327.5mm; flush pointing all faces	m	0.12	13.17	-	43.64	**56.81**	*273.45*
U1.7.7	Plinths							
U1.7.7.01	102.5mm thick; set forward 25mm from wall face; 450mm high; flush pointing face and top of projection	m	0.06	6.59	-	-	**6.59**	-
U1.7.7.02	102.5mm thick; set forward 25mm from wall face; 900mm high; flush pointing face and top of projection	m	0.12	13.17	-	-	**13.17**	-
U1.7.8	Fair facings							
U1.7.8.01	in stretcher bond including flush pointing as the work proceeds	m^2	0.06	6.59	-	-	**6.59**	-
U1.7.8.02	in stretcher bond including weatherstruck pointing as the work proceeds	m^2	0.07	7.69	-	-	**7.69**	-
U1.7.8.03	in English bond including flush pointing as the work proceeds	m^2	0.09	9.88	-	-	**9.88**	-
U1.7.8.04	in English bond including weatherstruck pointing as the work proceeds	m^2	0.10	10.98	-	-	**10.98**	-

U1 Common Brickwork continued...

		Unit	Labour Hours	Labour Net £	Plant Net £	Materials Net £	Unit Net £	CO_2 Kg
U1.7	**Surface features**							
U1.7.8	Fair facings							
U1.7.8.05	in Flemish bond including flush pointing as the work proceeds	m^2	0.08	9.00	-	-	9.00	-
U1.7.8.06	in Flemish bond including weatherstruck pointing as the work proceeds	m^2	0.08	9.22	-	-	9.22	-
U1.7.8.07	in stretcher bond including raking out joints and flush repointing with coloured gauged mortar	m^2	0.15	16.47	-	1.95	18.42	*7.08*
U1.7.8.08	in stretcher bond including raking out joints and weatherstruck repointing with coloured gauged mortar	m^2	0.16	17.57	-	1.95	19.52	*7.08*
U1.8	**Ancillaries**							
U1.8.1	Joint reinforcement							
U1.8.1.01	Exmet galvanised brick reinforcement; 24 gauge; horizontal; 100mm wide	m	0.04	4.39	-	1.03	5.42	*2.82*
U1.8.1.02	as above; 225mm wide	m	0.05	5.49	-	2.06	7.55	*5.64*
U1.8.1.03	as above; 305mm wide	m	0.06	6.59	-	3.09	9.68	*8.46*
U1.8.1.04	as above; 450mm wide	m	0.07	7.69	-	4.12	11.81	*11.28*
U1.8.1.05	as above; 900mm wide	m	0.14	15.37	-	8.24	23.61	*22.56*
U1.8.2	Damp proof courses							
U1.8.2.01	Bitumen damp proof course to, BS 743, Table 1; 100mm laps in cement mortar (1:3); pointing where exposed; Hessian based; reference 'A'; horizontal; 115mm wide	m	0.01	1.32	-	1.30	2.62	*4.75*
U1.8.2.02	as above; 225mm wide	m	0.01	2.20	-	2.60	4.80	*9.51*
U1.8.2.03	as above; 330mm wide	m	0.02	4.39	-	3.90	8.29	*14.26*
U1.8.2.04	as above; 450mm wide	m	0.02	6.04	-	5.21	11.25	*19.02*
U1.8.2.05	as above; 900mm wide	m	0.05	7.14	-	10.41	17.55	*38.04*
U1.8.2.06	Bitumen damp proof course to, BS 743, Table 1; 100mm laps in cement mortar (1:3); pointing where exposed; Hessian based; reference 'A'; vertical; 115mm wide	m	0.01	1.65	-	1.30	2.95	*4.75*
U1.8.2.07	as above; 225mm wide	m	0.02	2.42	-	2.60	5.02	*9.51*
U1.8.2.08	as above; 330mm wide	m	0.04	4.94	-	3.90	8.84	*14.26*
U1.8.2.09	as above; 450mm wide	m	0.05	6.59	-	5.21	11.80	*19.02*
U1.8.2.10	as above; 900mm wide	m	0.10	7.69	-	10.41	18.10	*38.04*

U1 Common Brickwork continued...

		Unit	Labour Hours	Labour Net £	Plant Net £	Materials Net £	Unit Net £	CO_2 Kg
U1.8	**Ancillaries**							
U1.8.2	Damp proof courses							
U1.8.2.11	Bitumen damp proof course to, BS 743, Table 1; 100mm laps in cement mortar (1:3); pointing where exposed; Fibre based; reference 'B'; horizontal; 115mm wide	m	0.01	0.66	-	1.00	1.66	*4.75*
U1.8.2.12	as above; 225mm wide	m	0.01	1.32	-	2.00	3.32	*9.51*
U1.8.2.13	as above; 330mm wide	m	0.02	1.98	-	3.00	4.98	*14.26*
U1.8.2.14	as above; 450mm wide	m	0.02	2.63	-	4.01	6.64	*19.02*
U1.8.2.15	as above; 900mm wide	m	0.05	5.27	-	8.01	13.28	*38.04*
U1.8.2.16	Bitumen damp proof course to, BS 743, Table 1; 100mm laps in cement mortar (1:3); pointing where exposed; Fibre based; reference 'B'; vertical; 115mm wide	m	0.01	1.32	-	1.00	2.32	*4.75*
U1.8.2.17	as above; 225mm wide	m	0.02	2.63	-	2.00	4.63	*9.51*
U1.8.2.18	as above; 330mm wide	m	0.04	3.95	-	3.00	6.95	*14.26*
U1.8.2.19	as above; 450mm wide	m	0.05	5.27	-	4.01	9.28	*19.02*
U1.8.2.20	as above; 900mm wide	m	0.10	10.54	-	8.01	18.55	*38.04*
U1.8.2.21	Hyload pitch polymer damp proof course; 100mm laps, sealed with Hyload contact adhesive; in cement mortar (1:3); pointing where exposed; Horizontal; 115mm wide	m	0.01	0.66	-	1.31	1.97	*4.75*
U1.8.2.22	as above; 225mm wide	m	0.01	1.32	-	2.62	3.94	*9.51*
U1.8.2.23	as above; 330mm wide	m	0.02	1.98	-	3.93	5.91	*14.26*
U1.8.2.24	as above; 450mm wide	m	0.02	2.63	-	5.25	7.88	*19.02*
U1.8.2.25	as above; 900mm wide	m	0.05	5.27	-	10.49	15.76	*38.04*
U1.8.2.26	Hyload pitch polymer damp proof course; 100mm laps, sealed with Hyload contact adhesive; in cement mortar (1:3); pointing where exposed; Vertical; 115mm wide	m	0.01	1.32	-	1.31	2.63	*4.75*
U1.8.2.27	as above; 225mm wide	m	0.02	2.63	-	2.62	5.25	*9.51*
U1.8.2.28	as above; 330mm wide	m	0.04	3.95	-	3.93	7.88	*14.26*
U1.8.2.29	as above; 450mm wide	m	0.05	5.27	-	5.25	10.52	*19.02*
U1.8.2.30	as above; 900mm wide	m	0.10	10.54	-	10.49	21.03	*38.04*

U1 Common Brickwork continued...

		Unit	Labour Hours	Labour Net £	Plant Net £	Materials Net £	Unit Net £	CO_2 Kg
U1.8	**Ancillaries**							
U1.8.3	Movement joints							
U1.8.3.01	Expansion joints; filling with Fillcrete joint filler; 20mm thick expansion joint; vertical; 102.5mm wide	m	0.06	6.92	-	2.23	**9.15**	*0.12*
U1.8.3.02	as above; 215mm wide	m	0.10	11.42	-	4.47	**15.89**	*0.24*
U1.8.3.03	as above; 327.5mm wide	m	0.17	18.33	-	6.70	**25.03**	*0.36*
U1.8.3.04	as above; 440mm wide	m	0.25	27.56	-	8.93	**36.49**	*0.49*
U1.8.3.05	as above; 890mm wide	m	0.42	46.11	-	17.87	**63.98**	*0.97*
U1.8.4	Bonds to existing work							
U1.8.4.01	Bonding 102.5mm brickwork to existing 215mm common brickwork; cutting and toothing alternate courses	m^2	0.22	24.15	-	1.22	**25.37**	*7.60*
U1.8.4.02	Bonding 102.5mm brickwork to existing concrete wall; cutting mortice and grouting in 1nr mild steel galvanised cramp every third course	m^2	0.42	46.11	-	1.70	**47.81**	*7.88*
U1.8.4.03	Bonding 215mm brickwork to existing 215mm common brickwork; cutting and toothing alternate courses	m^2	0.37	41.06	-	2.03	**43.09**	*12.68*
U1.8.4.04	Bonding 215mm brickwork to existing concrete wall; cutting mortice and grouting in 1nr mild steel galvanised cramp every third course	m^2	0.57	62.25	-	2.51	**64.76**	*12.97*
U1.8.5	Infills of stated thickness							
U1.8.5.01	Concrete infill; Grade 25, 20mm aggregate; 50mm thick	m^2	0.20	21.96	-	4.31	**26.27**	*15.60*
U1.8.5.02	as above; 100mm thick	m^2	0.30	32.94	-	8.62	**41.56**	*31.20*
U1.8.5.03	as above; 150mm thick	m^2	0.40	43.92	-	12.93	**56.85**	*46.80*
U1.8.5.04	as above; 200mm thick	m^2	0.50	54.90	-	17.23	**72.13**	*62.40*
U1.8.7	Built-in pipes and ducts, cross-sectional area: not exceeding 0.05m^2							
U1.8.7.01	supply excluded; 102.5mm brickwork; cross-sectional area; not exceeding 0.025m^2	Nr	0.12	13.17	-	0.48	**13.65**	*2.81*
U1.8.7.02	supply excluded; 102.5mm brickwork; cross-sectional area; 0.025 - 0.25m^2	Nr	0.12	13.17	-	0.48	**13.65**	*2.81*
U1.8.7.03	150mm diameter clay pipe to, BS 65, 102.5mm brickwork; cross-sectional area; not exceeding 0.025m^2	Nr	0.09	9.88	-	9.38	**19.26**	*6.76*
U1.8.7.04	supply excluded; 215mm brickwork; cross-sectional area; not exceeding 0.025m^2	Nr	0.10	10.98	-	0.24	**11.22**	*1.41*
U1.8.7.05	supply excluded; 215mm brickwork; cross-sectional area; 0.025 - 0.25m^2	Nr	0.12	13.17	-	0.48	**13.65**	*2.81*

U1 Common Brickwork continued...

		Unit	Labour Hours	Labour Net £	Plant Net £	Materials Net £	Unit Net £	CO_2 Kg
U1.8	**Ancillaries**							
U1.8.7	Built-in pipes and ducts, cross-sectional area: not exceeding 0.05m²							
U1.8.7.06	150mm diameter clay pipe to, BS 65, 215mm brickwork; cross-sectional area; not exceeding 0.025m²	Nr	0.10	10.98	-	14.31	25.29	*11.54*
U1.8.8	Built-in pipes and ducts, cross-sectional area: exceeding 0.05m²							
U1.8.8.01	supply excluded; 102.5mm brickwork; cross-sectional area; 0.40m²	Nr	0.16	17.57	-	0.60	18.17	*3.51*
U1.8.8.02	supply excluded; 215mm brickwork; cross-sectional area; 0.40m²	Nr	0.14	15.37	-	0.66	16.03	*3.87*

U2 Facing Brickwork

		Unit	Labour Hours	Labour Net £	Plant Net £	Materials Net £	Unit Net £	CO_2 Kg
U2.1	**Thickness: not exceeding: 150mm**							
U2.1.1	vertical straight walls							
U2.1.1.01	BS 3921; PC £325 per 1000 in cement mortar (1:3); 102.5mm thick in stretcher bond	m²	0.33	36.45	-	20.97	57.42	*96.68*
U2.1.2	vertical curved walls							
U2.1.2.01	BS 3921; PC £325 per 1000 in cement mortar (1:3); 102.5mm thick in stretcher bond; curved walls; 5m mean radius	m²	0.58	63.68	-	22.44	86.12	*93.85*
U2.1.2.02	as above; 10m mean radius	m²	1.05	115.28	-	44.17	159.45	*191.00*
U2.2	**Thickness: 150 - 250mm**							
U2.2.1	vertical straight walls							
U2.2.1.01	BS 3921; PC £325 per 1000 in cement mortar (1:3); 215mm thick in stretcher bond	m²	0.69	75.76	-	41.93	117.69	*193.37*
U2.2.1.02	BS 3921; PC £325 per 1000 in cement mortar (1:3); 215mm thick in Flemish bond	m²	0.63	69.17	-	41.93	111.10	*193.37*
U2.2.2	vertical curved walls							
U2.2.2.01	BS 3921; PC £325 per 1000 in cement mortar (1:3); 215mm thick in English bond; curved walls; 5m mean radius	m²	1.20	131.75	-	46.02	177.77	*189.36*
U2.2.2.02	as above; 10m mean radius	m²	1.03	113.08	-	46.02	159.10	*189.36*
U2.2.2.03	BS 3921; PC £325 per 1000 in cement mortar (1:3); 215mm thick in Flemish bond; curved walls; 5m mean radius	m²	1.11	121.87	-	46.02	167.89	*189.36*
U2.2.2.04	as above; 10m mean radius	m²	0.95	104.30	-	46.02	150.32	*189.36*
U2.2.5	Vertical facing to concrete							
U2.2.5.01	building in 4nr wall ties/m2; casting into concrete	m²	0.65	71.36	-	31.71	103.07	*197.16*

U2 Facing Brickwork continued...

		Unit	Labour Hours	Labour Net £	Plant Net £	Materials Net £	Unit Net £	CO_2 Kg
U2.3	**Thickness: 250 - 500mm**							
U2.3.1	vertical straight walls							
U2.3.1.01	BS 3921; PC £325 per 1000 in cement mortar (1:3); 327.5mm thick in stretcher bond	m^2	0.73	80.15	-	62.90	143.05	*290.05*
U2.3.2	vertical curved walls							
U2.3.2.01	BS 3921; PC £325 per 1000 in cement mortar (1:3); 327.5mm thick in stretcher bond; curved walls; 5m mean radius	m^2	1.26	138.34	-	67.26	205.60	*273.57*
U2.3.2.02	as above; 10m mean radius	m^2	1.08	118.57	-	67.26	185.83	*273.57*
U2.3.5	Vertical facing to concrete							
U2.3.5.01	BS 3921; PC £325 per 1000 in cement mortar (1:3); 327.5mm thick; building in 4nr wall ties/m^2; casting into concrete	m^2	0.93	102.10	-	62.77	164.87	*286.19*
U2.6	**Columns and piers of stated cross-sectional dimensions**							
U2.6.1	215 x 215mm							
U2.6.1.01	BS 3921; PC £325 per 1000 in cement mortar (1:3)	m	0.15	16.47	-	9.01	25.48	*40.83*
U2.6.2	327.5 x 215mm							
U2.6.2.01	BS 3921; PC £325 per 1000 in cement mortar (1:3)	m	0.23	25.25	-	13.36	38.61	*60.51*
U2.6.3	327.5 x 327.5							
U2.6.3.01	BS 3921; PC £325 per 1000 in cement mortar (1:3)	m	0.34	37.33	-	17.82	55.15	*80.89*
U2.6.4	440 x 440mm							
U2.6.4.01	BS 3921; PC £325 per 1000 in cement mortar (1:3)	m	0.54	59.29	-	39.90	99.19	*180.47*
U2.7	**Surface features**							
U2.7.1	Copings and sills, material stated							
U2.7.1.01	Brick on edge coping; flush pointing top and both sides; 225mm wide	m	0.08	8.56	-	3.28	11.84	*15.25*
U2.7.2	Rebates and chases							
U2.7.2.01	Forming fair chase 25 x 25mm wide	m	0.26	28.33	-	-	28.33	-
U2.7.4	Band courses							
U2.7.4.01	Projecting plain band set forward 25mm from wall face; 225mm wide; flush pointing one side and top and bottom of projection	m	0.04	4.17	-	-	4.17	-
U2.7.6	Pilasters							
U2.7.6.01	attached to wall face; 215 x 112.5mm; flush pointing all faces	m	0.04	4.17	-	58.46	62.63	*273.45*
U2.7.6.02	attached to wall face; 890 x 327.5mm; flush pointing all faces	m	0.15	16.58	-	14.61	31.19	*67.89*

U2 Facing Brickwork continued...

		Unit	Labour Hours	Labour Net £	Plant Net £	Materials Net £	Unit Net £	CO_2 Kg
U2.7	**Surface features**							
U2.7.7	Plinths							
U2.7.7.01	102.5mm thick; set forward 25mm from wall face; 450mm high; flush pointing face and top of projection	m	0.07	8.12	-	-	8.12	-
U2.7.7.02	102.5mm thick; set forward 25mm from wall face; 900mm high; flush pointing face and top of projection	m	0.16	17.02	-	-	17.02	-
U2.7.8	Fair facings							
U2.7.8.01	in stretcher bond including flush pointing as the work proceeds	m^2	0.08	8.45	-	-	8.45	-
U2.7.8.02	in stretcher bond including weatherstruck pointing as the work proceeds	m^2	0.08	8.45	-	-	8.45	-
U2.7.8.03	in English bond including flush pointing as the work proceeds	m^2	0.12	12.74	-	-	12.74	-
U2.7.8.04	in English bond including weatherstruck pointing as the work proceeds	m^2	0.12	12.74	-	-	12.74	-
U2.7.8.05	in Flemish bond including flush pointing as the work proceeds	m^2	0.11	11.64	-	-	11.64	-
U2.7.8.06	in Flemish bond including weatherstruck pointing as the work proceeds	m^2	0.11	11.64	-	-	11.64	-
U2.7.8.07	in stretcher bond including raking out joints and flush repointing with coloured gauged mortar	m^2	0.09	9.66	-	1.95	11.61	*7.08*
U2.7.8.08	in stretcher bond including raking out joints and weatherstruck repointing with coloured gauged mortar	m^2	0.09	9.66	-	1.95	11.61	*7.08*
U2.8	**Ancillaries**							
U2.8.1	Joint reinforcement							
U2.8.1.01	Exmet galvanised brick reinforcement; 24 gauge; horizontal; 100mm wide	m	0.04	4.39	-	1.03	5.42	*2.82*
U2.8.1.02	as above; 225mm wide	m	0.05	5.49	-	2.06	7.55	*5.64*
U2.8.1.03	as above; 305mm wide	m	0.06	6.59	-	3.09	9.68	*8.46*
U2.8.1.04	as above; 450mm wide	m	0.07	7.69	-	4.12	11.81	*11.28*
U2.8.1.05	as above; 900mm wide	m	0.14	15.37	-	8.24	23.61	*22.56*
U2.8.2	Damp proof courses							
U2.8.2.01	Bitumen damp proof course to, BS 743, Table 1; 100mm laps in cement mortar (1:3); pointing where exposed; Hessian based; reference 'A'; horizontal; 115mm wide	m	0.01	1.32	-	1.30	2.62	*4.75*
U2.8.2.02	as above; 225mm wide	m	0.01	2.20	-	2.60	4.80	*9.51*
U2.8.2.03	as above; 330mm wide	m	0.02	4.39	-	3.90	8.29	*14.26*
U2.8.2.04	as above; 450mm wide	m	0.02	6.04	-	5.21	11.25	*19.02*

U2 Facing Brickwork continued...

		Unit	Labour Hours	Labour Net £	Plant Net £	Materials Net £	Unit Net £	CO_2 Kg
U2.8	**Ancillaries**							
U2.8.2	Damp proof courses							
U2.8.2.05	as previous item; 900mm wide	m	0.05	7.14	-	10.41	**17.55**	*38.04*
U2.8.2.06	Bitumen damp proof course to, BS 743, Table 1; 100mm laps in cement mortar (1:3); pointing where exposed; Hessian based; reference 'A'; vertical; 115mm wide	m	0.01	1.65	-	1.30	**2.95**	*4.75*
U2.8.2.07	as above; 225mm wide	m	0.02	2.42	-	2.60	**5.02**	*9.51*
U2.8.2.08	as above; 330mm wide	m	0.04	4.94	-	3.90	**8.84**	*14.26*
U2.8.2.09	as above; 450mm wide	m	0.05	6.59	-	5.21	**11.80**	*19.02*
U2.8.2.10	as above; 900mm wide	m	0.10	7.69	-	10.41	**18.10**	*38.04*
U2.8.2.11	Bitumen damp proof course to, BS 743, Table 1; 100mm laps in cement mortar (1:3); pointing where exposed; Fibre based; reference 'B'; horizontal; 115mm wide	m	0.01	0.66	-	1.00	**1.66**	*4.75*
U2.8.2.12	as above; 225mm wide	m	0.01	1.32	-	2.00	**3.32**	*9.51*
U2.8.2.13	as above; 330mm wide	m	0.02	1.98	-	3.00	**4.98**	*14.26*
U2.8.2.14	as above; 450mm wide	m	0.02	2.63	-	4.01	**6.64**	*19.02*
U2.8.2.15	as above; 900mm wide	m	0.05	5.27	-	8.01	**13.28**	*38.04*
U2.8.2.16	Bitumen damp proof course to, BS 743, Table 1; 100mm laps in cement mortar (1:3); pointing where exposed; Fibre based; reference 'B'; vertical; 115mm wide	m	0.01	1.32	-	1.00	**2.32**	*4.75*
U2.8.2.17	as above; 225mm wide	m	0.02	2.63	-	2.00	**4.63**	*9.51*
U2.8.2.18	as above; 330mm wide	m	0.04	3.95	-	3.00	**6.95**	*14.26*
U2.8.2.19	as above; 450mm wide	m	0.05	5.27	-	4.01	**9.28**	*19.02*
U2.8.2.20	as above; 900mm wide	m	0.10	10.54	-	8.01	**18.55**	*38.04*
U2.8.2.21	Hyload pitch polymer damp proof course; 100mm laps, sealed with Hyload contact adhesive; in cement mortar (1:3); pointing where exposed; Horizontal; 115mm wide	m	0.01	0.66	-	1.31	**1.97**	*4.75*
U2.8.2.22	as above; 225mm wide	m	0.01	1.32	-	2.62	**3.94**	*9.51*
U2.8.2.23	as above; 330mm wide	m	0.02	1.98	-	3.93	**5.91**	*14.26*
U2.8.2.24	as above; 450mm wide	m	0.02	2.63	-	5.25	**7.88**	*19.02*
U2.8.2.25	as above; 900mm wide	m	0.05	5.27	-	10.49	**15.76**	*38.04*

U2 Facing Brickwork continued...

		Unit	Labour Hours	Labour Net £	Plant Net £	Materials Net £	Unit Net £	CO_2 *Kg*
U2.8	**Ancillaries**							
U2.8.2	Damp proof courses							
U2.8.2.26	Hyload pitch polymer damp proof course; 100mm laps, sealed with Hyload contact adhesive; in cement mortar (1:3); pointing where exposed; Vertical; 115mm wide	m	0.01	1.32	-	1.31	2.63	*4.75*
U2.8.2.27	as above; 225mm wide	m	0.02	2.63	-	2.62	5.25	*9.51*
U2.8.2.28	as above; 330mm wide	m	0.04	3.95	-	3.93	7.88	*14.26*
U2.8.2.29	as above; 450mm wide	m	0.05	5.27	-	5.25	10.52	*19.02*
U2.8.2.30	as above; 900mm wide	m	0.10	10.54	-	10.49	21.03	*38.04*
U2.8.3	Movement joints							
U2.8.3.01	Expansion joints; filling with Fillcrete joint filler; 20mm thick expansion joint; vertical; 102.5mm wide	m	0.06	6.92	-	2.23	9.15	*0.12*
U2.8.3.02	as above; 215mm wide	m	0.10	11.42	-	4.47	15.89	*0.24*
U2.8.3.03	as above; 327.5mm wide	m	0.17	18.33	-	6.70	25.03	*0.36*
U2.8.3.04	as above; 440mm wide	m	0.25	27.56	-	8.93	36.49	*0.49*
U2.8.3.05	as above; 890mm wide	m	0.42	46.11	-	17.87	63.98	*0.97*
U2.8.4	Bonds to existing work							
U2.8.4.01	Bonding 102.5mm brickwork to existing 215mm common brickwork; cutting and toothing alternate courses	m^2	0.24	26.57	-	1.60	28.17	*7.60*
U2.8.4.02	Bonding 102.5mm brickwork to existing concrete wall; cutting mortice and grouting in 1nr mild steel galvanised cramp every third course	m^2	0.46	50.72	-	2.08	52.80	*7.88*
U2.8.4.03	Bonding 215mm brickwork to existing 215mm facing brickwork; cutting and toothing alternate courses	m^2	0.41	45.01	-	1.60	46.61	*7.60*
U2.8.4.04	Bonding 215mm brickwork to existing concrete wall; cutting mortice and grouting in 1nr mild steel galvanised cramp every third course	m^2	0.64	70.49	-	2.08	72.57	*7.88*
U2.8.5	Infills of stated thickness							
U2.8.5.01	Concrete infill; Grade 25, 20mm aggregate; 50mm thick	m^2	0.20	21.96	-	4.31	26.27	*15.60*
U2.8.5.02	as above; 100mm thick	m^2	0.30	32.94	-	8.62	41.56	*31.20*
U2.8.5.03	as above; 150mm thick	m^2	0.40	43.92	-	12.93	56.85	*46.80*
U2.8.5.04	as above; 200mm thick	m^2	0.50	54.90	-	17.23	72.13	*62.40*

U2 Facing Brickwork continued...

		Unit	Labour Hours	Labour Net £	Plant Net £	Materials Net £	Unit Net £	CO_2 Kg
U2.8	**Ancillaries**							
U2.8.7	Built-in pipes and ducts, cross-sectional area: not exceeding 0.05m²							
U2.8.7.01	Built-in pipes and ducts (supply excluded); 102.5mm brickwork; cross-sectional area; not exceeding 0.025m²	Nr	0.09	9.66	-	0.36	10.02	*2.11*
U2.8.7.02	Built-in pipes and ducts (supply excluded); 102.5mm brickwork; cross-sectional area; 0.025 - 0.25m²	Nr	0.13	14.49	-	0.48	14.97	*2.81*
U2.8.7.03	Built-in pipes and ducts; 150mm diameter clay pipe to, BS 65, 102.5mm brickwork; cross-sectional area; not exceeding 0.025m²	Nr	0.07	7.69	-	9.38	17.07	*6.76*
U2.8.7.04	Built-in pipes and ducts (supply excluded); 215mm brickwork; cross-sectional area; not exceeding 0.025m²	Nr	0.11	12.08	-	0.24	12.32	*1.41*
U2.8.7.05	Built-in pipes and ducts (supply excluded); 215mm brickwork; cross-sectional area; 0.025 - 0.25m²	Nr	0.13	14.27	-	0.48	14.75	*2.81*
U2.8.7.06	Built-in pipes and ducts; 150mm diameter clay pipe to, BS 65, 215mm brickwork; cross-sectional area; not exceeding 0.025m²	Nr	0.11	12.08	-	9.86	21.94	*9.57*
U2.8.8	Built-in pipes and ducts, cross-sectional area: exceeding 0.05m²							
U2.8.8.01	Built-in pipes and ducts (supply excluded); 102.5mm brickwork; cross-sectional area; 0.40m²	Nr	0.13	14.49	-	0.48	14.97	*2.81*
U2.8.8.02	Built-in pipes and ducts (supply excluded); 215mm brickwork; cross-sectional area; 0.40m²	Nr	0.15	16.91	-	0.66	17.57	*3.87*

U3 Engineering Brickwork

		Unit	Labour Hours	Labour Net £	Plant Net £	Materials Net £	Unit Net £	CO_2 Kg
U3.1	**Thickness: not exceeding: 150mm**							
U3.1.1	vertical straight walls							
U3.1.1.01	Class A Engineering bricks, BS 3921; PC £375 per 1000 in cement mortar (1:3); 102.5mm thick	m²	0.28	31.18	-	23.92	55.10	*96.68*
U3.1.1.02	Class B Engineering bricks, BS 3921; PC £275 per 1000 in cement mortar (1:3); 102.5mm thick	m²	0.28	31.18	-	20.04	51.22	*91.69*
U3.1.2	vertical curved walls							
U3.1.2.01	Class A Engineering bricks, BS 3921; PC £375 per 1000 in cement mortar (1:3); 102.5mm thick; curved walls; 5m mean radius	m²	0.50	54.90	-	25.94	80.84	*91.69*
U3.1.2.02	as above; 10m mean radius	m²	0.43	47.21	-	25.94	73.15	*91.69*

U3 Engineering Brickwork continued...

		Unit	Labour Hours	Labour Net £	Plant Net £	Materials Net £	Unit Net £	CO_2 Kg
U3.1	**Thickness: not exceeding: 150mm**							
U3.1.2	vertical curved walls							
U3.1.2.03	Class B Engineering bricks, BS 3921; PC £275 per 1000 in cement mortar (1:3); 102.5mm thick; curved walls; 5m mean radius	m^2	0.50	54.90	-	20.04	74.94	*91.69*
U3.1.2.04	as above; 10m mean radius	m^2	0.43	47.21	-	20.04	67.25	*91.69*
U3.2	**Thickness: 150 - 250mm**							
U3.2.1	vertical straight walls							
U3.2.1.01	Class A Engineering bricks, BS 3921; PC £375 per 1000 in cement mortar (1:3); 215mm thick	m^2	0.51	55.99	-	47.83	103.82	*193.37*
U3.2.1.02	Class B Engineering bricks, BS 3921; PC £275 per 1000 in cement mortar (1:3); 215mm thick	m^2	0.51	55.99	-	40.08	96.07	*183.38*
U3.2.2	vertical curved walls							
U3.2.2.01	Class A Engineering bricks, BS 3921; PC £375 per 1000 in cement mortar (1:3); 215mm thick; curved walls; 5m mean radius	m^2	0.89	97.71	-	51.88	149.59	*183.38*
U3.2.2.02	as above; 10m mean radius	m^2	0.76	83.44	-	51.88	135.32	*183.38*
U3.2.2.03	Class B Engineering bricks, BS 3921; PC £275 per 1000 in cement mortar (1:3); 215mm thick; curved walls; 5m mean radius	m^2	0.89	97.71	-	40.08	137.79	*183.38*
U3.2.2.04	as above; 10m mean radius	m^2	0.76	83.44	-	40.08	123.52	*183.38*
U3.3	**Thickness: 250 - 500mm**							
U3.3.1	vertical straight walls							
U3.3.1.01	Class A Engineering bricks, BS 3921; PC £375 per 1000 in cement mortar (1:3); 327.5mm thick	m^2	0.66	72.46	-	77.82	150.28	*275.07*
U3.3.1.02	Class B Engineering bricks, BS 3921; PC £275 per 1000 in cement mortar (1:3); 327.5mm thick	m^2	0.65	71.14	-	60.12	131.26	*275.07*
U3.3.1.03	Class A Engineering bricks, BS 3921; PC £375 per 1000 in cement mortar (1:3); 440mm thick	m^2	0.87	95.08	-	95.67	190.75	*386.73*
U3.3.1.04	Class B Engineering bricks, BS 3921; PC £275 per 1000 in cement mortar (1:3); 440mm thick	m^2	0.87	95.08	-	80.16	175.24	*366.76*

U3 Engineering Brickwork continued...

		Unit	Labour Hours	Labour Net £	Plant Net £	Materials Net £	Unit Net £	CO_2 Kg
U3.3	**Thickness: 250 - 500mm**							
U3.3.2	vertical curved walls							
U3.3.2.01	Class A Engineering bricks, BS 3921; PC £375 per 1000 in cement mortar (1:3); 327.5mm thick; curved walls; 5m mean radius	m^2	1.13	124.06	-	77.82	**201.88**	*275.07*
U3.3.2.02	as above; 10m mean radius	m^2	0.97	106.50	-	77.82	**184.32**	*275.07*
U3.3.2.03	Class B Engineering bricks, BS 3921; PC £275 per 1000 in cement mortar (1:3); 327.5mm thick; curved walls; 5m mean radius	m^2	1.13	124.06	-	60.12	**184.18**	*275.07*
U3.3.2.04	as above; 10m mean radius	m^2	0.97	106.50	-	60.12	**166.62**	*275.07*
U3.3.2.05	Class A Engineering bricks, BS 3921; PC £375 per 1000 in cement mortar (1:3); 440mm thick; curved walls; 5m mean radius	m^2	1.52	166.88	-	103.76	**270.64**	*366.76*
U3.3.2.06	as above; 10m mean radius	m^2	1.31	143.82	-	103.76	**247.58**	*366.76*
U3.3.2.07	Class B Engineering bricks, BS 3921; PC £275 per 1000 in cement mortar (1:3); 440mm thick; curved walls; 5m mean radius	m^2	1.13	124.06	-	80.16	**204.22**	*366.76*
U3.3.2.08	as above; 10m mean radius	m^2	1.31	143.82	-	80.16	**223.98**	*366.76*
U3.3.5	vertical facing to concrete							
U3.3.5.01	Class A Engineering bricks, BS 3921; PC £375 per 1000 in cement mortar (1:3); 327.5mm thick; building in 4nr wall ties/m2; casting into concrete	m^2	0.83	91.13	-	72.25	**163.38**	*290.35*
U3.3.5.02	Class B Engineering bricks, BS 3921; PC £275 per 1000 in cement mortar (1:3); 327.5mm thick; building in 4nr wall ties/m2; casting into concrete	m^2	0.83	91.13	-	54.55	**145.68**	*290.35*
U3.4	**Thickness exceeding: 500mm - 1m**							
U3.4.1	vertical straight walls							
U3.4.1.01	Class A Engineering bricks, BS 3921; PC £375 per 1000 in cement mortar (1:3); 890mm thick	m^2	1.48	162.71	-	191.33	**354.04**	*773.47*
U3.4.1.02	Class B Engineering bricks, BS 3921; PC £275 per 1000 in cement mortar (1:3); 890mm thick	m^2	1.48	162.71	-	160.32	**323.03**	*733.52*
U3.4.2	vertical curved walls							
U3.4.2.01	Class A Engineering bricks, BS 3921; PC £375 per 1000 in cement mortar (1:3); 890mm thick; curved walls; 5m mean radius	m^2	2.65	291.16	-	191.33	**482.49**	*773.47*
U3.4.2.02	as above; 10m mean radius	m^2	2.65	291.16	-	144.13	**435.29**	*773.47*
U3.4.2.03	Class B Engineering bricks, BS 3921; PC £275 per 1000 in cement mortar (1:3); 890mm thick; curved walls; 5m mean radius	m^2	2.59	284.36	-	160.32	**444.68**	*733.52*

U3 Engineering Brickwork continued...

		Unit	Labour Hours	Labour Net £	Plant Net £	Materials Net £	Unit Net £	CO_2 Kg
U3.4	**Thickness exceeding: 500mm - 1m**							
U3.4.2	vertical curved walls							
U3.4.2.04	as previous item; 10m mean radius	m^2	2.22	243.73	-	160.32	**404.05**	*733.52*
U3.4.3	Battered straight walls							
U3.4.3.01	Class A Engineering bricks, BS 3921; PC £375 per 1000 in cement mortar (1:3); 890mm thick; battered walls; one face battered at an angle of 1:20	m^2	2.59	284.58	-	191.33	**475.91**	*773.47*
U3.4.3.02	Class B Engineering bricks, BS 3921; PC £275 per 1000 in cement mortar (1:3); 890mm thick; battered walls; one face battered at an angle of 1:20	m^2	2.65	290.94	-	160.32	**451.26**	*733.52*
U3.5	**Thickness: exceeding 1m**							
U3.5.1	vertical straight walls							
U3.5.1.01	Class A Engineering bricks, BS 3921; PC £375 per 1000 in cement mortar (1:3)	m^3	1.50	164.69	-	221.62	**386.31**	*894.97*
U3.5.1.02	Class B Engineering bricks, BS 3921; PC £275 per 1000 in cement mortar (1:3)	m^3	1.52	166.66	-	166.82	**333.48**	*894.97*
U3.6	**Columns and piers of stated cross-sectional dimensions**							
U3.6.1	215 x 215mm							
U3.6.1.01	Class A Engineering bricks, BS 3921; PC £375 per 1000 in cement mortar (1:3)	m	0.17	18.55	-	10.96	**29.51**	*44.34*
U3.6.1.02	Class B Engineering bricks, BS 3921; PC £275 per 1000 in cement mortar (1:3)	m	0.17	18.55	-	8.26	**26.81**	*44.34*
U3.6.2	327.5 x 215mm							
U3.6.2.01	Class A Engineering bricks, BS 3921; PC £375 per 1000 in cement mortar (1:3)	m	0.25	27.45	-	16.25	**43.70**	*65.78*
U3.6.2.02	Class B Engineering bricks, BS 3921; PC £275 per 1000 in cement mortar (1:3)	m	0.25	27.45	-	12.25	**39.70**	*65.78*
U3.6.3	327.5 x 327.5mm							
U3.6.3.01	Class A Engineering bricks, BS 3921; PC £375 per 1000 in cement mortar (1:3)	m	0.38	41.28	-	24.41	**65.69**	*98.85*
U3.6.3.02	Class B Engineering bricks, BS 3921; PC £275 per 1000 in cement mortar (1:3)	m	0.37	40.62	-	18.41	**59.03**	*98.85*
U3.6.4	440 x 440mm							
U3.6.4.01	Class A Engineering bricks, BS 3921; PC £375 per 1000 in cement mortar (1:3)	m	0.68	74.44	-	43.72	**118.16**	*176.66*
U3.6.4.02	Class B Engineering bricks, BS 3921; PC £275 per 1000 in cement mortar (1:3)	m	0.68	74.44	-	52.72	**127.16**	*281.78*

U3 Engineering Brickwork continued...

		Unit	Labour Hours	Labour Net £	Plant Net £	Materials Net £	Unit Net £	CO_2 Kg
U3.6	**Columns and piers of stated cross-sectional dimensions**							
U3.6.5	890 x 890mm							
U3.6.5.01	Class A Engineering bricks, BS 3921; PC £375 per 1000 in cement mortar (1:3)	m	2.35	257.79	-	172.67	430.46	*697.23*
U3.6.5.02	Class B Engineering bricks, BS 3921; PC £275 per 1000 in cement mortar (1:3)	m	2.35	257.79	-	129.97	387.76	*697.23*
U3.7	**Surface features**							
U3.7.1	Copings and sills, material stated							
U3.7.1.01	Class A Engineering bricks, BS 3921; PC £375 per 1000 in cement mortar (1:3); Brick on edge coping; flush pointing top and both sides; 225mm wide	m	0.07	7.25	-	3.73	10.98	*15.25*
U3.7.1.02	as above; Sill laid flat; flush with wall; flush pointing top and one side; 75mm wide	m	0.22	24.15	-	-	24.15	-
U3.7.1.03	Class B Engineering bricks, BS 3921; PC £275 per 1000 in cement mortar (1:3); Brick on edge coping; flush pointing top and both sides; 225mm wide	m	0.07	7.25	-	2.83	10.08	*15.25*
U3.7.1.04	as above; Sill laid flat; flush with wall; flush pointing top and one side; 75mm wide	m	0.22	24.15	-	-	24.15	-
U3.7.2	Rebates and chases							
U3.7.2.01	Class A Engineering bricks, BS 3921; PC £375 per 1000 in cement mortar (1:3); Forming fair chase 25 x 25mm wide	m	0.03	3.62	-	-	3.62	-
U3.7.2.02	Class B Engineering bricks, BS 3921; PC £275 per 1000 in cement mortar (1:3); Forming fair chase 25 x 25mm wide	m	0.03	3.62	-	-	3.62	-
U3.7.6	Pilasters							
U3.7.6.01	Class A Engineering bricks, BS 3921; PC £375 per 1000 in cement mortar (1:3); Pilaster attached to wall face; 215 x 112.5mm; flush pointing all faces	m	0.03	3.62	-	4.41	8.03	*23.90*
U3.7.6.02	as above; Pilaster attached to wall face; 890 x 327.5mm; flush pointing all faces	m	0.13	14.49	-	50.66	65.15	*273.45*
U3.7.6.03	Class B Engineering bricks, BS 3921; PC £275 per 1000 in cement mortar (1:3); Pilaster attached to wall face; 215 x 112.5mm; flush pointing all faces	m	0.03	3.62	-	4.41	8.03	*23.90*
U3.7.6.04	as above; Pilaster attached to wall face; 890 x 327.5mm; flush pointing all faces	m	0.13	14.49	-	50.66	65.15	*273.45*

U3 Engineering Brickwork continued...

		Unit	Labour Hours	Labour Net £	Plant Net £	Materials Net £	Unit Net £	CO_2 Kg
U3.7	**Surface features**							
U3.7.7	Plinths							
U3.7.7.01	Class A Engineering bricks, BS 3921; PC £375 per 1000 in cement mortar (1:3); Plinth 102.5mm thick; set forward 25mm from wall face; 450mm high; flush pointing face and top of projection	m	0.07	7.25	-	-	7.25	-
U3.7.7.02	as above; Plinth 102.5mm thick; set forward 25mm from wall face; 900mm high; flush pointing face and top of projection	m	0.13	14.49	-	-	14.49	-
U3.7.7.03	Class B Engineering bricks, BS 3921; PC £275 per 1000 in cement mortar (1:3); Plinth 102.5mm thick; set forward 25mm from wall face; 450mm high; flush pointing face and top of projection	m	0.07	7.25	-	-	7.25	-
U3.7.7.04	as above; Plinth 102.5mm thick; set forward 25mm from wall face; 900mm high; flush pointing face and top of projection	m	0.13	14.49	-	-	14.49	-
U3.7.8	Fair facings							
U3.7.8.01	Class A Engineering bricks, BS 3921; PC £375 per 1000 in cement mortar (1:3); Fair facing in stretcher bond including flush pointing as the work proceeds	m^2	0.07	7.25	-	-	7.25	-
U3.7.8.02	as above; in stretcher bond including weatherstruck pointing as the work proceeds	m^2	0.08	8.34	-	-	8.34	-
U3.7.8.03	as above; in English bond including flush pointing as the work proceeds	m^2	0.10	10.76	-	-	10.76	-
U3.7.8.04	as above; in English bond including weatherstruck pointing as the work proceeds	m^2	0.11	12.08	-	-	12.08	-
U3.7.8.05	as above; in Flemish bond including flush pointing as the work proceeds	m^2	0.09	9.88	-	-	9.88	-
U3.7.8.06	as above; in Flemish bond including weatherstruck pointing as the work proceeds	m^2	0.10	10.98	-	-	10.98	-
U3.7.8.07	as above; in stretcher bond including raking out joints and flush repointing with coloured gauged mortar	m^2	0.16	18.01	-	1.95	19.96	*7.08*
U3.7.8.08	as above; in stretcher bond including raking out joints and weatherstruck repointing with coloured gauged mortar	m^2	0.18	19.32	-	1.95	21.27	*7.08*
U3.7.8.09	Class B Engineering bricks, BS 3921; PC £275 per 1000 in cement mortar (1:3); Fair facing in stretcher bond including flush pointing as the work proceeds	m^2	0.07	7.25	-	-	7.25	-

U3 Engineering Brickwork continued...

		Unit	Labour Hours	Labour Net £	Plant Net £	Materials Net £	Unit Net £	CO_2 Kg
U3.7	**Surface features**							
U3.7.8	Fair facings							
U3.7.8.10	as previous item; in stretcher bond including weatherstruck pointing as the work proceeds	m²	0.08	8.34	-	-	8.34	-
U3.7.8.11	as above; in English bond including flush pointing as the work proceeds	m²	0.10	10.76	-	-	10.76	-
U3.7.8.12	as above; in English bond including weatherstruck pointing as the work proceeds	m²	0.11	12.08	-	-	12.08	-
U3.7.8.13	as above; in Flemish bond including flush pointing as the work proceeds	m²	0.09	9.88	-	-	9.88	-
U3.7.8.14	as above; in Flemish bond including weatherstruck pointing as the work proceeds	m²	0.10	10.98	-	-	10.98	-
U3.7.8.15	as above; in stretcher bond including raking out joints and flush repointing with coloured gauged mortar	m²	0.16	18.01	-	1.95	19.96	*7.08*
U3.7.8.16	as above; in stretcher bond including raking out joints and weatherstruck repointing with coloured gauged mortar	m²	0.18	19.32	-	1.95	21.27	*7.08*
U3.8	**Ancillaries**							
U3.8.1	Joint reinforcement							
U3.8.1.01	Exmet galvanised brick reinforcement; 24 gauge; horizontal; 100mm wide	m	0.04	4.39	-	1.03	5.42	*2.82*
U3.8.1.02	as above; 225mm wide	m	0.05	5.49	-	2.06	7.55	*5.64*
U3.8.1.03	as above; 305mm wide	m	0.06	6.59	-	3.09	9.68	*8.46*
U3.8.1.04	as above; 450mm wide	m	0.07	7.69	-	4.12	11.81	*11.28*
U3.8.1.05	as above; 900mm wide	m	0.14	15.37	-	8.24	23.61	*22.56*
U3.8.2	Damp proof courses							
U3.8.2.01	Bitumen damp proof course to, BS 743, Table 1; 100mm laps in cement mortar (1:3); pointing where exposed; Hessian based; reference 'A'; horizontal; 115mm wide	m	0.01	1.32	-	1.30	2.62	*4.75*
U3.8.2.02	as above; 225mm wide	m	0.01	2.20	-	2.60	4.80	*9.51*
U3.8.2.03	as above; 330mm wide	m	0.02	4.39	-	3.90	8.29	*14.26*
U3.8.2.04	as above; 450mm wide	m	0.02	6.04	-	5.21	11.25	*19.02*
U3.8.2.05	as above; 900mm wide	m	0.05	7.14	-	10.41	17.55	*38.04*
U3.8.2.06	Bitumen damp proof course to, BS 743, Table 1; 100mm laps in cement mortar (1:3); pointing where exposed; Hessian based; reference 'A'; vertical; 115mm wide	m	0.01	1.65	-	1.30	2.95	*4.75*

U3 Engineering Brickwork continued...

		Unit	Labour Hours	Labour Net £	Plant Net £	Materials Net £	Unit Net £	CO_2 Kg
U3.8	**Ancillaries**							
U3.8.2	Damp proof courses							
U3.8.2.07	as previous item; 225mm wide	m	0.02	2.42	-	2.60	**5.02**	*9.51*
U3.8.2.08	as above; 330mm wide	m	0.04	4.94	-	3.90	**8.84**	*14.26*
U3.8.2.09	as above; 450mm wide	m	0.05	6.59	-	5.21	**11.80**	*19.02*
U3.8.2.10	as above; 900mm wide	m	0.10	7.69	-	10.41	**18.10**	*38.04*
U3.8.2.11	Bitumen damp proof course to, BS 743, Table 1; 100mm laps in cement mortar (1:3); pointing where exposed; Fibre based; reference 'B'; horizontal; 115mm wide	m	0.01	0.66	-	1.00	**1.66**	*4.75*
U3.8.2.12	as above; 225mm wide	m	0.01	1.32	-	2.00	**3.32**	*9.51*
U3.8.2.13	as above; 330mm wide	m	0.02	1.98	-	3.00	**4.98**	*14.26*
U3.8.2.14	as above; 450mm wide	m	0.02	2.63	-	4.01	**6.64**	*19.02*
U3.8.2.15	as above; 900mm wide	m	0.05	5.27	-	8.01	**13.28**	*38.04*
U3.8.2.16	Bitumen damp proof course to, BS 743, Table 1; 100mm laps in cement mortar (1:3); pointing where exposed; Fibre based; reference 'B'; vertical; 115mm wide	m	0.01	1.32	-	1.00	**2.32**	*4.75*
U3.8.2.17	as above; 225mm wide	m	0.02	2.63	-	2.00	**4.63**	*9.51*
U3.8.2.18	as above; 330mm wide	m	0.04	3.95	-	3.00	**6.95**	*14.26*
U3.8.2.19	as above; 450mm wide	m	0.05	5.27	-	4.01	**9.28**	*19.02*
U3.8.2.20	as above; 900mm wide	m	0.10	10.54	-	8.01	**18.55**	*38.04*
U3.8.2.21	Hyload pitch polymer damp proof course; 100mm laps, sealed with Hyload contact adhesive; in cement mortar (1:3); pointing where exposed; Horizontal; 115mm wide	m	0.01	0.66	-	1.31	**1.97**	*4.75*
U3.8.2.22	as above; 225mm wide	m	0.01	1.32	-	2.62	**3.94**	*9.51*
U3.8.2.23	as above; 330mm wide	m	0.02	1.98	-	3.93	**5.91**	*14.26*
U3.8.2.24	as above; 450mm wide	m	0.02	2.63	-	5.25	**7.88**	*19.02*
U3.8.2.25	as above; 900mm wide	m	0.05	5.27	-	10.49	**15.76**	*38.04*
U3.8.2.26	Hyload pitch polymer damp proof course; 100mm laps, sealed with Hyload contact adhesive; in cement mortar (1:3); pointing where exposed; Vertical; 115mm wide	m	0.01	1.32	-	1.31	**2.63**	*4.75*
U3.8.2.27	as above; 225mm wide	m	0.02	2.63	-	2.62	**5.25**	*9.51*
U3.8.2.28	as above; 300mm wide	m	0.04	3.95	-	3.93	**7.89**	*14.26*

U3 Engineering Brickwork continued...

		Unit	Labour Hours	Labour Net £	Plant Net £	Materials Net £	Unit Net £	CO_2 Kg
U3.8	**Ancillaries**							
U3.8.2	Damp proof courses							
U3.8.2.29	as previous item; 450mm wide	m	0.05	5.27	-	5.25	**10.52**	*19.02*
U3.8.2.30	as above; 900mm wide	m	0.10	10.54	-	10.49	**21.03**	*38.04*
U3.8.3	Movement joints							
U3.8.3.01	Expansion joints; filling with Fillcrete joint filler; 20mm thick expansion joint; vertical; 102.5mm wide	m	0.06	6.92	-	2.23	**9.15**	*0.12*
U3.8.3.02	as above; 215mm wide	m	0.10	11.42	-	4.47	**15.89**	*0.24*
U3.8.3.03	as above; 327.5mm wide	m	0.17	18.33	-	6.70	**25.03**	*0.36*
U3.8.3.04	as above; 440mm wide	m	0.25	27.56	-	8.93	**36.49**	*0.49*
U3.8.3.05	as above; 890mm wide	m	0.42	46.11	-	17.87	**63.98**	*0.97*
U3.8.4	Bonds to existing work							
U3.8.4.01	Class A Engineering bricks, BS 3921; PC £375 per 1000 in cement mortar (1:3); bonding 102.5mm brickwork to existing 215mm common brickwork; cutting and toothing alternate courses	m^2	0.24	26.57	-	1.80	**28.37**	*7.60*
U3.8.4.02	as above; bonding 102.5mm brickwork to existing concrete wall; cutting mortice and grouting in 1nr mild steel galvanised cramp every third course	m^2	0.46	50.50	-	2.28	**52.78**	*7.88*
U3.8.4.03	as above; bonding 215mm brickwork to existing 215mm facing brickwork; cutting and toothing alternate courses	m^2	0.41	45.01	-	3.52	**48.53**	*12.97*
U3.8.4.04	as above; bonding 215mm brickwork to existing concrete wall; cutting mortice and grouting in 1nr mild steel galvanised cramp every third course	m^2	0.63	69.61	-	3.52	**73.13**	*12.97*
U3.8.4.05	Class B Engineering bricks, BS 3921; PC £275 per 1000 in cement mortar (1:3); bonding 102.5mm brickwork to existing 215mm common brickwork; cutting and toothing alternate courses	m^2	0.24	26.57	-	1.40	**27.97**	*7.60*
U3.8.4.06	as above; bonding 102.5mm brickwork to existing concrete wall; cutting mortice and grouting in 1nr mild steel galvanised cramp every third course	m^2	0.46	50.50	-	1.88	**52.38**	*7.88*
U3.8.4.07	as above; bonding 215mm brickwork to existing 215mm facing brickwork; cutting and toothing alternate courses	m^2	0.41	45.01	-	2.82	**47.83**	*12.97*
U3.8.4.08	as above; bonding 215mm brickwork to existing concrete wall; cutting mortice and grouting in 1nr mild steel galvanised cramp every third course	m^2	0.63	69.61	-	2.82	**72.43**	*12.97*

U3 Engineering Brickwork continued...

		Unit	Labour Hours	Labour Net £	Plant Net £	Materials Net £	Unit Net £	CO_2 *Kg*
U3.8	**Ancillaries**							
U3.8.5	Infills of stated thickness							
U3.8.5.01	Concrete infill; Grade 25, 20mm aggregate; 50mm thick	m^2	0.20	21.96	-	4.31	**26.27**	*15.60*
U3.8.5.02	as above; 100mm thick	m^2	0.30	32.94	-	8.62	**41.56**	*31.20*
U3.8.5.03	as above; 150mm thick	m^2	0.40	43.92	-	12.93	**56.85**	*46.80*
U3.8.5.04	as above; 200mm thick	m^2	0.50	54.90	-	17.23	**72.13**	*62.40*
U3.8.7	Built-in pipes and ducts, cross-sectional area: not exceeding 0.05m^2							
U3.8.7.01	Class A Engineering bricks, BS 3921; PC £375 per 1000 in cement mortar (1:3); supply excluded; 102.5mm brickwork; cross-sectional area; not exceeding 0.025m^2	Nr	0.13	14.49	-	0.36	**14.85**	*2.11*
U3.8.7.02	as above; supply excluded; 102.5mm brickwork; cross-sectional area; 0.025 - 0.25m^2	Nr	0.13	14.49	-	0.48	**14.97**	*2.81*
U3.8.7.03	as above; 150mm diameter clay pipe to, BS 65, 102.5mm brickwork; cross-sectional area; not exceeding 0.025m^2	Nr	0.13	14.49	-	0.36	**14.85**	*2.11*
U3.8.7.04	as above; supply excluded; 215mm brickwork; cross-sectional area; not exceeding 0.025m^2	Nr	0.13	14.49	-	0.48	**14.97**	*2.81*
U3.8.7.05	as above; supply excluded; 215mm brickwork; cross-sectional area; 0.025 - 0.25m^2	Nr	0.13	14.27	-	0.60	**14.87**	*3.51*
U3.8.7.06	as above; 150mm diameter clay pipe to, BS 65, 215mm brickwork; cross-sectional area; not exceeding 0.025m^2	Nr	0.11	12.08	-	9.80	**21.88**	*9.22*
U3.8.7.07	Class B Engineering bricks, BS 3921; PC £275 per 1000 in cement mortar (1:3); supply excluded; 102.5mm brickwork; cross-sectional area; not exceeding 0.025m^2	Nr	0.09	9.88	-	0.30	**10.18**	*1.76*
U3.8.7.08	as above; supply excluded; 102.5mm brickwork; cross-sectional area; 0.025 - 0.25m^2	Nr	0.13	14.27	-	0.60	**14.87**	*3.51*
U3.8.7.09	as above; 150mm diameter clay pipe to, BS 65, 102.5mm brickwork; cross-sectional area; not exceeding 0.025m^2	Nr	0.10	10.98	-	0.90	**11.88**	*5.27*
U3.8.7.10	as above; supply excluded; 215mm brickwork; cross-sectional area; not exceeding 0.025m^2	Nr	0.11	12.08	-	0.36	**12.44**	*2.11*
U3.8.7.11	as above; supply excluded; 215mm brickwork; cross-sectional area; 0.025 - 0.25m^2	Nr	0.13	14.27	-	0.60	**14.87**	*3.51*
U3.8.7.12	as above; 150mm diameter clay pipe to, BS 65, 215mm brickwork; cross-sectional area; not exceeding 0.025m^2	Nr	0.11	12.08	-	10.09	**22.17**	*10.97*

U3 Engineering Brickwork continued...

		Unit	Labour Hours	Labour Net £	Plant Net £	Materials Net £	Unit Net £	*CO_2 Kg*
U3.8	**Ancillaries**							
U3.8.8	Built-in pipes and ducts, cross-sectional area: exceeding 0.05m^2							
U3.8.8.01	Class A Engineering bricks, BS 3921; PC £375 per 1000 in cement mortar (1:3); supply excluded; 102.5mm brickwork; cross-sectional area; 0.40m^2	Nr	0.18	19.32	-	0.48	19.80	*2.81*
U3.8.8.02	as above; supply excluded; 215mm brickwork; cross-sectional area; 0.40m^2	Nr	0.15	16.91	-	0.66	17.57	*3.87*
U3.8.8.03	Class B Engineering bricks, BS 3921; PC £275 per 1000 in cement mortar (1:3); supply excluded; 102.5mm brickwork; cross-sectional area; 0.40m^2	Nr	0.18	19.32	-	0.48	19.80	*2.81*
U3.8.8.04	as above; supply excluded; 215mm brickwork; cross-sectional area; 0.40m^2	Nr	0.15	16.91	-	0.66	17.57	*3.87*

U4 Lightweight Blockwork

		Unit	Labour Hours	Labour Net £	Plant Net £	Materials Net £	Unit Net £	*CO_2 Kg*
U4.1	**Thickness: not exceeding: 150mm**							
U4.1.1	vertical straight walls							
U4.1.1.01	Precast concrete blocks, BS 6073, solid; compressive strength 4.2N/mm^2, face size 440 x 215mm; in gauged mortar (1:2:9); 100mm thick	m^2	0.16	16.71	-	8.63	25.34	*17.15*
U4.1.1.02	as above; hollow; compressive strength 4.2N/mm^2, face size 440 x 215mm; in gauged mortar (1:2:9); 100mm thick	m^2	0.14	14.62	-	8.99	23.61	*17.15*
U4.1.1.03	as above, solid; fair faced; compressive strength 4.2N/mm^2, face size 440 x 215mm; in gauged mortar (1:2:9); 100mm thick	m^2	0.17	17.44	-	9.52	26.96	*17.15*
U4.1.1.04	as above, hollow fair faced; compressive strength 4.2N/mm^2, face size 440 x 215mm; in gauged mortar (1:2:9); 100mm thick	m^2	0.16	16.39	-	12.12	28.51	*14.10*
U4.1.1.05	Precast concrete blocks, BS 6073, solid; compressive strength 4.2N/mm^2, face size 440 x 215mm; in gauged mortar (1:2:9); 140mm thick	m^2	0.18	18.80	-	12.69	31.49	*26.87*
U4.1.1.06	as above; hollow; compressive strength 4.2N/mm^2, face size 440 x 215mm; in gauged mortar (1:2:9); 140mm thick	m^2	0.17	17.75	-	15.38	33.13	*26.87*
U4.1.1.07	as above, solid; fair faced; compressive strength 4.2N/mm^2, face size 440 x 215mm; in gauged mortar (1:2:9); 140mm thick	m^2	0.20	20.88	-	13.94	34.82	*26.87*
U4.1.1.08	as above, hollow; fair faced; compressive strength 4.2N/mm^2, face size 440 x 215mm; in gauged mortar (1:2:9); 140mm thick	m^2	0.26	21.15	-	16.75	43.90	*21.97*

U4 Lightweight Blockwork continued...

		Unit	Labour Hours	Labour Net £	Plant Net £	Materials Net £	Unit Net £	*CO_2 Kg*
U4.1	**Thickness: not exceeding: 150mm**							
U4.1.2	vertical curved walls							
U4.1.2.01	Precast concrete blocks, BS 6073, solid; compressive strength 4.2N/mm², face size 440 x 215mm; in gauged mortar (1:2:9); curved walls; 5m mean radius; 140mm thick	m^2	0.27	28.19	-	8.63	36.82	*17.15*
U4.1.2.02	as above; curved walls; 10m mean radius; 140mm thick	m^2	0.24	25.06	-	8.63	33.69	*17.15*
U4.1.2.03	Precast concrete blocks, BS 6073, hollow; compressive strength 4.2N/mm², face size 440 x 215mm; in gauged mortar (1:2:9); curved walls; 5m mean radius; 140mm thick	m^2	0.24	25.06	-	8.99	34.05	*17.15*
U4.1.2.04	as above; curved walls; 10m mean radius; 140mm thick	m^2	0.20	20.88	-	8.99	29.87	*17.15*
U4.1.2.05	Precast concrete blocks, BS 6073, solid; fair faced; compressive strength 4.2N/mm², face size 440 x 215mm; in gauged mortar (1:2:9); curved walls; 5m mean radius; 140mm thick	m^2	0.29	30.28	-	9.52	39.80	*17.15*
U4.1.2.06	as above; curved walls; 10m mean radius; 140mm thick	m^2	0.25	26.11	-	9.52	35.63	*17.15*
U4.1.2.07	Precast concrete blocks, BS 6073, hollow fair faced; compressive strength 4.2N/mm², face size 440 x 215mm; in gauged mortar (1:2:9); curved walls; 5m mean radius; 140mm thick	m^2	0.23	24.02	-	12.12	36.14	*14.10*
U4.1.2.08	as above; curved walls; 10m mean radius; 140mm thick	m^2	0.20	20.88	-	12.12	33.00	*14.10*
U4.1.2.09	Precast concrete blocks, BS 6073, solid; compressive strength 4.2N/mm², face size 440 x 215mm; in gauged mortar (1:2:9); curved walls; 5m mean radius; 215mm thick	m^2	0.31	32.37	-	12.69	45.06	*26.87*
U4.1.2.10	as above; curved walls; 10m mean radius; 215mm thick	m^2	0.27	28.19	-	12.69	40.88	*26.87*
U4.1.2.11	Precast concrete blocks, BS 6073, hollow; compressive strength 4.2N/mm², face size 440 x 215mm; in gauged mortar (1:2:9); curved walls; 5m mean radius; 215mm thick	m^2	0.29	30.28	-	15.38	45.66	*26.87*
U4.1.2.12	as above; curved walls; 10m mean radius; 215mm thick	m^2	0.25	26.11	-	15.38	41.49	*26.87*
U4.1.2.13	Precast concrete blocks, BS 6073, solid; fair faced; compressive strength 4.2N/mm², face size 440 x 215mm; in gauged mortar (1:2:9); curved walls; 5m mean radius; 215mm thick	m^2	0.35	36.55	-	13.94	50.49	*26.87*
U4.1.2.14	as above; curved walls; 10m mean radius; 215mm thick	m^2	0.30	31.33	-	13.94	45.27	*26.87*

U4 Lightweight Blockwork continued...

		Unit	Labour Hours	Labour Net £	Plant Net £	Materials Net £	Unit Net £	CO_2 Kg
U4.1	**Thickness: not exceeding: 150mm**							
U4.1.2	vertical curved walls							
U4.1.2.15	Precast concrete blocks, BS 6073, hollow fair faced; compressive strength 4.2N/mm², face size 440 x 215mm; in gauged mortar (1:2:9); curved walls; 5m mean radius; 215mm thick	m^2	0.33	34.46	-	16.75	51.21	*21.97*
U4.1.2.16	as above; curved walls; 10m mean radius; 215mm thick	m^2	0.28	29.24	-	16.75	45.99	*21.97*
U4.2	**Thickness: 150 - 250mm**							
U4.2.1	vertical straight walls							
U4.2.1.01	Precast concrete blocks, BS 6073, solid; compressive strength 4.2N/mm², face size 440 x 215mm; in gauged mortar (1:2:9); 215mm thick	m^2	0.23	24.02	-	19.99	44.01	*37.29*
U4.2.1.02	as above, hollow; compressive strength 4.2N/mm², face size 440 x 215mm; in gauged mortar (1:2:9); 215mm thick	m^2	0.22	22.97	-	23.34	46.31	*37.29*
U4.2.1.03	as above, solid; fair faced; compressive strength 4.2N/mm², face size 440 x 215mm; in gauged mortar (1:2:9); 215mm thick	m^2	0.23	24.02	-	22.35	46.37	*37.29*
U4.2.1.04	as above, hollow fair faced; compressive strength 4.2N/mm², face size 440 x 215mm; in gauged mortar (1:2:9); 215mm thick	m^2	0.21	21.82	-	25.54	47.36	*30.54*
U4.2.2	vertical curved walls							
U4.2.2.01	Precast concrete blocks, BS 6073, solid; compressive strength 4.2N/mm², face size 440 x 215mm; in gauged mortar (1:2:9); 215mm thick; curved walls; 5m mean radius	m^2	0.40	41.77	-	19.99	61.76	*37.29*
U4.2.2.02	as above; 10m mean radius	m^2	0.34	35.50	-	19.99	55.49	*37.29*
U4.2.2.03	Precast concrete blocks, BS 6073, hollow; compressive strength 4.2N/mm², face size 440 x 215mm; in gauged mortar (1:2:9); 215mm thick; curved walls; 5m mean radius	m^2	0.38	39.68	-	23.34	63.02	*37.29*
U4.2.2.04	as above; 10m mean radius	m^2	0.33	34.46	-	23.34	57.80	*37.29*
U4.2.2.05	Precast concrete blocks, BS 6073, solid; fair faced; compressive strength 4.2N/mm², face size 440 x 215mm; in gauged mortar (1:2:9); 215mm thick; curved walls; 5m mean radius	m^2	0.40	41.77	-	22.35	64.12	*37.29*
U4.2.2.06	as above; 10m mean radius	m^2	0.34	35.50	-	22.35	57.85	*37.29*

U4 Lightweight Blockwork continued...

		Unit	Labour Hours	Labour Net £	Plant Net £	Materials Net £	Unit Net £	CO_2 Kg
U4.2	**Thickness: 150 - 250mm**							
U4.2.2	vertical curved walls							
U4.2.2.07	Precast concrete blocks, BS 6073, hollow fair faced; compressive strength 4.2N/mm², face size 440 x 215mm; in gauged mortar (1:2:9); 215mm thick; curved walls; 5m mean radius	m^2	0.37	38.64	-	25.54	**64.18**	*30.54*
U4.2.2.08	as above; 10m mean radius	m^2	0.31	32.37	-	25.54	**57.91**	*30.54*
U4.7	**Surface features**							
U4.7.6	Pilasters							
U4.7.6.01	Precast concrete blocks, BS 6073, solid; compressive strength 4.2N/mm², face size 440 x 215mm; in gauged mortar (1:2:9); Pilaster attached to wall face; 440 x 100mm; flush pointing all faces	m	0.07	7.52	-	3.17	**10.69**	*6.31*
U4.7.6.02	as above; Pilaster attached to wall face; 890 x 140mm; flush pointing all faces	m	0.20	20.68	-	11.30	**31.98**	*23.94*
U4.7.6.03	Precast concrete blocks, BS 6073, hollow; compressive strength 4.2N/mm², face size 440 x 215mm; in gauged mortar (1:2:9); Pilaster attached to wall face; 440 x 100mm; flush pointing all faces	m	0.07	7.52	-	3.17	**10.69**	*6.31*
U4.7.6.04	as above; Pilaster attached to wall face; 890 x 140mm; flush pointing all faces	m	0.20	20.68	-	11.30	**31.98**	*23.94*
U4.7.6.05	Precast concrete blocks, BS 6073, solid; fair faced; compressive strength 4.2N/mm², face size 440 x 215mm; in gauged mortar (1:2:9); Pilaster attached to wall face; 440 x 100mm; flush pointing all faces	m	0.07	7.52	-	3.40	**10.92**	*6.31*
U4.7.6.06	as above; Pilaster attached to wall face; 890 x 140mm; flush pointing all faces	m	0.20	20.68	-	12.07	**32.75**	*23.94*
U4.7.6.07	Precast concrete blocks, BS 6073, hollow fair faced; compressive strength 4.2N/mm², face size 440 x 215mm; in gauged mortar (1:2:9); Pilaster attached to wall face; 440 x 100mm; flush pointing all faces	m	0.07	7.52	-	4.33	**11.85**	*6.31*
U4.7.6.08	as above; Pilaster attached to wall face; 890 x 140mm; flush pointing all faces	m	0.20	20.68	-	14.50	**35.18**	*23.94*

U4 Lightweight Blockwork continued...

		Unit	Labour Hours	Labour Net £	Plant Net £	Materials Net £	Unit Net £	CO_2 Kg
U4.7	**Surface features**							
U4.7.7	Plinths							
U4.7.7.01	Precast concrete blocks, BS 6073, solid; compressive strength 4.2N/mm², face size 440 x 215mm; in gauged mortar (1:2:9); Plinth 100mm thick; set forward 25mm from wall face; 440mm high; flush pointing face and top of projection	m	0.07	7.41	-	-	7.41	-
U4.7.7.02	as above; Plinth 100mm thick; set forward 25mm from wall face; 890mm high; flush pointing face and top of projection	m	0.11	10.96	-	-	10.96	-
U4.7.7.03	Precast concrete blocks, BS 6073, hollow; compressive strength 4.2N/mm², face size 440 x 215mm; in gauged mortar (1:2:9); Plinth 100mm thick; set forward 25mm from wall face; 440mm high; flush pointing face and top of projection	m	0.07	7.41	-	-	7.41	-
U4.7.7.04	as above; Plinth 100mm thick; set forward 25mm from wall face; 890mm high; flush pointing face and top of projection	m	0.11	10.96	-	-	10.96	-
U4.7.7.05	Precast concrete blocks, BS 6073, solid; fair faced; compressive strength 4.2N/mm², face size 440 x 215mm; in gauged mortar (1:2:9); Plinth 100mm thick; set forward 25mm from wall face; 440mm high; flush pointing face and top of projection	m	0.07	7.41	-	-	7.41	-
U4.7.7.06	as above; Plinth 100mm thick; set forward 25mm from wall face; 890mm high; flush pointing face and top of projection	m	0.11	10.96	-	-	10.96	-
U4.7.7.07	Precast concrete blocks, BS 6073, hollow fair faced; compressive strength 4.2N/mm², face size 440 x 215mm; in gauged mortar (1:2:9); Plinth 100mm thick; set forward 25mm from wall face; 440mm high; flush pointing face and top of projection	m	0.07	7.41	-	-	7.41	-
U4.7.7.08	as above; Plinth 100mm thick; set forward 25mm from wall face; 890mm high; flush pointing face and top of projection	m	0.11	10.96	-	-	10.96	-
U4.7.8	Fair facings							
U4.7.8.01	Precast concrete blocks, BS 6073, solid; compressive strength 4.2N/mm², face size 440 x 215mm; in gauged mortar (1:2:9); Fair facing in stretcher bond including flush pointing as the work proceeds	m²	0.06	6.58	-	-	6.58	-

U4 Lightweight Blockwork continued...

		Unit	Labour Hours	Labour Net £	Plant Net £	Materials Net £	Unit Net £	CO_2 Kg
U4.7	**Surface features**							
U4.7.8	Fair facings							
U4.7.8.02	Precast concrete blocks, BS 6073, hollow; compressive strength 4.2N/mm², face size 440 x 215mm; in gauged mortar (1:2:9); Fair facing in stretcher bond including flush pointing as the work proceeds	m²	0.06	6.58	-	-	**6.58**	-
U4.7.8.03	Precast concrete blocks, BS 6073, solid; fair faced; compressive strength 4.2N/mm², face size 440 x 215mm; in gauged mortar (1:2:9); Fair facing in stretcher bond including flush pointing as the work proceeds	m²	0.06	6.58	-	-	**6.58**	-
U4.7.8.04	Precast concrete blocks, BS 6073, hollow fair faced; compressive strength 4.2N/mm², face size 440 x 215mm; in gauged mortar (1:2:9); Fair facing in stretcher bond including flush pointing as the work proceeds	m²	0.06	6.58	-	-	**6.58**	-
U4.8	**Ancillaries**							
U4.8.1	Joint reinforcement							
U4.8.1.01	Exmet galvanised brick reinforcement; 24 gauge; horizontal; 100mm wide	m	0.04	4.39	-	1.03	**5.42**	*2.82*
U4.8.1.02	as above; 225mm wide	m	0.05	5.49	-	2.06	**7.55**	*5.64*
U4.8.1.03	as above; 305mm wide	m	0.06	6.59	-	3.09	**9.68**	*8.46*
U4.8.1.04	as above; 450mm wide	m	0.07	7.69	-	4.12	**11.81**	*11.28*
U4.8.1.05	as above; 900mm wide	m	0.14	15.37	-	8.24	**23.61**	*22.56*
U4.8.2	Damp proof courses							
U4.8.2.01	Bitumen damp proof course to, BS 743, Table 1; 100mm laps in cement mortar (1:3); pointing where exposed; Hessian based; reference 'A'; horizontal; 115mm wide	m	0.01	1.32	-	1.30	**2.62**	*4.75*
U4.8.2.02	as above; 225mm wide	m	0.01	2.20	-	2.60	**4.80**	*9.51*
U4.8.2.03	as above; 330mm wide	m	0.02	4.39	-	3.90	**8.29**	*14.26*
U4.8.2.04	as above; 450mm wide	m	0.02	6.04	-	5.21	**11.25**	*19.02*
U4.8.2.05	as above; 900mm wide	m	0.05	7.14	-	10.41	**17.55**	*38.04*
U4.8.2.06	Bitumen damp proof course to, BS 743, Table 1; 100mm laps in cement mortar (1:3); pointing where exposed; Hessian based; reference 'A'; vertical; 115mm wide	m	0.01	1.65	-	1.30	**2.95**	*4.75*
U4.8.2.07	as above; 225mm wide	m	0.02	2.42	-	2.60	**5.02**	*9.51*
U4.8.2.08	as above; 330mm wide	m	0.04	4.94	-	3.90	**8.84**	*14.26*

U4 Lightweight Blockwork continued...

		Unit	Labour Hours	Labour Net £	Plant Net £	Materials Net £	Unit Net £	CO_2 Kg
U4.8	**Ancillaries**							
U4.8.2	Damp proof courses							
U4.8.2.09	as previous item; 450mm wide	m	0.05	6.59	-	5.21	11.80	*19.02*
U4.8.2.10	as above; 900mm wide	m	0.10	7.69	-	10.41	18.10	*38.04*
U4.8.2.11	Bitumen damp proof course to, BS 743, Table 1; 100mm laps in cement mortar (1:3); pointing where exposed; Fibre based; reference 'B'; horizontal; 115mm wide	m	0.01	0.66	-	1.00	1.66	*4.75*
U4.8.2.12	as above; 225mm wide	m	0.01	1.32	-	2.00	3.32	*9.51*
U4.8.2.13	as above; 330mm wide	m	0.02	1.98	-	3.00	4.98	*14.26*
U4.8.2.14	as above; 450mm wide	m	0.02	2.63	-	4.01	6.64	*19.02*
U4.8.2.15	as above; 900mm wide	m	0.05	5.27	-	8.01	13.28	*38.04*
U4.8.2.16	Bitumen damp proof course to, BS 743, Table 1; 100mm laps in cement mortar (1:3); pointing where exposed; Fibre based; reference 'B'; vertical; 115mm wide	m	0.01	1.32	-	1.00	2.32	*4.75*
U4.8.2.17	as above; 225mm wide	m	0.02	2.63	-	2.00	4.63	*9.51*
U4.8.2.18	as above; 330mm wide	m	0.04	3.95	-	3.00	6.95	*14.26*
U4.8.2.19	as above; 450mm wide	m	0.05	5.27	-	4.01	9.28	*19.02*
U4.8.2.20	as above; 900mm wide	m	0.10	10.54	-	8.01	18.55	*38.04*
U4.8.2.21	Hyload pitch polymer damp proof course; 100mm laps, sealed with Hyload contact adhesive; in cement mortar (1:3); pointing where exposed; Horizontal; 115mm wide	m	0.01	0.66	-	1.31	1.97	*4.75*
U4.8.2.22	as above; 225mm wide	m	0.01	1.32	-	2.62	3.94	*9.51*
U4.8.2.23	as above; 330mm wide	m	0.02	1.98	-	3.93	5.91	*14.26*
U4.8.2.24	as above; 450mm wide	m	0.02	2.63	-	5.25	7.88	*19.02*
U4.8.2.25	as above; 900mm wide	m	0.05	5.27	-	10.49	15.76	*38.04*
U4.8.2.26	Hyload pitch polymer damp proof course; 100mm laps, sealed with Hyload contact adhesive; in cement mortar (1:3); pointing where exposed; Vertical; 115mm wide	m	0.01	1.32	-	1.31	2.63	*4.75*
U4.8.2.27	as above; 225mm wide	m	0.02	2.63	-	2.62	5.25	*9.51*
U4.8.2.28	as above; 330mm wide	m	0.04	3.95	-	3.93	7.88	*14.26*
U4.8.2.29	as above; 450mm wide	m	0.05	5.27	-	5.25	10.52	*19.02*
U4.8.2.30	as above; 900mm wide	m	0.10	10.54	-	10.49	21.03	*38.04*

U4 Lightweight Blockwork continued...

		Unit	Labour Hours	Labour Net £	Plant Net £	Materials Net £	Unit Net £	CO_2 Kg
U4.8	**Ancillaries**							
U4.8.3	Movement joints							
U4.8.3.01	Expansion joints; filling with Fillcrete joint filler; 20mm thick expansion joint; vertical; 102.5mm wide	m	0.06	6.92	-	2.23	**9.15**	*0.12*
U4.8.3.02	as above; 215mm wide	m	0.10	11.42	-	4.47	**15.89**	*0.24*
U4.8.3.03	as above; 327.5mm wide	m	0.17	18.33	-	6.70	**25.03**	*0.36*
U4.8.3.04	as above; 440mm wide	m	0.25	27.56	-	8.93	**36.49**	*0.49*
U4.8.3.05	as above; 890mm wide	m	0.42	46.11	-	17.87	**63.98**	*0.97*
U4.8.4	Bonds to existing work							
U4.8.4.01	Precast concrete blocks, BS 6073, solid; compressive strength 4.2N/mm², face size 440 x 215mm; in gauged mortar (1:2:9); bonding 100mm blockwork to existing 215mm facing brickwork; cutting and toothing alternate courses	m^2	0.07	7.41	-	0.19	**7.60**	*0.62*
U4.8.4.02	as above; bonding 140mm blockwork to existing 215mm facing brickwork; cutting and toothing alternate courses	m^2	0.08	8.77	-	0.23	**9.00**	*0.72*
U4.8.4.03	Precast concrete blocks, BS 6073, hollow; compressive strength 4.2N/mm², face size 440 x 215mm; in gauged mortar (1:2:9); bonding 100mm blockwork to existing 215mm facing brickwork; cutting and toothing alternate courses	m^2	0.07	7.41	-	0.26	**7.67**	*0.72*
U4.8.4.04	as above; bonding 140mm blockwork to existing 215mm facing brickwork; cutting and toothing alternate courses	m^2	0.08	8.77	-	0.26	**9.03**	*0.72*
U4.8.4.05	Precast concrete blocks, BS 6073, solid; fair faced; compressive strength 4.2N/mm², face size 440 x 215mm; in gauged mortar (1:2:9); bonding 100mm blockwork to existing 215mm facing brickwork; cutting and toothing alternate courses	m^2	0.07	7.41	-	0.20	**7.61**	*0.62*
U4.8.4.06	as above; bonding 140mm blockwork to existing 215mm facing brickwork; cutting and toothing alternate courses	m^2	0.08	8.77	-	0.24	**9.01**	*0.72*
U4.8.4.07	Precast concrete blocks, BS 6073, hollow fair faced; compressive strength 4.2N/mm², face size 440 x 215mm; in gauged mortar (1:2:9); bonding 100mm blockwork to existing 215mm facing brickwork; cutting and toothing alternate courses	m^2	0.07	7.41	-	0.22	**7.63**	*0.62*

U4 Lightweight Blockwork continued...

		Unit	Labour Hours	Labour Net £	Plant Net £	Materials Net £	Unit Net £	CO_2 Kg
U4.8	**Ancillaries**							
U4.8.4	Bonds to existing work							
U4.8.4.08	as previous item; bonding 140mm blockwork to existing 215mm facing brickwork; cutting and toothing alternate courses	m^2	0.08	8.77	-	0.27	**9.04**	*0.72*
U4.8.5	Infills of stated thickness							
U4.8.5.01	Concrete infill; Grade 25, 20mm aggregate; 50mm thick	m^2	0.20	21.96	-	4.31	**26.27**	*15.60*
U4.8.5.02	as above; 100mm thick	m^2	0.30	32.94	-	8.62	**41.56**	*31.20*
U4.8.5.03	as above; 150mm thick	m^2	0.40	43.92	-	12.93	**56.85**	*46.80*
U4.8.5.04	as above; 200mm thick	m^2	0.50	54.90	-	17.23	**72.13**	*62.40*
U4.8.7	Built-in pipes and ducts, cross-sectional area: not exceeding $0.05m^2$							
U4.8.7.01	Precast concrete blocks, BS 6073, solid; compressive strength $4.2N/mm^2$, face size 440 x 215mm; in gauged mortar (1:2:9); 100mm blockwork; cross-sectional area; not exceeding $0.025m^2$	Nr	0.13	13.05	-	0.43	**13.48**	*1.89*
U4.8.7.02	as above; supply excluded; 100mm blockwork; cross-sectional area; 0.025 - $0.25m^2$	Nr	0.13	13.05	-	0.43	**13.48**	*1.89*
U4.8.7.03	as above; 150mm diameter clay pipe to, BS 65, 100mm blockwork; cross-sectional area; not exceeding $0.025m^2$	Nr	0.17	17.75	-	0.54	**18.29**	*2.36*
U4.8.7.04	Precast concrete blocks, BS 6073, hollow; compressive strength $4.2N/mm^2$, face size 440 x 215mm; in gauged mortar (1:2:9); supply excluded; 100mm blockwork; cross-sectional area; not exceeding $0.025m^2$	Nr	0.08	8.35	-	0.54	**8.89**	*2.36*
U4.8.7.05	as above; supply excluded; 100mm blockwork; cross-sectional area; 0.025 - $0.25m^2$	Nr	0.13	13.57	-	0.54	**14.11**	*2.36*
U4.8.7.06	as above; 150mm diameter clay pipe to, BS 65, 100mm blockwork; cross-sectional area; not exceeding $0.025m^2$	Nr	0.10	10.44	-	0.54	**10.98**	*2.36*
U4.8.7.07	Precast concrete blocks, BS 6073, solid; fair faced; compressive strength $4.2N/mm^2$, face size 440 x 215mm; in gauged mortar (1:2:9); supply excluded; 100mm blockwork; cross-sectional area; not exceeding $0.025m^2$	Nr	0.08	8.35	-	0.54	**8.89**	*2.36*
U4.8.7.08	as above; supply excluded; 100mm blockwork; cross-sectional area; 0.025 - $0.25m^2$	Nr	0.13	13.57	-	0.54	**14.11**	*2.36*
U4.8.7.09	as above; 150mm diameter clay pipe to, BS 65, 100mm blockwork; cross-sectional area; not exceeding $0.025m^2$	Nr	0.10	10.44	-	0.54	**10.98**	*2.36*

U4 Lightweight Blockwork continued...

		Unit	Labour Hours	Labour Net £	Plant Net £	Materials Net £	Unit Net £	CO_2 Kg
U4.8	**Ancillaries**							
U4.8.7	Built-in pipes and ducts, cross-sectional area: not exceeding 0.05m²							
U4.8.7.10	Precast concrete blocks, BS 6073, hollow fair faced; compressive strength 4.2N/mm², face size 440 x 215mm; in gauged mortar (1:2:9); supply excluded; 100mm blockwork; cross-sectional area; not exceeding 0.025m²	Nr	0.08	8.35	-	0.54	**8.89**	*2.36*
U4.8.7.11	as above; supply excluded; 100mm blockwork; cross-sectional area; 0.025 - 0.25m²	Nr	0.13	13.57	-	0.54	**14.11**	*2.36*
U4.8.7.12	as above; 150mm diameter clay pipe to, BS 65, 100mm blockwork; cross-sectional area; not exceeding 0.025m²	Nr	0.10	10.44	-	0.54	**10.98**	*2.36*
U4.8.8	Built-in pipes and ducts, cross-sectional area: exceeding 0.05m²							
U4.8.8.01	Precast concrete blocks, BS 6073, solid; compressive strength 4.2N/mm², face size 440 x 215mm; in gauged mortar (1:2:9); 100mm blockwork; cross-sectional area; 0.40m²	Nr	0.17	17.44	-	0.54	**17.98**	*2.36*
U4.8.8.02	as above, hollow; compressive strength 4.2N/mm², face size 440 x 215mm; in gauged mortar (1:2:9); 100mm blockwork; cross-sectional area; 0.40m²	Nr	0.17	17.75	-	0.54	**18.29**	*2.36*
U4.8.8.03	as above, BS 6073, solid; fair faced; compressive strength 4.2N/mm², face size 440 x 215mm; in gauged mortar (1:2:9); 100mm blockwork; cross-sectional area; 0.40m2	Nr	0.17	17.75	-	0.54	**18.29**	*2.36*
U4.8.8.04	as above, BS 6073, hollow fair faced; compressive strength 4.2N/mm², face size 440 x 215mm; in gauged mortar (1:2:9); 100mm blockwork; cross-sectional area; 0.40m²	Nr	0.17	17.75	-	0.54	**18.29**	*2.36*

U5 Dense Concrete Blockwork

		Unit	Labour Hours	Labour Net £	Plant Net £	Materials Net £	Unit Net £	CO_2 Kg
U5.1	**Thickness: not exceeding: 150mm**							
U5.1.1	vertical straight walls							
U5.1.1.01	Precast concrete blocks, BS 6073, solid; compressive strength 7 N/mm², face size 440 x 215mm; in gauged mortar (1:2:9); 100mm thick	m²	0.19	19.63	-	14.31	**33.94**	*42.31*
U5.1.1.02	as above; 140mm thick	m²	0.23	24.02	-	20.74	**44.76**	*60.41*
U5.1.1.03	Precast concrete blocks, BS 6073, hollow; compressive strength 7 N/mm², face size 440 x 215mm; in gauged mortar (1:2:9); 100mm thick	m²	0.18	18.59	-	12.91	**31.50**	*36.29*
U5.1.1.04	as above; 140mm thick	m²	0.22	22.97	-	17.99	**40.96**	*43.21*

U5 Dense Concrete Blockwork continued...

		Unit	Labour Hours	Labour Net £	Plant Net £	Materials Net £	Unit Net £	CO_2 Kg
U5.1	**Thickness: not exceeding: 150mm**							
U5.1.2	vertical curved walls							
U5.1.2.01	Precast concrete blocks, BS 6073, solid; compressive strength 7 N/mm², face size 440 x 215mm; in gauged mortar (1:2:9); 100mm thick; curved walls; 5m mean radius	m²	0.33	34.46	-	14.31	**48.77**	*42.31*
U5.1.2.02	as above; curved walls; 10m mean radius	m²	0.28	29.24	-	14.31	**43.55**	*42.31*
U5.1.2.03	Precast concrete blocks, BS 6073, solid; compressive strength 7 N/mm², face size 440 x 215mm; in gauged mortar (1:2:9); 140mm thick; curved walls; 5m mean radius	m²	0.40	41.77	-	20.74	**62.51**	*60.41*
U5.1.2.04	as above; curved walls; 10m mean radius	m²	0.34	35.50	-	20.74	**56.24**	*60.41*
U5.1.2.05	Precast concrete blocks, BS 6073, hollow; compressive strength 7 N/mm², face size 440 x 215mm; in gauged mortar (1:2:9); 100mm thick; curved walls; 5m mean radius	m²	0.31	32.37	-	12.91	**45.28**	*36.29*
U5.1.2.06	as above; curved walls; 10m mean radius	m²	0.27	28.19	-	12.91	**41.10**	*36.29*
U5.1.2.07	Precast concrete blocks, BS 6073, hollow; compressive strength 7 N/mm², face size 440 x 215mm; in gauged mortar (1:2:9); 140mm thick; curved walls; 5m mean radius	m²	0.38	39.68	-	17.99	**57.67**	*43.21*
U5.1.2.08	as above; curved walls; 10m mean radius	m²	0.33	34.46	-	17.99	**52.45**	*43.21*
U5.2	**Thickness: 150 - 250mm**							
U5.2.1	vertical straight walls							
U5.2.1.01	Precast concrete blocks, BS 6073, solid; compressive strength 7 N/mm², face size 440 x 215mm; in gauged mortar (1:2:9); 215mm thick	m²	0.30	31.33	-	31.75	**63.08**	*70.19*
U5.2.1.02	Precast concrete blocks, BS 6073, hollow; compressive strength 7 N/mm², face size 440 x 215mm; in gauged mortar (1:2:9); 215mm thick	m²	0.29	30.28	-	25.23	**55.51**	*48.69*
U5.2.2	vertical curved walls							
U5.2.2.01	Precast concrete blocks, BS 6073, solid; compressive strength 7 N/mm², face size 440 x 215mm; in gauged mortar (1:2:9); 215mm thick; curved walls; 5m mean radius	m²	0.53	55.34	-	31.75	**87.09**	*70.19*
U5.2.2.02	as above; curved walls; 10m mean radius	m²	0.45	46.99	-	31.75	**78.74**	*70.19*

U5 Dense Concrete Blockwork continued...

		Unit	Labour Hours	Labour Net £	Plant Net £	Materials Net £	Unit Net £	CO_2 Kg
U5.2	**Thickness: 150 - 250mm**							
U5.2.2	vertical curved walls							
U5.2.2.03	Precast concrete blocks, BS 6073, hollow; compressive strength 7 N/mm², face size 440 x 215mm; in gauged mortar (1:2:9); 215mm thick; curved walls; 5m mean radius	m²	0.42	43.86	-	25.23	**69.09**	*48.69*
U5.2.2.04	as above; curved walls; 10m mean radius	m²	0.39	40.72	-	25.23	**65.95**	*48.69*
U5.7	**Surface features**							
U5.7.6	Pilasters							
U5.7.6.01	Precast concrete blocks, BS 6073, solid; compressive strength 7 N/mm², face size 440 x 215mm; in gauged mortar (1:2:9); Pilaster attached to wall face; 440 x 100mm; flush pointing all faces	m	0.08	8.77	-	5.26	**14.03**	*15.54*
U5.7.6.02	as above; Pilaster attached to wall face; 890 x 140mm; flush pointing all faces	m	0.25	26.21	-	18.46	**44.67**	*53.79*
U5.7.6.03	Precast concrete blocks, BS 6073, hollow; compressive strength 7 N/mm², face size 440 x 215mm; in gauged mortar (1:2:9); Pilaster attached to wall face; 440 x 100mm; flush pointing all faces	m	0.08	8.77	-	4.74	**13.51**	*13.33*
U5.7.6.04	as above; Pilaster attached to wall face; 890 x 140mm; flush pointing all faces	m	0.25	26.21	-	16.02	**42.23**	*38.48*
U5.7.7	Plinths							
U5.7.7.01	Precast concrete blocks, BS 6073, solid; compressive strength 7 N/mm², face size 440 x 215mm; in gauged mortar (1:2:9); Plinth 100mm thick; set forward 25mm from wall face; 440mm high; flush pointing face and top of projection	m	0.08	8.77	-	-	**8.77**	-
U5.7.7.02	as above; Plinth 100mm thick; set forward 25mm from wall face; 890mm high; flush pointing face and top of projection	m	0.13	13.05	-	-	**13.05**	-
U5.7.7.03	Precast concrete blocks, BS 6073, hollow; compressive strength 7 N/mm², face size 440 x 215mm; in gauged mortar (1:2:9); Plinth 100mm thick; set forward 25mm from wall face; 440mm high; flush pointing face and top of projection	m	0.08	8.77	-	-	**8.77**	-
U5.7.7.04	as above; Plinth 100mm thick; set forward 25mm from wall face; 890mm high; flush pointing face and top of projection	m	0.13	13.05	-	-	**13.05**	-

U5 Dense Concrete Blockwork continued...

		Unit	Labour Hours	Labour Net £	Plant Net £	Materials Net £	Unit Net £	CO_2 Kg
U5.7	**Surface features**							
U5.7.8	Fair facings							
U5.7.8.01	Precast concrete blocks, BS 6073, solid; compressive strength 7 N/mm², face size 440 x 215mm; in gauged mortar (1:2:9); Fair facing in stretcher bond including flush pointing as the work proceeds	m²	0.08	8.77	-	-	8.77	-
U5.7.8.02	Precast concrete blocks, BS 6073, hollow; compressive strength 7 N/mm², face size 440 x 215mm; in gauged mortar (1:2:9); Fair facing in stretcher bond including flush pointing as the work proceeds	m²	0.08	8.77	-	-	8.77	-
U5.8	**Ancillaries**							
U5.8.1	Joint reinforcement							
U5.8.1.01	Exmet galvanised brick reinforcement; 24 gauge; horizontal; 100mm wide	m	0.04	4.39	-	1.03	5.42	*2.82*
U5.8.1.02	as above; 225mm wide	m	0.05	5.49	-	2.06	7.55	*5.64*
U5.8.1.03	as above; 305mm wide	m	0.06	6.59	-	3.09	9.68	*8.46*
U5.8.1.04	as above; 450mm wide	m	0.07	7.69	-	4.12	11.81	*11.28*
U5.8.1.05	as above; 900mm wide	m	0.14	15.37	-	8.24	23.61	*22.56*
U5.8.2	Damp proof courses							
U5.8.2.01	Bitumen damp proof course to, BS 743, Table 1; 100mm laps in cement mortar (1:3); pointing where exposed; Hessian based; reference 'A'; horizontal; 115mm wide	m	0.01	1.32	-	1.30	2.62	*4.75*
U5.8.2.02	as above; 225mm wide	m	0.01	2.20	-	2.60	4.80	*9.51*
U5.8.2.03	as above; 330mm wide	m	0.02	4.39	-	3.90	8.29	*14.26*
U5.8.2.04	as above; 450mm wide	m	0.02	6.04	-	5.21	11.25	*19.02*
U5.8.2.05	as above; 900mm wide	m	0.05	7.14	-	10.41	17.55	*38.04*
U5.8.2.06	Bitumen damp proof course to, BS 743, Table 1; 100mm laps in cement mortar (1:3); pointing where exposed; Hessian based; reference 'A'; vertical; 115mm wide	m	0.01	1.65	-	1.30	2.95	*4.75*
U5.8.2.07	as above; 225mm wide	m	0.02	2.42	-	2.60	5.02	*9.51*
U5.8.2.08	as above; 330mm wide	m	0.04	4.94	-	3.90	8.84	*14.26*
U5.8.2.09	as above; 450mm wide	m	0.05	6.59	-	5.21	11.80	*19.02*
U5.8.2.10	as above; 900mm wide	m	0.10	7.69	-	10.41	18.10	*38.04*

U5 Dense Concrete Blockwork continued...

		Unit	Labour Hours	Labour Net £	Plant Net £	Materials Net £	Unit Net £	CO_2 Kg
U5.8	**Ancillaries**							
U5.8.2	Damp proof courses							
U5.8.2.11	Bitumen damp proof course to, BS 743, Table 1; 100mm laps in cement mortar (1:3); pointing where exposed; Fibre based; reference 'B'; horizontal; 115mm wide	m	0.01	0.66	-	1.00	**1.66**	*4.75*
U5.8.2.12	as above; 225mm wide	m	0.01	1.32	-	2.00	**3.32**	*9.51*
U5.8.2.13	as above; 330mm wide	m	0.02	1.98	-	3.00	**4.98**	*14.26*
U5.8.2.14	as above; 450mm wide	m	0.02	2.63	-	4.01	**6.64**	*19.02*
U5.8.2.15	as above; 900mm wide	m	0.05	5.27	-	8.01	**13.28**	*38.04*
U5.8.2.16	Bitumen damp proof course to, BS 743, Table 1; 100mm laps in cement mortar (1:3); pointing where exposed; Fibre based; reference 'B'; vertical; 115mm wide	m	0.01	1.32	-	1.00	**2.32**	*4.75*
U5.8.2.17	as above; 225mm wide	m	0.02	2.63	-	2.00	**4.63**	*9.51*
U5.8.2.18	as above; 330mm wide	m	0.04	3.95	-	3.00	**6.95**	*14.26*
U5.8.2.19	as above; 450mm wide	m	0.05	5.27	-	4.01	**9.28**	*19.02*
U5.8.2.20	as above; 900mm wide	m	0.10	10.54	-	8.01	**18.55**	*38.04*
U5.8.2.21	Hyload pitch polymer damp proof course; 100mm laps, sealed with Hyload contact adhesive; in cement mortar (1:3); pointing where exposed; Horizontal; 115mm wide	m	0.01	0.66	-	1.31	**1.97**	*4.75*
U5.8.2.22	as above; 225mm wide	m	0.01	1.32	-	2.62	**3.94**	*9.51*
U5.8.2.23	as above; 330mm wide	m	0.02	1.98	-	3.93	**5.91**	*14.26*
U5.8.2.24	as above; 450mm wide	m	0.02	2.63	-	5.25	**7.88**	*19.02*
U5.8.2.25	as above; 900mm wide	m	0.05	5.27	-	10.49	**15.76**	*38.04*
U5.8.2.26	Hyload pitch polymer damp proof course; 100mm laps, sealed with Hyload contact adhesive; in cement mortar (1:3); pointing where exposed; Vertical; 115mm wide	m	0.01	1.32	-	1.31	**2.63**	*4.75*
U5.8.2.27	as above; 225mm wide	m	0.02	2.63	-	2.62	**5.25**	*9.51*
U5.8.2.28	as above; 330mm wide	m	0.04	3.95	-	3.93	**7.88**	*14.26*
U5.8.2.29	as above; 450mm wide	m	0.05	5.27	-	5.25	**10.52**	*19.02*
U5.8.2.30	as above; 900mm wide	m	0.10	10.54	-	10.49	**21.03**	*38.04*

U5 Dense Concrete Blockwork continued...

		Unit	Labour Hours	Labour Net £	Plant Net £	Materials Net £	Unit Net £	CO_2 Kg
U5.8	**Ancillaries**							
U5.8.3	Movement joints							
U5.8.3.01	Expansion joints; filling with Fillcrete joint filler; 20mm thick expansion joint; vertical; 102.5mm wide	m	0.06	6.92	-	2.23	9.15	*0.12*
U5.8.3.02	as above; 215mm wide	m	0.10	11.42	-	4.47	15.89	*0.24*
U5.8.3.03	as above; 327.5mm wide	m	0.17	18.33	-	6.70	25.03	*0.36*
U5.8.3.04	as above; 440mm wide	m	0.25	27.56	-	8.93	36.49	*0.49*
U5.8.3.05	as above; 890mm wide	m	0.42	46.11	-	17.87	63.98	*0.97*
U5.8.4	Bonds to existing work							
U5.8.4.01	Precast concrete blocks, BS 6073, solid; compressive strength 7 N/mm^2, face size 440 x 215mm; in gauged mortar (1:2:9); bonding 100mm blockwork to existing 215mm facing brickwork; cutting and toothing alternate courses	m^2	0.08	7.83	-	0.25	8.08	*0.88*
U5.8.4.02	as above; Bonding 140mm blockwork to existing 215mm facing brickwork; cutting and toothing alternate courses	m^2	0.09	9.19	-	0.31	9.50	*1.05*
U5.8.4.03	Precast concrete blocks, BS 6073, hollow; compressive strength 7 N/mm^2, face size 440 x 215mm; in gauged mortar (1:2:9); bonding 100mm blockwork to existing 215mm facing brickwork; cutting and toothing alternate courses	m^2	0.08	7.83	-	0.23	8.06	*0.82*
U5.8.4.04	as above; Bonding 140mm blockwork to existing 215mm facing brickwork; cutting and toothing alternate courses	m^2	0.09	9.19	-	0.28	9.47	*0.88*
U5.8.5	Infills of stated thickness							
U5.8.5.01	Concrete infill; Grade 25, 20mm aggregate; 50mm thick	m^2	0.20	21.96	-	4.31	26.27	*15.60*
U5.8.5.02	as above; 100mm thick	m^2	0.30	32.94	-	8.62	41.56	*31.20*
U5.8.5.03	as above; 150mm thick	m^2	0.40	43.92	-	12.93	56.85	*46.80*
U5.8.5.04	as above; 200mm thick	m^2	0.50	54.90	-	17.23	72.13	*62.40*
U5.8.7	Built-in pipes and ducts, cross-sectional area: not exceeding 0.05m2							
U5.8.7.01	Precast concrete blocks, BS 6073, solid; compressive strength 7 N/mm^2, face size 440 x 215mm; in gauged mortar (1:2:9); supply excluded; 100mm clockwork; cross-sectional area; not exceeding $0.025m^2$	Nr	0.15	15.25	-	0.43	15.68	*1.89*
U5.8.7.02	as above; supply excluded; 100mm clockwork; cross-sectional area; 0.025 - $0.25m^2$	Nr	0.15	15.25	-	0.43	15.68	*1.89*

U5 Dense Concrete Blockwork continued...

		Unit	Labour Hours	Labour Net £	Plant Net £	Materials Net £	Unit Net £	CO_2 Kg
U5.8	**Ancillaries**							
U5.8.7	Built-in pipes and ducts, cross-sectional area: not exceeding 0.05m²							
U5.8.7.03	as previous item; 150mm diameter clay pipe to, BS 65, 100mm blockwork; cross-sectional area; not exceeding 0.025m²	Nr	0.13	13.57	-	0.54	14.11	*2.36*
U5.8.7.04	Precast concrete blocks, BS 6073, hollow; compressive strength 7 N/mm², face size 440 x 215mm; in gauged mortar (1:2:9); supply excluded; 100mm clockwork; cross-sectional area; not exceeding 0.025m²	Nr	0.09	9.40	-	0.54	9.94	*2.36*
U5.8.7.05	as above; supply excluded; 100mm clockwork; cross-sectional area; 0.025 - 0.25m²	Nr	0.15	15.66	-	0.54	16.20	*2.36*
U5.8.7.06	as above; 150mm diameter clay pipe to, BS 65, 100mm blockwork; cross-sectional area; not exceeding 0.025m²	Nr	0.13	13.57	-	0.54	14.11	*2.36*
U5.8.8	Built-in pipes and ducts, cross-sectional area: exceeding 0.05m²							
U5.8.8.01	Precast concrete blocks, BS 6073, solid; compressive strength 7 N/mm², face size 440 x 215mm; in gauged mortar (1:2:9); supply excluded; 100mm clockwork; cross-sectional area; 0.40m²	Nr	0.18	19.21	-	0.54	19.75	*2.36*
U5.8.8.02	as above; hollow; compressive strength 7 N/mm², face size 440 x 215mm; in gauged mortar (1:2:9); supply excluded; 100mm clockwork; cross-sectional area; 0.40m²	Nr	0.18	18.80	-	0.54	19.34	*2.36*

U6 Artificial Stone Blockwork

		Unit	Labour Hours	Labour Net £	Plant Net £	Materials Net £	Unit Net £	CO_2 Kg
U6.1	**Thickness: not exceeding: 150mm**							
U6.1.1	vertical straight walls							
U6.1.1.01	Cast stonework; Bradstone walling blocks; Cotswold shades, random course in cement lime mortar (1:2:9); traditional walling; flush pointing, as the work proceeds; 100mm thick	m²	0.36	37.17	-	38.69	75.86	*13.09*
U6.1.2	vertical curved walls							
U6.1.2.01	Cast stonework; Bradstone walling blocks; Cotswold shades, random course in cement lime mortar (1:2:9); traditional walling; flush pointing, as the work proceeds; 100mm thick; curved walls; 5m mean radius	m²	0.62	64.74	-	38.69	103.43	*13.09*
U6.1.2.02	as above; curved walls; 10m mean radius	m²	0.91	95.02	-	77.89	172.91	*26.48*

U6 Artificial Stone Blockwork continued...

		Unit	Labour Hours	Labour Net £	Plant Net £	Materials Net £	Unit Net £	CO_2 Kg
U6.1	**Thickness: not exceeding: 150mm**							
U6.1.5	Vertical facing to concrete							
U6.1.5.01	Cast stonework; Bradstone walling blocks; Cotswold shades, random course in cement lime mortar (1:2:9); traditional walling; flush pointing, as the work proceeds; 100mm thick; facing to concrete; building in 4nr fish tailed ties/m^2; casting into concrete	m^2	0.56	58.48	-	39.19	97.67	*13.39*
U6.7	**Surface features**							
U6.7.2	Rebates and chases							
U6.7.2.01	Cast stonework; Bradstone walling blocks; Cotswold shades, random course in cement lime mortar (1:2:9); traditional walling; flush pointing, as the work proceeds; Forming fair rebate 25 x 10mm deep	m	0.11	10.96	-	-	10.96	-
U6.7.4	Band courses							
U6.7.4.01	Cast stonework; Bradstone walling blocks; Cotswold shades, random course in cement lime mortar (1:2:9); traditional walling; flush pointing, as the work proceeds; Projecting band set forward 25mm from wall face; one course wide; flush pointing one side a	m	0.05	5.43	-	-	5.43	-
U6.7.6	Pilasters							
U6.7.6.01	Cast stonework; Bradstone walling blocks; Cotswold shades, random course in cement lime mortar (1:2:9); traditional walling; flush pointing, as the work proceeds; Pilaster attached to wall face; 300 x 110mm; flush pointing all faces	m	0.05	5.43	-	11.59	17.02	*3.83*
U6.7.6.02	as above; Pilaster attached to wall face; 600 x 220mm; flush pointing all faces	m	0.26	27.36	-	46.13	73.49	*14.38*
U6.7.7	Plinths							
U6.7.7.01	Cast stonework; Bradstone walling blocks; Cotswold shades, random course in cement lime mortar (1:2:9); traditional walling; flush pointing, as the work proceeds; Plinth 100mm thick; set forward 25mm from wall face; 450mm high; flush pointing face and top	m	0.13	13.16	-	-	13.16	-
U6.7.7.02	as above; Plinth 100mm thick; set forward 25mm from wall face; 900mm high; flush pointing face and top of projection	m	0.27	27.78	-	-	27.78	-

U6 Artificial Stone Blockwork continued...

		Unit	Labour Hours	Labour Net £	Plant Net £	Materials Net £	Unit Net £	CO_2 Kg
U6.8	**Ancillaries**							
U6.8.1	Joint reinforcement							
U6.8.1.01	Exmet galvanised brick reinforcement; 24 gauge; horizontal; 100mm wide	m	0.04	4.39	-	1.03	**5.42**	*2.82*
U6.8.1.02	as above; 225mm wide	m	0.05	5.49	-	2.06	**7.55**	*5.64*
U6.8.1.03	as above; 305mm wide	m	0.06	6.59	-	3.09	**9.68**	*8.46*
U6.8.1.04	as above; 450mm wide	m	0.07	7.69	-	4.12	**11.81**	*11.28*
U6.8.1.05	as above; 900mm wide	m	0.14	15.37	-	8.24	**23.61**	*22.56*
U6.8.2	Damp proof courses							
U6.8.2.01	Bitumen damp proof course to, BS 743, Table 1; 100mm laps in cement mortar (1:3); pointing where exposed; Hessian based; reference 'A'; horizontal; 115mm wide	m	0.01	1.32	-	1.30	**2.62**	*4.75*
U6.8.2.02	as above; 225mm wide	m	0.01	2.20	-	2.60	**4.80**	*9.51*
U6.8.2.03	as above; 330mm wide	m	0.02	4.39	-	3.90	**8.29**	*14.26*
U6.8.2.04	as above; 450mm wide	m	0.02	6.04	-	5.21	**11.25**	*19.02*
U6.8.2.05	as above; 900mm wide	m	0.05	7.14	-	10.41	**17.55**	*38.04*
U6.8.2.06	Bitumen damp proof course to, BS 743, Table 1; 100mm laps in cement mortar (1:3); pointing where exposed; Hessian based; reference 'A'; vertical; 115mm wide	m	0.01	1.65	-	1.30	**2.95**	*4.75*
U6.8.2.07	as above; 225mm wide	m	0.02	2.42	-	2.60	**5.02**	*9.51*
U6.8.2.08	as above; 330mm wide	m	0.04	4.94	-	3.90	**8.84**	*14.26*
U6.8.2.09	as above; 450mm wide	m	0.05	6.59	-	5.21	**11.80**	*19.02*
U6.8.2.10	as above; 900mm wide	m	0.10	7.69	-	10.41	**18.10**	*38.04*
U6.8.2.11	Bitumen damp proof course to, BS 743, Table 1; 100mm laps in cement mortar (1:3); pointing where exposed; Fibre based; reference 'B'; horizontal; 115mm wide	m	0.01	0.66	-	1.00	**1.66**	*4.75*
U6.8.2.12	as above; 225mm wide	m	0.01	1.32	-	2.00	**3.32**	*9.51*
U6.8.2.13	as above; 330mm wide	m	0.02	1.98	-	3.00	**4.98**	*14.26*
U6.8.2.14	as above; 450mm wide	m	0.02	2.63	-	4.01	**6.64**	*19.02*
U6.8.2.15	as above; 900mm wide	m	0.05	5.27	-	8.01	**13.28**	*38.04*

U6 Artificial Stone Blockwork continued...

		Unit	Labour Hours	Labour Net £	Plant Net £	Materials Net £	Unit Net £	CO_2 Kg
U6.8	**Ancillaries**							
U6.8.2	Damp proof courses							
U6.8.2.16	Bitumen damp proof course to, BS 743, Table 1; 100mm laps in cement mortar (1:3); pointing where exposed; Fibre based; reference 'B'; vertical; 115mm wide	m	0.01	1.32	-	1.00	2.32	*4.75*
U6.8.2.17	as above; 225mm wide	m	0.02	2.63	-	2.00	4.63	*9.51*
U6.8.2.18	as above; 330mm wide	m	0.04	3.95	-	3.00	6.95	*14.26*
U6.8.2.19	as above; 450mm wide	m	0.05	5.27	-	4.01	9.28	*19.02*
U6.8.2.20	as above; 900mm wide	m	0.10	10.54	-	8.01	18.55	*38.04*
U6.8.2.21	Hyload pitch polymer damp proof course; 100mm laps, sealed with Hyload contact adhesive; in cement mortar (1:3); pointing where exposed; Horizontal; 115mm wide	m	0.01	0.66	-	1.31	1.97	*4.75*
U6.8.2.22	as above; 225mm wide	m	0.01	1.32	-	2.62	3.94	*9.51*
U6.8.2.23	as above; 330mm wide	m	0.02	1.98	-	3.93	5.91	*14.26*
U6.8.2.24	as above; 450mm wide	m	0.02	2.63	-	5.25	7.88	*19.02*
U6.8.2.25	as above; 900mm wide	m	0.05	5.27	-	10.49	15.76	*38.04*
U6.8.2.26	Hyload pitch polymer damp proof course; 100mm laps, sealed with Hyload contact adhesive; in cement mortar (1:3); pointing where exposed; Vertical; 115mm wide	m	0.01	1.32	-	1.31	2.63	*4.75*
U6.8.2.27	as above; 225mm wide	m	0.02	2.63	-	2.62	5.25	*9.51*
U6.8.2.28	as above; 330mm wide	m	0.04	3.95	-	3.93	7.88	*14.26*
U6.8.2.29	as above; 450mm wide	m	0.05	5.27	-	5.25	10.52	*19.02*
U6.8.2.30	as above; 900mm wide	m	0.10	10.54	-	10.49	21.03	*38.04*
U6.8.3	Movement joints							
U6.8.3.01	Expansion joints; filling with Fillcrete joint filler; 20mm thick expansion joint; vertical; 102.5mm wide	m	0.06	6.92	-	2.23	9.15	*0.12*
U6.8.3.02	as above; 215mm wide	m	0.10	11.42	-	4.47	15.89	*0.24*
U6.8.3.03	as above; 327.5mm wide	m	0.17	18.33	-	6.70	25.03	*0.36*
U6.8.3.04	as above; 440mm wide	m	0.25	27.56	-	8.93	36.49	*0.49*
U6.8.3.05	as above; 890mm wide	m	0.42	46.11	-	17.87	63.98	*0.97*

U6 Artificial Stone Blockwork continued...

		Unit	Labour Hours	Labour Net £	Plant Net £	Materials Net £	Unit Net £	CO_2 Kg
U6.8	**Ancillaries**							
U6.8.4	Bonds to existing work							
U6.8.4.01	Cast stonework; Bradstone walling blocks; Cotswold shades, random course in cement lime mortar (1:2:9); traditional walling; flush pointing, as the work proceeds; Bonding 100mm cast stone to existing 100mm cast stone; cutting and toothing alternate course	m^2	0.10	10.44	-	0.49	10.93	*0.58*
U6.8.5	Infills of stated thickness							
U6.8.5.01	Concrete infill; Grade 25, 20mm aggregate; 50mm thick	m^2	0.20	21.96	-	4.31	26.27	*15.60*
U6.8.5.02	as above; 100mm thick	m^2	0.30	32.94	-	8.62	41.56	*31.20*
U6.8.5.03	as above; 150mm thick	m^2	0.40	43.92	-	12.93	56.85	*46.80*
U6.8.5.04	as above; 200mm thick	m^2	0.50	54.90	-	17.23	72.13	*62.40*
U6.8.7	Built-in pipes and ducts, cross-sectional area: not exceeding $0.05m^2$							
U6.8.7.01	Cast stonework; Bradstone walling blocks; Cotswold shades, random course in cement lime mortar (1:2:9); traditional walling; flush pointing, as the work proceeds; supply excluded; 100mm cast stone; cross-sectional area; not exceeding $0.025m^2$	Nr	0.09	9.40	-	0.54	9.94	*2.36*
U6.8.7.02	as above; supply excluded; 100mm cast stone; cross-sectional area; 0.025 - $0.25m^2$	Nr	0.15	15.66	-	0.54	16.20	*2.36*
U6.8.7.03	as above; 150mm diameter clay pipe to, BS 65, 100mm cross-sectional area; not exceeding $0.025m^2$	Nr	0.13	13.57	-	0.54	14.11	*2.36*
U6.8.8	Built-in pipes and ducts, cross-sectional area: exceeding $0.05m^2$							
U6.8.8.01	Cast stonework; Bradstone walling blocks; Cotswold shades, random course in cement lime mortar (1:2:9); traditional walling; flush pointing, as the work proceeds; Built-in pipes and ducts (supply excluded); 100mm cast stone; cross-sectional area; $0.40m^2$	Nr	0.18	18.80	-	0.54	19.34	*2.36*

U7 Ashlar Masonry

Note(s): The following Specialist prices are for natural stonework labour and materials fixed in position and should be regarded as indicative. The prices allow for the stone to be delivered in full loads within 60 miles of the stone masons depot.

		Unit	Labour Hours	Labour Net £	Plant Net £	Materials Net £	Unit Net £	CO_2 *Kg*
U7.1	**Thickness: not exceeding: 150mm**							
U7.1.1	vertical straight walls							
U7.1.1.01	Natural stonework; Portland Whitbed with one exposed face in cement lime putty (2:5:7) with crushed stone dust; smooth finish; flush pointing one side as the work proceeds; 75mm thick	m^2	0.95	104.30	8.19	36.95	149.44	*23.18*
U7.1.1.02	as above; 100mm thick	m^2	1.25	137.24	10.77	47.20	195.21	*25.50*
U7.1.1.03	as above; 150mm thick	m^2	1.50	164.69	12.93	67.70	245.32	*28.38*
U7.1.2	vertical curved walls							
U7.1.2.01	Natural stonework; Portland Whitbed with one exposed face in cement lime putty (2:5:7) with crushed stone dust; smooth finish; flush pointing one side as the work proceeds; 75mm thick; curved walls; 5m mean radius	m^2	1.75	192.13	15.08	36.95	244.16	*27.22*
U7.1.2.02	as above; curved walls; 10m mean radius	m^2	1.45	159.20	12.50	36.95	208.65	*25.70*
U7.1.2.03	Natural stonework; Portland Whitbed with one exposed face in cement lime putty (2:5:7) with crushed stone dust; smooth finish; flush pointing one side as the work proceeds; 100mm thick; curved walls; 5m mean radius	m^2	2.00	219.58	17.24	47.20	284.02	*29.28*
U7.1.2.04	as above; curved walls; 10m mean radius	m^2	1.75	192.13	15.08	47.20	254.41	*28.02*
U7.1.2.05	Natural stonework; Portland Whitbed with one exposed face in cement lime putty (2:5:7) with crushed stone dust; smooth finish; flush pointing one side as the work proceeds; 150mm thick; curved walls; 5m mean radius	m^2	2.50	274.48	21.55	67.70	363.73	*33.42*
U7.1.2.06	as above; curved walls; 10m mean radius	m^2	2.00	219.58	17.24	67.70	304.52	*30.90*
U7.1.5	vertical facing to concrete							
U7.1.5.01	Natural stonework; Portland Whitbed with one exposed face in cement lime putty (2:5:7) with crushed stone dust; smooth finish; flush pointing one side as the work proceeds; 75mm thick; facing to concrete; building in 4nr fish tailed ties/m^2; casting into concrete (by others)	m^2	1.50	164.69	-	36.95	201.64	*18.40*
U7.1.5.02	as above; 100mm thick; facing to concrete; building in 4nr fish tailed ties/m^2; casting into concrete (by others)	m^2	1.75	192.13	-	47.20	239.33	*19.21*

U7 Ashlar Masonry continued...

		Unit	Labour Hours	Labour Net £	Plant Net £	Materials Net £	Unit Net £	CO_2 Kg
U7.1	**Thickness: not exceeding: 150mm**							
U7.1.5	vertical facing to concrete							
U7.1.5.03	as previous item; 150mm thick; facing to concrete; building in 4nr fish tailed ties/m²; casting into concrete (by others)	m^2	2.00	219.58	-	67.70	**287.28**	*20.82*
U7.2	**Thickness: 150 - 250mm**							
U7.2.1	vertical straight walls							
U7.2.1.01	Natural stonework; Portland Whitbed with one exposed face in cement lime putty (2:5:7) with crushed stone dust; smooth finish; flush pointing one side as the work proceeds; 200mm thick	m^2	2.00	219.58	12.93	88.20	**320.71**	*29.99*
U7.2.2	vertical curved walls							
U7.2.2.01	Natural stonework; Portland Whitbed with one exposed face in cement lime putty (2:5:7) with crushed stone dust; smooth finish; flush pointing one side as the work proceeds; 200mm thick; curved walls; 5m mean radius	m^2	3.00	329.37	25.86	88.20	**443.43**	*37.55*
U7.2.2.02	as above; curved walls; 10m mean radius	m^2	2.50	274.48	21.55	88.20	**384.23**	*35.03*
U7.2.5	vertical facing to concrete							
U7.2.5.01	Natural stonework; Portland Whitbed with one exposed face in cement lime putty (2:5:7) with crushed stone dust; smooth finish; flush pointing one side as the work proceeds; 200mm thick; facing to concrete; building in 4nr fish tailed ties/m²; casting into concrete (by others)	m^2	2.00	219.58	17.24	88.20	**325.02**	*32.51*
U7.6	**Columns and piers of stated cross-sectional dimensions**							
U7.6.1	300 x 300mm							
U7.6.1.01	Natural stonework; Portland Whitbed with one exposed face in cement lime putty (2:5:7) with crushed stone dust; smooth finish; flush pointing one side as the work proceeds	m	2.00	219.58	17.24	43.10	**279.92**	*28.96*
U7.6.2	450 x 300mm							
U7.6.2.01	Natural stonework; Portland Whitbed with one exposed face in cement lime putty (2:5:7) with crushed stone dust; smooth finish; flush pointing one side as the work proceeds	m	2.50	274.48	21.55	61.55	**357.58**	*32.93*

U7 Ashlar Masonry continued...

		Unit	Labour Hours	Labour Net £	Plant Net £	Materials Net £	Unit Net £	CO_2 Kg
U7.6	**Columns and piers of stated cross-sectional dimensions**							
U7.6.3	450 x 450mm							
U7.6.3.01	Natural stonework; Portland Whitbed with one exposed face in cement lime putty (2:5:7) with crushed stone dust; smooth finish; flush pointing one side as the work proceeds	m	4.00	439.16	34.48	89.43	**563.07**	*42.68*
U7.6.4	900 x 900mm							
U7.6.4.01	Natural stonework; Portland Whitbed with one exposed face in cement lime putty (2:5:7) with crushed stone dust; smooth finish; flush pointing one side as the work proceeds	m	8.00	878.32	68.96	338.30	**1,285.58**	*82.44*
U7.7	**Surface features**							
U7.7.2	Rebates and chases							
U7.7.2.01	Natural stonework; Portland Whitbed with one exposed face in cement lime putty (2:5:7) with crushed stone dust; smooth finish; flush pointing one side as the work proceeds; Forming fair rebate 25 x 10mm deep	m	0.15	16.47	1.29	-	**17.76**	*0.76*
U7.7.4	Band courses							
U7.7.4.01	Natural stonework; Portland Whitbed with one exposed face in cement lime putty (2:5:7) with crushed stone dust; smooth finish; flush pointing one side as the work proceeds; Projecting band set forward 25mm from wall face; one course wide; flush pointing one side as the work proceeds	m	0.20	21.96	1.72	7.84	**31.52**	*17.11*
U7.7.6	Pilasters							
U7.7.6.01	Natural stonework; Portland Whitbed with one exposed face in cement lime putty (2:5:7) with crushed stone dust; smooth finish; flush pointing one side as the work proceeds; Pilaster attached to wall face; 300 x 110mm; flush pointing all faces	m	0.75	82.34	6.46	19.73	**108.53**	*20.82*
U7.7.6.02	as above; Pilaster attached to wall face; 600 x 220mm; flush pointing all faces	m	1.00	109.79	8.62	60.32	**178.73**	*25.28*
U7.7.7	Plinths							
U7.7.7.01	Natural stonework; Portland Whitbed with one exposed face in cement lime putty (2:5:7) with crushed stone dust; smooth finish; flush pointing one side as the work proceeds; Plinth 100mm thick; set forward 25mm from wall face; 450mm high; flush pointing faces	m	1.00	109.79	8.62	24.65	**143.06**	*22.47*

U7 Ashlar Masonry continued...

		Unit	Labour Hours	Labour Net £	Plant Net £	Materials Net £	Unit Net £	CO_2 Kg
U7.7	**Surface features**							
U7.7.7	Plinths							
U7.7.7.02	as previous item; Plinth 100mm thick; set forward 25mm from wall face; 900mm high; flush pointing face and top of projection	m	2.00	219.58	17.24	43.10	**279.92**	*28.96*
U7.8	**Ancillaries**							
U7.8.1	Joint reinforcement							
U7.8.1.01	Exmet galvanised brick reinforcement; 24 gauge; horizontal; 100mm wide	m	0.04	4.39	-	1.03	**5.42**	*2.82*
U7.8.1.02	as above; 225mm wide	m	0.05	5.49	-	2.06	**7.55**	*5.64*
U7.8.1.03	as above; 305mm wide	m	0.06	6.59	-	3.09	**9.68**	*8.46*
U7.8.1.04	as above; 450mm wide	m	0.07	7.69	-	4.12	**11.81**	*11.28*
U7.8.1.05	as above; 900mm wide	m	0.14	15.37	-	8.24	**23.61**	*22.56*
U7.8.2	Damp proof courses							
U7.8.2.01	Bitumen damp proof course to, BS 743, Table 1; 100mm laps in cement mortar (1:3); pointing where exposed; Hessian based; reference 'A'; horizontal; 115mm wide	m	0.01	1.32	-	1.30	**2.62**	*4.75*
U7.8.2.02	as above; 225mm wide	m	0.01	2.20	-	2.60	**4.80**	*9.51*
U7.8.2.03	as above; 330mm wide	m	0.02	4.39	-	3.90	**8.29**	*14.26*
U7.8.2.04	as above; 450mm wide	m	0.02	6.04	-	5.21	**11.25**	*19.02*
U7.8.2.05	as above; 900mm wide	m	0.05	7.14	-	10.41	**17.55**	*38.04*
U7.8.2.06	Bitumen damp proof course to, BS 743, Table 1; 100mm laps in cement mortar (1:3); pointing where exposed; Hessian based; reference 'A'; vertical; 115mm wide	m	0.01	1.65	-	1.30	**2.95**	*4.75*
U7.8.2.07	as above; 225mm wide	m	0.02	2.42	-	2.60	**5.02**	*9.51*
U7.8.2.08	as above; 330mm wide	m	0.04	4.94	-	3.90	**8.84**	*14.26*
U7.8.2.09	as above; 450mm wide	m	0.05	6.59	-	5.21	**11.80**	*19.02*
U7.8.2.10	as above; 900mm wide	m	0.10	7.69	-	10.41	**18.10**	*38.04*
U7.8.2.11	Bitumen damp proof course to, BS 743, Table 1; 100mm laps in cement mortar (1:3); pointing where exposed; Fibre based; reference 'B'; horizontal; 115mm wide	m	0.01	0.66	-	1.00	**1.66**	*4.75*
U7.8.2.12	as above; 225mm wide	m	0.01	1.32	-	2.00	**3.32**	*9.51*
U7.8.2.13	as above; 330mm wide	m	0.02	1.98	-	3.00	**4.98**	*14.26*
U7.8.2.14	as above; 450mm wide	m	0.02	2.63	-	4.01	**6.64**	*19.02*

U7 Ashlar Masonry continued...

		Unit	Labour Hours	Labour Net £	Plant Net £	Materials Net £	Unit Net £	CO_2 Kg
U7.8	**Ancillaries**							
U7.8.2	Damp proof courses							
U7.8.2.15	as previous item; 900mm wide	m	0.05	5.27	-	8.01	**13.28**	*38.04*
U7.8.2.16	Bitumen damp proof course to, BS 743, Table 1; 100mm laps in cement mortar (1:3); pointing where exposed; Fibre based; reference 'B'; vertical; 115mm wide	m	0.01	1.32	-	1.00	**2.32**	*4.75*
U7.8.2.17	as above; 225mm wide	m	0.02	2.63	-	2.00	**4.63**	*9.51*
U7.8.2.18	as above; 330mm wide	m	0.04	3.95	-	3.00	**6.95**	*14.26*
U7.8.2.19	as above; 450mm wide	m	0.05	5.27	-	4.01	**9.28**	*19.02*
U7.8.2.20	as above; 900mm wide	m	0.10	10.54	-	8.01	**18.55**	*38.04*
U7.8.2.21	Hyload pitch polymer damp proof course; 100mm laps, sealed with Hyload contact adhesive; in cement mortar (1:3); pointing where exposed; Horizontal; 115mm wide	m	0.01	0.66	-	1.31	**1.97**	*4.75*
U7.8.2.22	as above; 225mm wide	m	0.01	1.32	-	2.62	**3.94**	*9.51*
U7.8.2.23	as above; 330mm wide	m	0.02	1.98	-	3.93	**5.91**	*14.26*
U7.8.2.24	as above; 450mm wide	m	0.02	2.63	-	5.25	**7.88**	*19.02*
U7.8.2.25	as above; 900mm wide	m	0.05	5.27	-	10.49	**15.76**	*38.04*
U7.8.2.26	Hyload pitch polymer damp proof course; 100mm laps, sealed with Hyload contact adhesive; in cement mortar (1:3); pointing where exposed; Vertical; 115mm wide	m	0.01	1.32	-	1.31	**2.63**	*4.75*
U7.8.2.27	as above; 225mm wide	m	0.02	2.63	-	2.62	**5.25**	*9.51*
U7.8.2.28	as above; 330mm wide	m	0.04	3.95	-	3.93	**7.88**	*14.26*
U7.8.2.29	as above; 450mm wide	m	0.05	5.27	-	5.25	**10.52**	*19.02*
U7.8.2.30	as above; 900mm wide	m	0.10	10.54	-	10.49	**21.03**	*38.04*
U7.8.3	Movement joints							
U7.8.3.01	Expansion joints; filling with Fillcrete joint filler; 20mm thick expansion joint; vertical; 102.5mm wide	m	0.06	6.92	-	2.23	**9.15**	*0.12*
U7.8.3.02	as above; 215mm wide	m	0.10	11.42	-	4.47	**15.89**	*0.24*
U7.8.3.03	as above; 327.5mm wide	m	0.17	18.33	-	6.70	**25.03**	*0.36*
U7.8.3.04	as above; 440mm wide	m	0.25	27.56	-	8.93	**36.49**	*0.49*
U7.8.3.05	as above; 890mm wide	m	0.42	46.11	-	17.87	**63.98**	*0.97*

U7 Ashlar Masonry continued...

		Unit	Labour Hours	Labour Net £	Plant Net £	Materials Net £	Unit Net £	CO_2 Kg
U7.8	**Ancillaries**							
U7.8.4	Bonds to existing work							
U7.8.4.01	Bonding 75mm natural stonework to existing 200mm natural stonework; cutting and toothing alternate courses	m^2	0.33	36.56	2.87	-	39.43	*1.68*
U7.8.4.02	Bonding 100mm natural stonework to existing 200mm natural stonework; cutting and toothing alternate courses	m^2	0.33	36.56	2.87	-	39.43	*1.68*
U7.8.5	Infills of stated thickness							
U7.8.5.01	Concrete infill; Grade 25, 20mm aggregate; 50mm thick	m^2	0.20	21.96	-	4.31	26.27	*15.60*
U7.8.5.02	as above; 100mm thick	m^2	0.30	32.94	-	8.62	41.56	*31.20*
U7.8.5.03	as above; 150mm thick	m^2	0.40	43.92	-	12.93	56.85	*46.80*
U7.8.5.04	as above; 200mm thick	m^2	0.50	54.90	-	17.23	72.13	*62.40*
U7.8.7	Built-in pipes and ducts, cross-sectional area: not exceeding $0.05m^2$							
U7.8.7.01	Natural stonework; Portland Whitbed with one exposed face in cement lime putty (2:5:7) with crushed stone dust; smooth finish; flush pointing one side as the work proceeds; supply excluded; 75mm natural stonework; cross-sectional area; not exceeding $0.025m^2$	Nr	0.17	18.33	1.44	-	19.77	*0.84*
U7.8.7.02	as above; supply excluded; 75mm natural stonework; cross-sectional area; 0.025 - $0.25m^2$	Nr	0.17	18.33	1.44	-	19.77	*0.84*
U7.8.7.03	as above; 150mm diameter clay pipe to, BS 65, 75mm natural stonework; cross-sectional area; not exceeding $0.025m^2$	Nr	0.17	18.33	1.44	-	19.77	*0.84*
U7.8.8	Built-in pipes and ducts, cross-sectional area: exceeding $0.05m^2$							
U7.8.8.01	Natural stonework; Portland Whitbed with one exposed face in cement lime putty (2:5:7) with crushed stone dust; smooth finish; flush pointing one side as the work proceeds; supply excluded; 75mm natural stonework; cross-sectional area; $0.40m^2$	Nr	0.17	18.33	1.44	-	19.77	*0.84*

U8 Rubble Masonry

U8.2	**Thickness: 150 - 250mm**							
U8.2.5	vertical facing to concrete							
U8.2.5.01	Cotswold limestone, Farmington stone quarry uncoursed random rubble walling 100 - 200mm high with natural exposed faces; in cement lime mortar (1:2:9); facing and recessed pointing as the work							

U8 Rubble Masonry continued...

		Unit	Labour Hours	Labour Net £	Plant Net £	Materials Net £	Unit Net £	CO_2 Kg
U8.3	**Thickness: 250 - 500mm**							
U8.3.1	vertical straight walls							
U8.3.1.01	Cotswold limestone, Farmington stone quarry uncoursed random rubble walling 50 - 100mm high with natural exposed faces; laid dry; facing both sides; 375mm thick	m^2	0.57	59.00	-	163.34	**222.34**	*1,373.40*
U8.3.1.02	as above; 412mm thick	m^2	0.62	64.95	-	179.48	**244.43**	*1,509.11*
U8.3.1.03	as above; 450mm thick	m^2	0.68	70.80	-	196.01	**266.81**	*1,648.08*
U8.3.1.04	Cotswold limestone, Farmington stone quarry uncoursed random rubble walling 100 - 200mm high with natural exposed faces; in cement lime mortar (1:2:9); facing and recessed pointing as the work proceeds; 450mm thick	m^2	0.67	70.38	-	78.68	**149.06**	*747.55*
U8.3.1.05	as above; 500mm thick	m^2	0.73	76.44	-	87.66	**164.10**	*831.66*
U8.3.2	vertical curved walls							
U8.3.2.01	Cotswold limestone, Farmington stone quarry uncoursed random rubble walling 50 - 100mm high with natural exposed faces; laid dry; facing both sides; 375mm thick; curved walls; 5m mean radius	m^2	1.08	112.67	-	163.34	**276.01**	*1,373.40*
U8.3.2.02	as above; curved walls; 10m mean radius	m^2	0.85	88.44	-	163.34	**251.78**	*1,373.40*
U8.3.2.03	Cotswold limestone, Farmington stone quarry uncoursed random rubble walling 50 - 100mm high with natural exposed faces; laid dry; facing both sides; 412mm thick; curved walls; 5m mean radius	m^2	1.21	125.83	-	179.48	**305.31**	*1,509.11*
U8.3.2.04	as above; curved walls; 10m mean radius	m^2	0.93	97.22	-	179.48	**276.70**	*1,509.11*
U8.3.2.05	Cotswold limestone, Farmington stone quarry uncoursed random rubble walling 50 - 100mm high with natural exposed faces; laid dry; facing both sides; 450mm thick; curved walls; 5m mean radius	m^2	0.72	74.76	-	87.50	**162.26**	*735.75*
U8.3.2.06	as above; curved walls; 10m mean radius	m^2	0.74	77.38	-	87.50	**164.88**	*735.75*
U8.3.2.07	Cotswold limestone, Farmington stone quarry uncoursed random rubble walling 100 - 200mm high with natural exposed faces; in cement lime mortar (1:2:9); facing and recessed pointing as the work proceeds; 450mm thick; curved walls; 5m mean radius	m^2	0.83	86.36	-	78.68	**165.04**	*747.55*
U8.3.2.08	as above; curved walls; 10m mean radius	m^2	1.01	104.94	-	78.68	**183.62**	*747.55*

U8 Rubble Masonry continued...

		Unit	Labour Hours	Labour Net £	Plant Net £	Materials Net £	Unit Net £	CO_2 Kg
U8.3	**Thickness: 250 - 500mm**							
U8.3.2	vertical curved walls							
U8.3.2.09	Cotswold limestone, Farmington stone quarry uncoursed random rubble walling 100 - 200mm high with natural exposed faces; in cement lime mortar (1:2:9); facing and recessed pointing as the work proceeds; 500mm thick; curved walls; 5m mean radius	m^2	0.91	95.02	-	87.66	**182.68**	*831.66*
U8.3.2.10	as above; curved walls; 10m mean radius	m^2	1.11	115.38	-	87.66	**203.04**	*831.66*
U8.3.3	battered straight walls							
U8.3.3.01	Cotswold limestone, Farmington stone quarry uncoursed random rubble walling 50 - 100mm high with natural exposed faces; laid dry; facing both sides; 375mm thick; battered walls; one face battered at an angle of 1:20	m^2	0.60	62.23	-	163.34	**225.57**	*1,373.40*
U8.3.3.02	as above; battered walls; both faces battered at an angle of 1:20	m^2	0.62	64.43	-	163.34	**227.77**	*1,373.40*
U8.3.3.03	Cotswold limestone, Farmington stone quarry uncoursed random rubble walling 50 - 100mm high with natural exposed faces; laid dry; facing both sides; 412mm thick; battered walls; one face battered at an angle of 1:20	m^2	0.66	68.40	-	179.48	**247.88**	*1,509.11*
U8.3.3.04	as above; battered walls; both faces battered at an angle of 1:20	m^2	0.68	70.80	-	179.48	**250.28**	*1,509.11*
U8.3.3.05	Cotswold limestone, Farmington stone quarry uncoursed random rubble walling 50 - 100mm high with natural exposed faces; laid dry; facing both sides; 450mm thick; battered walls; one face battered at an angle of 1:20	m^2	1.30	135.33	-	87.50	**222.83**	*735.75*
U8.3.3.06	as above; battered walls; both faces battered at an angle of 1:20	m^2	1.02	106.20	-	87.50	**193.70**	*735.75*
U8.3.3.07	Cotswold limestone, Farmington stone quarry uncoursed random rubble walling 100 - 200mm high with natural exposed faces; in cement lime mortar (1:2:9); facing and recessed pointing as the work proceeds; 450mm thick; battered walls; one face battered at angle of 1:20	m^2	1.17	122.38	-	78.68	**201.06**	*747.55*
U8.3.3.08	as above; battered walls; both faces battered at an angle of 1:20	m^2	1.00	104.84	-	78.68	**183.52**	*747.55*

U8 Rubble Masonry continued...

		Unit	Labour Hours	Labour Net £	Plant Net £	Materials Net £	Unit Net £	CO_2 Kg
U8.3	**Thickness: 250 - 500mm**							
U8.3.3	battered straight walls							
U8.3.3.09	Cotswold limestone, Farmington stone quarry uncoursed random rubble walling 100 - 200mm high with natural exposed faces; in cement lime mortar (1:2:9); facing and recessed pointing as the work proceeds; 500mm thick; battered walls; one face battered at angle of 1:20	m^2	1.28	133.66	-	87.66	**221.32**	*831.66*
U8.3.3.10	as above; battered walls; both faces battered at an angle of 1:20	m^2	1.10	114.65	-	87.66	**202.31**	*831.66*
U8.4	**Thickness: 500mm - 1m**							
U8.4.1	vertical straight walls							
U8.4.1.01	Cotswold limestone, Farmington stone quarry uncoursed random rubble walling 100 - 200mm high with natural exposed faces; in cement lime mortar (1:2:9); facing and recessed pointing as the work proceeds; facing and recessed pointing as the work proceeds; 600mm thick	m^2	0.86	89.59	-	105.09	**194.68**	*997.52*
U8.4.2	vertical curved walls							
U8.4.2.01	Cotswold limestone, Farmington stone quarry uncoursed random rubble walling 100 - 200mm high with natural exposed faces; in cement lime mortar (1:2:9); facing and recessed pointing as the work proceeds; facing and recessed pointing as the work proceeds; 600mm thick; 5m mean radius	m^2	1.04	108.18	-	105.09	**213.27**	*997.52*
U8.4.2.02	as above; curved walls; 10m mean radius	m^2	1.23	128.54	-	105.09	**233.63**	*997.52*
U8.4.3	battered straight walls							
U8.4.3.01	Cotswold limestone, Farmington stone quarry uncoursed random rubble walling 100 - 200mm high with natural exposed faces; in cement lime mortar (1:2:9); facing and recessed pointing as the work proceeds; facing and recessed pointing as the work proceeds; 600mm thick	m^2	1.41	146.81	-	105.09	**251.90**	*997.52*
U8.4.3.02	as above; battered walls; both faces battered at an angle of 1:20	m^2	1.24	128.96	-	105.09	**234.05**	*997.52*

U8 Rubble Masonry continued...

		Unit	Labour Hours	Labour Net £	Plant Net £	Materials Net £	Unit Net £	CO_2 Kg
U8.7	**Surface features**							
U8.7.2	Rebates and chases							
U8.7.2.01	Cotswold limestone, Farmington stone quarry uncoursed random rubble walling 50 - 100mm high with natural exposed faces; laid dry; facing both sides; Forming fair rebate 25 x 10mm deep	m	0.13	13.05	-	-	**13.05**	-
U8.7.2.02	Cotswold limestone, Farmington stone quarry uncoursed random rubble walling 100 - 200mm high with natural exposed faces; in cement lime mortar (1:2:9); facing and recessed pointing as the work proceeds; Forming fair rebate 25 x 10mm deep	m	0.13	13.05	-	-	**13.05**	-
U8.7.4	Band courses							
U8.7.4.01	Cotswold limestone, Farmington stone quarry uncoursed random rubble walling 50 - 100mm high with natural exposed faces; laid dry; facing both sides; Projecting band set forward 25mm from wall face; one course wide; flush pointing one side and top and bottom of projection	m	0.06	6.58	-	-	**6.58**	-
U8.7.4.02	Cotswold limestone, Farmington stone quarry uncoursed random rubble walling 100 - 200mm high with natural exposed faces; in cement lime mortar (1:2:9); facing and recessed pointing as the work proceeds; Projecting band set forward 25mm from wall face; one course wide; flush pointing one side and top and bottom of projection	m	0.06	6.58	-	-	**6.58**	-
U8.7.6	Pilasters							
U8.7.6.01	Cotswold limestone, Farmington stone quarry uncoursed random rubble walling 50 - 100mm high with natural exposed faces; laid dry; facing both sides; Pilaster attached to wall face; 600 x 200mm; recessed pointing all faces	m	0.17	17.44	-	23.87	**41.31**	*198.56*
U8.7.6.02	as above; Pilaster attached to wall face; 900 x 300mm	m	0.29	30.60	-	53.04	**83.64**	*443.81*
U8.7.6.03	Cotswold limestone, Farmington stone quarry uncoursed random rubble walling 100 - 200mm high with natural exposed faces; in cement lime mortar (1:2:9); facing and recessed pointing as the work proceeds; Pilaster attached to wall face; 600 x 200mm; recessed pointing all faces	m	0.17	17.44	-	20.80	**38.24**	*198.56*
U8.7.6.04	as above; Pilaster attached to wall face; 900 x 300mm; recessed pointing all faces	m	0.29	30.60	-	46.67	**77.27**	*446.17*

U8 Rubble Masonry continued...

		Unit	Labour Hours	Labour Net £	Plant Net £	Materials Net £	Unit Net £	CO_2 Kg
U8.7	**Surface features**							
U8.7.7	Plinths							
U8.7.7.01	Cotswold limestone, Farmington stone quarry uncoursed random rubble walling 50 - 100mm high with natural exposed faces; laid dry; facing both sides; Plinth one course thick; set forward 25mm from wall face; 450mm high	m	0.17	17.44	-	-	**17.44**	-
U8.7.7.02	as above; Plinth one course thick; set forward 25mm from wall face; 900mm high	m	0.33	34.46	-	-	**34.46**	-
U8.7.7.03	Cotswold limestone, Farmington stone quarry uncoursed random rubble walling 100 - 200mm high with natural exposed faces; in cement lime mortar (1:2:9); facing and recessed pointing as the work proceeds; Plinth one course thick; set forward 25mm from wall	m	0.17	17.44	-	-	**17.44**	-
U8.7.7.04	as above; Plinth one course thick; set forward 25mm from wall face; 900mm high; recessed pointing face and top of projection	m	0.33	34.46	-	-	**34.46**	-
U8.8	**Ancillaries**							
U8.8.1	Joint reinforcement							
U8.8.1.01	Exmet galvanised brick reinforcement; 24 gauge; horizontal; 100mm wide	m	0.04	4.39	-	1.03	**5.42**	*2.82*
U8.8.1.02	as above; 225mm wide	m	0.05	5.49	-	2.06	**7.55**	*5.64*
U8.8.1.03	as above; 305mm wide	m	0.06	6.59	-	3.09	**9.68**	*8.46*
U8.8.1.04	as above; 450mm wide	m	0.07	7.69	-	4.12	**11.81**	*11.28*
U8.8.1.05	as above; 900mm wide	m	0.14	15.37	-	8.24	**23.61**	*22.56*
U8.8.2	Damp proof courses							
U8.8.2.01	Bitumen damp proof course to, BS 743, Table 1; 100mm laps in cement mortar (1:3); pointing where exposed; Hessian based; reference 'A'; horizontal; 115mm wide	m	0.01	1.32	-	1.30	**2.62**	*4.75*
U8.8.2.02	as above; 225mm wide	m	0.01	2.20	-	2.60	**4.80**	*9.51*
U8.8.2.03	as above; 330mm wide	m	0.02	4.39	-	3.90	**8.29**	*14.26*
U8.8.2.04	as above; 450mm wide	m	0.02	6.04	-	5.21	**11.25**	*19.02*
U8.8.2.05	as above; 900mm wide	m	0.05	7.14	-	10.41	**17.55**	*38.04*
U8.8.2.06	Bitumen damp proof course to, BS 743, Table 1; 100mm laps in cement mortar (1:3); pointing where exposed; Hessian based; reference 'A'; vertical; 115mm wide	m	0.01	1.65	-	1.30	**2.95**	*4.75*

U8 Rubble Masonry continued...

		Unit	Labour Hours	Labour Net £	Plant Net £	Materials Net £	Unit Net £	CO_2 Kg
U8.8	**Ancillaries**							
U8.8.2	Damp proof courses							
U8.8.2.07	as previous item; 225mm wide	m	0.02	2.42	-	2.60	**5.02**	*9.51*
U8.8.2.08	as above; 330mm wide	m	0.04	4.94	-	3.90	**8.84**	*14.26*
U8.8.2.09	as above; 450mm wide	m	0.05	6.59	-	5.21	**11.80**	*19.02*
U8.8.2.10	as above; 900mm wide	m	0.10	7.69	-	10.41	**18.10**	*38.04*
U8.8.2.11	Bitumen damp proof course to, BS 743, Table 1; 100mm laps in cement mortar (1:3); pointing where exposed; Fibre based; reference 'B'; horizontal; 115mm wide	m	0.01	0.66	-	1.00	**1.66**	*4.75*
U8.8.2.12	as above; 225mm wide	m	0.01	1.32	-	2.00	**3.32**	*9.51*
U8.8.2.13	as above; 330mm wide	m	0.02	1.98	-	3.00	**4.98**	*14.26*
U8.8.2.14	as above; 450mm wide	m	0.02	2.63	-	4.01	**6.64**	*19.02*
U8.8.2.15	as above; 900mm wide	m	0.05	5.27	-	8.01	**13.28**	*38.04*
U8.8.2.16	Bitumen damp proof course to, BS 743, Table 1; 100mm laps in cement mortar (1:3); pointing where exposed; Fibre based; reference 'B'; vertical; 115mm wide	m	0.01	1.32	-	1.00	**2.32**	*4.75*
U8.8.2.17	as above; 225mm wide	m	0.02	2.63	-	2.00	**4.63**	*9.51*
U8.8.2.18	as above; 330mm wide	m	0.04	3.95	-	3.00	**6.95**	*14.26*
U8.8.2.19	as above; 450mm wide	m	0.05	5.27	-	4.01	**9.28**	*19.02*
U8.8.2.20	as above; 900mm wide	m	0.10	10.54	-	8.01	**18.55**	*38.04*
U8.8.2.21	Hyload pitch polymer damp proof course; 100mm laps, sealed with Hyload contact adhesive; in cement mortar (1:3); pointing where exposed; Horizontal; 115mm wide	m	0.01	0.66	-	1.31	**1.97**	*4.75*
U8.8.2.22	as above; 225mm wide	m	0.01	1.32	-	2.62	**3.94**	*9.51*
U8.8.2.23	as above; 330mm wide	m	0.02	1.98	-	3.93	**5.91**	*14.26*
U8.8.2.24	as above; 450mm wide	m	0.02	2.63	-	5.25	**7.88**	*19.02*
U8.8.2.25	as above; 900mm wide	m	0.05	5.27	-	10.49	**15.76**	*38.04*
U8.8.2.26	Hyload pitch polymer damp proof course; 100mm laps, sealed with Hyload contact adhesive; in cement mortar (1:3); pointing where exposed; Vertical; 115mm wide	m	0.01	1.32	-	1.31	**2.63**	*4.75*
U8.8.2.27	as above; 225mm wide	m	0.02	2.63	-	2.62	**5.25**	*9.51*
U8.8.2.28	as above; 330mm wide	m	0.04	3.95	-	3.93	**7.88**	*14.26*

U8 Rubble Masonry continued...

		Unit	Labour Hours	Labour Net £	Plant Net £	Materials Net £	Unit Net £	CO_2 Kg
U8.8	**Ancillaries**							
U8.8.2	Damp proof courses							
U8.8.2.29	as previous item; 450mm wide	m	0.05	5.27	-	5.25	**10.52**	*19.02*
U8.8.2.30	as above; 900mm wide	m	0.10	10.54	-	10.49	**21.03**	*38.04*
U8.8.3	Movement joints							
U8.8.3.01	Expansion joints; filling with Fillcrete joint filler; 20mm thick expansion joint; vertical; 102.5mm wide	m	0.06	6.92	-	2.23	**9.15**	*0.12*
U8.8.3.02	as above; 215mm wide	m	0.10	11.42	-	4.47	**15.89**	*0.24*
U8.8.3.03	as above; 327.5mm wide	m	0.17	18.33	-	6.70	**25.03**	*0.36*
U8.8.3.04	as above; 440mm wide	m	0.25	27.56	-	8.93	**36.49**	*0.49*
U8.8.3.05	as above; 890mm wide	m	0.42	46.11	-	17.87	**63.98**	*0.97*
U8.8.4	Bonds to existing work							
U8.8.4.01	Cotswold limestone, Farmington stone quarry uncoursed random rubble walling 50 - 100mm high with natural exposed faces; laid dry; facing both sides; bonding 450mm rubble masonry to existing 450mm rubble masonry; cutting and toothing alternate courses	m^2	0.13	13.05	-	2.05	**15.10**	*16.82*
U8.8.4.02	as above; bonding 500mm rubble masonry to existing 500mm rubble masonry; cutting and toothing alternate courses	m^2	0.17	17.44	-	2.11	**19.55**	*17.06*
U8.8.4.03	Cotswold limestone, Farmington stone quarry uncoursed random rubble walling 100 - 200mm high with natural exposed faces; in cement lime mortar (1:2:9); facing and recessed pointing as the work proceeds; bonding 450mm rubble masonry to existing 450mm rubble masonry; cutting and toothing alternate courses	m^2	0.13	13.05	-	1.80	**14.85**	*16.82*
U8.8.4.04	as above; bonding 500mm rubble masonry to existing 500mm rubble masonry; cutting and toothing alternate courses	m^2	0.17	17.44	-	1.85	**19.29**	*17.06*
U8.8.5	Infills of stated thickness							
U8.8.5.01	Concrete infill; Grade 25, 20mm aggregate; 50mm thick	m^2	0.20	21.96	-	4.31	**26.27**	*15.60*
U8.8.5.02	as above; 100mm thick	m^2	0.30	32.94	-	8.62	**41.56**	*31.20*
U8.8.5.03	as above; 150mm thick	m^2	0.40	43.92	-	12.93	**56.85**	*46.80*
U8.8.5.04	as above; 200mm thick	m^2	0.50	54.90	-	17.23	**72.13**	*62.40*

U8 Rubble Masonry continued...

		Unit	Labour Hours	Labour Net £	Plant Net £	Materials Net £	Unit Net £	CO_2 Kg
U8.8	**Ancillaries**							
U8.8.7	Built-in pipes and ducts, cross-sectional area: not exceeding $0.05m^2$							
U8.8.7.01	Cotswold limestone, Farmington stone quarry uncoursed random rubble walling 50 - 100mm high with natural exposed faces; laid dry; facing both sides; supply excluded; 450mm rubble masonry; cross-sectional area; not exceeding $0.025m^2$	Nr	0.21	22.24	-	0.27	**22.51**	*1.18*
U8.8.7.02	as above; 150mm diameter clay pipe to, BS 65, 450mm rubble masonry; cross-sectional area; not exceeding $0.025m^2$	Nr	0.19	19.63	-	0.54	**20.17**	*2.36*
U8.8.7.03	Cotswold limestone, Farmington stone quarry uncoursed random rubble walling 100 - 200mm high with natural exposed faces; in cement lime mortar (1:2:9); facing and recessed pointing as the work proceeds; supply excluded; 450mm rubble masonry; cross-sectional area not exceeding $0.025m^2$	Nr	0.17	17.44	-	0.54	**17.98**	*2.36*
U8.8.7.04	as above; 150mm diameter clay pipe to, BS 65, 450mm rubble masonry; cross-sectional area; not exceeding $0.025m^2$	Nr	0.19	19.63	-	0.54	**20.17**	*2.36*
U8.8.8	Built-in pipes and ducts, cross-sectional area: exceeding $0.05m^2$							
U8.8.8.01	Cotswold limestone, Farmington stone quarry uncoursed random rubble walling 50 - 100mm high with natural exposed faces; laid dry; facing both sides; supply excluded; 450mm rubble masonry; cross-sectional area; 0.025 - $0.25m^2$	Nr	0.21	22.24	-	0.27	**22.51**	*1.18*
U8.8.8.02	as above; cross-sectional area; $0.40m^2$	Nr	0.29	30.60	-	0.32	**30.92**	*1.42*
U8.8.8.03	Cotswold limestone, Farmington stone quarry uncoursed random rubble walling 100 - 200mm high with natural exposed faces; in cement lime mortar (1:2:9); facing and recessed pointing as the work proceeds; supply excluded; 450mm rubble masonry; cross-sectional area; 0.025 - $0.25m^2$	Nr	0.21	22.24	-	0.54	**22.78**	*2.36*
U8.8.8.04	as above; cross-sectional area: $0.40m^2$	Nr	0.29	30.60	-	0.54	**31.14**	*2.36*

CLASS V:
PAINTING

Calculations used throughout Class V - Painting

Labour

		Qty		Rate		Total
L A0310ICE	**Painting Labour Gang**					
	Painter (chargehand)	1	x	17.93	=	£17.93
	Painter	2	x	16.68	=	£33.37
	Brush hand (labourer)	1	x	12.56	=	£12.56
	Total hourly cost of gang				**=**	**£63.86**

Class V - Painting

Note(s): 1) Labour rates are based on free access to the work. No allowance has been made for scaffolding or time required to gain access to the work. The rates include an element of normal clean up time.

2) All the rates shown are based on hand work; where spray painting is justified, that is where large areas have to be covered, the cost per metre can be substantially reduced. The following table shows gang hours to paint various surfaces one coat using one gun and non-lead paint.

Surface	Area Covered m^2/litre	Area m^2/hour	Gang Hours /m^2
Concrete	10	30	0.033
Brickwork	10	30	0.033
Plasterer	14	35	0.028
Metal (smooth)	19	40	0.025
Wood (planed)	16	38	0.026

3) Priming coats or first coats include the cost of labour in preparing surfaces.

V1 Lead, Iron or Zinc Based Primer Paint

		Unit	Labour Hours	Labour Net £	Plant Net £	Materials Net £	Unit Net £	CO_2 *Kg*
VI.I	**Metal, other than metal sections and pipework**							
VI.I.I	Upper surfaces inclined at an angle not exceeding 30 degrees to the horizontal							
VI.I.I.01	Lead substitute primer paint	m^2	0.08	4.98	-	0.99	5.97	*0.36*
VI.I.I.02	Lead substitute primer paint; moderately rusted surfaces, wire brushed	m^2	0.12	7.47	-	1.48	8.95	*0.53*
VI.I.I.03	Lead substitute primer paint; heavily rusted surfaces, wire brushed	m^2	0.14	9.13	-	2.96	12.09	*1.07*
VI.I.I.04	Iron based primer paint	m^2	0.08	4.79	-	0.41	5.20	*0.36*
VI.I.I.05	Zinc rich primer paint	m^2	0.08	4.79	-	0.54	5.33	*0.36*
VI.I.2	Upper surfaces inclined at 30 - 60 degrees to the horizontal							
VI.I.2.01	Lead substitute primer paint	m^2	0.08	4.98	-	0.99	5.97	*0.36*
VI.I.2.02	Lead substitute primer paint; moderately rusted surfaces, wire brushed	m^2	0.13	8.30	-	1.48	9.78	*0.53*
VI.I.2.03	Lead substitute primer paint; heavily rusted surfaces, wire brushed	m^2	0.15	9.52	-	2.96	12.48	*1.07*
VI.I.2.04	Iron based primer paint	m^2	0.08	4.98	-	0.41	5.39	*0.36*
VI.I.2.05	Zinc rich primer paint	m^2	0.08	4.98	-	0.54	5.52	*0.36*

V1 Lead, Iron or Zinc Based Primer Paint continued...

		Unit	Labour Hours	Labour Net £	Plant Net £	Materials Net £	Unit Net £	CO_2 Kg
V1.1	**Metal, other than metal sections and pipework**							
V1.1.3	Surfaces inclined at an angle exceeding 60 degrees to the horizontal							
V1.1.3.01	Lead substitute primer paint	m^2	0.08	5.11	-	0.99	6.10	*0.36*
V1.1.3.02	Lead substitute primer paint; moderately rusted surfaces, wire brushed	m^2	0.15	9.58	-	1.48	11.06	*0.53*
V1.1.3.03	Lead substitute primer paint; heavily rusted surfaces, wire brushed	m^2	0.16	9.96	-	2.96	12.92	*1.07*
V1.1.3.04	Iron based primer paint	m^2	0.08	5.11	-	0.41	5.52	*0.36*
V1.1.3.05	Zinc rich primer paint	m^2	0.08	5.11	-	0.54	5.65	*0.36*
V1.1.4	Soffit surfaces and lower surfaces inclined at an angle not exceeding 60 degrees to the horizontal							
V1.1.4.01	Lead substitute primer paint	m^2	0.10	6.39	-	0.99	7.38	*0.36*
V1.1.4.02	Lead substitute primer paint; moderately rusted surfaces, wire brushed	m^2	0.17	10.86	-	1.48	12.34	*0.53*
V1.1.4.03	Lead substitute primer paint; heavily rusted surfaces, wire brushed	m^2	0.19	12.20	-	2.96	15.16	*1.07*
V1.1.4.04	Iron based primer paint	m^2	0.10	6.39	-	0.41	6.80	*0.36*
V1.1.4.05	Zinc rich primer paint	m^2	0.10	6.39	-	0.54	6.93	*0.36*
V1.1.6	Surfaces of width not exceeding 300mm							
V1.1.6.01	Lead substitute primer paint	m	0.03	1.60	-	0.30	1.90	*0.11*
V1.1.6.02	Lead substitute primer paint; moderately rusted surfaces, wire brushed	m	0.07	4.53	-	0.49	5.02	*0.18*
V1.1.6.03	Lead substitute primer paint; heavily rusted surfaces, wire brushed	m	0.05	3.07	-	0.99	4.06	*0.36*
V1.1.6.04	Iron based primer paint	m	0.03	1.60	-	0.12	1.72	*0.11*
V1.1.6.05	Zinc rich primer paint	m	0.03	1.60	-	0.16	1.76	*0.11*
V1.1.7	Surfaces of width 300mm - 1m							
V1.1.7.01	Lead substitute primer paint	m	0.04	2.43	-	0.49	2.92	*0.18*
V1.1.7.02	Lead substitute primer paint; moderately rusted surfaces, wire brushed	m	0.06	3.64	-	0.69	4.33	*0.25*
V1.1.7.03	Lead substitute primer paint; heavily rusted surfaces, wire brushed	m	0.07	4.53	-	1.48	6.01	*0.53*
V1.1.7.04	Iron based primer paint	m	0.04	2.43	-	0.20	2.63	*0.18*
V1.1.7.05	Zinc rich primer paint	m	0.04	2.43	-	0.41	2.84	*0.27*
V1.1.8	Isolated groups of surfaces							
V1.1.8.01	Lead substitute primer paint; 500 x 300mm inspection covers and frames in wall; painting one side	Nr	0.15	9.58	-	1.97	11.55	*0.71*
V1.1.8.02	Lead substitute primer paint; moderately rusted surfaces, wire brushed; 500 x 300mm inspection covers and frames in wall; painting one side	Nr	0.17	10.98	-	2.96	13.94	*1.07*
V1.1.8.03	Lead substitute primer paint; heavily rusted surfaces, wire brushed; 500 x 300mm inspection covers and frames in wall; painting one side	Nr	0.29	18.52	-	5.92	24.44	*2.14*
V1.1.8.04	Iron based primer paint; 500 x 300mm inspection covers and frames in wall; painting one side	Nr	0.15	9.58	-	0.81	10.39	*0.71*
V1.1.8.05	Zinc rich primer paint; 500 x 300mm inspection covers and frames in wall; painting one side	Nr	0.15	9.58	-	0.54	10.12	*0.36*

V1 Lead, Iron or Zinc Based Primer Paint continued...

		Unit	Labour Hours	Labour Net £	Plant Net £	Materials Net £	Unit Net £	CO_2 Kg
V1.2	**Timber**							
V1.2.1	Upper surfaces inclined at an angle not exceeding 30 degrees to the horizontal							
V1.2.1.01	Wood primer; planed timber	m^2	0.08	4.79	-	0.61	5.40	*0.36*
V1.2.2	Upper surfaces inclined at 30 - 60 degrees to the horizontal							
V1.2.2.01	Wood primer; planed timber	m^2	0.08	4.98	-	0.61	5.59	*0.36*
V1.2.3	Surfaces inclined at an angle exceeding 60 degrees to the horizontal							
V1.2.3.01	Wood primer; planed timber	m^2	0.08	5.11	-	0.61	5.72	*0.36*
V1.2.4	Soffit surfaces and lower surfaces inclined at an angle not exceeding 60 degrees to the horizontal							
V1.2.4.01	Wood primer; planed timber	m^2	0.10	6.39	-	0.61	7.00	*0.36*
V1.2.6	Surfaces of width not exceeding 300mm							
V1.2.6.01	Wood primer; planed timber	m	0.03	1.60	-	0.18	1.78	*0.11*
V1.2.7	Surfaces of width 300mm - 1m							
V1.2.7.01	Wood primer; planed timber	m	0.04	2.43	-	0.30	2.73	*0.18*
V1.2.8	Isolated groups of surfaces							
V1.2.8.01	Wood primer; planed timber; 300 x 200mm hatch and frame in wall; painting one side	Nr	0.15	9.58	-	1.22	10.80	*0.71*
V1.3	**Smooth concrete**							
V1.3.1	Upper surfaces inclined at an angle not exceeding 30 degrees to the horizontal							
V1.3.1.01	Masonry sealer; Unprimed smooth concrete	m^2	0.08	4.79	-	0.95	5.74	*0.61*
V1.3.2	Upper surfaces inclined at 30 - 60 degrees to the horizontal							
V1.3.2.01	Masonry sealer; Unprimed smooth concrete	m^2	0.08	4.92	-	0.95	5.87	*0.61*
V1.3.3	Surfaces inclined at an angle exceeding 60 degrees to the horizontal							
V1.3.3.01	Masonry sealer; Unprimed smooth concrete	m^2	0.08	5.24	-	0.95	6.19	*0.61*
V1.3.4	Soffit surfaces and lower surfaces inclined at an angle not exceeding 60 degrees to the horizontal							
V1.3.4.01	Masonry sealer; Unprimed smooth concrete	m^2	0.10	6.39	-	0.95	7.34	*0.61*
V1.3.6	Surfaces of width not exceeding 300mm							
V1.3.6.01	Masonry sealer; Unprimed smooth concrete	m	0.03	1.60	-	0.34	1.94	*0.21*
V1.3.7	Surfaces of width 300mm - 1m							
V1.3.7.01	Masonry sealer; Unprimed smooth concrete	m	0.04	2.36	-	0.67	3.03	*0.43*
V1.3.8	Isolated groups of surfaces							
V1.3.8.01	Masonry sealer; Unprimed smooth concrete; stepped and splayed plinth overall size 450 x 450 x 450mm; painting all faces	Nr	0.15	9.58	-	1.91	11.49	*1.21*

V1 Lead, Iron or Zinc Based Primer Paint continued...

		Unit	Labour Hours	Labour Net £	Plant Net £	Materials Net £	Unit Net £	CO_2 Kg
V1.4	**Rough concrete**							
V1.4.1	Upper surfaces inclined at an angle not exceeding 30 degrees to the horizontal							
V1.4.1.01	Masonry sealer; unprimed rough concrete; sawn board finish	m^2	0.08	5.24	-	1.07	6.31	*0.68*
V1.4.2	Upper surfaces inclined at 30 - 60 degrees to the horizontal							
V1.4.2.01	Masonry sealer; unprimed rough concrete; sawn board finish	m^2	0.09	5.43	-	1.07	6.50	*0.68*
V1.4.3	Surfaces inclined at an angle exceeding 60 degrees to the horizontal							
V1.4.3.01	Masonry sealer; unprimed rough concrete; sawn board finish	m^2	0.09	5.75	-	1.07	6.82	*0.68*
V1.4.4	Soffit surfaces and lower surfaces inclined at an angle not exceeding 60 degrees to the horizontal							
V1.4.4.01	Masonry sealer; unprimed rough concrete; sawn board finish	m^2	0.11	7.02	-	1.07	8.09	*0.68*
V1.4.6	Surfaces of width not exceeding 300mm							
V1.4.6.01	Masonry sealer; unprimed rough concrete; sawn board finish	m	0.03	1.72	-	0.34	2.06	*0.21*
V1.4.7	Surfaces of width 300mm - 1m							
V1.4.7.01	Masonry sealer; unprimed rough concrete; sawn board finish	m	0.04	2.55	-	0.67	3.22	*0.43*
V1.4.8	Isolated groups of surfaces							
V1.4.8.01	Masonry sealer; unprimed rough concrete; sawn board finish; stepped and splayed plinth overall size 450 x 450 x 450mm; painting all faces	Nr	0.17	10.54	-	2.13	12.67	*1.35*
V1.5	**Masonry**							
V1.5.1	Upper surfaces inclined at an angle not exceeding 30 degrees to the horizontal							
V1.5.1.01	Masonry sealer; unprimed masonry	m^2	0.08	5.24	-	1.07	6.31	*0.68*
V1.5.2	Upper surfaces inclined at 30 - 60 degrees to the horizontal							
V1.5.2.01	Masonry sealer; unprimed masonry	m^2	0.09	5.43	-	1.07	6.50	*0.68*
V1.5.3	Surfaces inclined at an angle exceeding 60 degrees to the horizontal							
V1.5.3.01	Masonry sealer; unprimed masonry	m^2	0.09	5.75	-	1.07	6.82	*0.68*
V1.5.4	Soffit surfaces and lower surfaces inclined at an angle not exceeding 60 degrees to the horizontal							
V1.5.4.01	Masonry sealer; unprimed masonry	m^2	0.11	7.02	-	1.07	8.09	*0.68*
V1.5.6	Surfaces of width not exceeding 300mm							
V1.5.6.01	Masonry sealer; unprimed masonry	m	0.03	1.72	-	0.34	2.06	*0.21*
V1.5.7	Surfaces of width 300mm - 1m							
V1.5.7.01	Masonry sealer; unprimed masonry	m	0.04	2.55	-	0.67	3.22	*0.43*
V1.5.8	Isolated groups of surfaces							
V1.5.8.01	Masonry sealer; unprimed masonry; stepped and splayed plinth overall size 450 x 450 x 450mm; painting all faces	Nr	0.17	10.54	-	2.13	12.67	*1.35*

V1 Lead, Iron or Zinc Based Primer Paint continued...

		Unit	Labour Hours	Labour Net £	Plant Net £	Materials Net £	Unit Net £	CO_2 Kg
V1.6	**Brickwork and blockwork**							
V1.6.1	Upper surfaces inclined at an angle not exceeding 30 degrees to the horizontal							
V1.6.1.01	Masonry sealer; unprimed brickwork and blockwork	m^2	0.09	5.75	-	1.23	6.98	*0.78*
V1.6.2	Upper surfaces inclined at 30 - 60 degrees to the horizontal							
V1.6.2.01	Masonry sealer; unprimed brickwork and blockwork	m^2	0.10	6.07	-	1.23	7.30	*0.78*
V1.6.3	Surfaces inclined at an angle exceeding 60 degrees to the horizontal							
V1.6.3.01	Masonry sealer; unprimed brickwork and blockwork	m^2	0.10	6.39	-	1.23	7.62	*0.78*
V1.6.4	Soffit surfaces and lower surfaces inclined at an angle not exceeding 60 degrees to the horizontal							
V1.6.4.01	Masonry sealer; unprimed brickwork and blockwork	m^2	0.12	7.66	-	1.23	8.89	*0.78*
V1.6.6	Surfaces of width not exceeding 300mm							
V1.6.6.01	Masonry sealer; unprimed brickwork and blockwork	m	0.03	1.92	-	0.39	2.31	*0.25*
V1.6.7	Surfaces of width 300mm - 1m							
V1.6.7.01	Masonry sealer; unprimed brickwork and blockwork	m	0.05	2.87	-	0.62	3.49	*0.39*
V1.6.8	Isolated groups of surfaces							
V1.6.8.01	Masonry sealer; unprimed brickwork and blockwork; stepped and splayed plinth overall size 450 x 450 x 450mm; painting all faces	Nr	0.18	11.49	-	2.47	13.96	*1.57*
V1.7	**Metal sections**							
V1.7.1	Generally							
V1.7.1.01	Lead substitute primer paint	m^2	0.10	6.39	-	0.99	7.38	*0.36*
V1.7.1.02	Lead substitute primer paint; moderately rusted surfaces, wire brushed	m^2	0.12	7.60	-	1.48	9.08	*0.53*
V1.7.1.03	Lead substitute primer paint; heavily rusted surfaces, wire brushed	m^2	0.15	9.71	-	2.96	12.67	*1.07*
V1.7.1.04	Iron based primer paint	m^2	0.10	6.39	-	0.41	6.80	*0.36*
V1.7.1.05	Zinc rich primer paint	m^2	0.08	4.79	-	0.54	5.33	*0.36*
V1.8	**Pipework**							
V1.8.1	Generally							
V1.8.1.01	Lead substitute primer paint	m^2	0.10	6.39	-	0.99	7.38	*0.36*
V1.8.1.02	Lead substitute primer paint; moderately rusted surfaces, wire brushed	m^2	0.12	7.60	-	1.48	9.08	*0.53*
V1.8.1.03	Lead substitute primer paint; heavily rusted surfaces, wire brushed	m^2	0.15	9.71	-	2.96	12.67	*1.07*
V1.8.1.04	Iron based primer paint	m^2	0.10	6.39	-	0.41	6.80	*0.36*

V2 Etch Primer Paint

		Unit	Labour Hours	Labour Net £	Plant Net £	Materials Net £	Unit Net £	CO_2 Kg
V2.1	**Metal, other than metal sections and pipework**							
V2.1.1	Upper surfaces inclined at an angle not exceeding 30 degrees to the horizontal							
V2.1.1.01	Zinc coated or aluminium surfaces	m^2	0.08	4.79	-	1.06	5.85	*0.53*

V2 Etch Primer Paint continued...

		Unit	Labour Hours	Labour Net £	Plant Net £	Materials Net £	Unit Net £	CO_2 Kg
V2.1	**Metal, other than metal sections and pipework**							
V2.1.2	Upper surfaces inclined at 30 - 60 degrees to the horizontal							
V2.1.2.01	Zinc coated or aluminium surfaces	m^2	0.08	4.98	-	1.06	**6.04**	*0.53*
V2.1.3	Surfaces inclined at an angle exceeding 60 degrees to the horizontal							
V2.1.3.01	Zinc coated or aluminium surfaces	m^2	0.08	5.11	-	1.06	**6.17**	*0.53*
V2.1.4	Soffit surfaces and lower surfaces inclined at an angle not exceeding 60 degrees to the horizontal							
V2.1.4.01	Zinc coated or aluminium surfaces	m^2	0.10	6.39	-	1.06	**7.45**	*0.53*
V2.1.6	Surfaces of width not exceeding 300mm							
V2.1.6.01	Zinc coated or aluminium surfaces	m	0.03	1.60	-	0.35	**1.95**	*0.18*
V2.1.7	Surfaces of width 300mm - 1m							
V2.1.7.01	Zinc coated or aluminium surfaces	m	0.04	2.43	-	0.50	**2.93**	*0.25*
V2.1.8	Isolated groups of surfaces							
V2.1.8.01	Zinc coated or aluminium surfaces; 300 x 200mm access hatch and frame in wall; painting one side	Nr	0.15	9.58	-	0.21	**9.79**	*0.11*
V2.7	**Metal sections**							
V2.7.1	Generally							
V2.7.1.01	Zinc coated or aluminium surfaces	m^2	0.08	5.24	-	1.06	**6.30**	*0.53*
V2.8	**Pipework**							
V2.8.1	Generally							
V2.8.1.01	Zinc coated or aluminium surfaces	m^2	0.08	5.24	-	1.06	**6.30**	*0.53*

V3 Oil Paint

		Unit	Labour Hours	Labour Net £	Plant Net £	Materials Net £	Unit Net £	CO_2 Kg
V3.1	**Metal, other than metal sections and pipework**							
V3.1.1	Upper surfaces inclined at an angle not exceeding 30 degrees to the horizontal							
V3.1.1.01	in three coats; primed metal	m^2	0.09	5.56	-	2.00	**7.56**	*1.00*
V3.1.2	Upper surfaces inclined at 30 - 60 degrees to the horizontal							
V3.1.2.01	in three coats; primed metal	m^2	0.09	5.75	-	2.00	**7.75**	*1.00*
V3.1.3	Surfaces inclined at an angle exceeding 60 degrees to the horizontal							
V3.1.3.01	in three coats; primed metal	m^2	0.10	6.07	-	2.00	**8.07**	*1.00*
V3.1.4	Soffit surfaces and lower surfaces inclined at an angle not exceeding 60 degrees to the horizontal							
V3.1.4.01	in three coats; primed metal	m^2	0.12	7.47	-	2.00	**9.47**	*1.00*
V3.1.6	Surfaces of width not exceeding 300mm							
V3.1.6.01	in three coats; primed metal	m	0.03	1.92	-	0.64	**2.56**	*0.32*
V3.1.7	Surfaces of width 300mm - 1m							
V3.1.7.01	in three coats; primed metal	m	0.04	2.68	-	1.29	**3.97**	*0.64*
V3.1.8	Isolated groups of surfaces							
V3.1.8.01	in three coats; primed metal; 300 x 200mm access hatch and frame in wall; painting one side	Nr	0.18	11.49	-	4.01	**15.50**	*1.99*

V3 Oil Paint continued...

		Unit	Labour Hours	Labour Net £	Plant Net £	Materials Net £	Unit Net £	CO_2 Kg
V3.2	**Timber**							
V3.2.1	Upper surfaces inclined at an angle not exceeding 30 degrees to the horizontal							
V3.2.1.01	in three coats; planed, primed timber	m^2	0.09	5.56	-	2.00	7.56	*1.00*
V3.2.2	Upper surfaces inclined at 30 - 60 degrees to the horizontal							
V3.2.2.01	in three coats; planed, primed timber	m^2	0.09	5.75	-	2.00	7.75	*1.00*
V3.2.3	Surfaces inclined at an angle exceeding 60 degrees to the horizontal							
V3.2.3.01	in three coats; planed, primed timber	m^2	0.10	6.07	-	2.00	8.07	*1.00*
V3.2.4	Soffit surfaces and lower surfaces inclined at an angle not exceeding 60 degrees to the horizontal							
V3.2.4.01	in three coats; planed, primed timber	m^2	0.12	7.47	-	2.00	9.47	*1.00*
V3.2.6	Surfaces of width not exceeding 300mm							
V3.2.6.01	in three coats; planed, primed timber	m	0.03	1.92	-	0.64	2.56	*0.32*
V3.2.7	Surfaces of width 300mm - 1m							
V3.2.7.01	in three coats; planed, primed timber	m	0.04	2.68	-	1.29	3.97	*0.64*
V3.2.8	Isolated groups of surfaces							
V3.2.8.01	in three coats; planed, primed timber; 300 x 200mm access hatch and frame in wall; painting one side	Nr	0.18	11.49	-	4.01	15.50	*1.99*
V3.7	**Metal sections**							
V3.7.1	Generally							
V3.7.1.01	Oil paint in three coats; planed, primed timber	m^2	0.12	7.47	-	2.00	9.47	*1.00*
V3.8	**Pipework**							
V3.8.1	Generally							
V3.8.1.01	Oil paint in three coats; planed, primed timber	m^2	0.12	7.47	-	2.00	9.47	*1.00*

V4 Alkyd Gloss Paint

		Unit	Labour Hours	Labour Net £	Plant Net £	Materials Net £	Unit Net £	CO_2 Kg
V4.1	**Metal, other than metal sections and pipework**							
V4.1.1	Upper surfaces inclined at an angle not exceeding 30 degrees to the horizontal							
V4.1.1.01	in three coats; primed metal	m^2	0.09	5.56	-	2.00	7.56	*1.00*
V4.1.2	Upper surfaces inclined at 30 - 60 degrees to the horizontal							
V4.1.2.01	in three coats; primed metal	m^2	0.09	5.75	-	2.00	7.75	*1.00*
V4.1.3	Surfaces inclined at an angle exceeding 60 degrees to the horizontal							
V4.1.3.01	in three coats; primed metal	m^2	0.10	6.07	-	2.00	8.07	*1.00*
V4.1.4	Soffit surfaces and lower surfaces inclined at an angle not exceeding 60 degrees to the horizontal							
V4.1.4.01	in three coats; primed metal	m^2	0.12	7.47	-	2.00	9.47	*1.00*
V4.1.6	Surfaces of width not exceeding 300mm							
V4.1.6.01	in three coats; primed metal	m	0.03	1.92	-	0.64	2.56	*0.32*

V4 Alkyd Gloss Paint continued...

		Unit	Labour Hours	Labour Net £	Plant Net £	Materials Net £	Unit Net £	CO_2 Kg
V4.1	**Metal, other than metal sections and pipework**							
V4.1.7	Surfaces of width 300mm - 1m							
V4.1.7.01	in three coats; primed metal	m	0.04	2.68	-	1.29	3.97	*0.64*
V4.1.8	Isolated groups of surfaces							
V4.1.8.01	in three coats; primed metal; 300 x 200mm access hatch and frame in wall; painting one side	Nr	0.18	11.49	-	4.01	15.50	*1.99*
V4.2	**Timber**							
V4.2.1	Upper surfaces inclined at an angle not exceeding 30 degrees to the horizontal							
V4.2.1.01	in three coats; primed timber	m^2	0.09	5.56	-	2.00	7.56	*1.00*
V4.2.2	Upper surfaces inclined at 30 - 60 degrees to the horizontal							
V4.2.2.01	in three coats; primed timber	m^2	0.09	5.75	-	2.00	7.75	*1.00*
V4.2.3	Surfaces inclined at an angle exceeding 60 degrees to the horizontal							
V4.2.3.01	in three coats; primed timber	m^2	0.10	6.07	-	2.00	8.07	*1.00*
V4.2.4	Soffit surfaces and lower surfaces inclined at an angle not exceeding 60 degrees to the horizontal							
V4.2.4.01	in three coats; primed timber	m^2	0.12	7.47	-	2.00	9.47	*1.00*
V4.2.6	Surfaces of width not exceeding 300mm							
V4.2.6.01	in three coats; primed timber	m	0.03	1.92	-	0.64	2.56	*0.32*
V4.2.7	Surfaces of width 300mm - 1m							
V4.2.7.01	in three coats; primed timber	m	0.04	2.68	-	1.29	3.97	*0.64*
V4.2.8	Isolated groups of surfaces							
V4.2.8.01	in three coats; primed timber; 300 x 200mm access hatch and frame in wall; painting one side	Nr	0.18	11.49	-	4.01	15.50	*1.99*
V4.3	**Smooth concrete**							
V4.3.1	Upper surfaces inclined at an angle not exceeding 30 degrees to the horizontal							
V4.3.1.01	one coat sealer; two coats finish	m^2	0.11	7.22	-	1.50	8.72	*0.85*
V4.3.2	Upper surfaces inclined at 30 - 60 degrees to the horizontal							
V4.3.2.01	one coat sealer; two coats finish	m^2	0.12	7.47	-	1.50	8.97	*0.85*
V4.3.3	Surfaces inclined at an angle exceeding 60 degrees to the horizontal							
V4.3.3.01	one coat sealer; two coats finish	m^2	0.12	7.79	-	1.50	9.29	*0.85*
V4.3.4	Soffit surfaces and lower surfaces inclined at an angle not exceeding 60 degrees to the horizontal							
V4.3.4.01	one coat sealer; two coats finish	m^2	0.15	9.39	-	1.50	10.89	*0.85*
V4.3.6	Surfaces of width not exceeding 300mm							
V4.3.6.01	one coat sealer; two coats finish	m	0.04	2.36	-	0.50	2.86	*0.28*
V4.3.7	Surfaces of width 300mm - 1m							
V4.3.7.01	one coat sealer; two coats finish	m	0.06	3.51	-	0.75	4.26	*0.43*
V4.3.8	Isolated groups of surfaces							
V4.3.8.01	one coat sealer; two coats finish; 2000 x 215 x 200mm deep lintel in wall; painting one face and soffit	Nr	0.31	19.92	-	0.90	20.82	*0.61*

V4 Alkyd Gloss Paint continued...

		Unit	Labour Hours	Labour Net £	Plant Net £	Materials Net £	Unit Net £	*CO_2 Kg*
V4.4	**Rough concrete**							
V4.4.1	Upper surfaces inclined at an angle not exceeding 30 degrees to the horizontal							
V4.4.1.01	one coat sealer; two coats finish; sawn board finish	m^2	0.12	7.47	-	1.50	**8.97**	*0.85*
V4.4.2	Upper surfaces inclined at 30 - 60 degrees to the horizontal							
V4.4.2.01	one coat sealer; two coats finish; sawn board finish	m^2	0.12	7.85	-	1.50	**9.35**	*0.85*
V4.4.3	Surfaces inclined at an angle exceeding 60 degrees to the horizontal							
V4.4.3.01	one coat sealer; two coats finish; sawn board finish	m^2	0.13	8.11	-	1.50	**9.61**	*0.85*
V4.4.4	Soffit surfaces and lower surfaces inclined at an angle not exceeding 60 degrees to the horizontal							
V4.4.4.01	one coat sealer; two coats finish; sawn board finish	m^2	0.15	9.39	-	1.50	**10.89**	*0.85*
V4.4.6	Surfaces of width not exceeding 300mm							
V4.4.6.01	one coat sealer; two coats finish; sawn board finish	m	0.04	2.36	-	0.50	**2.86**	*0.28*
V4.4.7	Surfaces of width 300mm - 1m							
V4.4.7.01	one coat sealer; two coats finish; sawn board finish	m	0.06	3.64	-	0.75	**4.39**	*0.43*
V4.4.8	Isolated groups of surfaces							
V4.4.8.01	one coat sealer; two coats finish; sawn board finish; 2000 x 215 x 200mm deep lintel in wall; painting one face and soffit	Nr	0.31	19.99	-	2.12	**22.11**	*1.21*
V4.5	**Masonry**							
V4.5.1	Upper surfaces inclined at an angle not exceeding 30 degrees to the horizontal							
V4.5.1.01	one coat sealer; two coats finish	m^2	0.12	7.47	-	1.50	**8.97**	*0.85*
V4.5.2	Upper surfaces inclined at 30 - 60 degrees to the horizontal							
V4.5.2.01	one coat sealer; two coats finish	m^2	0.12	7.85	-	1.50	**9.35**	*0.85*
V4.5.3	Surfaces inclined at an angle exceeding 60 degrees to the horizontal							
V4.5.3.01	one coat sealer; two coats finish	m^2	0.13	8.11	-	1.50	**9.61**	*0.85*
V4.5.4	Soffit surfaces and lower surfaces inclined at an angle not exceeding 60 degrees to the horizontal							
V4.5.4.01	one coat sealer; two coats finish	m^2	0.15	9.39	-	1.50	**10.89**	*0.85*
V4.5.6	Surfaces of width not exceeding 300mm							
V4.5.6.01	one coat sealer; two coats finish	m	0.04	2.36	-	0.50	**2.86**	*0.28*
V4.5.7	Surfaces of width 300mm - 1m							
V4.5.7.01	one coat sealer; two coats finish	m	0.06	3.64	-	0.75	**4.39**	*0.43*
V4.5.8	Isolated groups of surfaces							
V4.5.8.01	one coat sealer; two coats finish; stepped and spayed plinth overall size 450 x 450 x 450mm; painting all faces	Nr	0.31	19.99	-	0.90	**20.89**	*0.61*
V4.6	**Brickwork and blockwork**							
V4.6.1	Upper surfaces inclined at an angle not exceeding 30 degrees to the horizontal							
V4.6.1.01	one coat sealer; two coats finish	m^2	0.12	7.47	-	1.50	**8.97**	*0.85*

V4 Alkyd Gloss Paint continued...

		Unit	Labour Hours	Labour Net £	Plant Net £	Materials Net £	Unit Net £	CO_2 Kg
V4.6	**Brickwork and blockwork**							
V4.6.2	Upper surfaces inclined at 30 - 60 degrees to the horizontal							
V4.6.2.01	one coat sealer; two coats finish	m^2	0.12	7.85	-	1.50	9.35	*0.85*
V4.6.3	Surfaces inclined at an angle exceeding 60 degrees to the horizontal							
V4.6.3.01	one coat sealer; two coats finish	m^2	0.13	8.11	-	1.50	9.61	*0.85*
V4.6.4	Soffit surfaces and lower surfaces inclined at an angle not exceeding 60 degrees to the horizontal							
V4.6.4.01	one coat sealer; two coats finish	m^2	0.15	9.52	-	1.50	11.02	*0.85*
V4.6.6	Surfaces of width not exceeding 300mm							
V4.6.6.01	one coat sealer; two coats finish	m	0.04	2.36	-	0.50	2.86	*0.28*
V4.6.7	Surfaces of width 300mm - 1m							
V4.6.7.01	one coat sealer; two coats finish	m	0.06	3.64	-	0.75	4.39	*0.43*
V4.6.8	Isolated groups of surfaces							
V4.6.8.01	one coat sealer; two coats finish; stepped and spayed plinth overall size 450 x 450 x 450mm; painting all faces	Nr	0.31	19.99	-	2.12	22.11	*1.21*
V4.7	**Metal sections**							
V4.7.1	Generally							
V4.7.1.01	one coat sealer; two coats finish	m^2	0.09	5.94	-	1.29	7.23	*0.64*
V4.8	**Pipework**							
V4.8.1	Generally							
V4.8.1.01	one coat sealer; two coats finish	m^2	0.09	5.94	-	1.29	7.23	*0.64*

V5 Emulsion Paint

		Unit	Labour Hours	Labour Net £	Plant Net £	Materials Net £	Unit Net £	CO_2 Kg
V5.2	**Timber**							
V5.2.1	Upper surfaces inclined at an angle not exceeding 30 degrees to the horizontal							
V5.2.1.01	in three coats; planed, primed timber	m^2	0.08	5.11	-	0.91	6.02	*0.71*
V5.2.2	Upper surfaces inclined at 30 - 60 degrees to the horizontal							
V5.2.2.01	in three coats; planed, primed timber	m^2	0.08	5.11	-	0.91	6.02	*0.71*
V5.2.3	Surfaces inclined at an angle exceeding 60 degrees to the horizontal							
V5.2.3.01	in three coats; planed, primed timber	m^2	0.08	5.11	-	0.91	6.02	*0.71*
V5.2.4	Soffit surfaces and lower surfaces inclined at an angle not exceeding 60 degrees to the horizontal							
V5.2.4.01	in three coats; planed, primed timber	m^2	0.11	7.02	-	0.91	7.93	*0.71*
V5.2.6	Surfaces of width not exceeding 300mm							
V5.2.6.01	in three coats; planed, primed timber	m	0.02	1.28	-	0.32	1.60	*0.25*
V5.2.7	Surfaces of width 300mm - 1m							
V5.2.7.01	in three coats; planed, primed timber	m	0.03	1.92	-	0.46	2.38	*0.36*

V5 Emulsion Paint continued...

		Unit	Labour Hours	Labour Net £	Plant Net £	Materials Net £	Unit Net £	CO_2 Kg
V5.2	**Timber**							
V5.2.8	Isolated groups of surfaces							
V5.2.8.01	in three coats; planed, primed timber; 300 x 200mm access hatch and frame in wall; painting one side	Nr	0.16	10.22	-	1.82	12.04	*1.42*
V5.3	**Smooth concrete**							
V5.3.1	Upper surfaces inclined at an angle not exceeding 30 degrees to the horizontal							
V5.3.1.01	in three coats; primed smooth concrete	m^2	0.08	5.11	-	0.46	5.57	*0.36*
V5.3.2	Upper surfaces inclined at 30 - 60 degrees to the horizontal							
V5.3.2.01	in three coats; primed smooth concrete	m^2	0.08	5.11	-	0.46	5.57	*0.36*
V5.3.3	Surfaces inclined at an angle exceeding 60 degrees to the horizontal							
V5.3.3.01	in three coats; primed smooth concrete	m^2	0.08	5.11	-	0.46	5.57	*0.36*
V5.3.4	Soffit surfaces and lower surfaces inclined at an angle not exceeding 60 degrees to the horizontal							
V5.3.4.01	in three coats; primed smooth concrete	m^2	0.11	7.02	-	0.46	7.48	*0.36*
V5.3.6	Surfaces of width not exceeding 300mm							
V5.3.6.01	in three coats; primed smooth concrete	m	0.02	1.28	-	0.14	1.42	*0.11*
V5.3.7	Surfaces of width 300mm - 1m							
V5.3.7.01	in three coats; primed smooth concrete	m	0.03	1.92	-	0.23	2.15	*0.18*
V5.3.8	Isolated groups of surfaces							
V5.3.8.01	in three coats; primed smooth concrete; 2000 x 215 x 200mm deep lintel in wall; painting one face and soffit	Nr	0.16	10.22	-	0.68	10.90	*0.53*
V5.6	**Brickwork and blockwork**							
V5.6.1	Upper surfaces inclined at an angle not exceeding 30 degrees to the horizontal							
V5.6.1.01	in three coats	m^2	0.11	6.83	-	0.46	7.29	*0.36*
V5.6.2	Upper surfaces inclined at 30 - 60 degrees to the horizontal							
V5.6.2.01	in three coats	m^2	0.12	7.34	-	0.46	7.80	*0.36*
V5.6.3	Surfaces inclined at an angle exceeding 60 degrees to the horizontal							
V5.6.3.01	in three coats	m^2	0.12	7.47	-	0.46	7.93	*0.36*
V5.6.4	Soffit surfaces and lower surfaces inclined at an angle not exceeding 60 degrees to the horizontal							
V5.6.4.01	in three coats	m^2	0.15	9.58	-	0.55	10.13	*0.43*
V5.6.6	Surfaces of width not exceeding 300mm							
V5.6.6.01	in three coats	m	0.04	2.55	-	0.14	2.69	*0.11*
V5.6.7	Surfaces of width 300mm - 1m							
V5.6.7.01	in three coats	m	0.05	3.19	-	0.27	3.46	*0.21*
V5.6.8	Isolated groups of surfaces							
V5.6.8.01	in three coats; stepped and spayed plinth overall size 450 x 450 x 450mm; painting all faces	Nr	0.22	13.73	-	1.09	14.82	*0.85*

V6 Cement Paint

		Unit	Labour Hours	Labour Net £	Plant Net £	Materials Net £	Unit Net £	CO_2 Kg
V6.3	**Smooth concrete**							
V6.3.1	Upper surfaces inclined at an angle not exceeding 30 degrees to the horizontal							
V6.3.1.01	in three coats	m^2	0.06	3.83	-	0.92	4.75	*0.71*
V6.3.2	Upper surfaces inclined at 30 - 60 degrees to the horizontal							
V6.3.2.01	in three coats	m^2	0.06	3.83	-	0.92	4.75	*0.71*
V6.3.3	Surfaces inclined at an angle exceeding 60 degrees to the horizontal							
V6.3.3.01	in three coats	m^2	0.06	3.83	-	0.92	4.75	*0.71*
V6.3.4	Soffit surfaces and lower surfaces inclined at an angle not exceeding 60 degrees to the horizontal							
V6.3.4.01	in three coats	m^2	0.08	5.11	-	0.92	6.03	*0.71*
V6.3.6	Surfaces of width not exceeding 300mm							
V6.3.6.01	in three coats	m	0.02	1.28	-	3.23	4.51	*2.49*
V6.3.7	Surfaces of width 300mm - 1m							
V6.3.7.01	in three coats	m	0.04	2.55	-	0.46	3.01	*0.36*
V6.3.8	Isolated groups of surfaces							
V6.3.8.01	in three coats; 2000 x 215 x 200mm deep lintel in wall; painting one face and soffit	Nr	0.12	7.66	-	1.85	9.51	*1.42*
V6.4	**Rough concrete**							
V6.4.1	Upper surfaces inclined at an angle not exceeding 30 degrees to the horizontal							
V6.4.1.01	in three coats; primed rough concrete; sawn board finish	m^2	0.08	5.11	-	1.16	6.27	*0.89*
V6.4.2	Upper surfaces inclined at 30 - 60 degrees to the horizontal							
V6.4.2.01	in three coats; primed rough concrete; sawn board finish	m^2	0.08	5.11	-	1.16	6.27	*0.89*
V6.4.3	Surfaces inclined at an angle exceeding 60 degrees to the horizontal							
V6.4.3.01	in three coats; primed rough concrete; sawn board finish	m^2	0.08	5.11	-	1.16	6.27	*0.89*
V6.4.4	Soffit surfaces and lower surfaces inclined at an angle not exceeding 60 degrees to the horizontal							
V6.4.4.01	in three coats; primed rough concrete; sawn board finish	m^2	0.10	6.39	-	1.16	7.55	*0.89*
V6.4.6	Surfaces of width not exceeding 300mm							
V6.4.6.01	in three coats; primed rough concrete; sawn board finish	m	0.03	1.92	-	0.32	2.24	*0.25*
V6.4.7	Surfaces of width 300mm - 1m							
V6.4.7.01	in three coats; primed rough concrete; sawn board finish	m	0.04	2.55	-	0.55	3.10	*0.43*
V6.4.8	Isolated groups of surfaces							
V6.4.8.01	in three coats; primed rough concrete; sawn board finish; 2000 x 215 x 200mm deep lintel in wall; painting one face and soffit	Nr	0.16	10.22	-	2.31	12.53	*1.78*
V6.5	**Masonry**							
V6.5.1	Upper surfaces inclined at an angle not exceeding 30 degrees to the horizontal							
V6.5.1.01	in three coats; primed masonry	m^2	0.08	5.11	-	1.16	6.27	*0.89*
V6.5.2	Upper surfaces inclined at 30 - 60 degrees to the horizontal							
V6.5.2.01	in three coats; primed masonry	m^2	0.08	5.11	-	1.16	6.27	*0.89*

V6 Cement Paint continued...

		Unit	Labour Hours	Labour Net £	Plant Net £	Materials Net £	Unit Net £	CO_2 Kg
V6.5	**Masonry**							
V6.5.3	Surfaces inclined at an angle exceeding 60 degrees to the horizontal							
V6.5.3.01	in three coats; primed masonry	m^2	0.08	5.11	-	1.16	**6.27**	*0.89*
V6.5.4	Soffit surfaces and lower surfaces inclined at an angle not exceeding 60 degrees to the horizontal							
V6.5.4.01	in three coats; primed masonry	m^2	0.10	6.39	-	1.16	**7.55**	*0.89*
V6.5.6	Surfaces of width not exceeding 300mm							
V6.5.6.01	in three coats; primed masonry	m	0.03	1.92	-	0.32	**2.24**	*0.25*
V6.5.7	Surfaces of width 300mm - 1m							
V6.5.7.01	in three coats; primed masonry	m	0.04	2.55	-	0.55	**3.10**	*0.43*
V6.5.8	Isolated groups of surfaces							
V6.5.8.01	in three coats; primed masonry; stepped and spayed plinth overall size 450 x 450 x 450mm; painting all faces	Nr	0.16	10.22	-	2.31	**12.53**	*1.78*
V6.6	**Brickwork and blockwork**							
V6.6.1	Upper surfaces inclined at an angle not exceeding 30 degrees to the horizontal							
V6.6.1.01	in three coats; primed brickwork and blockwork	m^2	0.08	5.30	-	1.39	**6.69**	*1.07*
V6.6.2	Upper surfaces inclined at 30 - 60 degrees to the horizontal							
V6.6.2.01	in three coats; primed brickwork and blockwork	m^2	0.09	5.43	-	1.39	**6.82**	*1.07*
V6.6.3	Surfaces inclined at an angle exceeding 60 degrees to the horizontal							
V6.6.3.01	in three coats; primed brickwork and blockwork	m^2	0.09	5.75	-	1.39	**7.14**	*1.07*
V6.6.4	Soffit surfaces and lower surfaces inclined at an angle not exceeding 60 degrees to the horizontal							
V6.6.4.01	in three coats; primed brickwork and blockwork	m^2	0.11	6.83	-	1.39	**8.22**	*1.07*
V6.6.6	Surfaces of width not exceeding 300mm							
V6.6.6.01	in three coats; primed brickwork and blockwork	m	0.03	1.72	-	0.46	**2.18**	*0.36*
V6.6.7	Surfaces of width 300mm - 1m							
V6.6.7.01	in three coats; primed brickwork and blockwork	m	0.04	2.55	-	0.69	**3.24**	*0.53*
V6.6.8	Isolated groups of surfaces							
V6.6.8.01	in three coats; primed brickwork and blockwork; stepped and spayed plinth overall size 450 x 450 x 450mm; painting all faces	Nr	0.17	10.54	-	1.39	**11.93**	*1.07*

V7 Epoxy or Polyurethane Paint

		Unit	Labour Hours	Labour Net £	Plant Net £	Materials Net £	Unit Net £	CO_2 Kg
V7.2	**Timber**							
V7.2.1	Upper surfaces inclined at an angle not exceeding 30 degrees to the horizontal							
V7.2.1.01	Polyurethane varnish in two coats; planed, primed timber	m^2	0.09	5.75	-	0.96	**6.71**	*0.50*
V7.2.2	Upper surfaces inclined at 30 - 60 degrees to the horizontal							
V7.2.2.01	Polyurethane varnish in two coats; planed, primed timber	m^2	0.09	5.75	-	0.96	**6.71**	*0.50*

V7 Epoxy or Polyurethane Paint continued...

		Unit	Labour Hours	Labour Net £	Plant Net £	Materials Net £	Unit Net £	CO_2 Kg
V7.2	**Timber**							
V7.2.3	Surfaces inclined at an angle exceeding 60 degrees to the horizontal							
V7.2.3.01	Polyurethane varnish in two coats; planed, primed timber	m^2	0.09	5.75	-	0.96	6.71	*0.50*
V7.2.4	Soffit surfaces and lower surfaces inclined at an angle not exceeding 60 degrees to the horizontal							
V7.2.4.01	Polyurethane varnish in two coats; planed, primed timber	m^2	0.12	7.66	-	0.96	8.62	*0.50*
V7.2.6	Surfaces of width not exceeding 300mm							
V7.2.6.01	Polyurethane varnish in two coats; planed, primed timber	m	0.03	1.92	-	0.34	2.26	*0.18*
V7.2.7	Surfaces of width 300mm - 1m							
V7.2.7.01	Polyurethane varnish in two coats; planed, primed timber	m	0.04	2.55	-	0.48	3.03	*0.25*
V7.2.8	Isolated groups of surfaces							
V7.2.8.01	Polyurethane varnish in two coats; planed, primed timber; 300 x 200mm access hatch and frame in wall; painting one side	Nr	0.18	11.49	-	1.93	13.42	*1.00*

V8 Bituminous or Coal Tar Paint

		Unit	Labour Hours	Labour Net £	Plant Net £	Materials Net £	Unit Net £	CO_2 Kg
V8.1	**Metal, other than metal sections and pipework**							
V8.1.1	Upper surfaces inclined at an angle not exceeding 30 degrees to the horizontal							
V8.1.1.01	to BS 3416, in two coats	m^2	0.09	5.75	-	0.62	6.37	*0.71*
V8.1.1.02	to BS 3416, heavy duty; in two coats	m^2	0.14	8.75	-	4.76	13.51	*4.17*
V8.1.2	Upper surfaces inclined at 30 - 60 degrees to the horizontal							
V8.1.2.01	to BS 3416, in two coats	m^2	0.09	5.75	-	0.62	6.37	*0.71*
V8.1.2.02	to BS 3416, heavy duty; in two coats	m^2	0.14	9.13	-	4.76	13.89	*4.17*
V8.1.3	Surfaces inclined at an angle exceeding 60 degrees to the horizontal							
V8.1.3.01	to BS 3416, in two coats	m^2	0.09	5.75	-	0.62	6.37	*0.71*
V8.1.3.02	to BS 3416, heavy duty; in two coats	m^2	0.15	9.58	-	4.76	14.34	*4.17*
V8.1.4	Soffit surfaces and lower surfaces inclined at an angle not exceeding 60 degrees to the horizontal							
V8.1.4.01	to BS 3416, in two coats	m^2	0.12	7.66	-	0.62	8.28	*0.71*
V8.1.4.02	to BS 3416, heavy duty; in two coats	m^2	0.18	11.69	-	4.76	16.45	*4.17*
V8.1.6	Surfaces of width not exceeding 300mm							
V8.1.6.01	to BS 3416, in two coats	m	0.02	1.47	-	0.22	1.69	*0.25*
V8.1.6.02	to BS 3416, heavy duty; in two coats	m	0.05	2.87	-	1.63	4.50	*1.42*
V8.1.7	Surfaces of width 300mm - 1m							
V8.1.7.01	to BS 3416, in two coats	m	0.03	2.11	-	0.47	2.58	*0.53*
V8.1.7.02	to BS 3416, heavy duty; in two coats	m	0.07	4.28	-	2.44	6.72	*2.14*
V8.1.8	Isolated groups of surfaces							
V8.1.8.01	to BS 3416, in two coats; rolled steel joist 2000 x 215 x 200mm deep; painting one face and soffit	Nr	0.18	11.49	-	1.24	12.73	*1.42*

V8 Bituminous or Coal Tar Paint continued...

		Unit	Labour Hours	Labour Net £	Plant Net £	Materials Net £	Unit Net £	CO_2 Kg
V8.1	**Metal, other than metal sections and pipework**							
V8.1.8	Isolated groups of surfaces							
V8.1.8.02	to BS 3416, heavy duty; in two coats; rolled steel joist 2000 x 215 x 200mm deep; painting one face and soffit	Nr	0.28	17.56	-	9.52	27.08	*8.33*
V8.2	**Metal, other than metal sections and pipework**							
V8.2.1	Upper surfaces inclined at an angle not exceeding 30 degrees to the horizontal							
V8.2.1.01	to BS 3416, in two coats; primed timber	m^2	0.09	5.75	-	0.62	6.37	*0.71*
V8.2.1.02	to BS 3416, heavy duty; in two coats; primed planed timber	m^2	0.14	8.75	-	4.76	13.51	*4.17*
V8.2.2	Upper surfaces inclined at 30 - 60 degrees to the horizontal							
V8.2.2.01	to BS 3416, in two coats; primed timber	m^2	0.09	5.75	-	0.62	6.37	*0.71*
V8.2.2.02	to BS 3416, heavy duty; in two coats; primed planed timber	m^2	0.14	9.13	-	4.76	13.89	*4.17*
V8.2.3	Surfaces inclined at an angle exceeding 60 degrees to the horizontal							
V8.2.3.01	to BS 3416, in two coats; primed timber	m^2	0.09	5.75	-	0.62	6.37	*0.71*
V8.2.3.02	to BS 3416, heavy duty; in two coats; primed planed timber	m^2	0.15	9.58	-	4.76	14.34	*4.17*
V8.2.4	Soffit surfaces and lower surfaces inclined at an angle not exceeding 60 degrees to the horizontal							
V8.2.4.01	to BS 3416, in two coats; primed timber	m^2	0.12	7.66	-	0.62	8.28	*0.71*
V8.2.4.02	to BS 3416, heavy duty; in two coats; primed planed timber	m^2	0.18	11.69	-	4.76	16.45	*4.17*
V8.2.6	Surfaces of width not exceeding 300mm							
V8.2.6.01	to BS 3416, in two coats; primed timber	m	0.03	1.92	-	0.22	2.14	*0.25*
V8.2.6.02	to BS 3416, heavy duty; in two coats; primed planed timber	m	0.05	2.87	-	1.63	4.50	*1.42*
V8.2.7	Surfaces of width 300mm - 1m							
V8.2.7.01	to BS 3416, in two coats; primed timber	m	0.04	2.55	-	0.47	3.02	*0.53*
V8.2.7.02	to BS 3416, heavy duty; in two coats; primed planed timber	m	0.07	4.28	-	2.44	6.72	*2.14*
V8.2.8	Isolated groups of surfaces							
V8.2.8.01	to BS 3416, in two coats; primed timber; beam 2000 x 215 x 200mm deep; painting one face and soffit	Nr	0.18	11.49	-	1.24	12.73	*1.42*
V8.2.8.02	to BS 3416, heavy duty; in two coats; primed planed timber; beam 2000 x 215 x 200mm deep; painting one face and soffit	Nr	0.28	17.56	-	9.52	27.08	*8.33*
V8.3	**Smooth concrete**							
V8.3.1	Upper surfaces inclined at an angle not exceeding 30 degrees to the horizontal							
V8.3.1.01	to BS 3416, in two coats	m^2	0.07	4.66	-	0.68	5.34	*0.78*
V8.3.1.02	to BS 3416, heavy duty; in two coats; sealed smooth concrete	m^2	0.15	9.77	-	5.21	14.98	*4.56*

V8 Bituminous or Coal Tar Paint continued...

		Unit	Labour Hours	Labour Net £	Plant Net £	Materials Net £	Unit Net £	CO_2 Kg
V8.3	**Smooth concrete**							
V8.3.2	Upper surfaces inclined at 30 - 60 degrees to the horizontal							
V8.3.2.01	to BS 3416, in two coats	m^2	0.08	4.79	-	0.68	**5.47**	*0.78*
V8.3.2.02	to BS 3416, heavy duty; in two coats; sealed smooth concrete	m^2	0.16	10.22	-	5.21	**15.43**	*4.56*
V8.3.3	Surfaces inclined at an angle exceeding 60 degrees to the horizontal							
V8.3.3.01	to BS 3416, in two coats	m^2	0.08	5.11	-	0.68	**5.79**	*0.78*
V8.3.3.02	to BS 3416, heavy duty; in two coats; sealed smooth concrete	m^2	0.17	10.66	-	5.21	**15.87**	*4.56*
V8.3.4	Soffit surfaces and lower surfaces inclined at an angle not exceeding 60 degrees to the horizontal							
V8.3.4.01	to BS 3416, in two coats	m^2	0.10	6.39	-	0.68	**7.07**	*0.78*
V8.3.4.02	to BS 3416, heavy duty; in two coats; sealed smooth concrete	m^2	0.23	14.69	-	5.21	**19.90**	*4.56*
V8.3.6	Surfaces of width not exceeding 300mm							
V8.3.6.01	to BS 3416, in two coats	m	0.04	2.55	-	0.22	**2.77**	*0.25*
V8.3.6.02	to BS 3416, heavy duty; in two coats; sealed smooth concrete	m	0.05	3.19	-	1.75	**4.94**	*1.53*
V8.3.7	Surfaces of width 300mm - 1m							
V8.3.7.01	to BS 3416, in two coats	m	0.04	2.36	-	0.34	**2.70**	*0.39*
V8.3.7.02	to BS 3416, heavy duty; in two coats; sealed smooth concrete	m	0.08	4.79	-	2.60	**7.39**	*2.28*
V8.3.8	Isolated groups of surfaces							
V8.3.8.01	to BS 3416, in two coats; beam 2000 x 215 x 200mm deep, concrete lintel in wall; painting one face and soffit	Nr	0.18	11.49	-	1.37	**12.86**	*1.57*
V8.3.8.02	to BS 3416, heavy duty; in two coats; sealed smooth concrete; beam 2000 x 215 x 200mm deep concrete lintel in wall; painting one face and soffit	Nr	0.28	17.56	-	10.42	**27.98**	*9.11*
V8.4	**Rough concrete**							
V8.4.1	Upper surfaces inclined at an angle not exceeding 30 degrees to the horizontal							
V8.4.1.01	to BS 3416, in two coats; sawn board finish	m^2	0.08	5.11	-	1.62	**6.73**	*1.85*
V8.4.1.02	to BS 3416, heavy duty; in two coats; sealed rough concrete; sawn board finish	m^2	0.17	10.54	-	5.29	**15.83**	*4.63*
V8.4.2	Upper surfaces inclined at 30 - 60 degrees to the horizontal							
V8.4.2.01	to BS 3416, in two coats; sawn board finish	m^2	0.08	5.30	-	1.62	**6.92**	*1.85*
V8.4.2.02	to BS 3416, heavy duty; in two coats; sealed rough concrete; sawn board finish	m^2	0.17	11.05	-	5.29	**16.34**	*4.63*
V8.4.3	Surfaces inclined at an angle exceeding 60 degrees to the horizontal							
V8.4.3.01	to BS 3416, in two coats; sawn board finish	m^2	0.09	5.56	-	1.62	**7.18**	*1.85*
V8.4.3.02	to BS 3416, heavy duty; in two coats; sealed rough concrete; sawn board finish	m^2	0.18	11.49	-	5.29	**16.78**	*4.63*

V8 Bituminous or Coal Tar Paint continued...

		Unit	Labour Hours	Labour Net £	Plant Net £	Materials Net £	Unit Net £	CO_2 Kg
V8.4	**Rough concrete**							
V8.4.4	Soffit surfaces and lower surfaces inclined at an angle not exceeding 60 degrees to the horizontal							
V8.4.4.01	to BS 3416, in two coats; sawn board finish	m^2	0.11	7.02	-	1.62	**8.64**	*1.85*
V8.4.4.02	to BS 3416, heavy duty; in two coats; sealed rough concrete; sawn board finish	m^2	0.22	14.05	-	5.29	**19.34**	*4.63*
V8.4.6	Surfaces of width not exceeding 300mm							
V8.4.6.01	to BS 3416, in two coats; sawn board finish	m	0.03	1.60	-	0.53	**2.13**	*0.61*
V8.4.6.02	to BS 3416, heavy duty; in two coats; sealed rough concrete; sawn board finish	m	0.06	3.51	-	1.67	**5.18**	*1.46*
V8.4.7	Surfaces of width 300mm - 1m							
V8.4.7.01	to BS 3416, in two coats; sawn board finish	m	0.04	2.55	-	0.81	**3.36**	*0.93*
V8.4.7.02	to BS 3416, heavy duty; in two coats; sealed rough concrete; sawn board finish	m	0.08	5.30	-	2.65	**7.95**	*2.31*
V8.4.8	Isolated groups of surfaces							
V8.4.8.01	to BS 3416, in two coats; sawn board finish; 2000 x 215 x 200mm deep, concrete beam in wall; painting one face and soffit	Nr	0.16	10.22	-	0.50	**10.72**	*0.57*
V8.4.8.02	to BS 3416, heavy duty; in two coats; sealed rough concrete; sawn board finish; 2000 x 215 x 200mm deep concrete beam in wall; painting one face and soffit	Nr	0.33	21.07	-	10.58	**31.65**	*9.26*
V8.5	**Masonry**							
V8.5.1	Upper surfaces inclined at an angle not exceeding 30 degrees to the horizontal							
V8.5.1.01	to BS 3416, in two coats	m^2	0.08	5.11	-	1.62	**6.73**	*1.85*
V8.5.1.02	to BS 3416, heavy duty; in two coats; sealed masonry	m^2	0.17	10.54	-	5.29	**15.83**	*4.63*
V8.5.2	Upper surfaces inclined at 30 - 60 degrees to the horizontal							
V8.5.2.01	to BS 3416, in two coats	m^2	0.08	5.30	-	1.62	**6.92**	*1.85*
V8.5.2.02	to BS 3416, heavy duty; in two coats; sealed masonry	m^2	0.17	11.05	-	5.29	**16.34**	*4.63*
V8.5.3	Surfaces inclined at an angle exceeding 60 degrees to the horizontal							
V8.5.3.01	to BS 3416, in two coats	m^2	0.09	5.56	-	1.62	**7.18**	*1.85*
V8.5.3.02	to BS 3416, heavy duty; in two coats; sealed masonry	m^2	0.18	11.49	-	5.29	**16.78**	*4.63*
V8.5.4	Soffit surfaces and lower surfaces inclined at an angle not exceeding 60 degrees to the horizontal							
V8.5.4.01	to BS 3416, in two coats	m^2	0.11	7.02	-	1.62	**8.64**	*1.85*
V8.5.4.02	to BS 3416, heavy duty; in two coats; sealed masonry	m^2	0.22	14.05	-	5.29	**19.34**	*4.63*
V8.5.6	Surfaces of width not exceeding 300mm							
V8.5.6.01	to BS 3416, in two coats	m	0.03	1.60	-	0.53	**2.13**	*0.61*
V8.5.6.02	to BS 3416, heavy duty; in two coats; sealed masonry	m	0.06	3.51	-	1.67	**5.18**	*1.46*

V8 Bituminous or Coal Tar Paint continued...

		Unit	Labour Hours	Labour Net £	Plant Net £	Materials Net £	Unit Net £	CO_2 Kg
V8.5	**Masonry**							
V8.5.7	Surfaces of width 300mm - 1m							
V8.5.7.01	to BS 3416, in two coats	m	0.04	2.55	-	0.81	3.36	*0.93*
V8.5.7.02	to BS 3416, heavy duty; in two coats; sealed masonry	m	0.08	5.30	-	2.65	7.95	*2.31*
V8.5.8	Isolated groups of surfaces							
V8.5.8.01	to BS 3416, in two coats; stepped and spayed plinth overall size 450 x 450 x 450mm; painting all faces	Nr	0.16	10.22	-	0.50	10.72	*0.57*
V8.5.8.02	to BS 3416, heavy duty; in two coats; sealed masonry; stepped and spayed plinth overall size 450 x 450 x 450mm; painting all faces	Nr	0.33	21.07	-	10.58	31.65	*9.26*
V8.6	**Brickwork and blockwork**							
V8.6.1	Upper surfaces inclined at an angle not exceeding 30 degrees to the horizontal							
V8.6.1.01	to BS 3416, in two coats	m^2	0.10	6.39	-	0.81	7.20	*0.93*
V8.6.1.02	to BS 3416, heavy duty; in two coats; sealed brickwork and blockwork	m^2	0.18	11.49	-	6.35	17.84	*5.55*
V8.6.2	Upper surfaces inclined at 30 - 60 degrees to the horizontal							
V8.6.2.01	to BS 3416, in two coats	m^2	0.01	0.64	-	0.81	1.45	*0.93*
V8.6.2.02	to BS 3416, heavy duty; in two coats; sealed brickwork and blockwork	m^2	0.19	12.13	-	6.35	18.48	*5.55*
V8.6.3	Surfaces inclined at an angle exceeding 60 degrees to the horizontal							
V8.6.3.01	to BS 3416, in two coats	m^2	0.10	6.39	-	0.81	7.20	*0.93*
V8.6.3.02	to BS 3416, heavy duty; in two coats; sealed brickwork and blockwork	m^2	0.20	12.58	-	6.35	18.93	*5.55*
V8.6.4	Soffit surfaces and lower surfaces inclined at an angle not exceeding 60 degrees to the horizontal							
V8.6.4.01	to BS 3416, in two coats	m^2	0.13	8.30	-	0.81	9.11	*0.93*
V8.6.4.02	to BS 3416, heavy duty; in two coats; sealed brickwork and blockwork	m^2	0.24	15.52	-	6.35	21.87	*5.55*
V8.6.6	Surfaces of width not exceeding 300mm							
V8.6.6.01	to BS 3416, in two coats	m	0.03	1.92	-	0.28	2.20	*0.32*
V8.6.6.02	to BS 3416, heavy duty; in two coats; sealed brickwork and blockwork	m	0.06	3.83	-	2.08	5.91	*1.82*
V8.6.7	Surfaces of width 300mm - 1m							
V8.6.7.01	to BS 3416, in two coats	m	0.04	2.55	-	0.40	2.95	*0.46*
V8.6.7.02	to BS 3416, heavy duty; in two coats; sealed brickwork and blockwork	m	0.09	5.75	-	3.17	8.92	*2.78*
V8.6.8	Isolated groups of surfaces							
V8.6.8.01	to BS 3416, in two coats; stepped and spayed plinth overall size 450 x 450 x 450mm; painting all faces	Nr	0.20	12.77	-	1.62	14.39	*1.85*
V8.6.8.02	to BS 3416, heavy duty; in two coats; sealed brickwork and blockwork; stepped and spayed plinth overall size 450 x 450 x 450mm; painting all faces	Nr	0.36	22.67	-	12.70	35.37	*11.11*

V8 Bituminous or Coal Tar Paint continued...

		Unit	Labour Hours	Labour Net £	Plant Net £	Materials Net £	Unit Net £	CO_2 Kg
V8.7	**Metal sections**							
V8.7.1	**Generally**							
V8.7.1.01	to BS 3416, in two coats	m^2	0.10	6.39	-	0.62	**7.01**	*0.71*
V8.7.1.02	to BS 3416, heavy duty; in two coats; sealed brickwork and blockwork	m^2	0.07	4.66	-	0.62	**5.28**	*0.71*
V8.8	**Pipework**							
V8.8.1	**Generally**							
V8.8.1.01	to BS 3416, in two coats	m^2	0.10	6.39	-	0.62	**7.01**	*0.71*
V8.8.1.02	to BS 3416, heavy duty; in two coats; sealed brickwork and blockwork	m^2	0.07	4.66	-	0.62	**5.28**	*0.71*

CLASS W:
WATERPROOFING

Calculations used throughout Class W - Waterproofing

Labour

		Qty		Rate		Total
L A0315ICE	**Paint spray Labour Gang**					
	Spray painter	1	x	16.68	=	£16.68
	Total hourly cost of gang				**=**	**£16.68**
L A0320ICE	**Waterproofing Labour Gang**					
	Ganger	1	x	16.99	=	£16.99
	Labourer (General Operative)	3	x	12.56	=	£37.68
	Total hourly cost of gang				**=**	**£54.67**
L A0324ICE	**Tiling Labour Gang (protective layer)**					
	Tiler	2	x	16.68	=	£33.37
	Labourer (General Operative)	1	x	12.56	=	£12.56
	Total hourly cost of gang				**=**	**£45.93**
L A0325ICE	**Plastering Labour Gang**					
	Plasterer	1	x	16.68	=	£16.68
	Labourer (General Operative)	1	x	12.56	=	£12.56
	Total hourly cost of gang				**=**	**£29.24**

Class W - Waterproofing

W1 Damp Proofing

		Unit	Labour Hours	Labour Net £	Plant Net £	Materials Net £	Unit Net £	CO_2 Kg
W1.3	**Waterproof sheeting**							
W1.3.1	Upper surfaces inclined at an angle not exceeding 30 degrees to the horizontal							
W1.3.1.01	Polythene in one layer, 1200 gauge	m^2	0.01	0.16	-	0.68	**0.84**	*0.55*
W1.3.2	Upper surfaces inclined at 30 - 60 degrees to the horizontal							
W1.3.2.01	Polythene in one layer, 1200 gauge	m^2	0.01	0.38	-	0.68	**1.06**	*0.55*
W1.3.3	Surfaces inclined at an angle exceeding 60 degrees to the horizontal							
W1.3.3.01	Polythene in one layer, 1200 gauge	m^2	0.01	0.55	-	0.68	**1.23**	*0.55*
W1.3.4	Curved surfaces							
W1.3.4.01	Polythene in one layer, 1200 gauge	m^2	0.02	1.09	-	0.68	**1.77**	*0.55*
W1.3.5	Domed surfaces							
W1.3.5.01	Polythene in one layer, 1200 gauge	m^2	0.02	1.09	-	0.68	**1.77**	*0.55*
W1.3.6	Surfaces of width not exceeding 300mm							
W1.3.6.01	Polythene in one layer, 1200 gauge	m	0.01	0.16	-	0.14	**0.30**	*0.11*
W1.3.7	Surfaces of width 300mm - 1m							
W1.3.7.01	Polythene in one layer, 1200 gauge	m	0.01	0.55	-	0.48	**1.03**	*0.39*
W1.3.8	Isolated groups of surfaces							
W1.3.8.01	Polythene in one layer, 1200 gauge; sump below basement level; 600 x 400 x 400mm to sides and base	Nr	0.02	1.09	-	0.76	**1.85**	*0.62*
W1.5	**Rendering in ordinary cement mortar**							
W1.5.1	Upper surfaces inclined at an angle not exceeding 30 degrees to the horizontal							
W1.5.1.01	cement mortar (1:3); treated with water resistant additive; 25mm thick screed in one coat to concrete; trowelled	m^2	0.23	6.64	-	5.31	**11.95**	*16.29*
W1.5.2	Upper surfaces inclined at 30 - 60 degrees to the horizontal							
W1.5.2.01	cement mortar (1:3); treated with water resistant additive; 25mm thick screed in one coat to concrete; trowelled	m^2	0.34	9.94	-	5.31	**15.25**	*16.29*
W1.5.3	Surfaces inclined at an angle exceeding 60 degrees to the horizontal							
W1.5.3.01	cement mortar (1:3); treated with water resistant additive; 25mm thick in two coats to brickwork; trowelled	m^2	0.58	16.81	-	5.31	**22.12**	*16.29*
W1.5.4	Curved surfaces							
W1.5.4.01	cement mortar (1:3); treated with water resistant additive; 25mm thick in two coats to brickwork; trowelled	m^2	0.86	25.20	-	5.31	**30.51**	*16.29*

W1 Damp Proofing continued...

		Unit	Labour Hours	Labour Net £	Plant Net £	Materials Net £	Unit Net £	CO_2 Kg
W1.5	**Rendering in ordinary cement mortar**							
W1.5.5	Domed surfaces							
W1.5.5.01	cement mortar (1:3); treated with water resistant additive; 25mm thick in two coats to brickwork; trowelled	m^2	1.15	33.63	-	5.31	**38.94**	*16.29*
W1.5.6	Surfaces of width not exceeding 300mm							
W1.5.6.01	cement mortar (1:3); treated with water resistant additive; 25mm thick in two coats to brickwork; trowelled	m	0.18	5.12	-	1.76	**6.88**	*5.16*
W1.5.7	Surfaces of width 300mm - 1m							
W1.5.7.01	cement mortar (1:3); treated with water resistant additive; 25mm thick in two coats to brickwork; trowelled	m	0.35	10.23	-	2.92	**13.15**	*10.25*
W1.5.8	Isolated groups of surfaces							
W1.5.8.01	cement mortar (1:3); treated with water resistant additive; 25mm thick in two coats to brickwork; trowelled; stepped brick plinth; overall size 450 x 450 x 450mm; to all faces	Nr	1.15	33.63	-	9.12	**42.75**	*32.43*
W1.6	**Rendering in waterproof cement mortar**							
W1.6.3	Surfaces inclined at an angle exceeding 60 degrees to the horizontal							
W1.6.3.01	cement lime mortar (1:1:6); treated with water resistant additive; 25mm thick in two coats to brickwork; trowelled	m^2	0.57	16.67	-	3.38	**20.05**	*8.68*
W1.6.4	Curved surfaces							
W1.6.4.01	cement lime mortar (1:1:6); treated with water resistant additive; 25mm thick in two coats to brickwork; trowelled	m^2	0.86	25.15	-	3.38	**28.53**	*8.68*
W1.6.5	Domed surfaces							
W1.6.5.01	cement lime mortar (1:1:6); treated with water resistant additive; 25mm thick in two coats to brickwork; trowelled	m^2	1.14	33.33	-	3.38	**36.71**	*8.68*
W1.6.6	Surfaces of width not exceeding 300mm							
W1.6.6.01	cement lime mortar (1:1:6); treated with water resistant additive; 25mm thick in two coats to brickwork; trowelled	m	0.17	4.97	-	1.08	**6.05**	*2.62*
W1.6.7	Surfaces of width 300mm - 1m							
W1.6.7.01	cement lime mortar (1:1:6); treated with water resistant additive; 25mm thick in two coats to brickwork; trowelled	m	0.35	10.23	-	1.68	**11.91**	*4.34*

W1 Damp Proofing continued...

		Unit	Labour Hours	Labour Net £	Plant Net £	Materials Net £	Unit Net £	CO_2 Kg
W1.6	**Rendering in waterproof cement mortar**							
W1.6.8	Isolated groups of surfaces							
W1.6.8.01	cement lime mortar (1:1:6); treated with water resistant additive; 25mm thick in two coats to brickwork; trowelled; stepped brick plinth; overall size 450 x 450 x 450mm; to all faces	Nr	1.14	33.33	-	8.89	**42.22**	*32.23*

W2 Tanking

		Unit	Labour Hours	Labour Net £	Plant Net £	Materials Net £	Unit Net £	CO_2 Kg
W2.1	**Asphalt**							
W2.1.1	Upper surfaces inclined at an angle not exceeding 30 degrees to the horizontal							
W2.1.1.01	to BS 6925; 20mm thick in two coats to brickwork; raking out joints to form key	m^2	0.55	16.08	-	9.41	**25.49**	*25.65*
W2.1.1.02	to BS 5625; 20mm thick in two coats laid on prepared concrete surface	m^2	0.50	14.62	-	8.58	**23.20**	*23.40*
W2.1.2	Upper surfaces inclined at 30 - 60 degrees to the horizontal							
W2.1.2.01	to BS 6925; 20mm thick in two coats to brickwork; raking out joints to form key	m^2	0.82	23.98	-	9.41	**33.39**	*25.65*
W2.1.2.02	to BS 5625; 20mm thick in two coats laid on prepared concrete surface	m^2	0.75	21.93	-	8.58	**30.51**	*23.40*
W2.1.3	Surfaces inclined at an angle exceeding 60 degrees to the horizontal							
W2.1.3.01	to BS 6925; 20mm thick in two coats to brickwork; raking out joints to form key	m^2	1.39	40.64	-	9.41	**50.05**	*25.65*
W2.1.3.02	to BS 5625; 20mm thick in two coats laid on prepared concrete surface	m^2	1.30	38.01	-	8.58	**46.59**	*23.40*
W2.1.4	Curved surfaces							
W2.1.4.01	to BS 6925; 20mm thick in two coats to brickwork; raking out joints to form key	m^2	1.59	46.49	-	9.41	**55.90**	*25.65*
W2.1.4.02	to BS 5625; 20mm thick in two coats laid on prepared concrete surface	m^2	1.60	46.78	-	8.58	**55.36**	*23.40*
W2.1.5	Domed surfaces							
W2.1.5.01	to BS 6925; 20mm thick in two coats to brickwork; raking out joints to form key	m^2	2.18	63.74	-	9.41	**73.15**	*25.65*
W2.1.5.02	to BS 5625; 20mm thick in two coats laid on prepared concrete surface	m^2	2.20	64.33	-	8.58	**72.91**	*23.40*
W2.1.6	Surfaces of width not exceeding 300mm							
W2.1.6.01	to BS 6925; 20mm thick in two coats to brickwork; raking out joints to form key	m	0.29	8.33	-	3.13	**11.46**	*8.55*
W2.1.6.02	to BS 5625; 20mm thick in two coats laid on prepared concrete surface	m	0.20	5.85	-	3.14	**8.99**	*8.55*
W2.1.7	Surfaces of width 300mm - 1m							
W2.1.7.01	to BS 6925; 20mm thick in two coats to brickwork; raking out joints to form key	m	0.42	12.28	-	4.79	**17.07**	*13.05*
W2.1.7.02	to BS 5625; 20mm thick in two coats laid on prepared concrete surface	m	0.30	8.77	-	4.29	**13.06**	*11.70*

W2 Tanking continued...

		Unit	Labour Hours	Labour Net £	Plant Net £	Materials Net £	Unit Net £	CO_2 Kg
W2.1	**Asphalt**							
W2.1.8	Isolated groups of surfaces							
W2.1.8.01	to BS 6925; 20mm thick in two coats to brickwork; raking out joints to form key; brick sump below basement level; 600 x 400 x 400mm to sides and base	Nr	2.18	63.74	-	28.22	**91.96**	*76.95*
W2.1.8.02	to BS 5625; 20mm thick in two coats laid on prepared concrete surface; concrete sump below basement level; 600 x 400 x 400mm to sides and base	Nr	2.20	64.33	-	25.74	**90.07**	*70.20*

W3 Roofing

		Unit	Labour Hours	Labour Net £	Plant Net £	Materials Net £	Unit Net £	CO_2 Kg
W3.1	**Asphalt**							
W3.1.1	Upper surfaces inclined at an angle not exceeding 30 degrees to the horizontal							
W3.1.1.01	Mastic asphalt, BS 6925; 20mm thick in two coats laid on prepared concrete surface	m^2	0.50	14.62	-	8.05	**22.67**	*23.40*
W3.1.1.02	as above; heavy gauge polythene membrane; sheathing felt, BS 747, type IB, 18kg roll, expanded polystyrene insulation 25mm thick; on concrete surface	m^2	0.39	21.32	-	14.50	**35.82**	*28.75*
W3.1.2	Upper surfaces inclined at 30 - 60 degrees to the horizontal							
W3.1.2.01	Mastic asphalt, BS 6925; 20mm thick in two coats laid on prepared concrete surface	m^2	0.75	21.93	-	8.05	**29.98**	*23.40*
W3.1.2.02	as above; heavy gauge polythene membrane; sheathing felt, BS 747, type IB, 18kg roll, expanded polystyrene insulation 25mm thick; on concrete surface	m^2	0.59	32.26	-	14.50	**46.76**	*28.75*
W3.1.3	Surfaces inclined at an angle exceeding 60 degrees to the horizontal							
W3.1.3.01	Mastic asphalt, BS 6925; 20mm thick in two coats laid on prepared concrete surface	m^2	1.30	38.01	-	8.05	**46.06**	*23.40*
W3.1.3.02	as above; heavy gauge polythene membrane; sheathing felt, BS 747, type IB, 18kg roll, expanded polystyrene insulation 25mm thick; on concrete surface	m^2	0.98	53.58	-	14.50	**68.08**	*28.75*
W3.1.4	Curved surfaces							
W3.1.4.01	Mastic asphalt, BS 6925; 20mm thick in two coats laid on prepared concrete surface	m^2	1.60	46.78	-	8.05	**54.83**	*23.40*
W3.1.5	Domed surfaces							
W3.1.5.01	Mastic asphalt, BS 6925; 20mm thick in two coats laid on prepared concrete surface	m^2	2.20	64.33	-	8.05	**72.38**	*23.40*
W3.1.6	Surfaces of width not exceeding 300mm							
W3.1.6.01	Mastic asphalt, BS 6925; 20mm thick in two coats laid on prepared concrete surface	m	0.20	5.85	-	2.63	**8.48**	*7.65*

W3 Roofing continued...

		Unit	Labour Hours	Labour Net £	Plant Net £	Materials Net £	Unit Net £	CO_2 Kg
W3.1	**Asphalt**							
W3.1.6	Surfaces of width not exceeding 300mm							
W3.1.6.02	as above; heavy gauge polythene membrane; sheathing felt, BS 747, type IB, 18kg roll, expanded polystyrene insulation 25mm thick; on concrete surface	m	0.13	7.11	-	4.82	**11.93**	*9.47*
W3.1.7	Surfaces of width 300mm - 1m							
W3.1.7.01	Mastic asphalt, BS 6925; 20mm thick in two coats laid on prepared concrete surface	m	0.30	8.77	-	5.26	**14.03**	*15.30*
W3.1.7.02	as above; heavy gauge polythene membrane; sheathing felt, BS 747, type IB, 18kg roll, expanded polystyrene insulation 25mm thick; on concrete surface	m	0.26	14.21	-	10.23	**24.44**	*19.42*
W3.1.8	Isolated groups of surfaces							
W3.1.8.01	Mastic asphalt, BS 6925; 20mm thick in two coats laid on prepared concrete surface; stepped penthouse roof; overall size 800 x 500 x 150mm high step	Nr	2.20	64.33	-	16.09	**80.42**	*46.80*
W3.1.8.02	as above; heavy gauge polythene membrane; sheathing felt, BS 747, type IB, 18kg roll, expanded polystyrene insulation 25mm thick; on concrete surface; stepped penthouse roof; overall size 800 x 500 x 150mm high step	Nr	1.60	87.47	-	28.38	**115.85**	*55.70*
W3.2	**Sheet metal**							
W3.2.6	Surfaces of width not exceeding 300mm							
W3.2.6.01	Milled lead sheet, BS EN 12588, lead wedge fixings; Flashings; 200mm girth; one edge dressed along the verge of single lap tiling; one edge wedged into raked out joints of brickwork	m	0.36	16.35	-	10.75	**27.10**	*5.43*
W3.2.6.02	as above; Flashings; 300mm girth; one edge dressed along the verge of single lap tiling; one edge wedged into raked out joints of brickwork	m	0.41	18.69	-	16.08	**34.77**	*8.14*

W4 Protective Layers

		Unit	Labour Hours	Labour Net £	Plant Net £	Materials Net £	Unit Net £	CO_2 Kg
W4.2	**Flexible sheeting**							
W4.2.1	Upper surfaces inclined at an angle not exceeding 30 degrees to the horizontal							
W4.2.1.01	Polythene in one layer 4000 gauge	m^2	0.01	0.38	-	1.68	**2.06**	*0.55*
W4.2.1.02	Lotrak 10/7 ground stabilising matting	m^2	0.01	0.38	-	0.65	**1.03**	*0.25*
W4.2.2	Upper surfaces inclined at 30 - 60 degrees to the horizontal							
W4.2.2.01	Polythene in one layer 4000 gauge	m^2	0.01	0.60	-	1.68	**2.28**	*0.55*

W4 Protective Layers continued...

		Unit	Labour Hours	Labour Net £	Plant Net £	Materials Net £	Unit Net £	CO_2 Kg
W4.2	**Flexible sheeting**							
W4.2.2	Upper surfaces inclined at 30 - 60 degrees to the horizontal							
W4.2.2.02	Lotrak 10/7 ground stabilising matting	m^2	0.01	0.60	-	0.65	**1.25**	*0.25*
W4.2.3	Surfaces inclined at an angle exceeding 60 degrees to the horizontal							
W4.2.3.01	Polythene in one layer 4000 gauge	m^2	0.02	0.82	-	1.68	**2.50**	*0.55*
W4.2.3.02	Lotrak 10/7 ground stabilising matting	m^2	0.02	0.82	-	0.65	**1.47**	*0.25*
W4.2.4	Curved surfaces							
W4.2.4.01	Polythene in one layer 4000 gauge	m^2	0.02	0.82	-	1.68	**2.50**	*0.55*
W4.2.4.02	Lotrak 10/7 ground stabilising matting	m^2	0.02	0.82	-	0.65	**1.47**	*0.25*
W4.2.5	Domed surfaces							
W4.2.5.01	Polythene in one layer 4000 gauge	m^2	0.02	0.93	-	1.68	**2.61**	*0.55*
W4.2.5.02	Lotrak 10/7 ground stabilising matting	m^2	0.02	1.04	-	0.65	**1.69**	*0.24*
W4.2.6	Surfaces of width not exceeding 300mm							
W4.2.6.01	Polythene in one layer 4000 gauge	m	0.01	0.38	-	0.57	**0.95**	*0.19*
W4.2.6.02	Lotrak 10/7 ground stabilising matting	m	0.01	0.55	-	0.22	**0.77**	*0.08*
W4.2.7	Surfaces of width 300mm - 1m							
W4.2.7.01	Polythene in one layer 4000 gauge	m	0.01	0.38	-	1.13	**1.51**	*0.37*
W4.2.7.02	Lotrak 10/7 ground stabilising matting	m	0.01	0.55	-	0.44	**0.99**	*0.16*
W4.2.8	Isolated groups of surfaces							
W4.2.8.01	Polythene in one layer 4000 gauge; sump below basement level; 600 x 400 x 400mm to sides and base	Nr	0.02	1.09	-	3.36	**4.45**	*1.10*
W4.2.8.02	Lotrak 10/7 ground stabilising matting; 150mm laps; sump below basement level; 600 x 400 x 400mm to sides and base	Nr	0.02	1.26	-	1.30	**2.56**	*0.49*
W4.3	**Sand**							
W4.3.1	Upper surfaces inclined at an angle not exceeding 30 degrees to the horizontal							
W4.3.1.01	25mm thick to granular base	m^2	0.00	0.16	-	0.63	**0.79**	*0.21*
W4.3.8	Isolated groups of surfaces							
W4.3.8.01	to base of stepped concrete plinth 450 x 450mm	Nr	0.01	0.55	-	1.26	**1.81**	*0.42*
W4.4	**Sand and cement screed**							
W4.4.1	Upper surfaces inclined at an angle not exceeding 30 degrees to the horizontal							
W4.4.1.01	Sand and cement (1:3) screed; treated with water resistant additive; 50mm thick to prepared concrete surface	m^2	0.56	16.37	-	8.12	**24.49**	*32.59*

W4 Protective Layers continued...

		Unit	Labour Hours	Labour Net £	Plant Net £	Materials Net £	Unit Net £	*CO_2 Kg*
W4.4	**Sand and cement screed**							
W4.4.2	Upper surfaces inclined at 30 - 60 degrees to the horizontal							
W4.4.2.01	Sand and cement (1:3) screed; treated with water resistant additive; 50mm thick to prepared concrete surface	m^2	0.84	24.56	-	8.12	**32.68**	*32.59*
W4.4.7	Surfaces of width 300mm - 1m							
W4.4.7.01	Sand and cement (1:3) screed; treated with water resistant additive; 50mm thick to prepared concrete surface	m	0.36	10.53	-	13.26	**23.79**	*19.34*
W4.4.8	Isolated groups of surfaces							
W4.4.8.01	Sand and cement (1:3) screed; treated with water resistant additive; 50mm thick to prepared concrete surface; to base of stepped concrete plinth 450 x 450mm	Nr	1.12	32.75	-	14.62	**47.37**	*64.51*
W4.5	**Tiles**							
W4.5.1	Upper surfaces inclined at an angle not exceeding 30 degrees to the horizontal							
W4.5.1.01	Plain tiles; 265 x 165mm; overlapping broken bonded; twice nailed each title to timber battens; 38 x 25mm softwood battens, plugged and screwed through 1000 gauge polythene membrane to concrete background	m^2	0.69	31.69	-	33.74	**65.43**	*23.16*
W4.5.2	Upper surfaces inclined at 30 - 60 degrees to the horizontal							
W4.5.2.01	Plain tiles; 265 x 165mm; overlapping broken bonded; twice nailed each title to timber battens; 38 x 25mm softwood battens, plugged and screwed through 1000 gauge polythene membrane to concrete background	m^2	0.74	33.76	-	33.74	**67.50**	*23.16*
W4.5.3	Surfaces inclined at an angle exceeding 60 degrees to the horizontal							
W4.5.3.01	Plain tiles; 265 x 165mm; overlapping broken bonded; twice nailed each title to timber battens; 38 x 25mm softwood battens, plugged and screwed through 1000 gauge polythene membrane to concrete background	m^2	1.04	47.54	-	33.74	**81.28**	*23.16*
W4.5.4	Curved surfaces							
W4.5.4.01	Plain tiles; 265 x 165mm; overlapping broken bonded; twice nailed each title to timber battens; 38 x 25mm softwood battens, plugged and screwed through 1000 gauge polythene membrane to concrete background	m^2	1.04	47.54	-	33.74	**81.28**	*23.16*

W4 Protective Layers continued...

		Unit	Labour Hours	Labour Net £	Plant Net £	Materials Net £	Unit Net £	CO_2 Kg
W4.5	**Tiles**							
W4.5.6	Surfaces of width not exceeding 300mm							
W4.5.6.01	Plain tiles; 265 x 165mm; overlapping broken bonded; twice nailed each title to timber battens; 38 x 25mm softwood battens, plugged and screwed through 1000 gauge polythene membrane to concrete background	m	0.23	10.56	-	11.45	22.01	*7.88*
W4.5.7	Surfaces of width 300mm - 1m							
W4.5.7.01	Plain tiles; 265 x 165mm; overlapping broken bonded; twice nailed each title to timber battens; 38 x 25mm softwood battens, plugged and screwed through 1000 gauge polythene membrane to concrete background	m	0.46	21.13	-	22.90	44.03	*15.76*

W5 Sprayed or Brushed Waterproofing

		Unit	Labour Hours	Labour Net £	Plant Net £	Materials Net £	Unit Net £	CO_2 Kg
W5.1	**Two coats R.I.W. solution**							
W5.1.1	Large horizontal or vertical areas; applied by spray gun (see class V painting for details)							
W5.1.1.01	To concrete surfaces	m^2	0.05	2.73	-	3.41	6.14	*0.36*

CLASS X:

MISCELLANEOUS WORK

Calculations used throughout Class X - Miscellaneous Work

Labour

		Qty		Rate		Total
L X0003ICE	**Rock Gabion Labour Gang**					
	Ganger	1	x	16.99	=	£16.99
	Labourer (General Operative)	4	x	12.56	=	£50.24
	Plant Operator (Class 3)	0.5	x	15.63	=	£7.82
	Total hourly cost of gang				**=**	**£75.05**
L A0332ICE	**Fencing / Gate Installation Labour Gang**					
	Ganger	0.5	x	16.99	=	£8.49
	Labourer (Skill Rate 4)	0.5	x	13.53	=	£6.77
	Labourer (General Operative)	1	x	12.56	=	£12.56
	Plant Operator (Class 4)	1	x	14.75	=	£14.75
	Total hourly cost of gang				**=**	**£42.57**

Plant

		Qty		Rate		Total
P A1329ICE	**Gabion Plant Gang**					
	Cranes Crawler - NCK 305B - 20t	1	x	45.36	=	£45.36
	Total hourly cost of gang				**=**	**£45.36**
P X0001ICE	**Fencing / Gate Installation Plant Gang**					
	Agricultural Tractor: Fencing Auger	1	x	23.44	=	£23.44
	Trailer - Massey Tipping	1	x	1.69	=	£1.69
	Total hourly cost of gang				**=**	**£25.13**

Class X - Miscellaneous Work

X1 Fences

Note(s): The prices for work in this section are guide prices for approximate estimating purposes only. The prices are inclusive of labour and materials and are applicable to sites over 30 miles but not exceeding 60 miles radius from the point of supply.

1) All treated posts have been kiln dried where necessary to ensure a moisture content of below 28% and treated with a copper chrome arsenic preservative to a net dry salt retention of 6.4kg per m^2. Specify Jakcured treated timber.

2) The prices for fencing include all necessary post hole excavation, disposal of surplus soil and concrete bases, whererequired by specification.

3) Extras would be deemed to be included in the linear items measured for fencing under the CESMM3.

		Unit	Labour Hours	Labour Net £	Plant Net £	Materials Net £	Unit Net £	CO_2 Kg
X1.1	**Timber post and rail**							
X1.1.1	Height: not exceeding 1m							
X1.1.1.01	Wooden palisade fencing BS 1722, part 5, with intermediate posts at 3m centres; 75 x 20mm rectangular pales with square tops spaced 75mm apart; height: 1.00m; treated wooden posts	m	0.47	19.88	0.89	18.38	**39.15**	*13.77*
X1.1.1.02	as above; extra for end post	Nr	0.38	16.18	5.14	24.54	**45.86**	*59.98*
X1.1.1.03	as above; extra for angle post	Nr	0.47	20.09	6.83	22.90	**49.82**	*41.97*
X1.1.1.04	Cleft chestnut pale fencing BS 1722, part 4, with intermediate posts at maximum centres and spacings as Table 1; height: 0.90m; untreated chestnut, pointed for driving	m	0.30	12.81	0.05	4.29	**17.15**	*5.10*
X1.1.1.05	as above; extra for straining posts and struts: end post and one strut	Nr	0.49	20.86	0.11	7.67	**28.64**	*4.80*
X1.1.1.06	as above; extra for straining posts and struts: corner post and two struts	Nr	0.58	24.48	0.16	12.09	**36.73**	*7.38*
X1.1.1.07	as above; extra for one line of barbed wire: wooden posts	m	0.03	1.06	-	0.27	**1.33**	*1.03*
X1.1.1.08	as above; extra for two lines of barbed wire: wooden posts	m	0.05	2.13	-	0.54	**2.67**	*2.06*
X1.1.2	Height: 1 - 1.25m							
X1.1.2.01	Timber post and rail fencing; BS 1722 part 7, morticed type; intermediate main posts at 2.85m centres, one prick post between each main post; height: 1.10m (3 rails); treated softwood posts and rails; prick posts pointed for driving	m	0.36	15.15	0.05	5.83	**21.03**	*4.18*
X1.1.2.02	as above; extra for end post	Nr	0.31	13.28	0.11	13.80	**27.19**	*8.52*
X1.1.2.03	as above; extra for angle post	Nr	0.37	15.54	0.16	20.01	**35.71**	*12.35*
X1.1.2.04	as above; extra for intersection post	Nr	0.31	13.28	0.11	20.01	**33.40**	*12.35*

X1 Fences continued...

		Unit	Labour Hours	Labour Net £	Plant Net £	Materials Net £	Unit Net £	CO_2 Kg
X1.1	**Timber post and rail**							
X1.1.2	Height: 1 - 1.25m							
X1.1.2.05	Timber post and rail fencing; BS 1722 part 7, morticed type; intermediate main posts at 2.85m centres, one prick post between each main post; height: 1.10m (3 rails); untreated Oak posts and rails; prick posts pointed for driving	m	0.53	22.60	0.05	15.75	**38.40**	*5.11*
X1.1.2.06	as above; extra for end post	Nr	0.31	13.28	0.11	22.77	**36.16**	*7.40*
X1.1.2.07	as above; extra for angle post	Nr	0.37	15.54	0.16	33.02	**48.72**	*10.74*
X1.1.2.08	as above; extra for intersection post	Nr	0.31	13.28	0.11	33.02	**46.41**	*10.74*
X1.1.2.09	Timber post and rail fencing; BS 1722 part 7, morticed type; intermediate main posts at 2.85m centres, one prick post between each main post; height: 1.10m (4 rails); treated softwood posts and rails; prick posts pointed for driving	m	0.38	16.05	0.05	6.94	**23.04**	*5.06*
X1.1.2.10	as above; extra for end post	Nr	0.35	14.77	0.11	14.08	**28.96**	*8.69*
X1.1.2.11	as above; extra for angle post	Nr	0.40	17.16	0.16	20.53	**37.85**	*12.67*
X1.1.2.12	as above; extra for intersection post	Nr	0.35	14.77	0.11	20.53	**35.41**	*12.67*
X1.1.2.13	Timber post and rail fencing; BS 1722 part 7, morticed type; intermediate main posts at 2.85m centres, one prick post between each main post; height: 1.10m (4 rails); untreated Oak posts and rails; prick posts pointed for driving	m	0.41	17.37	0.05	19.61	**37.03**	*6.36*
X1.1.2.14	as above; extra for end post	Nr	0.33	14.18	0.11	22.77	**37.06**	*7.40*
X1.1.2.15	as above; extra for angle post	Nr	0.39	16.60	0.16	33.02	**49.78**	*10.74*
X1.1.2.16	as above; extra for intersection post	Nr	0.33	14.18	0.11	33.02	**47.31**	*10.74*
X1.1.2.17	Wooden post and rail fencing, BS 1722, part 7, nailed type; intermediate main posts at 1.80m centres; height: 1.10m (3 rails); treated softwood posts and rails	m	0.30	12.73	0.05	5.00	**17.78**	*3.69*
X1.1.2.18	as above; extra for end post	Nr	0.33	14.18	0.11	8.62	**22.91**	*4.91*
X1.1.2.19	as above; extra for angle post	Nr	0.39	16.60	0.16	12.82	**29.58**	*7.23*
X1.1.2.20	as above; extra for intersection post	Nr	0.33	14.18	0.11	12.82	**27.11**	*7.23*
X1.1.2.21	Wooden post and rail fencing, BS 1722, part 7, nailed type; intermediate main posts at 1.80m centres; height: 1.10m (3 rails); treated softwood posts and rails, posts pointed for driving	m	0.31	13.20	0.05	5.00	**18.25**	*3.69*

X1 Fences continued...

		Unit	Labour Hours	Labour Net £	Plant Net £	Materials Net £	Unit Net £	CO_2 Kg
X1.1	**Timber post and rail**							
X1.1.2	Height: 1 - 1.25m							
X1.1.2.22	as previous item; extra for end post	Nr	0.32	13.79	0.11	8.62	**22.52**	*4.91*
X1.1.2.23	as above; extra for angle post	Nr	0.38	16.18	0.16	12.82	**29.16**	*7.23*
X1.1.2.24	as above; extra for intersection post	Nr	0.32	13.79	0.11	12.82	**26.72**	*7.23*
X1.1.2.25	Wooden post and rail fencing, BS 1722, part 7, nailed type; intermediate main posts at 1.80m centres; height: 1.10m (3 rails); untreated Oak posts and rails	m	0.58	24.48	0.05	15.75	**40.28**	*5.11*
X1.1.2.26	as above; extra for end post	Nr	0.31	13.28	0.11	22.77	**36.16**	*7.40*
X1.1.2.27	as above; extra for angle post	Nr	0.34	14.52	0.16	33.02	**47.70**	*10.74*
X1.1.2.28	as above; extra for intersection post	Nr	0.32	13.79	0.11	33.02	**46.92**	*10.74*
X1.1.2.29	Wooden post and rail fencing, BS 1722, part 7, nailed type; intermediate main posts at 1.80m centres; height: 1.10m (3 rails); untreated Oak posts and rails; posts pointed for driving	m	0.68	28.99	0.05	15.75	**44.79**	*5.11*
X1.1.2.30	as above; extra for end post	Nr	0.32	13.62	0.11	22.77	**36.50**	*7.40*
X1.1.2.31	as above; extra for angle post	Nr	0.38	15.96	0.16	33.02	**49.14**	*10.74*
X1.1.2.32	as above; extra for intersection post	Nr	0.32	13.62	0.11	33.02	**46.75**	*10.74*
X1.1.2.33	Wooden post and rail fencing, BS 1722, part 7, nailed type; intermediate main posts at 1.80m centres; height: 1.10m (4 rails); treated softwood posts and rails	m	0.35	15.07	0.05	6.15	**21.27**	*4.61*
X1.1.2.34	as above; extra for end post	Nr	0.35	14.77	0.11	8.62	**23.50**	*4.91*
X1.1.2.35	as above; extra for angle post	Nr	0.40	17.16	0.16	13.04	**30.36**	*7.49*
X1.1.2.36	as above; extra for intersection post	Nr	0.35	14.77	0.11	13.04	**27.92**	*7.49*
X1.1.2.37	Wooden post and rail fencing, BS 1722, part 7, nailed type; intermediate main posts at 1.80m centres; height: 1.10m (4 rails); treated softwood posts and rails, posts pointed for driving	m	0.35	14.69	0.05	6.15	**20.89**	*4.61*
X1.1.2.38	as above; extra for end post	Nr	0.34	14.43	0.11	8.62	**23.16**	*4.91*
X1.1.2.39	as above; extra for angle post	Nr	0.39	16.73	0.16	13.04	**29.93**	*7.49*
X1.1.2.40	as above; extra for intersection post	Nr	0.34	14.43	0.11	13.04	**27.58**	*7.49*
X1.1.2.41	Wooden post and rail fencing, BS 1722, part 7, nailed type; intermediate main posts at 1.80m centres; height: 1.10m (4 rails); untreated Oak posts and rails	m	0.50	21.37	0.05	19.61	**41.03**	*6.36*
X1.1.2.42	as above; extra for end post	Nr	0.33	14.18	0.11	22.77	**37.06**	*7.40*

X1 Fences continued...

		Unit	Labour Hours	Labour Net £	Plant Net £	Materials Net £	Unit Net £	CO_2 Kg
XI.I	**Timber post and rail**							
XI.I.2	Height: I - I.25m							
XI.I.2.43	as previous items; extra for angle post	Nr	0.39	16.60	0.16	33.02	**49.78**	*10.74*
XI.I.2.44	as above; extra for intersection post	Nr	0.33	14.18	0.11	33.02	**47.31**	*10.74*
XI.I.2.45	Wooden post and rail fencing, BS I722, part 7, nailed type; intermediate main posts at I.80m centres; height: I.I0m (4 rails); untreated Oak posts and rails; posts pointed for driving	m	0.49	20.86	0.05	19.61	**40.52**	*6.36*
XI.I.2.46	as above; extra for end post	Nr	0.32	13.79	0.11	22.77	**36.67**	*7.40*
XI.I.2.47	as above; extra for angle post	Nr	0.38	16.18	0.16	33.02	**49.36**	*10.74*
XI.I.2.48	as above; extra for intersection post	Nr	0.32	13.79	0.11	33.02	**46.92**	*10.74*
XI.I.2.49	Wooden palisade fencing BS I722, part 5, with intermediate posts at 3m centres; 75 x 20mm rectangular pales with square tops spaced 75mm apart; height: I.20m; treated wooden posts	m	0.49	20.69	0.89	18.38	**39.96**	*13.77*
XI.I.2.50	as above; extra for end post	Nr	0.40	16.82	5.14	24.54	**46.50**	*59.98*
XI.I.2.5I	as above; extra for angle post	Nr	0.49	20.86	6.83	22.90	**50.59**	*41.97*
XI.I.2.52	Cleft chestnut pale fencing BS I722, part 4, with intermediate posts at maximum centres and spacings as Table I; height: I.05m; untreated chestnut, pointed for driving	m	0.30	12.81	0.05	4.65	**17.51**	*5.80*
XI.I.2.53	as above; extra for straining posts and struts: end post and one strut	Nr	0.49	20.86	0.11	9.15	**30.12**	*5.31*
XI.I.2.54	as above; extra for straining posts and struts: corner post and two struts	Nr	0.57	24.09	0.16	13.75	**38.00**	*8.15*
XI.I.2.55	Cleft chestnut pale fencing BS I722, part 4, with intermediate posts at maximum centres and spacings as Table I; height: I.20m; untreated chestnut, pointed for driving	m	0.30	12.81	0.05	5.40	**18.26**	*6.59*
XI.I.2.56	as above; extra for straining posts and struts: end post and one strut	Nr	0.52	22.05	0.11	9.15	**31.31**	*5.31*
XI.I.2.57	as above; extra for straining posts and struts: corner post and two struts	Nr	0.64	27.12	0.16	13.35	**40.63**	*7.64*
XI.I.3	Height: I.25 - I.5m							
XI.I.3.0I	BS I722 part 7, morticed type; intermediate main posts at 2.85m centres, one prick post between each main post; height: I.30m (4 rails); treated softwood posts and rails; prick posts pointed for driving	m	0.41	17.37	0.05	7.39	**24.81**	*5.33*
XI.I.3.02	as above; extra for end post	Nr	0.35	14.77	0.11	16.56	**31.44**	*10.22*

X1 Fences continued...

		Unit	Labour Hours	Labour Net £	Plant Net £	Materials Net £	Unit Net £	CO_2 Kg
X1.1	**Timber post and rail**							
X1.1.3	Height: 1.25 - 1.5m							
X1.1.3.03	as previous item; extra for angle post	Nr	0.40	17.16	0.16	24.15	**41.47**	*14.91*
X1.1.3.04	as above; extra for intersection post	Nr	0.35	14.77	0.11	24.15	**39.03**	*14.91*
X1.1.3.05	BS 1722 part 7, morticed type; intermediate main posts at 2.85m centres, one prick post between each main post; height: 1.30m (4 rails); untreated Oak posts and rails; prick posts pointed for driving	m	0.50	21.37	0.05	20.37	**41.79**	*6.60*
X1.1.3.06	as above; extra for end post	Nr	0.35	14.77	0.11	27.32	**42.20**	*8.88*
X1.1.3.07	as above; extra for angle post	Nr	0.40	17.16	0.16	39.47	**56.79**	*12.83*
X1.1.3.08	as above; extra for intersection post	Nr	0.35	14.77	0.11	39.85	**54.73**	*12.96*
X1.1.3.09	Wooden post and rail fencing, BS 1722, part 7, nailed type; intermediate main posts at 1.80m centres; height: 1.30m (4 rails); treated softwood posts and rails	m	0.35	15.07	0.05	6.15	**21.27**	*4.61*
X1.1.3.10	as above; extra for end post	Nr	0.35	14.77	0.11	8.62	**23.50**	*4.91*
X1.1.3.11	as above; extra for angle post	Nr	0.40	17.16	0.16	13.04	**30.36**	*7.49*
X1.1.3.12	as above; extra for intersection post	Nr	0.35	14.77	0.11	13.04	**27.92**	*7.49*
X1.1.3.13	Wooden post and rail fencing, BS 1722, part 7, nailed type; intermediate main posts at 1.80m centres; height: 1.30m (4 rails); treated softwood posts and rails, posts pointed for driving	m	0.35	14.69	0.05	6.15	**20.89**	*4.61*
X1.1.3.14	as above; extra for end post	Nr	0.34	14.43	0.11	8.62	**23.16**	*4.91*
X1.1.3.15	as above; extra for angle post	Nr	0.39	16.73	0.16	13.04	**29.93**	*7.49*
X1.1.3.16	as above; extra for intersection post	Nr	0.34	14.43	0.11	13.04	**27.58**	*7.49*
X1.1.3.17	Wooden post and rail fencing, BS 1722, part 7, nailed type; intermediate main posts at 1.80m centres; height: 1.30m (4 rails); untreated Oak posts and rails	m	0.50	21.37	0.05	20.37	**41.79**	*6.60*
X1.1.3.18	as above; extra for end post	Nr	0.33	14.18	0.11	27.32	**41.61**	*8.88*
X1.1.3.19	as above; extra for angle post	Nr	0.39	16.60	0.16	39.47	**56.23**	*12.83*
X1.1.3.20	as above; extra for intersection post	Nr	0.33	14.18	0.11	39.85	**54.14**	*12.96*
X1.1.3.21	Wooden post and rail fencing, BS 1722, part 7, nailed type; intermediate main posts at 1.80m centres; height: 1.30m (4 rails); untreated Oak posts and rails; posts pointed for driving	m	0.49	20.86	0.05	20.37	**41.28**	*6.60*
X1.1.3.22	as above; extra for end post	Nr	0.32	13.79	0.11	27.32	**41.22**	*8.88*

X1 Fences continued...

		Unit	Labour Hours	Labour Net £	Plant Net £	Materials Net £	Unit Net £	*CO_2 Kg*
X1.1	**Timber post and rail**							
X1.1.3	Height: 1.25 - 1.5m							
X1.1.3.23	as previous item; extra for angle post	Nr	0.38	16.18	0.16	39.47	**55.81**	*12.83*
X1.1.3.24	as above; extra for intersection post	Nr	0.32	13.79	0.11	39.85	**53.75**	*12.96*
X1.1.3.25	Wooden palisade fencing BS 1722, part 5, with intermediate posts at 3m centres; 75 x 20mm rectangular pales with square tops spaced 75mm apart; height: 1.40m; treated wooden posts	m	0.49	20.77	0.89	24.04	**45.70**	*15.17*
X1.1.3.26	as above; extra for end post	Nr	0.42	17.88	5.14	26.64	**49.66**	*61.53*
X1.1.3.27	as above; extra for angle post	Nr	0.50	21.29	6.83	25.65	**53.77**	*44.29*
X1.1.3.28	Cleft chestnut pale fencing BS 1722, part 4, with intermediate posts at maximum centres and spacings as Table 1; height: 1.35m; untreated chestnut, pointed for driving	m	0.30	12.81	0.05	7.10	**19.96**	*7.47*
X1.1.3.29	as above; extra for straining posts and struts: end post and one strut	Nr	0.52	22.05	0.11	10.78	**32.94**	*6.34*
X1.1.3.30	as above; extra for straining posts and struts: corner post and two struts	Nr	0.64	27.12	0.16	15.38	**42.66**	*9.18*
X1.1.4	Height: 1.5 - 2.0m							
X1.1.4.01	Wooden palisade fencing BS 1722, part 5, with intermediate posts at 3m centres; 75 x 20mm rectangular pales with square tops spaced 75mm apart; height: 1.60m; treated wooden posts	m	0.49	20.77	0.89	27.07	**48.73**	*15.77*
X1.1.4.02	as above; extra for end post	Nr	0.47	20.01	5.14	26.64	**51.79**	*61.53*
X1.1.4.03	as above; extra for angle post	Nr	0.60	25.54	6.83	25.65	**58.02**	*44.29*
X1.1.4.04	Wooden palisade fencing BS 1722, part 5, with intermediate posts at 3m centres; 75 x 20mm rectangular pales with square tops spaced 75mm apart; height: 1.80m; treated wooden posts	m	0.54	23.03	0.89	27.57	**51.49**	*16.03*
X1.1.4.05	as above; extra for end post	Nr	0.45	19.16	5.14	29.83	**54.13**	*63.08*
X1.1.4.06	as above; extra for angle post	Nr	0.53	22.39	7.69	30.53	**60.61**	*46.95*
X1.1.4.07	Cleft chestnut pale fencing BS 1722, part 4, with intermediate posts at maximum centres and spacings as Table 1; height: 1.80m; untreated chestnut, pointed for driving	m	0.30	12.81	0.05	8.81	**21.67**	*9.85*
X1.1.4.08	as above; extra for straining posts and struts: end post and one strut	Nr	0.52	22.05	0.11	13.45	**35.61**	*7.89*
X1.1.4.09	as above; extra for straining posts and struts: corner post and two struts	Nr	0.64	27.12	0.16	19.50	**46.78**	*11.51*

X1 Fences continued...

		Unit	Labour Hours	Labour Net £	Plant Net £	Materials Net £	Unit Net £	CO_2 Kg
X1.2	**Timber post and wire**							
X1.2.1	Height: not exceeding 1m							
X1.2.1.01	Strained wire fencing, BS 1722 part 2, with 4mm galvanised wire; intermediate posts at 3m centres; height: 0.85m (3 wires); treated round softwood posts; pointed for driving	m	0.21	9.07	0.05	1.23	**10.35**	*1.34*
X1.2.1.02	as above; extra for straining posts and struts: end post and one strut	Nr	0.46	19.58	0.11	7.35	**27.04**	*3.65*
X1.2.1.03	as above; extra for straining posts and struts: corner post and two struts	Nr	0.57	24.09	0.16	12.05	**36.30**	*5.64*
X1.2.1.04	Strained wire fencing, BS 1722 part 2, with 4mm galvanised wire; intermediate posts at 3m centres; height: 0.85m (3 wires); treated sawn softwood posts; pointed for driving	m	0.21	9.07	0.05	1.93	**11.05**	*1.69*
X1.2.1.05	as above; extra for straining posts and struts: end post and one strut	Nr	0.46	19.58	0.11	10.22	**29.91**	*5.57*
X1.2.1.06	as above; extra for straining posts and struts: corner post and two struts	Nr	0.57	24.09	0.16	15.67	**39.92**	*8.40*
X1.2.1.07	Strained wire fencing, BS 1722 part 2, with 4mm galvanised wire; intermediate posts at 3m centres; height: 1.00m (6 wires); treated round softwood posts; pointed for driving	m	0.22	9.32	0.05	1.69	**11.06**	*2.17*
X1.2.1.08	as above; extra for straining posts and struts: end post and one strut	Nr	0.47	19.88	0.11	10.40	**30.39**	*4.73*
X1.2.1.09	as above; extra for straining posts and struts: corner post and two struts	Nr	0.58	24.73	0.16	18.30	**43.19**	*8.24*
X1.2.1.10	Strained wire fencing, BS 1722 part 2, with 4mm galvanised wire; intermediate posts at 3m centres; height: 1.00m (6 wires); treated sawn softwood posts; pointed for driving	m	0.22	9.32	0.05	2.44	**11.81**	*2.61*
X1.2.1.11	as above; extra for straining posts and struts: end post and one strut	Nr	0.47	19.88	0.11	13.20	**33.19**	*6.85*
X1.2.1.12	as above; extra for straining posts and struts: corner post and two struts	Nr	0.58	24.73	0.16	24.59	**49.48**	*11.64*
X1.2.1.13	Chain link fencing, BS 1722, part 1, with galvanised mesh, line and tying wire, intermediate posts at 3m centres; height: 0.90m (medium 2 line wires); treated softwood posts	m	0.30	12.69	0.16	3.16	**16.01**	*6.96*
X1.2.1.14	as above; extra for straining posts and struts: end post and one strut	Nr	0.85	36.18	0.11	10.22	**46.51**	*5.57*

X1 Fences continued...

		Unit	Labour Hours	Labour Net £	Plant Net £	Materials Net £	Unit Net £	CO_2 Kg
X1.2	**Timber post and wire**							
X1.2.2	Height: 1 - 1.25m							
X1.2.2.01	Chain link fencing, BS 1722, part 1, with galvanised mesh, line and tying wire, intermediate posts at 3m centres; height: 1.20m (heavy 3 line wires); treated softwood posts	m	0.34	14.47	0.16	4.37	19.00	*9.27*
X1.2.2.02	as above; extra for straining posts and struts: end post and one strut	Nr	0.85	36.18	0.11	12.17	48.46	*6.60*
X1.2.3	Height: 1.25 - 1.5m							
X1.2.3.01	Strained wire fencing, BS 1722 part 2, with 4mm galvanised wire; intermediate posts at 3m centres; height: 1.40m (8 wires); treated round softwood posts; pointed for driving	m	0.23	9.62	0.05	2.52	12.19	*2.93*
X1.2.3.02	as above; extra for straining posts and struts: end post and one strut	Nr	0.47	20.18	0.11	13.85	34.14	*6.16*
X1.2.3.03	as above; extra for straining posts and struts: corner post and two struts	Nr	0.59	24.99	0.16	23.80	48.95	*10.18*
X1.2.3.04	Strained wire fencing, BS 1722 part 2, with 4mm galvanised wire; intermediate posts at 3m centres; height: 1.40m (8 wires); treated sawn softwood posts; pointed for driving	m	0.23	9.62	0.05	3.24	12.91	*3.42*
X1.2.3.05	as above; extra for straining posts and struts: end post and one strut	Nr	0.47	20.18	0.11	18.05	38.34	*8.92*
X1.2.3.06	as above; extra for straining posts and struts: corner post and two struts	Nr	0.59	24.99	0.16	30.05	55.20	*14.22*
X1.2.3.07	Straining wire fencing, BS 1722 part 2, dropper pattern with 4mm wire; intermediate posts at 5m centres; height: 1.40m (8 wires); treated round softwood posts, pointed for driving, cleft chestnut pale dropper	m	0.23	9.62	0.05	4.79	14.46	*5.19*
X1.2.3.08	Straining wire fencing, BS 1722 part 2, dropper pattern with 4mm wire; intermediate posts at 5m centres; height: 1.40m (8 wires); treated sawn softwood posts, pointed for driving treated wooden batten dropper	m	0.23	9.62	0.05	4.79	14.46	*5.19*
X1.2.3.09	Chain link fencing, BS 1722, part 1, with galvanised mesh, line and tying wire, intermediate posts at 3m centres; height: 1.40m (medium 3 line wires); treated softwood posts	m	0.43	18.09	0.16	4.83	23.08	*10.77*
X1.2.3.10	as above; extra for straining posts and struts: end post and one strut	Nr	0.85	36.18	0.11	13.80	50.09	*7.63*

X1 Fences continued...

		Unit	Labour Hours	Labour Net £	Plant Net £	Materials Net £	Unit Net £	CO_2 Kg
X1.2	**Timber post and wire**							
X1.2.4	Height: 1.5 - 2.0m							
X1.2.4.01	Chain link fencing, BS 1722, part 1, with galvanised mesh, line and tying wire, intermediate posts at 3m centres; height: 1.80m (heavy 3 line wires); treated softwood posts	m	0.45	19.16	0.16	7.74	**27.06**	*13.59*
X1.2.4.02	as above; extra for straining posts and struts: end post and one strut	Nr	0.90	38.31	0.15	16.34	**54.80**	*8.66*
X1.2.5	Height: 2 - 2.5m							
X1.2.5.01	Chain link fencing, BS 1722, part 1, with galvanised mesh, line and tying wire, intermediate posts at 3m centres; 2.13m (heavy 3 line wires); treated softwood posts	m	0.45	19.16	0.16	10.00	**29.32**	*15.83*
X1.2.5.02	as above; extra for straining posts and struts: end post and one strut	Nr	0.90	38.31	0.15	18.35	**56.81**	*9.70*
X1.3	**Concrete post and wire**							
X1.3.1	Height: not exceeding 1m							
X1.3.1.01	Strained wire fencing, BS 1722, part 2, with 4mm galvanised wire; intermediate posts at 3m centres; height: 0.85m (3 wires); concrete posts	m	0.32	13.58	0.89	5.72	**20.19**	*12.21*
X1.3.1.02	as above; extra for straining posts and struts: end post and one strut	Nr	0.62	26.39	4.18	32.12	**62.69**	*64.90*
X1.3.1.03	as above; extra for straining posts and struts: corner post and two struts	Nr	0.83	35.33	7.93	35.22	**78.48**	*51.33*
X1.3.1.04	Strained wire fencing, BS 1722, part 2, with 4mm galvanised wire; intermediate posts at 3m centres; height: 1.00m (6 wires); concrete posts	m	0.33	13.96	0.89	6.97	**21.82**	*13.76*
X1.3.1.05	as above; extra for straining posts and struts: end post and one strut	Nr	0.65	27.80	5.14	36.56	**69.50**	*69.93*
X1.3.1.06	as above; extra for straining posts and struts: corner post and two struts	Nr	0.83	35.25	7.93	41.10	**84.28**	*56.47*
X1.3.1.07	Chain link fencing, BS 1722, part 1, with galvanised mesh, line and tying wire; intermediate posts at 3m centres; height: 0.90m (medium 2 line wires); concrete posts	m	0.30	12.69	0.89	7.46	**21.04**	*17.65*
X1.3.1.08	as above; extra for straining posts and struts: end post and one strut	Nr	0.62	26.39	4.32	32.46	**63.17**	*66.04*
X1.3.1.09	as above; extra for straining posts and struts: corner post and two struts	Nr	0.83	35.33	7.93	35.22	**78.48**	*51.33*
X1.3.1.10	Wooden palisade fencing BS 1722, part 5, with intermediate posts at 3m centres; 75 x 20mm rectangular pales with square tops spaced 75mm apart; height: 1.00m; concrete posts	m	0.47	19.88	0.89	19.29	**40.06**	*14.73*

X1 Fences continued...

		Unit	Labour Hours	Labour Net £	Plant Net £	Materials Net £	Unit Net £	CO_2 Kg
X1.3	**Concrete post and wire**							
X1.3.1	Height: not exceeding 1m							
X1.3.1.11	as previous item; extra for end post	Nr	0.38	16.18	5.14	26.21	**47.53**	*46.21*
X1.3.1.12	as above; extra for angle post	Nr	0.47	20.09	6.83	34.22	**61.14**	*51.52*
X1.3.1.13	Cleft chestnut pale fencing BS 1722, part 4, with intermediate posts at maximum centres and spacings as Table 1; height: 0.90m; concrete posts	m	0.23	9.62	1.92	12.58	**24.12**	*24.32*
X1.3.1.14	as above; extra for straining posts and struts: end post and one strut	Nr	0.58	24.48	2.12	21.09	**47.69**	*31.86*
X1.3.1.15	as above; extra for straining posts and struts: corner post and two struts	Nr	0.63	26.95	2.12	27.23	**56.30**	*36.19*
X1.3.1.16	Cleft chestnut pale fencing BS 1722, part 4, with intermediate posts at maximum centres and spacings as Table 1; height: 0.90m; untreated chestnut, pointed for driving; additional costs of barbed wire fixed above the fencing; posts increased in length by 150mm for each line of barbed wire: one line of barbed wire: concrete posts	m	0.05	2.13	-	0.27	**2.40**	*1.03*
X1.3.1.17	as above; two lines of barbed wire: concrete posts	m	0.10	4.26	-	0.54	**4.80**	*2.06*
X1.3.2	Height: 1 - 1.25m							
X1.3.2.01	Chain link fencing, BS 1722, part 1, with galvanised mesh, line and tying wire; intermediate posts at 3m centres; height: 1.20m (heavy 3 line wires); concrete posts	m	0.33	13.96	0.89	8.97	**23.82**	*20.52*
X1.3.2.02	as above; extra for straining posts and struts: end post and one strut	Nr	0.76	32.44	5.14	36.56	**74.14**	*69.93*
X1.3.2.03	as above; extra for straining posts and struts: corner post and two struts	Nr	0.89	37.97	3.79	41.10	**82.86**	*54.74*
X1.3.2.04	Wooden palisade fencing BS 1722, part 6, with intermediate posts at 3m centres; 75 x 20mm rectangular pales with square tops spaced 75mm apart; height: 1.20m; concrete posts	m	0.48	20.31	0.89	22.47	**43.67**	*16.26*
X1.3.2.05	as above; extra for end post	Nr	0.42	17.88	5.14	27.72	**50.74**	*47.95*
X1.3.2.06	as above; extra for angle post	Nr	0.49	20.86	6.83	36.98	**64.67**	*55.86*
X1.3.2.07	Cleft chestnut pale fencing BS 1722, part 4, with intermediate posts at maximum centres and spacings as Table 1; height: 1.05m; concrete posts	m	0.24	10.26	1.92	11.40	**23.58**	*27.55*
X1.3.2.08	as above; extra for straining posts and struts: end post and one strut	Nr	0.60	25.71	2.12	21.93	**49.76**	*32.94*
X1.3.2.09	as above; extra for straining posts and struts: corner post and two struts	Nr	0.75	32.01	2.12	28.91	**63.04**	*38.36*

X1 Fences continued...

		Unit	Labour Hours	Labour Net £	Plant Net £	Materials Net £	Unit Net £	CO_2 Kg
X1.3	**Concrete post and wire**							
X1.3.2	Height: 1 - 1.25m							
X1.3.2.10	Cleft chestnut pale fencing BS 1722, part 4, with intermediate posts at maximum centres and spacings as Table 1; height: 1.20m; concrete posts	m	0.30	12.81	1.92	12.16	**26.89**	*28.74*
X1.3.2.11	as above; extra for straining posts and struts: end post and one strut	Nr	0.60	25.71	2.12	23.12	**50.95**	*34.03*
X1.3.2.12	as above; extra for straining posts and struts: corner post and two struts	Nr	0.89	37.67	2.17	31.87	**71.71**	*42.56*
X1.3.3	Height: 1.25 - 1.5m							
X1.3.3.01	Strained wire fencing, BS 1722, part 2, with 4mm galvanised wire; intermediate posts at 3m centres; height: 1.40m (8 wires); concrete posts	m	0.34	14.26	0.89	7.36	**22.51**	*14.22*
X1.3.3.02	as above; extra for straining posts and struts: end post and one strut	Nr	0.80	34.06	4.18	37.00	**75.24**	*60.81*
X1.3.3.03	as above; extra for straining posts and struts: corner post and two struts	Nr	0.88	37.46	3.99	48.73	**90.18**	*61.79*
X1.3.3.04	Straining wire fencing, BS 1722, part 2, dropper pattern with 4mm wire; intermediate posts at 5m centres; concrete posts; cleft chestnut pale droppers	m	0.34	14.26	0.82	8.23	**23.31**	*15.10*
X1.3.3.05	Chain link fencing, BS 1722, part 1, with galvanised mesh, line and tying wire; intermediate posts at 3m centres; height: 1.40m (medium 3 line wires); concrete posts	m	0.33	13.96	0.89	9.54	**24.39**	*22.32*
X1.3.3.06	as above; extra for straining posts and struts: end post and one strut	Nr	0.76	32.44	5.14	38.54	**76.12**	*72.46*
X1.3.3.07	as above; extra for straining posts and struts: corner post and two struts	Nr	0.89	37.97	3.79	44.27	**86.03**	*58.35*
X1.3.3.08	Wooden palisade fencing BS 1722, part 6, with intermediate posts at 3m centres; 75 x 20mm rectangular pales with square tops spaced 75mm apart; height: 1.40m; concrete posts: extra for end post	m	0.49	20.77	0.89	29.82	**51.48**	*22.63*
X1.3.3.09	as above; extra for end post	Nr	0.42	17.88	5.14	36.39	**59.41**	*72.01*
X1.3.3.10	as above; extra for angle post	Nr	0.45	19.16	6.83	40.70	**66.69**	*60.19*
X1.3.3.11	Cleft chestnut pale fencing BS 1722, part 4, with intermediate posts at maximum centres and spacings as Table 1; height: 1.35m; concrete posts	m	0.30	12.81	1.92	13.45	**28.18**	*29.44*
X1.3.3.12	as above; extra for straining posts and struts: end post and one strut	Nr	0.60	25.71	2.12	24.36	**52.19**	*35.47*
X1.3.3.13	as above; extra for straining posts and struts: corner post and two struts	Nr	0.89	37.67	2.17	33.11	**72.95**	*44.00*

X1 Fences continued...

		Unit	Labour Hours	Labour Net £	Plant Net £	Materials Net £	Unit Net £	CO_2 Kg
X1.3	**Concrete post and wire**							
X1.3.4	Height: 1.5 - 2.0m							
X1.3.4.01	Chain link fencing, BS 1722, part 1, with galvanised mesh, line and tying wire; intermediate posts at 3m centres; height: 1.80m (heavy 3 line wires); concrete posts	m	0.34	14.26	0.89	12.66	27.81	*25.24*
X1.3.4.02	as above; extra for straining posts and struts: end post and one strut	Nr	0.86	36.65	4.32	42.61	83.58	*75.12*
X1.3.4.03	as above; extra for straining posts and struts: corner post and two struts	Nr	1.02	43.25	7.93	50.57	101.75	*64.72*
X1.3.4.04	Chain link fencing, BS 1722, part 1, with galvanised mesh, line and tying wire, 3 lines of barbed wire protection at top; intermediate posts at 3m centres; height: 1.80m (heavy 3 line wires); concrete posts; steel extension arms	m	0.37	15.84	0.89	16.07	32.80	*29.43*
X1.3.4.05	as above; extra for straining posts and struts: end post and one strut	Nr	0.90	38.23	5.14	43.91	87.28	*77.37*
X1.3.4.06	as above; extra for straining posts and struts: corner post and two struts	Nr	1.02	43.25	7.93	52.61	103.79	*86.06*
X1.3.4.07	Chain link fencing, BS 1722, part 1, with galvanised mesh, line and tying wire, 3 lines of barbed wire protection at top; intermediate posts at 3m centres; height: 1.80m (heavy 3 line wires); concrete posts with cranked tops	m	0.38	16.35	0.89	13.39	30.63	*27.23*
X1.3.4.08	as above; extra for straining posts and struts: end post and one strut	Nr	0.92	39.04	5.14	41.50	85.68	*74.99*
X1.3.4.09	as above; extra for straining posts and struts: corner post and two struts	Nr	1.00	42.74	7.69	47.76	98.19	*63.60*
X1.3.4.10	Wooden palisade fencing BS 1722, part 6, with intermediate posts at 3m centres; 75 x 20mm rectangular pales with square tops spaced 75mm apart; height: 1.60m; concrete posts: extra for end post	m	0.50	21.24	0.89	33.25	55.38	*24.76*
X1.3.4.11	as above; extra for end post	Nr	0.42	17.88	5.14	38.59	61.61	*74.90*
X1.3.4.12	as above; extra for angle post	Nr	0.49	20.82	5.06	44.00	69.88	*63.64*
X1.3.4.13	Wooden palisade fencing BS 1722, part 6, with intermediate posts at 3m centres; 75 x 20mm rectangular pales with square tops spaced 75mm apart; height: 1.80m; concrete posts: extra for end post	m	0.54	23.03	0.89	33.59	57.51	*26.28*
X1.3.4.14	as above; extra for end post	Nr	0.45	19.16	5.14	39.51	63.81	*77.79*
X1.3.4.15	as above; extra for angle post	Nr	0.53	22.39	5.06	45.38	72.83	*67.97*

X1 Fences continued...

		Unit	Labour Hours	Labour Net £	Plant Net £	Materials Net £	Unit Net £	CO_2 Kg
X1.3	**Concrete post and wire**							
X1.3.4	Height: 1.5 - 2.0m							
X1.3.4.16	Cleft chestnut pale fencing BS 1722, part 4, with intermediate posts at maximum centres and spacings as Table 1; height: 1.80m; concrete posts	m	0.35	14.90	1.92	14.90	**31.72**	*32.52*
X1.3.4.17	as above; extra for straining posts and struts: end post and one strut	Nr	0.65	27.67	2.12	25.99	**55.78**	*38.00*
X1.3.4.18	as above; extra for straining posts and struts: corner post and two struts	Nr	0.89	37.67	2.17	35.27	**75.11**	*47.61*
X1.3.5	Height: 2 - 2.5m							
X1.3.5.01	Chain link fencing, BS 1722, part 1, with galvanised mesh, line and tying wire; intermediate posts at 3m centres; height: 2.13m (heavy 3 line wires); concrete posts	m	0.39	16.64	0.89	16.32	**33.85**	*29.35*
X1.3.5.02	as above; extra for straining posts and struts: end post and one strut	Nr	0.92	39.04	5.14	47.12	**91.30**	*80.04*
X1.3.5.03	as above; extra for straining posts and struts: corner post and two struts	Nr	1.02	43.25	7.93	59.17	**110.35**	*71.94*
X1.3.5.04	Chain link fencing, BS 1722, part 1, with galvanised mesh, line and tying wire, 3 lines of barbed wire protection at top; intermediate posts at 3m centres; height: 2.13m (heavy 3 line wires); concrete posts; steel extension arms	m	0.40	17.16	0.89	18.52	**36.57**	*31.90*
X1.3.5.05	as above; extra for straining posts and struts: end post and one strut	Nr	0.98	41.85	5.14	50.12	**97.11**	*82.43*
X1.3.5.06	as above; extra for straining posts and struts: corner post and two struts	Nr	1.07	45.51	7.69	58.77	**111.97**	*73.20*
X1.3.5.07	Chain link fencing, BS 1722, part 1, with galvanised mesh, line and tying wire, 3 lines of barbed wire protection at top; intermediate posts at 3m centres; height: 2.13m (heavy 3 line wires); concrete posts with cranked tops	m	0.46	19.58	0.89	13.85	**34.32**	*27.61*
X1.3.5.08	as above; extra for straining posts and struts: end post and one strut	Nr	1.00	42.66	5.14	45.35	**93.15**	*78.60*
X1.3.5.09	as above; extra for straining posts and struts: corner post and two struts	Nr	1.17	49.72	7.69	54.00	**111.41**	*69.38*
X1.4	**Metal post and wire**							
X1.4.1	Height: not exceeding 1m							
X1.4.1.01	Strained wire fencing, BS 1722, part 2, with 4mm galvanised wire; intermediate posts at 3m centres; height: 0.85m (3 wires); galvanised steel angle posts pointed for driving	m	0.29	12.43	0.89	5.31	**18.63**	*17.36*
X1.4.1.02	as above; extra for straining posts and struts with welded base plates: end post and one strut	Nr	0.61	26.01	4.83	29.30	**60.14**	*90.70*

X1 Fences continued...

		Unit	Labour Hours	Labour Net £	Plant Net £	Materials Net £	Unit Net £	CO_2 Kg
X1.4	**Metal post and wire**							
X1.4.1	Height: not exceeding 1m							
X1.4.1.03	as previous item; extra for straining posts and struts with welded base plates: corner post and two struts	Nr	0.68	28.99	7.08	44.12	**80.19**	*132.07*
X1.4.1.04	Strained wire fencing, BS 1722, part 2, with 4mm galvanised wire; intermediate posts at 3m centres; height: 1.00m (6 wires); galvanised steel angle posts pointed for driving	m	0.29	12.43	0.89	5.76	**19.08**	*18.19*
X1.4.1.05	as above; extra for straining posts and struts with welded base plates: end post and one strut	Nr	0.65	27.71	4.83	29.30	**61.84**	*90.70*
X1.4.1.06	as above; extra for straining posts and struts with welded base plates: corner post and two struts	Nr	0.73	31.08	7.08	44.12	**82.28**	*132.07*
X1.4.1.07	Chain link fencing, BS 1722, part 1, with galvanised mesh, line and tying wire, intermediate posts at 3m centres; height: 0.90m (medium 2 line wires); galvanised steel angle posts pointed for driving	m	0.23	9.92	0.89	10.19	**21.00**	*18.23*
X1.4.1.08	as above; extra for straining posts and struts with welded base plates: end post and one strut	Nr	0.61	26.01	4.83	29.30	**60.14**	*90.70*
X1.4.1.09	as above; extra for straining posts and struts with welded base plates: corner post and two struts	Nr	0.68	28.99	7.08	44.12	**80.19**	*132.07*
X1.4.2	Height: 1 - 1.25m							
X1.4.2.01	Chain link fencing, BS 1722, part 1, with galvanised mesh, line and tying wire, intermediate posts at 3m centres; height: 1.20m (heavy 3 line wires); galvanised steel angle posts pointed for driving	m	0.31	13.24	0.89	7.91	**22.04**	*25.31*
X1.4.2.02	as above; extra for straining posts and struts with welded base plates: end post and one strut	Nr	0.67	28.39	4.83	29.30	**62.52**	*90.70*
X1.4.2.03	as above; extra for straining posts and struts with welded base plates: corner post and two struts	Nr	0.78	33.12	7.08	44.12	**84.32**	*132.07*
X1.4.3	Height: 1.25 - 1.5m							
X1.4.3.01	Strained wire fencing, BS 1722, part 2, with 4mm galvanised wire; intermediate posts at 3m centres; height: 1.40m (8 wires); galvanised steel angle posts pointed for driving	m	0.27	11.58	0.89	13.05	**25.52**	*41.28*
X1.4.3.02	as above; extra for straining posts and struts with welded base plates: end post and one strut	Nr	0.65	27.71	4.83	33.23	**65.77**	*103.37*
X1.4.3.03	as above; extra for straining posts and struts with welded base plates: corner post and two struts	Nr	0.73	31.08	7.08	49.36	**87.52**	*148.96*

X1 Fences continued...

		Unit	Labour Hours	Labour Net £	Plant Net £	Materials Net £	Unit Net £	CO_2 Kg
X1.4	**Metal post and wire**							
X1.4.3	Height: 1.25 - 1.5m							
X1.4.3.04	Strained wire fencing, BS 1722, part 2, dropper pattern with 4mm wire; intermediate posts at 5m centres; Galvanised steel angle posts; pointed for driving: 20 x 3mm galvanised flat steel dropper	m	0.27	11.58	0.89	15.23	**27.70**	*42.86*
X1.4.3.05	Chain link fencing, BS 1722, part 1, with galvanised mesh, line and tying wire, intermediate posts at 3m centres; height: 1.40m (medium 3 line wires); galvanised steel angle posts pointed for driving	m	0.25	10.77	0.89	15.21	**26.87**	*49.17*
X1.4.3.06	as above; extra for straining posts and struts with welded base plates: end post and one strut	Nr	0.65	27.71	4.83	33.23	**65.77**	*103.37*
X1.4.3.07	as above; extra for straining posts and struts with welded base plates: corner post and two struts	Nr	0.73	31.08	7.08	49.36	**87.52**	*148.96*
X1.4.4	Height: 1.5 - 2.0m							
X1.4.4.01	Chain link fencing, BS 1722, part 1, with galvanised mesh, line and tying wire, intermediate posts at 3m centres; height: 1.80m (heavy 3 line wires); galvanised steel angle posts pointed for driving	m	0.25	10.77	0.89	19.04	**30.70**	*56.04*
X1.4.4.02	as above; extra for straining posts and struts with welded base plates: end post and one strut	Nr	0.81	34.65	5.14	37.17	**76.96**	*116.19*
X1.4.4.03	as above; extra for straining posts and struts with welded base plates: corner post and two struts	Nr	0.68	28.99	7.93	55.93	**92.85**	*170.47*
X1.4.4.04	Chain link fencing, BS 1722, part 1, with galvanised mesh, line and tying wire, 3 lines of barbed wire protection at top; intermediate posts at 3m centres; height: 1.80m (heavy 3 line wires); galvanised steel angle posts; steel extension arms; pointed for driving	m	0.27	11.32	0.83	22.17	**34.32**	*59.24*
X1.4.4.05	as above; extra for straining posts and struts with welded base plates: end post and one strut	Nr	1.03	43.68	5.14	42.45	**91.27**	*123.69*
X1.4.4.06	as above; extra for straining posts and struts with welded base plates: corner post and two struts	Nr	1.03	43.68	5.14	52.28	**101.10**	*155.36*
X1.4.4.07	Chain link fencing, BS 1722, part 1, with galvanised mesh, line and tying wire, 3 lines of barbed wire protection at top; intermediate posts at 3m centres; height: 1.80m (heavy 3 line wires); galvanised steel angle posts with cranked tops; pointed for driving	m	0.29	12.43	0.83	24.66	**37.92**	*62.62*
X1.4.4.08	as above; extra for straining posts and struts with welded base plates: end post and one strut	Nr	1.03	43.68	5.14	44.94	**93.76**	*127.07*

X1 Fences continued...

		Unit	Labour Hours	Labour Net £	Plant Net £	Materials Net £	Unit Net £	CO_2 Kg
X1.4	**Metal post and wire**							
X1.4.4	Height: 1.5 - 2.0m							
X1.4.4.09	as previous item; extra for straining posts and struts with welded base plates: corner post and two struts	Nr	1.03	43.68	5.14	54.77	103.59	*158.74*
X1.4.5	Height: 2 - 2.5m							
X1.4.5.01	Chain link fencing, BS 1722, part 1, with galvanised mesh, line and tying wire, intermediate posts at 3m centres; height: 2.13m (heavy 3 line wires); galvanised steel angle posts pointed for driving	m	0.26	11.11	0.89	20.35	32.35	*60.26*
X1.4.5.02	as above; extra for straining posts and struts with welded base plates: end post and one strut	Nr	0.81	34.65	5.14	39.13	78.92	*122.52*
X1.4.5.03	as above; extra for straining posts and struts with welded base plates: corner post and two struts	Nr	0.97	41.42	7.93	58.54	107.89	*178.92*
X1.4.5.04	Chain link fencing, BS 1722, part 1, with galvanised mesh, line and tying wire, 3 lines of barbed wire protection at top; intermediate posts at 3m centres; height: 2.13m (heavy 3 line wires); galvanised steel angle posts; steel extension arms; pointed for driving	m	0.27	11.32	0.83	25.24	37.39	*65.45*
X1.4.5.05	as above; extra for straining posts and struts with welded base plates: end post and one strut	Nr	1.03	43.68	5.14	44.41	93.23	*130.02*
X1.4.5.06	as above; extra for straining posts and struts with welded base plates: corner post and two struts	Nr	1.03	43.68	5.14	54.89	103.71	*163.81*
X1.4.5.07	Chain link fencing, BS 1722, part 1, with galvanised mesh, line and tying wire, 3 lines of barbed wire protection at top; intermediate posts at 3m centres; height: 2.13m (heavy 3 line wires); galvanised steel angle posts with cranked tops; pointed for driving	m	0.29	12.43	0.83	27.72	40.98	*69.25*
X1.4.5.08	as above; extra for straining posts and struts with welded base plates: end post and one strut	Nr	1.03	43.85	5.14	49.38	98.37	*137.20*
X1.4.5.09	as above; extra for straining posts and struts with welded base plates: corner post and two struts	Nr	1.09	46.40	5.14	62.35	113.89	*174.37*
X1.4.6	Height: 2.5 - 3m							
X1.4.6.01	Anti-intruder chain link fencing, BS 1722, part 10, with galvanised mesh, lines and tying wire; intermediate posts at 3m centres with cranked tops or extension arms; 3 lines barbed wire protection at top; bottom of mesh buried vertically 0.30m deep including trenching; 2.9m vertical height; concrete posts; cranked top; single protective top	m	0.58	24.48	0.89	24.75	50.12	*45.72*

X1 Fences continued...

		Unit	Labour Hours	Labour Net £	Plant Net £	Materials Net £	Unit Net £	CO_2 Kg
X1.4	**Metal post and wire**							
X1.4.6	Height: 2.5 - 3m							
X1.4.6.02	as previous item; extra for straining posts and struts: end post and one strut	Nr	1.34	56.87	5.14	49.24	**111.25**	*82.45*
X1.4.6.03	as above; extra for straining posts and struts: corner post and two struts	Nr	1.46	62.15	7.69	64.08	**133.92**	*94.39*
X1.4.6.04	Anti-intruder chain link fencing, BS 1722, part 10, with galvanised mesh, lines and tying wire; intermediate posts at 3m centres with cranked tops or extension arms; 3 lines barbed wire protection at top; bottom of mesh buried vertically 0.30m deep including trenching; 2.9m vertical height; concrete posts; steel extension arms; single protective top	m	0.58	24.48	0.89	27.75	**53.12**	*48.10*
X1.4.6.05	as above; extra for straining posts and struts: end post and one strut	Nr	1.40	59.60	5.14	52.24	**116.98**	*84.84*
X1.4.6.06	as above; extra for straining posts and struts: corner post and two struts	Nr	1.56	66.41	5.14	70.08	**141.63**	*98.15*
X1.4.6.07	Anti-intruder chain link fencing, BS 1722, part 10, with galvanised mesh, lines and tying wire; intermediate posts at 3m centres with cranked tops or extension arms; 3 lines barbed wire protection at top; bottom of mesh buried vertically 0.30m deep including trenching; 2.9m vertical height; galvanised steel angle posts with welded extension arms; spragged; single protective top	m	0.58	24.48	0.89	22.78	**48.15**	*55.58*
X1.4.6.08	as above; extra for straining posts and struts: end post and one strut, spragged; bolted tie and bars	Nr	1.48	63.00	5.14	47.04	**115.18**	*142.69*
X1.4.6.09	as above; extra for straining posts and struts: corner post and two struts; spragged; bolted tie bars	Nr	1.56	66.41	5.14	65.58	**137.13**	*184.26*
X1.4.6.10	Anti-intruder chain link fencing, BS 1722, part 10, with galvanised mesh, lines and tying wire; intermediate posts at 3m centres with cranked tops or extension arms; 3 lines barbed wire protection at top; bottom of mesh buried vertically 0.30m deep including trenching; 2.9m vertical height; concrete posts; cranked top; double protective top	m	0.63	26.90	0.89	25.29	**53.08**	*47.78*
X1.4.6.11	as above; extra for straining posts and struts: end post and one strut	Nr	1.40	59.60	5.14	49.24	**113.98**	*82.45*
X1.4.6.12	as above; extra for straining posts and struts: corner post and two struts	Nr	1.53	65.26	7.69	64.08	**137.03**	*94.39*

X1 Fences continued...

		Unit	Labour Hours	Labour Net £	Plant Net £	Materials Net £	Unit Net £	CO_2 Kg
X1.4	**Metal post and wire**							
X1.4.6	Height: 2.5 - 3m							
X1.4.6.13	Anti-intruder chain link fencing, BS 1722, part 10, with galvanised mesh, lines and tying wire; intermediate posts at 3m centres with cranked tops or extension arms; 3 lines barbed wire protection at top; bottom of mesh buried vertically 0.30m deep including trenching; 2.9m vertical height; concrete posts; steel extension arms; double protective top	m	0.63	26.90	0.89	28.29	**56.08**	*50.17*
X1.4.6.14	as above; extra for straining posts and struts: end post and one strut	Nr	1.55	65.98	5.14	52.24	**123.36**	*84.84*
X1.4.6.15	as above; extra for straining posts and struts: corner post and two struts	Nr	1.72	73.22	5.14	70.08	**148.44**	*98.15*
X1.4.6.16	Anti-intruder chain link fencing, BS 1722, part 10, with galvanised mesh, lines and tying wire; intermediate posts at 3m centres with cranked tops or extension arms; 3 lines barbed wire protection at top; bottom of mesh buried vertically 0.30m deep including trenching; 2.9m vertical height; galvanised steel angle posts with welded extension arms; spragged; double protective top	m	0.63	26.90	0.89	23.32	**51.11**	*57.64*
X1.4.6.17	as above; extra for straining posts and struts: end post and one strut, spragged; bolted tie and bars	Nr	1.72	73.22	5.14	47.04	**125.40**	*142.69*
X1.4.6.18	as above; extra for straining posts and struts: corner post and two struts; spragged; bolted tie bars	Nr	1.72	73.22	5.14	65.58	**143.94**	*184.26*
X1.4.6.19	Chain link fencing for tennis court surrounds, BS 1722, part 13, with galvanised mesh, line and tying wire; galvanised mild steel intermediate posts at 3m centres; Fencing 2.75m high; angle section posts pointed for driving	m	0.36	15.37	0.83	21.79	**37.99**	*28.19*
X1.4.6.20	Chain link fencing for tennis court surrounds, BS 1722, part 13, with galvanised mesh, line and tying wire; galvanised mild steel intermediate posts at 3m centres; Fencing 2.75m high; angle section posts with spragged ends	m	0.36	15.37	0.83	21.79	**37.99**	*28.19*
X1.4.6.21	as above; extra for angle section straining posts and struts: one way straining post or gate post with one strut; welded base plate	Nr	1.19	50.83	5.14	44.70	**100.67**	*144.53*
X1.4.6.22	as above; extra for angle section straining posts and struts: two way straining post or gate post with two struts; welded base plate	Nr	1.45	61.77	7.69	58.92	**128.38**	*176.28*

X1 Fences continued...

		Unit	Labour Hours	Labour Net £	Plant Net £	Materials Net £	Unit Net £	CO_2 Kg
X1.4	**Metal post and wire**							
X1.4.6	Height: 2.5 - 3m							
X1.4.6.23	as previous item; extra for gates: single 1.00 x 2.00m	Nr	0.60	25.63	0.83	271.38	297.84	*31.80*
X1.4.6.24	as above; extra for gates: double 1.80 x 2.00m	Nr	0.60	25.63	0.81	588.93	615.37	*52.33*
X1.6	**Timber close boarded**							
X1.6.1	Height: not exceeding 1m							
X1.6.1.01	Close boarded fencing, BS 1722, part 5, softwood pressure treated pales, horizontal rails, capping and gravel boards; intermediate posts at 3m centres; centre stump in each bay; height: 1.00m; concrete posts; morticed types	m	0.39	16.39	1.06	22.68	40.13	*26.92*
X1.6.1.02	as above; extra for: end post	Nr	0.45	19.16	2.82	11.07	33.05	*16.49*
X1.6.1.03	as above; extra for: angle post	Nr	0.45	19.16	2.82	11.07	33.05	*16.49*
X1.6.1.04	Close boarded fencing, BS 1722, part 5, softwood pressure treated pales, horizontal rails, capping and gravel boards; intermediate posts at 3m centres; centre stump in each bay; height: 1.00m; treated sawn softwood posts	m	0.38	16.18	1.06	19.87	37.11	*25.66*
X1.6.1.05	as above; extra for: end post	Nr	0.24	10.17	2.82	14.47	27.46	*17.52*
X1.6.1.06	as above; extra for: angle post	Nr	0.27	11.32	2.82	14.47	28.61	*17.52*
X1.6.1.07	Woven wood fencing, BS 1722, part 11, treated softwood panels between posts at 1.80m centres; height: 1.00m; concrete posts	m	0.40	17.20	0.71	13.76	31.67	*15.80*
X1.6.1.08	as above; extra for: end post	Nr	0.20	8.68	2.12	13.72	24.52	*26.80*
X1.6.1.09	as above; extra for: angle post	Nr	0.24	10.17	2.12	13.72	26.01	*26.80*
X1.6.1.10	Woven wood fencing, BS 1722, part 11, treated softwood panels between posts at 1.80m centres; height: 1.00m; treated sawn softwood posts	m	0.40	17.20	0.71	11.70	29.61	*13.52*
X1.6.1.11	as above; extra for: end post	Nr	0.20	8.68	2.12	9.89	20.69	*22.63*
X1.6.1.12	as above; extra for: angle post	Nr	0.24	10.17	2.12	9.89	22.18	*22.63*
X1.6.1.13	Woven wood fencing, BS 1722, part 11, treated softwood panels between posts at 1.80m centres; height: 1.00m; overlap panels; treated softwood panels between posts at 1.80m centres: Concrete posts	m	0.40	17.20	0.71	14.72	32.63	*15.79*
X1.6.1.14	as above; extra for: end post	Nr	0.20	8.68	2.12	13.72	24.52	*26.80*
X1.6.1.15	as above; extra for: angle post	Nr	0.24	10.17	2.12	13.72	26.01	*26.80*

X1 Fences continued...

		Unit	Labour Hours	Labour Net £	Plant Net £	Materials Net £	Unit Net £	CO_2 Kg
X1.6	**Timber close boarded**							
X1.6.1	Height: not exceeding 1m							
X1.6.1.16	Woven wood fencing, BS 1722, part 11, treated softwood panels between posts at 1.80m centres; height: 1.00m; overlap panels; treated softwood panels between posts at 1.80m centres: Treated softwood posts	m	0.40	17.20	0.71	12.59	**30.50**	*13.47*
X1.6.1.17	as above; extra for: end post	Nr	0.20	8.68	2.12	9.89	**20.69**	*22.63*
X1.6.1.18	as above; extra for: angle post	Nr	0.24	10.17	2.12	9.89	**22.18**	*22.63*
X1.6.1.19	Woven wood fencing, BS 1722, part 11, treated softwood panels between posts at 1.80m centres; height: 1.00m; trellis panel fencing; treated panels between posts at 1.80m centres: Concrete posts	m	0.40	17.20	0.71	16.55	**34.46**	*15.79*
X1.6.1.20	as above; extra for: end post	Nr	0.20	8.68	2.12	13.72	**24.52**	*26.80*
X1.6.1.21	as above; extra for: angle post	Nr	0.24	10.17	2.12	13.72	**26.01**	*26.80*
X1.6.1.22	Woven wood fencing, BS 1722, part 11, treated softwood panels between posts at 1.80m centres; height: 1.00m; trellis panel fencing; treated panels between posts at 1.80m centres: Treated softwood posts	m	0.40	17.20	0.71	14.42	**32.33**	*13.47*
X1.6.1.23	as above; extra for: end post	Nr	0.20	8.68	2.12	9.89	**20.69**	*22.63*
X1.6.1.24	as above; extra for: angle post	Nr	0.24	10.17	2.12	9.89	**22.18**	*22.63*
X1.6.2	Height: 1 - 1.25m							
X1.6.2.01	Close boarded fencing, BS 1722, part 5, softwood pressure treated pales, horizontal rails, capping and gravel boards; intermediate posts at 3m centres; centre stump in each bay; height: 1.20m; concrete posts; morticed types	m	0.39	16.39	1.06	24.49	**41.94**	*29.07*
X1.6.2.02	as above; extra for: end post	Nr	0.45	19.16	2.82	20.36	**42.34**	*22.75*
X1.6.2.03	as above; extra for: angle post	Nr	0.45	19.16	2.82	20.36	**42.34**	*22.75*
X1.6.2.04	Close boarded fencing, BS 1722, part 5, softwood pressure treated pales, horizontal rails, capping and gravel boards; intermediate posts at 3m centres; centre stump in each bay; height: 1.20m; treated sawn softwood posts	m	0.39	16.39	1.06	23.02	**40.47**	*27.56*
X1.6.2.05	as above; extra for: end post	Nr	0.45	19.16	2.82	15.93	**37.91**	*18.21*
X1.6.2.06	as above; extra for: angle post	Nr	0.45	19.16	2.82	15.93	**37.91**	*18.21*
X1.6.2.07	Woven wood fencing, BS 1722, part 11, treated softwood panels between posts at 1.80m centres; height: 1.20m; concrete posts	m	0.40	17.20	0.71	16.14	**34.05**	*17.35*

X1 Fences continued...

		Unit	Labour Hours	Labour Net £	Plant Net £	Materials Net £	Unit Net £	CO_2 Kg
X1.6	**Timber close boarded**							
X1.6.2	Height: 1 - 1.25m							
X1.6.2.08	as previous item; extra for: end post	Nr	0.20	8.68	2.12	16.13	**26.93**	*28.97*
X1.6.2.09	as above; extra for: angle post	Nr	0.24	10.17	2.12	16.13	**28.42**	*28.97*
X1.6.2.10	Woven wood fencing, BS 1722, part 11, treated softwood panels between posts at 1.80m centres; height: 1.20m; treated sawn softwood posts	m	0.40	17.20	0.71	13.66	**31.57**	*14.44*
X1.6.2.11	as above; extra for: end post	Nr	0.26	10.94	2.12	11.52	**24.58**	*23.66*
X1.6.2.12	as above; extra for: angle post	Nr	0.28	12.05	2.12	11.52	**25.69**	*23.66*
X1.6.2.13	Woven wood fencing, BS 1722, part 11, treated softwood panels between posts at 1.80m centres; height: 1.20m; overlap panels; treated softwood panels between posts at 1.80m centres: Concrete posts	m	0.40	17.20	0.71	16.56	**34.47**	*17.33*
X1.6.2.14	as above; extra for: end post	Nr	0.26	10.94	2.12	16.13	**29.19**	*28.97*
X1.6.2.15	as above; extra for: angle post	Nr	0.28	12.05	2.12	16.13	**30.30**	*28.97*
X1.6.2.16	Woven wood fencing, BS 1722, part 11, treated softwood panels between posts at 1.80m centres; height: 1.20m; overlap panels; treated softwood panels between posts at 1.80m centres: Treated softwood posts	m	0.40	17.20	0.71	13.99	**31.90**	*14.38*
X1.6.2.17	as above; extra for: end post	Nr	0.26	10.94	2.12	11.52	**24.58**	*23.66*
X1.6.2.18	as above; extra for: angle post	Nr	0.28	12.05	2.12	11.52	**25.69**	*23.66*
X1.6.2.19	Woven wood fencing, BS 1722, part 11, treated softwood panels between posts at 1.80m centres; height: 1.20m; trellis panel fencing; treated panels between posts at 1.80m centres: Concrete posts	m	0.40	17.20	0.71	19.46	**37.37**	*17.33*
X1.6.2.20	as above; extra for: end post	Nr	0.26	10.94	2.12	16.13	**29.19**	*28.97*
X1.6.2.21	as above; extra for: angle post	Nr	0.28	12.05	2.12	16.13	**30.30**	*28.97*
X1.6.2.22	Woven wood fencing, BS 1722, part 11, treated softwood panels between posts at 1.80m centres; height: 1.20m; trellis panel fencing; treated panels between posts at 1.80m centres: Treated softwood posts	m	0.40	17.20	0.71	16.90	**34.81**	*14.38*
X1.6.2.23	as above; extra for: end post	Nr	0.26	10.94	2.12	11.52	**24.58**	*23.66*
X1.6.2.24	as above; extra for: angle post	Nr	0.28	12.05	2.12	11.52	**25.69**	*23.66*

X1 Fences continued...

		Unit	Labour Hours	Labour Net £	Plant Net £	Materials Net £	Unit Net £	CO_2 Kg
X1.6	**Timber close boarded**							
X1.6.3	Height: 1.25 - 1.5m							
X1.6.3.01	Close boarded fencing, BS 1722, part 5, softwood pressure treated pales, horizontal rails, capping and gravel boards; intermediate posts at 3m centres; centre stump in each bay; height: 1.50m; concrete posts; morticed types	m	0.39	16.39	1.06	26.25	**43.70**	*31.22*
X1.6.3.02	as above; extra for: end post	Nr	0.47	20.14	2.82	21.00	**43.96**	*24.19*
X1.6.3.03	as above; extra for: angle post	Nr	0.47	20.14	2.82	21.00	**43.96**	*24.19*
X1.6.3.04	Close boarded fencing, BS 1722, part 5, softwood pressure treated pales, horizontal rails, capping and gravel boards; intermediate posts at 3m centres; centre stump in each bay; height: 1.50m; treated sawn softwood posts	m	0.39	16.39	1.06	25.04	**42.49**	*29.45*
X1.6.3.05	as above; extra for: end post	Nr	0.47	20.14	2.82	17.39	**40.35**	*18.90*
X1.6.3.06	as above; extra for: angle post	Nr	0.47	20.14	2.82	17.39	**40.35**	*18.90*
X1.6.3.07	Woven wood fencing, BS 1722, part 11, treated softwood panels between posts at 1.80m centres; height: 1.50m; concrete posts	m	0.58	24.86	0.71	17.62	**43.19**	*18.50*
X1.6.3.08	as above; extra for: end post	Nr	0.27	11.32	2.12	16.92	**30.36**	*30.42*
X1.6.3.09	as above; extra for: angle post	Nr	0.29	12.43	2.12	16.92	**31.47**	*30.42*
X1.6.3.10	Woven wood fencing, BS 1722, part 11, treated softwood panels between posts at 1.80m centres; height: 1.50m; treated sawn softwood posts	m	0.48	20.35	0.71	14.85	**35.91**	*14.95*
X1.6.3.11	as above; extra for: end post	Nr	0.27	11.32	2.12	11.74	**25.18**	*23.92*
X1.6.3.12	as above; extra for: angle post	Nr	0.29	12.43	2.12	11.74	**26.29**	*23.92*
X1.6.3.13	Woven wood fencing, BS 1722, part 11, treated softwood panels between posts at 1.80m centres; height: 1.50m; overlap panels; treated softwood panels between posts at 1.80m centres: Concrete posts	m	0.58	24.86	0.71	17.42	**42.99**	*18.41*
X1.6.3.14	as above; extra for: end post	Nr	0.27	11.32	2.12	16.92	**30.36**	*30.42*
X1.6.3.15	as above; extra for: angle post	Nr	0.29	12.43	2.12	16.92	**31.47**	*30.42*
X1.6.3.16	Woven wood fencing, BS 1722, part 11, treated softwood panels between posts at 1.80m centres; height: 1.50m; overlap panels; treated softwood panels between posts at 1.80m centres: Treated softwood posts	m	0.48	20.35	0.71	14.66	**35.72**	*14.86*
X1.6.3.17	as above; extra for: end post	Nr	0.27	11.32	2.12	11.74	**25.18**	*23.92*

X1 Fences continued...

		Unit	Labour Hours	Labour Net £	Plant Net £	Materials Net £	Unit Net £	CO_2 Kg
X1.6	**Timber close boarded**							
X1.6.3	Height: 1.25 - 1.5m							
X1.6.3.18	as previous item; extra for: angle post	Nr	0.29	12.43	2.12	11.74	**26.29**	*23.92*
X1.6.3.19	Woven wood fencing, BS 1722, part 11, treated softwood panels between posts at 1.80m centres; height: 1.50m; trellis panel fencing; treated panels between posts at 1.80m centres: Concrete posts	m	0.58	24.86	0.71	21.47	**47.04**	*18.41*
X1.6.3.20	as above; extra for: end post	Nr	0.27	11.32	2.12	16.92	**30.36**	*30.42*
X1.6.3.21	as above; extra for: angle post	Nr	0.29	12.43	2.12	16.92	**31.47**	*30.42*
X1.6.3.22	Woven wood fencing, BS 1722, part 11, treated softwood panels between posts at 1.80m centres; height: 1.50m; trellis panel fencing; treated panels between posts at 1.80m centres: Treated softwood posts	m	0.48	20.35	0.71	18.70	**39.76**	*14.86*
X1.6.3.23	as above; extra for: end post	Nr	0.27	11.32	2.12	11.74	**25.18**	*23.92*
X1.6.3.24	as above; extra for: angle post	Nr	0.29	12.43	2.12	11.74	**26.29**	*23.92*
X1.6.4	Height: 1.5 - 2.0m							
X1.6.4.01	Close boarded fencing, BS 1722, part 5, softwood pressure treated pales, horizontal rails, capping and gravel boards; intermediate posts at 3m centres; centre stump in each bay; height: 1.60m; concrete posts; morticed types	m	0.39	16.39	1.06	27.02	**44.47**	*32.05*
X1.6.4.02	as above; extra for: end post	Nr	0.50	21.07	2.82	21.00	**44.89**	*24.19*
X1.6.4.03	as above; extra for: angle post	Nr	0.50	21.07	2.82	21.00	**44.89**	*24.19*
X1.6.4.04	Close boarded fencing, BS 1722, part 5, softwood pressure treated pales, horizontal rails, capping and gravel boards; intermediate posts at 3m centres; centre stump in each bay; height: 1.60m; treated sawn softwood posts	m	0.39	16.39	1.06	25.81	**43.26**	*30.29*
X1.6.4.05	as above; extra for: end post	Nr	0.49	20.90	2.82	17.39	**41.11**	*18.90*
X1.6.4.06	as above; extra for: angle post	Nr	0.49	20.90	2.82	18.58	**42.30**	*19.63*
X1.6.4.07	Close boarded fencing, BS 1722, part 5, softwood pressure treated pales, horizontal rails, capping and gravel boards; intermediate posts at 3m centres; centre stump in each bay; height: 1.80m; concrete posts; morticed types	m	0.39	16.39	1.06	27.77	**45.22**	*33.37*
X1.6.4.08	as above; extra for: end post	Nr	0.54	22.99	2.82	21.29	**47.10**	*25.64*
X1.6.4.09	as above; extra for: angle post	Nr	0.54	22.99	2.82	21.29	**47.10**	*25.64*

X1 Fences continued...

		Unit	Labour Hours	Labour Net £	Plant Net £	Materials Net £	Unit Net £	CO_2 Kg
X1.6	**Timber close boarded**							
X1.6.4	Height: 1.5 - 2.0m							
X1.6.4.10	Close boarded fencing, BS 1722, part 5, softwood pressure treated pales, horizontal rails, capping and gravel boards; intermediate posts at 3m centres; centre stump in each bay; height: 1.80m; treated sawn softwood posts	m	0.39	16.39	1.06	26.96	**44.41**	*31.35*
X1.6.4.11	as above; extra for: end post	Nr	0.49	20.90	2.82	18.84	**42.56**	*19.59*
X1.6.4.12	as above; extra for: angle post	Nr	0.65	27.63	2.82	22.77	**53.22**	*23.17*
X1.6.4.13	Woven wood fencing, BS 1722, part 11, treated softwood panels between posts at 1.80m centres; height: 1.60m; concrete posts	m	0.58	24.86	0.71	18.11	**43.68**	*18.61*
X1.6.4.14	as above; extra for: end post	Nr	0.28	11.88	2.12	16.92	**30.92**	*30.42*
X1.6.4.15	as above; extra for: angle post	Nr	0.31	13.07	2.12	16.92	**32.11**	*30.42*
X1.6.4.16	Woven wood fencing, BS 1722, part 11, treated softwood panels between posts at 1.80m centres; height: 1.60m; treated sawn softwood posts	m	0.48	20.35	0.71	15.34	**36.40**	*15.07*
X1.6.4.17	as above; extra for: end post	Nr	0.28	11.88	2.12	11.74	**25.74**	*23.92*
X1.6.4.18	as above; extra for: angle post	Nr	0.31	13.07	2.12	11.74	**26.93**	*23.92*
X1.6.4.19	Woven wood fencing, BS 1722, part 11, treated softwood panels between posts at 1.80m centres; height: 1.60m; overlap panels; treated softwood panels between posts at 1.80m centres: Concrete posts	m	0.58	24.86	0.71	17.67	**43.24**	*18.52*
X1.6.4.20	as above; extra for: end post	Nr	0.28	11.88	2.12	16.92	**30.92**	*30.42*
X1.6.4.21	as above; extra for: angle post	Nr	0.31	13.07	2.12	16.92	**32.11**	*30.42*
X1.6.4.22	Woven wood fencing, BS 1722, part 11, treated softwood panels between posts at 1.80m centres; height: 1.60m; overlap panels; treated softwood panels between posts at 1.80m centres: Treated softwood posts	m	0.48	20.35	0.71	14.91	**35.97**	*14.98*
X1.6.4.23	as above; extra for: end post	Nr	0.28	11.88	2.12	11.74	**25.74**	*23.92*
X1.6.4.24	as above; extra for: angle post	Nr	0.31	13.07	2.12	11.74	**26.93**	*23.92*
X1.6.4.25	Woven wood fencing, BS 1722, part 11, treated softwood panels between posts at 1.80m centres; height: 1.60m; trellis panel fencing; treated panels between posts at 1.80m centres: Concrete posts	m	0.58	24.86	0.71	22.35	**47.92**	*18.52*
X1.6.4.26	as above; extra for: end post	Nr	0.28	11.88	2.12	16.92	**30.92**	*30.42*

X1 Fences continued...

		Unit	Labour Hours	Labour Net £	Plant Net £	Materials Net £	Unit Net £	CO_2 Kg
X1.6	**Timber close boarded**							
X1.6.4	Height: 1.5 - 2.0m							
X1.6.4.27	as previous item; extra for: angle post	Nr	0.31	13.07	2.12	16.92	**32.11**	*30.42*
X1.6.4.28	Woven wood fencing, BS 1722, part 11, treated softwood panels between posts at 1.80m centres; height: 1.60m; trellis panel fencing; treated panels between posts at 1.80m centres: Treated softwood posts	m	0.48	20.35	0.71	19.59	**40.65**	*14.98*
X1.6.4.29	as above; extra for: end post	Nr	0.28	11.88	2.12	11.74	**25.74**	*23.92*
X1.6.4.30	as above; extra for: angle post	Nr	0.31	13.07	2.12	11.74	**26.93**	*23.92*
X1.6.4.31	Woven wood fencing, BS 1722, part 11, treated softwood panels between posts at 1.80m centres; height: 1.80m; concrete posts	m	0.61	26.01	0.71	19.62	**46.34**	*19.65*
X1.6.4.32	as above; extra for: end post	Nr	0.28	11.88	2.12	18.76	**32.76**	*31.86*
X1.6.4.33	as above; extra for: angle post	Nr	0.30	12.81	2.12	18.76	**33.69**	*31.86*
X1.6.4.34	Woven wood fencing, BS 1722, part 11, treated softwood panels between posts at 1.80m centres; height: 1.80m; treated sawn softwood posts	m	0.62	26.56	0.71	9.39	**36.66**	*14.54*
X1.6.4.35	as above; extra for: end post	Nr	0.28	11.88	2.12	12.74	**26.74**	*24.43*
X1.6.4.36	as above; extra for: angle post	Nr	0.30	12.81	2.12	12.74	**27.67**	*24.43*
X1.6.4.37	Woven wood fencing, BS 1722, part 11, treated softwood panels between posts at 1.80m centres; height: 1.80m; overlap panels; treated softwood panels between posts at 1.80m centres: Concrete posts	m	0.61	26.01	0.71	18.95	**45.67**	*19.54*
X1.6.4.38	as above; extra for: end post	Nr	0.28	11.88	2.12	18.76	**32.76**	*31.86*
X1.6.4.39	as above; extra for: angle post	Nr	0.30	12.81	2.12	18.76	**33.69**	*31.86*
X1.6.4.40	Woven wood fencing, BS 1722, part 11, treated softwood panels between posts at 1.80m centres; height: 1.80m; overlap panels; treated softwood panels between posts at 1.80m centres: Treated softwood posts	m	0.62	26.56	0.71	17.27	**44.54**	*16.37*
X1.6.4.41	as above; extra for: end post	Nr	0.28	11.88	2.12	12.74	**26.74**	*24.43*
X1.6.4.42	as above; extra for: angle post	Nr	0.30	12.81	2.12	12.74	**27.67**	*24.43*
X1.6.4.43	Woven wood fencing, BS 1722, part 11, treated softwood panels between posts at 1.80m centres; height: 1.80m; trellis panel fencing; treated panels between posts at 1.80m centres: Concrete posts	m	0.56	23.84	0.71	24.27	**48.82**	*19.54*

X1 Fences continued...

		Unit	Labour Hours	Labour Net £	Plant Net £	Materials Net £	Unit Net £	CO_2 Kg
X1.6	**Timber close boarded**							
X1.6.4	Height: 1.5 - 2.0m							
X1.6.4.44	as previous item; extra for: end post	Nr	0.28	11.88	2.12	18.76	**32.76**	*31.86*
X1.6.4.45	as above; extra for: angle post	Nr	0.30	12.81	2.12	18.76	**33.69**	*31.86*
X1.6.4.46	Woven wood fencing, BS 1722, part 11, treated softwood panels between posts at 1.80m centres; height: 1.80m; trellis panel fencing; treated panels between posts at 1.80m centres: Treated softwood posts	m	0.56	23.84	0.71	22.59	**47.14**	*16.37*
X1.6.4.47	as above; extra for: end post	Nr	0.28	11.88	2.12	12.74	**26.74**	*24.43*
X1.6.4.48	as above; extra for: angle post	Nr	0.30	12.81	2.12	12.74	**27.67**	*24.43*
X1.7	**Metal guard rails**							
X1.7.2	Height: 1 - 1.25m							
X1.7.2.01	Mild steel (low carbon steel) fencing with round or square vertical and flat posts and horizontals, BS 1722, part 9; welded type railing panel with flat horizontals and round bar verticals pointed at top; 102 x 44 x 7.4 kg/m R.S.J. posts for concreting in the ground; 1.20m; 16mm Bar Bluntops; Calcium plumbate primed components	m	1.24	52.74	2.12	29.04	**83.90**	*80.91*
X1.7.2.02	as above; extra for: end standard	Nr	0.92	39.16	2.12	17.78	**59.06**	*42.52*
X1.7.2.03	Mild steel (low carbon steel) fencing with round or square vertical and flat posts and horizontals, BS 1722, part 9; welded type railing panel with flat horizontals and round bar verticals pointed at top; 102 x 44 x 7.4 kg/m R.S.J. posts for concreting in the ground; 1.20m; 16mm Bar Bluntops; Galvanised components	m	1.29	54.92	2.12	30.51	**87.55**	*80.64*
X1.7.2.04	as above; extra for: end standard	Nr	0.98	41.85	2.12	19.23	**63.20**	*42.45*
X1.7.3	Height: 1.25 - 1.5m							
X1.7.3.01	Mild steel (low carbon steel) fencing with round or square vertical and flat posts and horizontals, BS 1722, part 9; welded type railing panel with flat horizontals and round bar verticals pointed at top; 102 x 44 x 7.4 kg/m R.S.J. posts for concreting in the ground; 1.35; 20mm Bar Bluntops; Calcium plumbate primed components	m	1.31	55.77	2.12	39.16	**97.05**	*109.54*
X1.7.3.02	as above; extra for: end standard	Nr	0.92	39.16	2.12	21.87	**63.15**	*45.16*

X1 Fences continued...

		Unit	Labour Hours	Labour Net £	Plant Net £	Materials Net £	Unit Net £	CO_2 Kg
X1.7	**Metal guard rails**							
X1.7.3	Height: 1.25 - 1.5m							
X1.7.3.03	Mild steel (low carbon steel) fencing with round or square vertical and flat posts and horizontals, BS 1722, part 9; welded type railing panel with flat horizontals and round bar verticals pointed at top; 102 x 44 x 7.4 kg/m R.S.J. posts for concreting in the ground; 1.35m; 20mm Bar Bluntops; Galvanised components	m	1.48	63.00	2.12	40.98	**106.10**	*109.22*
X1.7.3.04	as above; extra for: end standard	Nr	0.98	41.85	2.12	23.93	**67.90**	*45.09*
X1.7.3.05	Mild steel (low carbon steel) fencing with round or square vertical and flat posts and horizontals, BS 1722, part 9; welded type railing panel with flat horizontals and round bar verticals pointed at top; 102 x 44 x 7.4 kg/m R.S.J. posts for concreting in the ground; 1.50m; 20mm Bar Bluntops; Calcium plumbate primed components	m	1.35	57.26	2.12	40.93	**100.31**	*114.72*
X1.7.3.06	as above; extra for: end standard	Nr	0.95	40.44	2.12	22.60	**65.16**	*46.47*
X1.7.3.07	Mild steel (low carbon steel) fencing with round or square vertical and flat posts and horizontals, BS 1722, part 9; welded type railing panel with flat horizontals and round bar verticals pointed at top; 102 x 44 x 7.4 kg/m R.S.J. posts for concreting in the ground; 1.50m; 20mm Bar Bluntops; Galvanised components	m	1.48	63.00	2.12	42.83	**107.95**	*114.40*
X1.7.3.08	as above; extra for: end standard	Nr	0.99	41.97	2.12	24.77	**68.86**	*46.40*
X1.7.4	Height: 1.5 - 2.0m							
X1.7.4.01	Mild steel (low carbon steel) fencing with round or square vertical and flat posts and horizontals, BS 1722, part 9; welded type railing panel with flat horizontals and round bar verticals pointed at top; 102 x 44 x 7.4 kg/m R.S.J. posts for concreting in the ground; 1.80m; 20mm Bar Bluntops; Calcium plumbate primed components	m	1.35	57.26	2.12	46.23	**105.61**	*130.28*
X1.7.4.02	as above; extra for: end standard	Nr	0.95	40.44	2.12	24.79	**67.35**	*50.43*

X1 Fences continued...

		Unit	Labour Hours	Labour Net £	Plant Net £	Materials Net £	Unit Net £	*CO_2 Kg*
X1.7	**Metal guard rails**							
X1.7.4	Height: 1.5 - 2.0m							
X1.7.4.03	Mild steel (low carbon steel) fencing with round or square vertical and flat posts and horizontals, BS 1722, part 9; welded type railing panel with flat horizontals and round bar verticals pointed at top; 102 x 44 x 7.4 kg/m R.S.J. posts for concreting in the ground; 1.80m; 20mm Bar Bluntops; Galvanised components	m	1.48	63.00	2.12	48.37	**113.49**	*129.96*
X1.7.4.04	as above; extra for: end standard	Nr	0.99	41.97	2.12	27.29	**71.38**	*50.35*
X1.7.4.05	Steel palisade fences, BS 1722, part 12, galvanised after manufacture; fences of corrugated pales with plain tops; height: 1.80m	m	0.83	35.42	0.89	86.92	**123.23**	*178.57*
X1.7.5	Height: 2 - 2.5m							
X1.7.5.01	Mild steel (low carbon steel) fencing with round or square vertical and flat posts and horizontals, BS 1722, part 9; welded type railing panel with flat horizontals and round bar verticals pointed at top; 102 x 44 x 7.4 kg/m R.S.J. posts for concreting in the ground; 2.10m; 22mm Bar Bluntops; Calcium plumbate primed components	m	1.35	57.26	2.12	64.55	**123.93**	*195.67*
X1.7.5.02	as above; extra for: end standard	Nr	0.95	40.44	2.12	26.98	**69.54**	*54.38*
X1.7.5.03	Mild steel (low carbon steel) fencing with round or square vertical and flat posts and horizontals, BS 1722, part 9; welded type railing panel with flat horizontals and round bar verticals pointed at top; 102 x 44 x 7.4 kg/m R.S.J. posts for concreting in the ground; 2.10m; 22mm Bar Bluntops; Galvanised components	m	1.48	63.00	2.12	66.93	**132.05**	*195.35*
X1.7.5.04	as above; extra for: end standard	Nr	0.99	41.97	2.12	29.81	**73.90**	*54.31*
X1.7.5.05	Steel palisade fences, BS 1722, part 12, galvanised after manufacture; fences of corrugated pales with plain tops; height: 2.10m	m	0.83	35.42	0.89	95.20	**131.51**	*194.45*
X1.7.5.06	as above; height: 2.40m	m	0.83	35.42	0.89	103.42	**139.73**	*210.22*
X1.7.6	Height: 2.5 - 3m							
X1.7.6.01	Steel palisade fences, BS 1722, part 12, galvanised after manufacture; fences of corrugated pales with plain tops; height: 3.00m	m	0.83	35.42	0.89	119.90	**156.21**	*241.81*

X2 Gates and Stiles

		Unit	Labour Hours	Labour Net £	Plant Net £	Materials Net £	Unit Net £	CO_2 Kg
X2.4	**Metal Wicket Gates**							
X2.4.1	Width not exceeding 1.5m							
X2.4.1.01	Single gate width 1.00m; infilling with galvanised chain link mesh; Circular hollow section framing; fittings bolted to concrete or timber posts: bitumen coated; fence height: 0.90m	Nr	1.00	42.57	25.13	79.20	**146.90**	*32.88*
X2.4.1.02	as above; fence height: 1.2m	Nr	1.00	42.57	25.13	105.60	**173.30**	*41.13*
X2.4.1.03	as above; fence height: 1.8m	Nr	1.00	42.57	25.13	158.40	**226.10**	*57.62*
X2.4.1.04	as above; fence height: 2.18m	Nr	1.00	42.57	25.13	187.44	**255.14**	*66.69*
X2.4.1.05	Single gate width 1.00m; infilling with galvanised chain link mesh; Circular hollow section framing; fittings bolted to concrete or timber posts: galvanised; fence height: 0.90m	Nr	1.00	42.57	25.13	105.23	**172.93**	*43.19*
X2.4.1.06	as above; fence height: 1.2m	Nr	1.00	42.57	25.13	140.31	**208.01**	*54.88*
X2.4.1.07	as above; fence height: 1.8m	Nr	1.00	42.57	25.13	210.46	**278.16**	*78.24*
X2.4.1.08	as above; fence height: 2.18m	Nr	1.00	42.57	25.13	245.54	**313.24**	*89.92*
X2.4.1.09	Single gate width 1.00m; infilling with galvanised chain link mesh; Rectangular hollow section framing; fittings bolted to concrete or timber posts: bitumen coated; fence height: 0.90m	Nr	1.00	42.57	25.13	79.20	**146.90**	*32.88*
X2.4.1.10	as above; fence height: 1.2m	Nr	1.00	42.57	25.13	105.60	**173.30**	*41.13*
X2.4.1.11	as above; fence height: 1.8m	Nr	1.00	42.57	25.13	158.40	**226.10**	*57.62*
X2.4.1.12	as above; fence height: 2.18m	Nr	1.00	42.57	25.13	184.80	**252.50**	*65.87*
X2.4.1.13	Single gate width 1.00m; infilling with galvanised chain link mesh; Rectangular hollow section framing; fittings bolted to concrete or timber posts: galvanised; fence height: 0.90m	Nr	1.00	42.57	25.13	116.92	**184.62**	*47.09*
X2.4.1.14	as above; fence height: 1.2m	Nr	1.00	42.57	25.13	140.31	**208.01**	*54.88*
X2.4.1.15	as above; fence height: 1.8m	Nr	1.00	42.57	25.13	210.46	**278.16**	*78.24*
X2.4.1.16	as above; fence height: 2.18m	Nr	1.00	42.57	25.13	245.54	**313.24**	*89.92*
X2.4.1.17	Single gate width 1.00m; infilling with galvanised chain link mesh; additional costs of three lines of barbed wire above gates; extended stiles and extension arms 0.33m high: bitumen coated	Nr	0.20	8.51	-	6.00	**14.51**	*8.81*
X2.4.1.18	as above; galvanised	Nr	0.20	8.51	-	8.00	**16.51**	*28.61*
X2.4.1.19	Single gate width 1.00m; Gates in conjunction with anti-intruder chain link fencing, Infilling with: galvanised chain link mesh or plastic coated chain link mesh	Nr	1.00	42.57	25.13	274.15	**341.85**	*93.24*

X2 Gates and Stiles continued...

		Unit	Labour Hours	Labour Net £	Plant Net £	Materials Net £	Unit Net £	CO_2 Kg
X2.4	**Metal Wicket Gates**							
X2.4.1	Width not exceeding 1.5m							
X2.4.1.20	as previous item; Infilling with: galvanised mild steel wire fabric	Nr	1.00	42.57	25.13	274.15	**341.85**	*93.24*
X2.4.2	Width 1.5 - 2m							
X2.4.2.01	Single gate width 1.50m; Corrugated pales with plain tops; Steel gates and gate posts in conjunction with steel palisade fencing; galvanised after manufacture; Height: 1.80m	Nr	1.50	63.86	37.70	403.35	**504.91**	*109.16*
X2.4.2.02	as above; fence height: 2.1m	Nr	1.50	63.86	37.70	420.84	**522.40**	*114.46*
X2.4.2.03	as above; fence height: 2.4m	Nr	1.50	63.86	37.70	436.35	**537.91**	*119.45*
X2.4.2.04	as above; fence height: 3.0m	Nr	1.50	63.86	37.70	490.64	**592.20**	*133.06*
X2.4.3	Width 2 - 2.5m							
X2.4.3.01	Single gate width 2.00m; infilling with galvanised chain link mesh; Circular hollow section framing; fittings bolted to concrete or timber posts: bitumen coated; fence height: 0.90m	Nr	1.00	42.57	25.13	158.40	**226.10**	*57.62*
X2.4.3.02	as above; fence height: 1.2m	Nr	1.00	42.57	25.13	211.20	**278.90**	*74.11*
X2.4.3.03	as above; fence height: 1.8m	Nr	1.00	42.57	25.13	316.80	**384.50**	*107.10*
X2.4.3.04	as above; fence height: 2.18m	Nr	1.00	42.57	25.13	369.60	**437.30**	*123.59*
X2.4.3.05	Single gate width 2.00m; infilling with galvanised chain link mesh; Circular hollow section framing; fittings bolted to concrete or timber posts: galvanised; fence height: 0.90m	Nr	1.00	42.57	25.13	210.46	**278.16**	*78.24*
X2.4.3.06	as above; fence height: 1.2m	Nr	1.00	42.57	25.13	280.61	**348.31**	*101.61*
X2.4.3.07	as above; fence height: 1.8m	Nr	1.00	42.57	25.13	420.92	**488.62**	*148.33*
X2.4.3.08	as above; fence height: 2.18m	Nr	1.00	42.57	25.13	491.07	**558.77**	*171.70*
X2.4.3.09	Single gate width 2.00m; infilling with galvanised chain link mesh; Rectangular hollow section framing; fittings bolted to concrete or timber posts: bitumen coated; fence height: 0.90m	Nr	1.25	53.21	31.41	158.40	**243.02**	*59.66*
X2.4.3.10	as above; fence height: 1.2m	Nr	1.25	53.21	31.41	211.20	**295.82**	*76.15*
X2.4.3.11	as above; fence height: 1.8m	Nr	1.25	53.21	31.41	316.80	**401.42**	*109.13*
X2.4.3.12	as above; fence height: 2.18m	Nr	1.25	53.21	31.41	369.60	**454.22**	*125.62*
X2.4.3.13	Single gate width 2.00m; infilling with galvanised chain link mesh; Rectangular hollow section framing; fittings bolted to concrete or timber posts: galvanised; fence height: 0.90m	Nr	1.25	53.21	31.41	210.46	**295.08**	*80.28*

X2 Gates and Stiles continued...

		Unit	Labour Hours	Labour Net £	Plant Net £	Materials Net £	Unit Net £	CO_2 Kg
X2.4	**Metal Wicket Gates**							
X2.4.3	Width 2 - 2.5m							
X2.4.3.14	as previous item; fence height: 1.2m	Nr	1.25	53.21	31.41	280.61	**365.23**	*103.64*
X2.4.3.15	as above; fence height: 1.8m	Nr	1.25	53.21	31.41	420.92	**505.54**	*150.37*
X2.4.3.16	as above; fence height: 2.18m	Nr	1.25	53.21	31.41	491.07	**575.69**	*173.74*
X2.4.3.17	Single gate width 2.00m; infilling with galvanised chain link mesh; additional costs of three lines of barbed wire above gates; extended stiles and extension arms 0.33m high: bitumen coated	Nr	0.20	8.51	-	6.00	**14.51**	*8.81*
X2.4.3.18	as above; galvanised	Nr	0.20	8.51	-	8.00	**16.51**	*28.61*
X2.4.3.19	Single gate width 2.00m; Gates in conjunction with anti-intruder chain link fencing, Infilling with: galvanised chain link mesh or plastic coated chain link mesh	Nr	1.00	42.57	25.13	548.30	**616.00**	*178.34*
X2.4.3.20	as above; Infilling with: galvanised mild steel wire fabric	Nr	1.00	42.57	25.13	548.30	**616.00**	*178.34*
X2.4.5	Width 3 - 4m							
X2.4.5.01	Single gate width 3.00m; infilling with galvanised chain link mesh; Circular hollow section framing; fittings bolted to concrete or timber posts: bitumen coated; fence height: 0.90m	Nr	2.00	85.14	50.26	237.60	**373.00**	*90.51*
X2.4.5.02	as above; fence height: 1.2m	Nr	2.00	85.14	50.26	316.80	**452.20**	*115.24*
X2.4.5.03	as above; fence height: 1.8m	Nr	2.00	85.14	50.26	475.20	**610.60**	*164.72*
X2.4.5.04	as above; fence height: 2.18m	Nr	2.00	85.14	50.26	554.40	**689.80**	*189.46*
X2.4.5.05	Single gate width 3.00m; infilling with galvanised chain link mesh; Circular hollow section framing; fittings bolted to concrete or timber posts: galvanised; fence height: 0.90m	Nr	2.50	106.43	62.82	315.59	**484.84**	*125.34*
X2.4.5.06	as above; fence height: 1.2m	Nr	2.50	106.43	62.82	420.79	**590.04**	*160.33*
X2.4.5.07	as above; fence height: 1.8m	Nr	2.50	106.43	62.82	631.18	**800.43**	*230.32*
X2.4.5.08	as above; fence height: 2.18m	Nr	2.50	106.43	62.82	736.38	**905.63**	*265.31*
X2.4.5.09	Single gate width 3.00m; infilling with galvanised chain link mesh; Rectangular hollow section framing; fittings bolted to concrete or timber posts: bitumen coated; fence height: 0.90m	Nr	2.00	85.14	50.26	237.60	**373.00**	*90.51*
X2.4.5.10	as above; fence height: 1.2m	Nr	2.00	85.14	50.26	316.80	**452.20**	*115.24*
X2.4.5.11	as above; fence height: 1.8m	Nr	2.00	85.14	50.26	475.20	**610.60**	*164.72*

X2 Gates and Stiles continued...

		Unit	Labour Hours	Labour Net £	Plant Net £	Materials Net £	Unit Net £	CO_2 Kg
X2.4	**Metal Wicket Gates**							
X2.4.5	Width 3 - 4m							
X2.4.5.13	Single gate width 3.00m; infilling with galvanised chain link mesh; Rectangular hollow section framing; fittings bolted to concrete or timber posts: galvanised; fence height: 0.90m	Nr	2.50	106.43	62.82	315.59	484.84	*125.34*
X2.4.5.14	as above; fence height: 1.2m	Nr	2.50	106.43	62.82	420.79	590.04	*160.33*
X2.4.5.15	as above; fence height: 1.8m	Nr	2.50	106.43	62.82	631.18	800.43	*230.32*
X2.4.5.16	as above; fence height: 2.18m	Nr	2.50	106.43	62.82	736.38	905.63	*265.31*
X2.4.5.17	Single gate width 3.00m; infilling with galvanised chain link mesh; additional costs of three lines of barbed wire above gates; extended stiles and extension arms 0.33m high: bitumen coated	Nr	0.20	8.51	-	6.00	14.51	*8.81*
X2.4.5.18	as above; galvanised	Nr	0.20	8.51	-	8.00	16.51	*28.61*
X2.4.5.19	Single gate width 3.00m; Corrugated pales with plain tops; Steel gates and gate posts in conjunction with steel palisade fencing; galvanised after manufacture; Height: 1.80m	Nr	2.00	85.14	50.26	668.34	803.74	*169.92*
X2.4.5.20	as above; fence height: 2.1m	Nr	2.00	85.14	50.26	697.49	832.89	*179.62*
X2.4.5.21	as above; fence height: 2.4m	Nr	2.00	85.14	50.26	723.34	858.74	*188.79*
X2.4.5.22	as above; fence height: 3.0m	Nr	2.00	85.14	50.26	813.82	949.22	*213.19*
X2.4.6	Width 4 - 5m							
X2.4.6.01	Double gates width 4.00m; infilling with galvanised chain link mesh; Circular hollow section framing; fittings bolted to concrete or timber posts: bitumen coated; fence height: 0.90m	Nr	2.50	106.43	62.82	316.80	486.05	*119.32*
X2.4.6.02	as above; fence height: 1.2m	Nr	2.50	106.43	62.82	422.40	591.65	*152.30*
X2.4.6.03	as above; fence height: 1.8m	Nr	2.50	106.43	62.82	633.60	802.85	*218.27*
X2.4.6.04	as above; fence height: 2.18m	Nr	2.50	106.43	62.82	739.20	908.45	*251.25*
X2.4.6.05	Double gates width 4.00m; infilling with galvanised chain link mesh; Circular hollow section framing; fittings bolted to concrete or timber posts: galvanised; fence height: 0.90m	Nr	3.00	127.71	75.39	420.79	623.89	*164.41*
X2.4.6.06	as above; fence height: 1.2m	Nr	3.00	127.71	75.39	561.05	764.15	*211.06*
X2.4.6.07	as above; fence height: 1.8m	Nr	3.00	127.71	75.39	841.58	1,044.68	*304.37*
X2.4.6.08	as above; fence height: 2.18m	Nr	3.00	127.71	75.39	981.84	1,184.94	*351.03*

X2 Gates and Stiles continued...

		Unit	Labour Hours	Labour Net £	Plant Net £	Materials Net £	Unit Net £	CO_2 Kg
X2.4	**Metal Wicket Gates**							
X2.4.6	Width 4 - 5m							
X2.4.6.09	Double gates width 4.00m; infilling with galvanised chain link mesh; Rectangular hollow section framing; fittings bolted to concrete or timber posts: bitumen coated; fence height: 0.90m	Nr	2.50	106.43	62.82	316.80	**486.05**	*119.32*
X2.4.6.10	as above; fence height: 1.2m	Nr	2.50	106.43	62.82	422.40	**591.65**	*152.30*
X2.4.6.11	as above; fence height: 1.8m	Nr	2.50	106.43	62.82	633.60	**802.85**	*218.27*
X2.4.6.12	as above; fence height: 2.18m	Nr	2.50	106.43	62.82	739.20	**908.45**	*251.25*
X2.4.6.13	Double gates width 4.00m; infilling with galvanised chain link mesh; Rectangular hollow section framing; fittings bolted to concrete or timber posts: galvanised; fence height: 0.90m	Nr	3.00	127.71	75.39	420.79	**623.89**	*164.41*
X2.4.6.14	as above; fence height: 1.2m	Nr	3.00	127.71	75.39	561.05	**764.15**	*211.06*
X2.4.6.15	as above; fence height: 1.8m	Nr	3.00	127.71	75.39	841.58	**1,044.68**	*304.37*
X2.4.6.16	as above; fence height: 2.18m	Nr	3.00	127.71	75.39	981.84	**1,184.94**	*351.03*
X2.4.6.17	Double gates width 4.00m; infilling with galvanised chain link mesh; additional costs of three lines of barbed wire above gates; extended stiles and extension arms 0.33m high: bitumen coated	Nr	0.20	8.51	-	6.00	**14.51**	*8.81*
X2.4.6.18	as above; galvanised	Nr	0.20	8.51	-	8.00	**16.51**	*28.61*
X2.4.6.19	Double gates width 4.00m; Gates in conjunction with anti-intruder chain link fencing, Infilling with: galvanised chain link mesh or plastic coated chain link mesh	Nr	1.00	42.57	25.13	1,096.60	**1,164.30**	*348.53*
X2.4.6.20	as above; Infilling with: galvanised mild steel wire fabric	Nr	1.00	42.57	25.13	1,096.60	**1,164.30**	*348.53*
X2.4.6.21	Double gates width 4.50m; Corrugated pales with plain tops; Steel gates and gate posts in conjunction with steel palisade fencing; galvanised after manufacture; Height: 1.80m	Nr	2.00	85.14	50.26	886.97	**1,022.37**	*219.40*
X2.4.6.22	as above; fence height: 2.1m	Nr	2.00	85.14	50.26	947.47	**1,082.87**	*236.55*
X2.4.6.23	as above; fence height: 2.4m	Nr	2.00	85.14	50.26	995.87	**1,131.27**	*251.82*
X2.4.6.24	as above; fence height: 3.0m	Nr	2.00	85.14	50.26	1,166.37	**1,301.77**	*293.81*
X2.4.7	Width exceeding 5m							
X2.4.7.01	Double gates width 6.00m; infilling with galvanised chain link mesh; Circular hollow section framing; fittings bolted to concrete or timber posts: bitumen coated; fence height: 0.90m	Nr	3.00	127.71	75.39	475.20	**678.30**	*172.87*

X2 Gates and Stiles continued...

		Unit	Labour Hours	Labour Net £	Plant Net £	Materials Net £	Unit Net £	CO_2 Kg
X2.4	**Metal Wicket Gates**							
X2.4.7	Width exceeding 5m							
X2.4.7.02	as previous item; fence height: 1.2m	Nr	3.00	127.71	75.39	633.60	**836.70**	*222.34*
X2.4.7.03	as above; fence height: 1.8m	Nr	3.00	127.71	75.39	950.40	**1,153.50**	*321.29*
X2.4.7.04	as above; fence height: 2.18m	Nr	3.00	127.71	75.39	1,108.80	**1,311.90**	*370.76*
X2.4.7.05	Double gates width 6.00m; infilling with galvanised chain link mesh; Circular hollow section framing; fittings bolted to concrete or timber posts: galvanised; fence height: 0.90m	Nr	3.50	149.00	87.95	631.18	**868.13**	*238.46*
X2.4.7.06	as above; fence height: 1.2m	Nr	3.50	149.00	87.95	841.58	**1,078.53**	*308.45*
X2.4.7.07	as above; fence height: 1.8m	Nr	3.50	149.00	87.95	1,262.37	**1,499.32**	*448.41*
X2.4.7.08	as above; fence height: 2.18m	Nr	3.50	149.00	87.95	1,472.76	**1,709.71**	*518.40*
X2.4.7.09	Double gates width 6.00m; infilling with galvanised chain link mesh; Rectangular hollow section framing; fittings bolted to concrete or timber posts: bitumen coated; fence height: 0.90m	Nr	3.00	127.71	75.39	475.20	**678.30**	*172.87*
X2.4.7.10	as above; fence height: 1.2m	Nr	3.00	127.71	75.39	633.60	**836.70**	*222.34*
X2.4.7.11	as above; fence height: 1.8m	Nr	3.00	127.71	75.39	950.40	**1,153.50**	*321.29*
X2.4.7.12	as above; fence height: 2.18m	Nr	3.00	127.71	75.39	1,108.80	**1,311.90**	*370.76*
X2.4.7.13	Double gates width 6.00m; infilling with galvanised chain link mesh; Rectangular hollow section framing; fittings bolted to concrete or timber posts: galvanised; fence height: 0.90m	Nr	3.50	149.00	87.95	631.18	**868.13**	*238.46*
X2.4.7.14	as above; fence height: 1.2m	Nr	3.50	149.00	87.95	841.58	**1,078.53**	*308.45*
X2.4.7.15	as above; fence height: 1.8m	Nr	3.50	149.00	87.95	1,262.37	**1,499.32**	*448.41*
X2.4.7.16	as above; fence height: 2.18m	Nr	3.50	149.00	87.95	1,472.76	**1,709.71**	*518.40*
X2.4.7.17	Double gates width 6.00m; infilling with galvanised chain link mesh; additional costs of three lines of barbed wire above gates; extended stiles and extension arms 0.33m high: bitumen coated	Nr	0.20	8.51	-	6.00	**14.51**	*8.81*
X2.4.7.18	as above; galvanised	Nr	0.20	8.51	-	8.00	**16.51**	*28.61*
X2.4.7.19	Double gates width 6.00m; Gates in conjunction with anti-intruder chain link fencing, Infilling with: galvanised chain link mesh or plastic coated chain link mesh	Nr	1.50	63.86	37.70	1,638.90	**1,740.46**	*518.69*
X2.4.7.20	as above; Infilling with: galvanised mild steel wire fabric	Nr	1.50	63.86	37.70	1,638.90	**1,740.46**	*518.69*

X2 Gates and Stiles continued...

		Unit	Labour Hours	Labour Net £	Plant Net £	Materials Net £	Unit Net £	CO_2 Kg
X2.4	**Metal Wicket Gates**							
X2.4.7	Width exceeding 5m							
X2.4.7.21	Double gates width 6.00m; Corrugated pales with plain tops; Steel gates and gate posts in conjunction with steel palisade fencing; galvanised after manufacture; Height: 1.80m	Nr	2.00	85.14	50.26	995.87	**1,131.27**	*251.82*
X2.4.7.22	as above; fence height: 2.1m	Nr	2.00	85.14	50.26	1,028.87	**1,164.27**	*267.27*
X2.4.7.23	as above; fence height: 2.4m	Nr	2.00	85.14	50.26	1,078.37	**1,213.77**	*285.30*
X2.4.7.24	as above; fence height: 3.0m	Nr	2.00	85.14	50.26	1,435.87	**1,571.27**	*361.53*
X2.4.7.25	Double gates width 8.00m; infilling with galvanised chain link mesh; Circular hollow section framing; fittings bolted to concrete or timber posts: bitumen coated; fence height: 0.90m	Nr	3.50	149.00	87.95	633.60	**870.55**	*226.41*
X2.4.7.26	as above; fence height: 1.2m	Nr	3.50	149.00	87.95	844.80	**1,081.75**	*292.38*
X2.4.7.27	as above; fence height: 1.8m	Nr	3.50	149.00	87.95	1,267.20	**1,504.15**	*424.31*
X2.4.7.28	as above; fence height: 2.18m	Nr	3.50	149.00	87.95	1,478.40	**1,715.35**	*490.28*
X2.4.7.29	Double gates width 8.00m; infilling with galvanised chain link mesh; Circular hollow section framing; fittings bolted to concrete or timber posts: galvanised; fence height: 0.90m	Nr	4.00	170.28	100.52	841.58	**1,112.38**	*312.52*
X2.4.7.30	as above; fence height: 1.2m	Nr	4.00	170.28	100.52	1,122.11	**1,392.91**	*405.83*
X2.4.7.31	as above; fence height: 1.8m	Nr	4.00	170.28	100.52	1,683.16	**1,953.96**	*592.45*
X2.4.7.32	as above; fence height: 2.18m	Nr	4.00	170.28	100.52	1,963.69	**2,234.49**	*685.76*
X2.4.7.33	Double gates width 8.00m; infilling with galvanised chain link mesh; Rectangular hollow section framing; fittings bolted to concrete or timber posts: bitumen coated; fence height: 0.90m	Nr	3.50	149.00	87.95	633.60	**870.55**	*226.41*
X2.4.7.34	as above; fence height: 1.2m	Nr	3.50	149.00	87.95	844.80	**1,081.75**	*292.38*
X2.4.7.35	as above; fence height: 1.8m	Nr	3.50	149.00	87.95	1,267.20	**1,504.15**	*424.31*
X2.4.7.36	as above; fence height: 2.18m	Nr	3.50	149.00	87.95	1,478.40	**1,715.35**	*490.28*
X2.4.7.37	Double gates width 8.00m; infilling with galvanised chain link mesh; Rectangular hollow section framing; fittings bolted to concrete or timber posts: galvanised; fence height: 0.90m	Nr	4.00	170.28	100.52	841.58	**1,112.38**	*312.52*
X2.4.7.38	as above; fence height: 1.2m	Nr	4.00	170.28	100.52	1,122.11	**1,392.91**	*405.83*
X2.4.7.39	as above; fence height: 1.8m	Nr	4.00	170.28	100.52	1,683.16	**1,953.96**	*592.45*
X2.4.7.40	as above; fence height: 2.18m	Nr	4.00	170.28	100.52	1,963.69	**2,234.49**	*685.76*

X2 Gates and Stiles continued...

		Unit	Labour Hours	Labour Net £	Plant Net £	Materials Net £	Unit Net £	*CO_2 Kg*
X2.4	**Metal Wicket Gates**							
X2.4.7	Width exceeding 5m							
X2.4.7.41	Double gates width 8.00m; infilling with galvanised chain link mesh; additional costs of three lines of barbed wire above gates; extended stiles and extension arms 0.33m high: bitumen coated	Nr	0.20	8.51	-	6.00	14.51	*8.81*
X2.4.7.42	as above; galvanised	Nr	0.20	8.51	-	8.00	16.51	*28.61*
X2.4.7.43	Double gates width 8.00m; Gates in conjunction with anti-intruder chain link fencing, Infilling with: galvanised chain link mesh or plastic coated chain link mesh	Nr	1.50	63.86	37.70	2,181.20	2,282.76	*684.77*
X2.4.7.44	as above; Infilling with: galvanised mild steel wire fabric	Nr	1.50	63.86	37.70	2,181.20	2,282.76	*684.77*

X3 Drainage to Structures Above Ground

		Unit	Labour Hours	Labour Net £	Plant Net £	Materials Net £	Unit Net £	*CO_2 Kg*
X3.2	**Cast Iron**							
X3.2.1	Gutters							
X3.2.1.01	Fixing with standard brackets at heights not exceeding 3m; half round eaves gutters; Diameter: 100mm	m	0.25	6.76	-	22.68	29.44	*23.06*
X3.2.1.02	as above; Diameter: 150mm	m	0.30	8.12	-	43.88	52.00	*34.59*
X3.2.1.03	as above; Ogee eaves gutters; Diameter: 100mm	m	0.25	6.76	-	25.45	32.21	*23.55*
X3.2.1.04	as above; Ogee eaves gutters; Diameter: 150mm	m	0.30	8.12	-	29.20	37.32	*34.59*
X3.2.2	Fittings to gutters							
X3.2.2.01	Fixing with standard brackets at heights not exceeding 3m; half round eaves gutters; diameter 100mm; Stopped ends	Nr	0.03	0.81	-	4.36	5.17	*1.43*
X3.2.2.02	as above; square angles	Nr	0.04	1.08	-	12.28	13.36	*5.35*
X3.2.2.03	as above; outlets (drop end)	Nr	0.04	1.08	-	11.97	13.05	*4.39*
X3.2.2.04	as above; diameter 150mm; Stopped ends	Nr	0.03	0.81	-	7.42	8.23	*1.72*
X3.2.2.05	as above; square angles	Nr	0.04	1.08	-	27.22	28.30	*8.02*
X3.2.2.06	as above; outlets (drop end)	Nr	0.04	1.08	-	25.80	26.88	*6.59*
X3.2.2.07	as above; Ogee eaves gutters; diameter 100mm; Stopped ends	Nr	0.03	0.81	-	4.22	5.03	*1.20*
X3.2.2.08	as above; square angles	Nr	0.04	1.08	-	13.31	14.39	*5.62*
X3.2.2.09	as above; outlets (drop end)	Nr	0.04	1.08	-	13.05	14.13	*4.61*
X3.2.2.10	as above; diameter 150mm; Stopped ends	Nr	0.03	0.81	-	15.15	15.96	*1.81*
X3.2.2.11	as above; square angles	Nr	0.04	1.08	-	19.02	20.10	*8.42*
X3.2.2.12	as above; outlets (drop end)	Nr	0.04	1.08	-	15.26	16.34	*6.92*

X3 Drainage to Structures Above Ground continued...

		Unit	Labour Hours	Labour Net £	Plant Net £	Materials Net £	Unit Net £	CO_2 Kg
X3.2	**Cast Iron**							
X3.2.3	Downpipes							
X3.2.3.01	fixing with standard brackets at heights not exceeding 3m; ears cast on; fixing with pipe nails and hardwood distance pieces; nominal size; 75mm	m	0.28	7.58	-	52.42	60.00	*15.43*
X3.2.3.02	as above; nominal size; 100mm	m	0.28	7.58	-	67.21	74.79	*22.44*
X3.2.3.03	as above; nominal size; Rectangular section 100 x 75mm	m	0.28	7.58	-	172.74	180.32	*26.20*
X3.2.4	Fittings to downpipes							
X3.2.4.01	fixing with standard brackets at heights not exceeding 3m; nominal size 75mm; Shoes	Nr	0.18	4.87	-	27.97	32.84	*4.03*
X3.2.4.02	as above; nominal size 75mm; Obtuse bend	Nr	0.28	7.58	-	20.78	28.36	*2.29*
X3.2.4.03	as above; nominal size 75mm; Swan neck offset: 150mm projection	Nr	0.28	7.58	-	26.20	33.78	*4.71*
X3.2.4.04	as above; nominal size 75mm; Swan neck offset: 305mm projection	Nr	0.28	7.58	-	26.20	33.78	*4.71*
X3.2.4.05	as above; nominal size 75mm; Single equal branch	Nr	0.28	7.58	-	26.20	33.78	*4.71*
X3.2.4.06	as above; nominal size 100mm; Shoes	Nr	0.18	4.87	-	37.13	42.00	*4.74*
X3.2.4.07	as above; nominal size 100mm; Obtuse bend	Nr	0.18	4.87	-	29.35	34.22	*8.21*
X3.2.4.08	as above; nominal size 100mm; Swan neck offset: 150mm projection	Nr	0.18	4.87	-	50.38	55.25	*5.54*
X3.2.4.09	as above; nominal size 100mm; Swan neck offset: 305mm projection	Nr	0.18	4.87	-	50.38	55.25	*5.54*
X3.2.4.10	as above; nominal size 100mm; Single equal branch	Nr	0.18	4.87	-	50.38	55.25	*5.54*
X3.2.4.11	as above; nominal size 100 x 75 rectangular section; Shoes	Nr	0.18	4.87	-	104.74	109.61	*5.92*
X3.2.4.12	as above; nominal size 100 x 75 rectangular section; Side bend	Nr	0.18	4.87	-	99.73	104.60	*10.27*
X3.2.4.13	as above; nominal size 100 x 75 rectangular section; Front plinth offset	Nr	0.18	4.87	-	133.42	138.29	*6.93*
X3.2.4.14	as above; nominal size 100 x 75 rectangular section; Side plinth offset	Nr	0.18	4.87	-	133.42	138.29	*6.93*
X3.2.4.15	as above; rainwater heads; jointing to pipes; Hopper type flat; 75mm outlet	Nr	0.18	4.87	-	50.00	54.87	*3.73*
X3.2.4.16	as above; rainwater heads; jointing to pipes; Rectangular, 250 x 178 x 178mm; 75mm outlet	Nr	0.18	4.87	-	75.00	79.87	*6.25*
X3.2.4.17	as above; rainwater heads; jointing to pipes; Rectangular, 250 x 178 x 178mm; 100mm outlet	Nr	0.18	4.87	-	95.00	99.87	*8.35*

X3 Drainage to Structures Above Ground continued...

		Unit	Labour Hours	Labour Net £	Plant Net £	Materials Net £	Unit Net £	CO_2 Kg
X3.3	**Plastics**							
X3.3.1	Gutters							
X3.3.1.01	UPVC; fixing with standard brackets at heights not exceeding 3m; half round eaves gutters; nominal size; 112mm	m	0.18	4.87	-	9.77	**14.64**	*4.17*
X3.3.1.02	as above; half round eaves gutters; nominal size; 150mm	m	0.18	4.87	-	12.48	**17.35**	*7.64*
X3.3.2	Fittings to gutters							
X3.3.2.01	UPVC; fixing with standard brackets at heights not exceeding 3m; half round eaves gutters; nominal size 112m; Stopped ends	Nr	0.05	1.35	-	4.05	**5.40**	*0.15*
X3.3.2.02	as above; half round eaves gutters; nominal size 112m; Square angles	Nr	0.14	3.79	-	17.67	**21.46**	*1.13*
X3.3.2.03	as above; half round eaves gutters; nominal size 112m; Outlets	Nr	0.05	1.35	-	14.48	**15.83**	*0.38*
X3.3.2.04	as above; half round eaves gutters; diameter 150mm; Stopped ends	Nr	0.05	1.35	-	5.51	**6.86**	*0.29*
X3.3.2.05	as above; half round eaves gutters; diameter 150mm; Square angles	Nr	0.14	3.79	-	13.95	**17.74**	*1.38*
X3.3.2.06	as above; half round eaves gutters; diameter 150mm; Outlets	Nr	0.05	1.35	-	15.27	**16.62**	*1.25*
X3.3.3	Downpipes							
X3.3.3.01	UPVC; fixing with standard brackets at heights not exceeding 3m; fixing with standard brackets; nominal size; 68mm	m	0.15	4.06	-	7.44	**11.50**	*3.10*
X3.3.3.02	as above; nominal size; 100mm	m	0.15	4.06	-	16.95	**21.01**	*4.17*
X3.3.4	Fittings to downpipes							
X3.3.4.01	UPVC; fixing with standard brackets at heights not exceeding 3m; nominal size 68mm; Shoes	Nr	0.10	2.71	-	7.08	**9.79**	*0.18*
X3.3.4.02	as above; nominal size 68mm; Bends	Nr	0.16	4.33	-	8.19	**12.52**	*0.64*
X3.3.4.03	as above; nominal size 68mm; Offsets; 150mm projection	Nr	0.18	4.87	-	4.53	**9.40**	*0.46*
X3.3.4.04	as above; nominal size 68mm; Offsets; 300mm projection	Nr	0.18	4.87	-	4.53	**9.40**	*0.46*
X3.3.4.05	as above; nominal size 68mm; Branches	Nr	0.05	1.35	-	6.76	**8.11**	*0.39*
X3.3.4.06	as above; nominal size 110mm; Shoes	Nr	0.10	2.71	-	16.24	**18.95**	*1.13*
X3.3.4.07	as above; nominal size 110mm; Bends	Nr	0.16	4.33	-	20.09	**24.42**	*0.91*
X3.3.4.08	as above; nominal size 110mm; Offsets; 150mm projection	Nr	0.18	4.87	-	19.43	**24.30**	*1.13*
X3.3.4.09	as above; nominal size 110mm; Offsets; 300mm projection	Nr	0.18	4.87	-	19.43	**24.30**	*1.13*
X3.3.4.10	as above; nominal size 110mm; Branches	Nr	0.18	4.87	-	19.74	**24.61**	*0.12*

X4 Rock Filled Gabions

		Unit	Labour Hours	Labour Net £	Plant Net £	Materials Net £	Unit Net £	CO_2 Kg
X4.1	**Box of stated size**							
X4.1.1	placed on river bank above water level; Zinc wire mesh 80mm; random filled by hand with broken rock of cubic character; average mass 2 - 10kg							
X4.1.1.01	Size: 2 x 1 x 1m	Nr	0.80	60.03	17.14	78.83	**156.00**	*250.43*
X4.1.1.02	Size: 2 x 1 x 0.5m	Nr	0.65	48.78	13.93	47.11	**109.82**	*127.32*
X4.1.2	PVC coated wire mesh 80mm; random filled by hand with broken rock of cubic character; average mass 2 - 10kg							
X4.1.2.01	Size: 2 x 1 x 1m	Nr	0.80	60.03	17.14	86.74	**163.91**	*218.93*
X4.1.2.02	Size: 2 x 1 x 0.5m	Nr	0.65	48.78	13.93	53.75	**116.46**	*111.57*
X4.1.3	placed below water level and filled by grab; Zinc wire mesh 80mm; random filled by machine with broken rock of cubic character; average mass 2 - 10kg							
X4.1.3.01	Size: 2 x 1 x 1m	Nr	0.80	60.03	55.51	78.83	**194.37**	*254.18*
X4.2	**Matress of stated thickness**							
X4.2.1	gabions filled on bank then lifted into position below water level; distance 10m from bank top; galvanised wire mesh 60mm; random filled by hand with broken rock of cubic character; average mass 2 - 10kg							
X4.2.1.01	Size: 6 x 2m x 230mm	m^2	0.15	11.26	3.21	19.19	**33.66**	*26.95*
X4.2.1.02	Size: 6 x 2m x 300mm	m^2	0.15	11.26	3.21	22.53	**37.00**	*34.77*

CLASS Y:
SEWER AND WATER MAIN RENOVATION AND ANCILLARY WORKS

Calculations used throughout Class Y - Sewer and Water Main Renovation and Ancillary Works

Labour

		Qty		Rate		Total
L Y0004ICE	**Sewer Renovation Labour Gang**					
	Labourer (General Operative)	2	x	12.56	=	£25.12
	Labourer (Skill Rate 3)	2	x	14.34	=	£28.68
	Bricklayer	3	x	16.68	=	£50.05
	Banksman	1	x	13.53	=	£13.53
	Total hourly cost of gang				**=**	**£117.38**

Plant

		Qty		Rate		Total
P Y0005ICE	**Sewer Renovation Plant Gang**					
	Vactor Unit for Sewer Cleaning	1	x	7.94	=	£7.94
	Total hourly cost of gang				**=**	**£7.94**
P Y0006ICE	**Sewer Repair Plant Gang**					
	Robotic Sewer Repair Unit	1	x	69.08	=	£69.08
	Total hourly cost of gang				**=**	**£69.08**

Class Y - Sewer and Water Main Renovation and ancillary works

Y1 Preparation of Existing Sewers

Note(s): Cleaning

Cleaning is done in two stages

To remove all silt and adhesions prior to a survey of the existing sewer to establish the size of the lining units. Immediately prior to placing lining units to clean away any recent silt or sewage deposits to ensure efficient grouting to the annulus. Stage (i) usually requires 'heavy' jetting and vacuum cleaning or dredging. There is a variety of equipment/sub-contractors available depending on the size of sewer, length between the manholes etc., but usually the more expensive equipment has a compensatingly greater output and the cost will be determined more by the degree of situation rather than the size of sewer or length. Stage (ii) costs have been included in the laying operations. Guide Prices (Sub-contractors) for man-entry sewers 1200mm maximum diameter.

Normally re-lining is only contemplated where the existing structure is considered safe to work in. There should be minimal 'making good' following a cleaning operation and it would be done by the lining gang.

Plugging Laterals

The following are Specialist prices and are based on robotic methods for non man entry pipelines. Assume as a permanent plug in lieu of complete filling of a lateral with PFA/cement.

Local Internal Repairs

The following are Specialist prices and are based on robotic methods for non man entry pipelines. Including cutting and repointing.

		Unit	Labour Hours	Labour Net £	Plant Net £	Materials Net £	Unit Net £	CO_2 Kg
Y1.1	**Cleaning**							
Y1.1.1	Guide Prices (Sub-contractors) for man entry sewers 1200mm maximum diameter							
Y1.1.1.01	0 - 10% siltation	m	0.17	19.60	1.33	-	**20.93**	*1.36*
Y1.1.1.02	10 - 40% siltation	m	0.25	29.34	1.99	-	**31.33**	*2.04*
Y1.2	**Removing intrusions**							
Y1.2.1	Laterals, bore not exceeding 150mm							
Y1.2.1.01	GVC, concrete, cast iron or steel pipes	Nr	2.00	234.76	7.04	-	**241.80**	*3.02*
Y1.2.2	Laterals, stated profile and size exceeding 150mm in one or more dimension							
Y1.2.2.01	GVC, or concrete pipes not exceeding 300mm into the bore of the main sewer	Nr	3.00	352.14	10.56	-	**362.70**	*4.53*
Y1.2.3	Other stated artifical intrusions							
Y1.2.3.01	Mass brickwork	Nr	0.50	58.69	2.61	-	**61.30**	*3.30*
Y1.2.3.02	Mass concrete	Nr	0.75	88.03	3.91	-	**91.94**	*4.94*
Y1.2.3.03	Reinforced concrete	Nr	1.00	117.38	5.21	-	**122.59**	*6.59*
Y1.2.3.04	Isolated bricks	Nr	0.01	1.64	0.07	-	**1.71**	*0.09*
Y1.4	**Plugging laterals, material stated**							
Y1.4.1	Bore not exceeding 300mm							
Y1.4.1.01	Epoxy resin plug	Nr	1.00	117.38	-	369.63	**487.01**	*23.65*
Y1.4.1.02	Permanent concrete plug	Nr	0.50	58.69	-	3.90	**62.59**	*11.45*
Y1.6	**Local internal repairs**							
Y1.6.1	Area: not exceeding 0.1m^2							
Y1.6.1.01	Based on robotic methods for non man entry pipelines	Nr	1.00	117.38	69.08	184.80	**371.26**	*75.62*

Y1 Preparation of Existing Sewers continued...

		Unit	Labour Hours	Labour Net £	Plant Net £	Materials Net £	Unit Net £	CO_2 Kg
Y1.6	**Local internal repairs**							
Y1.6.2	Area: 0.1 - 0.25m2							
Y1.6.2.01	Based on robotic methods for non man entry pipelines	Nr	1.50	176.07	103.62	369.60	**649.29**	*119.33*

Y2 Stabilisation of Existing Sewers

Note(s): Pointing to be carried out by hand for small areas and by pressure pointing for large areas. Material cost is minimal compared with raking out and pointing labour costs. Prices will vary depending upon accessibility.

		Unit	Labour Hours	Labour Net £	Plant Net £	Materials Net £	Unit Net £	CO_2 Kg
Y2.1	**Pointing, materials stated**							
Y2.1.1	with cement mortar (1:3)							
Y2.1.1.01	including preparation of joints	m^2	0.25	29.34	0.65	1.31	**31.30**	*8.18*

Y3 Renovation of Existing Sewers

Note(s): Segmental lining

Linings are usually tailor-made to suit a given sewer. This is usually determined by passing a 3-dimensional template (the length of the proposed lining units) through the existing sewer to determine what lining of constant X-section will be suitable between any two manholes. The price charged for materials will depend upon the number of units which are to be provided which can be made from one run or former. 'The labour/plant cost of installation will depend on a number of factors: Minimum safety cover (ie. personnel) at shaft positions. If work is taking place at shaft positions while lining is carried out, then extra men would not be required for emergency use; if an existing shaft is being used for access then extra labour should be allowed over and above the lining crew to maintain (a) air flow through system (at least two manhole covers open and attended), (b) traffic direction, (c) gas monitoring and (d) escape facilities. The output in metres/shift does not vary greatly with diameter since large units are often easier to install because of the greater working room. The factors affecting output are: (a) Length between manholes. (b) Whether linings are in one piece or have an invert and soffit section. (c) Whether fixings are required to pin the units to existing brickwork. (d) Whether units are stiff/thick enough to withstand annulus grouting without internal strutting.

		Unit	Labour Hours	Labour Net £	Plant Net £	Materials Net £	Unit Net £	CO_2 Kg
Y3.3	**Segmental lining**							
Y3.3.3	Glass reinforced plastic							
Y3.3.3.01	1050 x 750 original size; One piece unit	m	0.05	5.87	1.61	383.32	**390.80**	*143.65*
Y3.3.3.02	900 x 600 original size; One piece unit	m	0.03	3.87	1.06	311.45	**316.38**	*114.89*
Y3.3.4	Glass reinforced concrete							
Y3.3.4.01	1050 x 750 original size; Two piece unit	m	0.10	11.74	3.21	360.00	**374.95**	*93.13*
Y3.3.4.02	900 x 600 original size; Two piece unit	m	0.07	7.86	2.15	290.00	**300.01**	*74.45*
Y3.6	**Annulus grouting, materials stated**							
Y3.6.1	Pozament GP3 or GP4							
Y3.6.1.01	Generally	m^3	0.10	11.74	0.68	270.00	**282.42**	*396.99*

Y4 Laterals to Renovated Sewers

		Unit	Labour Hours	Labour Net £	Plant Net £	Materials Net £	Unit Net £	CO_2 Kg
Y4.1	**Jointing**							
Y4.1.1	Bore: not exceeding 150mm							
Y4.1.1.01	Generally	Nr	0.30	35.21	1.06	25.00	**61.27**	*12.60*
Y4.1.2	Bore: 150 - 300mm							
Y4.1.2.01	Generally	Nr	0.55	64.56	1.94	35.00	**101.50**	*17.03*
Y4.1.3	Stated profile and size exceeding 300mm in one or more dimension							
Y4.1.3.01	bore: 450mm	Nr	0.80	93.90	2.82	55.00	**151.72**	*25.51*

Y5 Water Mains Renovation and Ancillary Works

Note(s): The following Specialist prices and are based on robotic methods for non man entry pipelines.

Cleaning

Cleaning is done in two stages. To remove all debris and encrustations prior to a survey of the existing main to establish the size of the lining units. Immediately prior to placing lining units to clean away any residual corrosion debris and encrustation to ensure efficient grouting to the annulus. Stage (i) usually requires power boring or scraping and plunging or high pressure jetting. There is a variety of equipment/sub-contractors available depending on the size of main, length between manholes etc., but usually the more expensive equipment has a compensatingly greater output and the cost will be determined more by the degree of siltation rather than the size of main or its length. 'Stage (ii) costs have been included in the laying operations. Guide Prices for non man entry mains up to 1200mm maximum diameter.

Removing Intructions

The following prices are based on the removal of intruding laterals by the KA-TE robotic system. All operations are monitored by a monochrome camera mounted on the robot and recorded on video tape.

Closed Circuit Television Surveys

These rates include the following:

Establishment, moving and setting up equipment at each exploratory hole and dismantling after completion. Reinstatement around each exploratory hole. Any standing time incurred by boring, drilling, grouting or probing equipment as a result of the survey. Editing, copying and supply of video tapes. Provision of all necessary equipment including adequate power supply and experienced operator. Covered accommodation for viewing monitoring screen.

		Unit	Labour Hours	Labour Net £	Plant Net £	Materials Net £	Unit Net £	CO_2 *Kg*
Y5.1	**Cleaning**							
Y5.1.2	Nominal bore: 200 - 300mm							
Y5.1.2.01	Siltation: not exceeding 35%	m	0.02	2.00	0.13	-	**2.13**	*0.14*
Y5.1.2.02	Siltation: not exceeding 35-50%	m	0.03	2.93	0.20	-	**3.13**	*0.20*
Y5.1.2.03	Siltation: not exceeding 50-65%	m	0.03	3.87	0.26	-	**4.13**	*0.27*
Y5.1.2.04	Siltation: over 65%	m	0.05	5.87	0.40	-	**6.27**	*0.41*
Y5.1.3	Nominal bore: 300 - 600mm							
Y5.1.3.01	Siltation: not exceeding 35%	m	0.03	3.87	0.26	-	**4.13**	*0.27*
Y5.1.3.02	Siltation: not exceeding 35-50%	m	0.05	5.87	0.40	-	**6.27**	*0.41*
Y5.1.3.03	Siltation: not exceeding 50-65%	m	0.07	7.86	0.53	-	**8.39**	*0.55*
Y5.1.3.04	Siltation: over 65%	m	0.10	11.74	0.79	-	**12.53**	*0.81*
Y5.1.4	Nominal bore: 600 - 900mm							
Y5.1.4.01	Siltation: not exceeding 35%	m	0.08	9.74	0.66	-	**10.40**	*0.68*
Y5.1.4.02	Siltation: not exceeding 35-50%	m	0.13	14.67	0.99	-	**15.66**	*1.02*
Y5.1.4.03	Siltation: not exceeding 50-65%	m	0.17	19.60	1.33	-	**20.93**	*1.36*
Y5.1.4.04	Siltation: over 65%	m	0.25	29.34	1.99	-	**31.33**	*2.04*
Y5.1.5	Nominal bore: 900 - 1200mm							
Y5.1.5.01	Siltation: not exceeding 35%	m	0.17	19.60	1.33	-	**20.93**	*1.36*
Y5.1.5.02	Siltation: not exceeding 35-50%	m	0.25	29.34	1.99	-	**31.33**	*2.04*
Y5.1.5.03	Siltation: not exceeding 50-65%	m	0.33	39.09	2.64	-	**41.73**	*2.71*
Y5.1.5.04	Siltation: over 65%	m	0.40	46.95	3.18	-	**50.13**	*3.26*

Y5 Water Mains Renovation and Ancillary Works continued...

		Unit	Labour Hours	Labour Net £	Plant Net £	Materials Net £	Unit Net £	CO_2 Kg
Y5.2	**Removing intrusions**							
Y5.2.1	Nominal bore: not exceeding 200mm							
Y5.2.1.01	Laterals of bore not exceeding 150mm; GVC, concrete, cast iron or steel pipes	Nr	2.00	234.76	7.04	-	241.80	*3.02*
Y5.2.2	Nominal bore: 200 - 300mm							
Y5.2.2.01	Laterals exceeding 200mm in one or more dimension; GVC, or concrete pipes not exceeding 300mm into the bore of the main pipe	Nr	3.00	352.14	10.56	-	362.70	*4.53*
Y5.2.2.02	Laterals exceeding 200mm in one or more dimension; Isolated bricks	Nr	3.00	352.14	10.56	-	362.70	*4.53*
Y5.4	**Closed-circuit television surveys**							
Y5.4.3	Nominal bore: 300 - 600mm							
Y5.4.3.01	for cast iron pipe; nominal bore 600mm	m	-	-	1.62	-	1.62	*0.14*
Y5.4.4	Nominal bore: 600 - 900mm							
Y5.4.4.01	for cast iron pipe; nominal bore 900mm	m	-	-	1.62	-	1.62	*0.14*
Y5.4.5	Nominal bore: 900 - 1200mm							
Y5.4.5.01	for cast iron pipe; nominal bore 1000mm	m	-	-	1.62	-	1.62	*0.14*
Y5.4.5.02	for cast iron pipe; nominal bore 1200mm	m	-	-	1.62	-	1.62	*0.14*
Y5.4.6	Nominal bore: stated exceeding 1200mm							
Y5.4.6.01	for cast iron pipe; nominal bore 1500mm	m	-	-	1.62	-	1.62	*0.14*
Y5.4.6.02	for cast iron pipe; nominal bore 1800mm	m	-	-	1.62	-	1.62	*0.14*

Y8 Interruptions

Note(s): Prices will depend greatly upon the amount of labour and plant that is tied up by the stopping of an operation. In certain circumstances labour and plant may be diverted on to other work.

		Unit	Labour Hours	Labour Net £	Plant Net £	Materials Net £	Unit Net £	CO_2 Kg
Y8.1	**Preparation of existing sewers**							
Y8.1.1	Cleaning							
Y8.1.1.01	Vacuum cleaning	Hr	1.00	117.38	7.94	-	125.32	*8.15*
Y8.2	**Stabilisation of existing sewers**							
Y8.2.1	Generally							
Y8.2.1.01	Pointing	Hr	1.00	117.38	2.61	-	119.99	*1.80*
Y8.3	**Renovation of existing sewers**							
Y8.3.4	Stated proprietary lining							
Y8.3.4.01	GRC and GRP linings	Hr	1.00	117.38	32.12	-	149.50	*4.26*

CLASS Z:
SIMPLE BUILDING WORKS INCIDENTAL TO CIVIL ENGINEERING WORK

Calculations used throughout Class Z - Simple Building Works Incidental to Civil Engineering Work

Labour

		Qty		Rate		Total
L A0120ICE	**General Earthworks Labour Gang**					
	Ganger	1	x	16.99	=	£16.99
	Labourer (General Operative)	1	x	12.56	=	£12.56
	Banksman	1	x	13.53	=	£13.53
	Total hourly cost of gang				**=**	**£43.08**
L A0300ICE	**Brickwork Labour Gang**					
	Bricklayer (chargehand)	1	x	17.93	=	£17.93
	Bricklayer	4	x	16.68	=	£66.73
	Labourer (General Operative)	2	x	12.56	=	£25.12
	Total hourly cost of gang				**=**	**£109.78**
L A0310ICE	**Painting Labour Gang**					
	Painter (chargehand)	1	x	17.93	=	£17.93
	Painter	2	x	16.68	=	£33.37
	Brush hand (labourer)	1	x	12.56	=	£12.56
	Total hourly cost of gang				**=**	**£63.86**
L A0325ICE	**Plastering Labour Gang**					
	Plasterer	1	x	16.68	=	£16.68
	Labourer (General Operative)	1	x	12.56	=	£12.56
	Total hourly cost of gang				**=**	**£29.24**
L Z0002ICE	**Patent Glazing Labour Gang**					
	Labourer (Skill Rate 4)	3	x	13.53	=	£40.59
	Craftsman WRA	1	x	16.68	=	£16.68
	Total hourly cost of gang				**=**	**£57.27**
L Z0005ICE	**Carpentry Labour Gang**					
	Craftsman WRA	5	x	16.68	=	£83.42
	Labourer (General Operative)	1	x	12.56	=	£12.56
	Ganger	1	x	16.99	=	£16.99
	Total hourly cost of gang				**=**	**£112.97**
L Z0006ICE	**Electrical Labour Gang**					
	Electrician	2	x	22.37	=	£44.74
	Apprentice	1	x	11.19	=	£11.19
	Total hourly cost of gang				**=**	**£55.93**
L Z0007ICE	**Floor Finishes Labour Gang**					
	Craftsman WRA	1	x	16.68	=	£16.68
	Labourer (General Operative)	1	x	12.56	=	£12.56
	Total hourly cost of gang				**=**	**£29.24**
L Z0008ICE	**HVAC Labour Gang**					
	HVAC Craftsman	2	x	17.90	=	£35.81
	Apprentice	1	x	11.19	=	£11.19
	Total hourly cost of gang				**=**	**£47.00**
L Z0010ICE	**Screeding Labour Gang**					
	Craftsman WRA	1	x	16.68	=	£16.68
	Labourer (General Operative)	1	x	12.56	=	£12.56
	Total hourly cost of gang				**=**	**£29.24**

L Z0011ICE	**Wall Tiling Labour Gang**					
	Ganger	1	x	16.99	=	£16.99
	Labourer (General Operative)	1	x	12.56	=	£12.56
	Total hourly cost of gang				**=**	**£29.55**

Plant

P A1124ICE	**General Excavation Plant Gang**					
	Hydraulic Excavator - Cat 166kW	1	x	41.41	=	£41.41
	Crawler Tractor / Dozer - Cat D6 LGP 160 Hp	0.5	x	48.61	=	£24.30
	Total hourly cost of gang				**=**	**£65.71**
P Z0002ICE	**Carpentry Plant Gang**					
	Generator - 10kvA Diesel	1	x	3.55	=	£3.55
	9" Circular Saw	1	x	0.98	=	£0.98
	Small Tools	1	x	1.50	=	£1.50
	Total hourly cost of gang				**=**	**£6.03**
P Z0004ICE	**Plastering Plant Gang**					
	Concrete Mixer - 5/3 Diesel	1	x	2.61	=	£2.61
	Total hourly cost of gang				**=**	**£2.61**
P Z0006ICE	**Screeding Plant Gang**					
	Concrete Mixer - 5/3 Diesel	1	x	2.61	=	£2.61
	Screed Pump	1	x	14.46	=	£14.46
	Total hourly cost of gang				=	£17.07

Class Z - Simple Building Works Incidental to Civil Engineering Work

Note(s): The prices contained in this class are intended to assist in the compilation of estimates for activities commonly found in simple building works incidental to civil engineering works. The items listed hereafter are all not measured strictly in accordance with Class Z of CESMM3 but are included as a representative sample based on a composite basis wherever possible, to provide an indication of the level of pricing. The prices do not include for any Preliminary type items. Attention should be given to guidance notes which follow some items.

Z1 Carpentry and Joinery

		Unit	Labour Hours	Labour Net £	Plant Net £	Materials Net £	Unit Net £	CO_2 *Kg*
Z1.1	**Structural and carcassing timber**							
Z1.1.1	Floors							
Z1.1.1.01	Suspended timber floors; including structural and carcassing timbers with boarding; sawn softwood joists at 600mm centres, ends built in; sawn softwood herringbone strutting 50 x 50mm to centre line of joists span; all timbers treated; Joint sizes: 175 x 50mm; Plywood, tongued and grooved joints; 18mm thick	m^2	0.32	36.15	1.93	11.84	**49.92**	*15.43*
Z1.1.1.02	as above; Joint sizes: 175 x 50mm; Chipboard, tongued and grooved joints; 18mm thick; pre-felted	m^2	0.24	27.11	1.44	9.54	**38.09**	*12.24*
Z1.1.1.03	as above; Joint sizes: 175 x 50mm; Softwood, wrought, tongued and grooved jointed; 150mm wide, 25mm thick	m^2	0.40	45.18	2.41	13.28	**60.87**	*15.28*
Z1.1.1.04	as above; Joint sizes: 200 x 50mm; Plywood, tongued and grooved joints; 18mm thick	m^2	0.32	36.15	1.93	12.67	**50.75**	*16.24*
Z1.1.1.05	as above; Joint sizes: 200 x 50mm; Chipboard, tongued and grooved joints; 18mm thick; pre-felted	m^2	0.24	27.11	1.44	10.37	**38.92**	*13.05*
Z1.1.1.06	as above; Joint sizes: 200 x 50mm; Softwood, wrought, tongued and grooved jointed; 150mm wide, 25mm thick	m^2	0.40	45.18	2.41	14.11	**61.70**	*16.09*
Z1.1.1.07	as above; Joint sizes: 225 x 50mm; Plywood, tongued and grooved joints; 18mm thick	m^2	0.32	36.15	1.93	13.49	**51.57**	*17.05*
Z1.1.1.08	as above; Joint sizes: 225 x 50mm; Chipboard, tongued and grooved joints; 18mm thick; pre-felted	m^2	0.24	27.11	1.44	11.19	**39.74**	*13.85*
Z1.1.1.09	as above; Joint sizes: 225 x 50mm; Softwood, wrought, tongued and grooved jointed; 150mm wide, 25mm thick	m^2	0.40	45.18	2.41	14.93	**62.52**	*16.89*

Z1 Carpentry and Joinery continued...

		Unit	Labour Hours	Labour Net £	Plant Net £	Materials Net £	Unit Net £	CO_2 Kg
Z1.1	**Structural and carcassing timber**							
Z1.1.2	Walls and partitions							
Z1.1.2.01	Timber internal stud partitions; including structural carcassing timbers within partitions; studs at 450mm centres, noggins at 1220mm centres; head and sole plate; all timbers treated; Stud sizes: 38 x 50mm; Hardwood, sawn	m^2	0.20	22.59	1.20	4.39	**28.18**	*3.81*
Z1.1.2.02	as above; Stud sizes: 38 x 50mm; Softwood, sawn	m^2	0.10	11.30	0.60	2.45	**14.35**	*2.62*
Z1.1.2.03	as above; Stud sizes: 50 x 75mm; Hardwood, sawn	m^2	0.30	33.89	1.81	8.12	**43.82**	*6.91*
Z1.1.2.04	as above; Stud sizes: 50 x 75mm; Softwood, sawn	m^2	0.15	16.94	0.90	4.58	**22.42**	*4.79*
Z1.1.2.05	as above; Stud sizes: 75 x 100mm; Hardwood, sawn	m^2	0.60	67.78	3.61	17.27	**88.66**	*14.62*
Z1.1.2.06	as above; Stud sizes: 75 x 100mm; Softwood, sawn	m^2	0.30	33.89	1.81	9.72	**45.42**	*10.15*
Z1.1.3	Flat roofs							
Z1.1.3.01	Timber flat roof; including structural and carcassing timbers with boarding; sawn softwood joists at 750mm centres, ends built in; sawn softwood herringbone strutting at mid span; 100 x 50mm wall plates, average 50 x 75mm firrings no insulation; no finishings, all timber treated; Joint sizes: 150 x 50mm; Plywood, butt joints; 18mm thick	m^2	0.32	36.15	1.93	12.28	**50.36**	*15.47*
Z1.1.3.02	as above; Joint sizes: 150 x 50mm; Chipboard, butt joints; 18mm thick; pre-felted	m^2	0.24	27.11	1.44	9.98	**38.53**	*12.27*
Z1.1.3.03	as above; Joint sizes: 150 x 50mm; Softwood, wrought, tongued and grooved jointed; 150mm wide, 25mm thick	m^2	0.40	45.18	2.41	13.73	**61.32**	*15.31*
Z1.1.3.04	as above; Joint sizes: 200 x 50mm; Plywood, butt joints; 18mm thick	m^2	0.36	40.67	2.17	13.33	**56.17**	*16.77*
Z1.1.3.05	as above; Joint sizes: 200 x 50mm; Chipboard, butt joints; 18mm thick; pre-felted	m^2	0.28	31.63	1.69	11.03	**44.35**	*13.58*
Z1.1.3.06	as above; Joint sizes: 200 x 50mm; Softwood, wrought, tongued and grooved jointed; 150mm wide, 25mm thick	m^2	0.44	49.70	2.65	14.77	**67.12**	*16.62*
Z1.1.3.07	as above; Joint sizes: 250 x 50mm; Plywood, butt joints; 18mm thick	m^2	0.40	45.18	2.41	14.39	**61.98**	*17.89*
Z1.1.3.08	as above; Joint sizes: 250 x 50mm; Chipboard, butt joints; 18mm thick; pre-felted	m^2	0.32	36.15	1.93	12.10	**50.18**	*14.70*
Z1.1.3.09	as above; Joint sizes: 250 x 50mm; Softwood, wrought, tongued and grooved jointed; 150mm wide, 25mm thick	m^2	0.48	54.22	2.89	15.84	**72.95**	*17.74*

Z1 Carpentry and Joinery continued...

		Unit	Labour Hours	Labour Net £	Plant Net £	Materials Net £	Unit Net £	CO_2 Kg
Z1.1	**Structural and carcassing timber**							
Z1.1.4	Pitched roofs							
Z1.1.4.01	Timber pitched roof in traditional sawn softwood construction; including structural and carcassing timbers; roof with hipped ends; purlins; ridge; rafters and ceiling joists at 450mm centres, blinders; struts; hangers; ties; wall plates; no insulation no coverings; all timber trated; Roof pitch: 22.5 degrees; Rafters at 1800mm centres spanning; 8000mm	m^2	0.25	28.24	1.50	12.31	**42.05**	*11.32*
Z1.1.4.02	as above; Roof pitch: 22.5 degrees; Rafters at 1800mm centres spanning; 10000mm	m^2	0.24	27.11	1.44	10.59	**39.14**	*9.87*
Z1.1.4.03	as above; Roof pitch: 35 degrees; Rafters at 1800mm centres spanning; 8000mm	m^2	0.28	31.74	1.69	14.58	**48.01**	*13.52*
Z1.1.4.04	as above; Roof pitch: 35 degrees; Rafters at 1800mm centres spanning; 10000mm	m^2	0.30	33.89	1.81	11.39	**47.09**	*10.71*
Z1.1.4.05	as above; Roof pitch: 45 degrees; Rafters at 1800mm centres spanning; 8000mm	m^2	0.31	35.36	1.88	15.47	**52.71**	*14.37*
Z1.1.4.06	as above; Roof pitch: 45 degrees; Rafters at 1800mm centres spanning; 10000mm	m^2	0.34	38.41	2.05	12.00	**52.46**	*11.34*
Z1.1.4.07	Timber pitched roof; including structural and carcassing timbers with trussed rafters; sawn softwood trussed rafters at 600mm centres, roof with gable ends; sawn softwood wall plates, bracing and binders; galvanised steel straps to gable walls; no insulation; np coverings; all timber treated; Roof pitch: 22.5 degrees; Trussed rafter spanning; 4600mm	m^2	0.08	8.70	0.46	15.96	**25.12**	*13.91*
Z1.1.4.08	as above; Roof pitch: 22.5 degrees; Trussed rafter spanning; 7000mm; Fink	m^2	0.08	8.70	0.46	27.28	**36.44**	*17.50*
Z1.1.4.09	as above; Roof pitch: 22.5 degrees; Trussed rafter spanning; 10000mm; Fink	m^2	0.08	8.70	0.46	38.86	**48.02**	*22.05*
Z1.1.4.10	as above; Roof pitch: 35 degrees; Trussed rafter spanning; 4600mm; Fink	m^2	0.09	9.60	0.51	17.22	**27.33**	*12.79*
Z1.1.4.11	as above; Roof pitch: 35 degrees; Trussed rafter spanning; 7000mm; Fink	m^2	0.09	9.60	0.51	30.36	**40.47**	*16.44*
Z1.1.4.12	as above; Roof pitch: 35 degrees; Trussed rafter spanning; 10000mm; Fink	m^2	0.10	11.52	0.61	43.73	**55.86**	*20.98*
Z1.1.4.13	as above; Roof pitch: 45 degrees; Trussed rafter spanning; 4600mm; Fink	m^2	0.12	13.67	0.73	18.26	**32.66**	*11.99*
Z1.1.4.14	as above; Roof pitch: 45 degrees; Trussed rafter spanning; 7000mm; Fink	m^2	0.12	13.67	0.73	32.86	**47.26**	*15.70*

Z1 Carpentry and Joinery continued...

		Unit	Labour Hours	Labour Net £	Plant Net £	Materials Net £	Unit Net £	*CO_2 Kg*
Z1.1	**Structural and carcassing timber**							
Z1.1.4	Pitched roofs							
Z1.1.4.15	as previous item; Roof pitch: 45 degrees; Trussed rafter spanning; 10000mm; Fink	m^2	0.12	13.67	0.73	47.67	**62.07**	*20.16*
Z1.1.5	Plates and bearers							
Z1.1.5.01	Untreated Softwood, sawn: 25 x 50mm	m	0.02	1.92	0.10	0.23	**2.25**	*0.33*
Z1.1.5.02	Untreated Softwood, sawn: 25 x 75mm	m	0.02	1.92	0.10	0.35	**2.37**	*0.47*
Z1.1.5.03	Untreated Softwood, sawn: 25 x 100mm	m	0.02	1.92	0.10	0.46	**2.48**	*0.61*
Z1.1.5.04	Untreated Softwood, sawn: 38 x 50mm	m	0.02	1.92	0.10	0.35	**2.37**	*0.47*
Z1.1.5.05	Untreated Softwood, sawn: 38 x 75mm	m	0.02	1.92	0.10	0.53	**2.55**	*0.69*
Z1.1.5.06	Untreated Softwood, sawn: 38 x 100mm	m	0.02	2.37	0.13	0.70	**3.20**	*0.92*
Z1.1.5.07	Untreated Softwood, sawn: 47 x 50mm	m	0.02	2.37	0.13	0.44	**2.94**	*0.59*
Z1.1.5.08	Untreated Softwood, sawn: 47 x 75mm	m	0.02	2.37	0.13	0.65	**3.15**	*0.86*
Z1.1.5.09	Untreated Softwood, sawn: 47 x 100mm	m	0.02	2.71	0.14	0.87	**3.72**	*1.13*
Z1.1.5.10	Untreated Softwood, sawn: 75 x 75mm	m	0.03	3.16	0.17	1.04	**4.37**	*1.35*
Z1.1.5.11	Untreated Softwood, sawn: 75 x 100mm	m	0.03	3.16	0.17	1.39	**4.72**	*1.78*
Z1.1.5.12	Untreated Softwood, sawn: 75 x 150mm	m	0.04	4.74	0.25	2.09	**7.08**	*2.68*
Z1.1.5.13	Untreated Softwood, sawn: 75 x 200mm	m	0.04	4.74	0.25	2.78	**7.77**	*3.54*
Z1.1.5.14	Untreated Softwood, sawn: 100 x 100mm	m	0.04	4.74	0.25	1.85	**6.84**	*2.39*
Z1.1.5.15	Untreated Softwood, sawn: 100 x 150mm	m	0.05	5.87	0.31	2.78	**8.96**	*3.56*
Z1.1.5.16	Untreated Softwood, sawn: 100 x 200mm	m	0.07	7.79	0.42	3.71	**11.92**	*4.75*
Z1.1.5.17	Untreated Softwood, sawn: 100 x 250mm	m	0.09	9.83	0.52	4.64	**14.99**	*5.93*
Z1.1.5.18	Treated Softwood, sawn: 25 x 50mm	m	0.02	1.92	0.10	0.34	**2.36**	*0.35*
Z1.1.5.19	Treated Softwood, sawn: 25 x 75mm	m	0.02	1.92	0.10	0.51	**2.53**	*0.50*
Z1.1.5.20	Treated Softwood, sawn: 25 x 100mm	m	0.02	1.92	0.10	0.69	**2.71**	*0.66*
Z1.1.5.21	Treated Softwood, sawn: 38 x 50mm	m	0.02	1.92	0.10	0.52	**2.54**	*0.51*
Z1.1.5.22	Treated Softwood, sawn: 38 x 75mm	m	0.02	1.92	0.10	0.78	**2.80**	*0.74*
Z1.1.5.23	Treated Softwood, sawn: 38 x 100mm	m	0.02	2.37	0.13	1.04	**3.54**	*0.99*
Z1.1.5.24	Treated Softwood, sawn: 47 x 50mm	m	0.02	2.37	0.13	0.64	**3.14**	*0.63*
Z1.1.5.25	Treated Softwood, sawn: 47 x 75mm	m	0.02	2.37	0.13	0.97	3.47 3.47	*0.92*
Z1.1.5.26	Treated Softwood, sawn: 47 x 100mm	m	0.02	2.71	0.14	1.29	**4.14**	*1.22*
Z1.1.5.27	Treated Softwood, sawn: 75 x 75mm	m	0.03	3.16	0.17	1.54	**4.87**	*1.46*

Z1 Carpentry and Joinery continued...

		Unit	Labour Hours	Labour Net £	Plant Net £	Materials Net £	Unit Net £	CO_2 Kg
Z1.1	**Structural and carcassing timber**							
Z1.1.5	Plates and bearers							
Z1.1.5.28	Treated Softwood, sawn: 75 x 100mm	m	0.04	4.74	0.25	2.06	7.05	*1.95*
Z1.1.5.29	Treated Softwood, sawn: 75 x 150mm	m	0.04	4.74	0.25	3.08	8.07	*2.88*
Z1.1.5.30	Treated Softwood, sawn: 75 x 200mm	m	0.04	4.74	0.25	4.11	9.10	*3.81*
Z1.1.5.31	Treated Softwood, sawn: 100 x 100mm	m	0.04	4.74	0.25	2.74	7.73	*2.57*
Z1.1.5.32	Treated Softwood, sawn: 100 x 150mm	m	0.05	5.87	0.31	4.11	10.29	*3.83*
Z1.1.5.33	Treated Softwood, sawn: 100 x 200mm	m	0.07	7.79	0.42	5.48	13.69	*5.11*
Z1.1.5.34	Treated Softwood, sawn: 100 x 250mm	m	0.09	9.83	0.52	6.86	17.21	*6.38*
Z1.1.6	Struts							
Z1.1.6.01	Untreated Softwood, sawn: 50 x 50mm	m	0.02	1.92	0.10	0.46	2.48	*0.61*
Z1.1.6.02	Untreated Softwood, sawn: 50 x 100mm	m	0.04	3.95	0.21	0.93	5.09	*1.23*
Z1.1.6.03	Untreated Softwood, sawn: 50 x 150mm	m	0.05	5.87	0.31	1.39	7.57	*1.27*
Z1.1.6.04	Untreated Softwood, sawn: 50 x 200mm	m	0.07	7.79	0.42	1.85	10.06	*2.68*
Z1.1.6.05	Untreated Softwood, sawn: 50 x 250mm	m	0.09	9.83	0.52	2.32	12.67	*3.06*
Z1.1.6.06	Treated Softwood, sawn: 50 x 50mm	m	0.02	1.92	0.10	0.69	2.71	*0.66*
Z1.1.6.07	Treated Softwood, sawn: 50 x 100mm	m	0.04	3.95	0.21	1.37	5.53	*1.23*
Z1.1.6.08	Treated Softwood, sawn: 50 x 150mm	m	0.05	5.87	0.31	2.06	8.24	*1.84*
Z1.1.6.09	Treated Softwood, sawn: 50 x 200mm	m	0.07	7.79	0.42	2.74	10.95	*2.63*
Z1.1.6.10	Treated Softwood, sawn: 50 x 250mm	m	0.09	9.83	0.52	3.43	13.78	*3.29*
Z1.1.7	Cleats							
Z1.1.7.01	Untreated Softwood, sawn: 50 x 100 x 200mm long	Nr	0.01	1.13	0.06	0.19	1.38	*1.17*
Z1.1.7.02	Untreated Softwood, sawn: 75 x 100 x 225mm long	Nr	0.01	1.58	0.08	0.31	1.97	*1.75*
Z1.1.7.03	Untreated Softwood, sawn: 75 x 150 x 300mm long	Nr	0.02	1.92	0.10	0.63	2.65	*2.62*
Z1.1.7.04	Untreated Softwood, sawn: 100 x 200 x 400mm long	Nr	0.02	2.37	0.13	1.48	3.98	*4.64*
Z1.1.7.05	Treated Softwood, sawn: 50 x 100 x 200mm long	Nr	0.01	1.13	0.06	0.27	1.46	*1.26*
Z1.1.7.06	Treated Softwood, sawn: 75 x 100 x 225mm long	Nr	0.01	1.58	0.08	0.46	2.12	*1.89*
Z1.1.7.07	Treated Softwood, sawn: 75 x 150 x 300mm long	Nr	0.02	1.92	0.10	0.93	2.95	*2.82*
Z1.1.7.08	Treated Softwood, sawn: 100 x 200 x 400mm long	Nr	0.02	2.37	0.13	2.19	4.69	*5.00*

Z1 Carpentry and Joinery continued...

		Unit	Labour Hours	Labour Net £	Plant Net £	Materials Net £	Unit Net £	CO_2 Kg
Z1.2	**Strip boarding**							
Z1.2.1	Floors							
Z1.2.1.01	Tongued and grooved joints; 150mm widths; Thickness: 22mm; Softwood, wrought	m^2	0.10	8.84	0.30	14.63	**23.77**	*7.00*
Z1.2.1.02	as above; 150mm widths; Thickness: 25mm; Softwood, wrought	m^2	0.10	8.84	0.30	15.41	**24.55**	*7.88*
Z1.2.1.03	as above; 75mm widths; Thickness: 22mm; Hardwood, wrought: Maple	m^2	0.34	31.53	1.20	21.56	**54.29**	*8.14*
Z1.2.1.04	as above; 75mm widths; Thickness: 22mm; Hardwood, wrought: Iroko	m^2	0.29	25.88	0.90	20.58	**47.36**	*8.03*
Z1.2.1.05	as above; 75mm widths; Thickness: 22mm; Hardwood, wrought: Oak	m^2	0.34	31.53	1.20	21.56	**54.29**	*8.14*
Z1.2.4	Soffits							
Z1.2.4.01	At eaves; butt joints; including 38 x 50mm sawn softwood treated bearers; Widths: over 150mm; Masterboard; 6mm thick	m^2	0.05	5.65	0.30	4.29	**10.24**	*4.62*
Z1.2.4.02	as above; Widths: over 150mm; Softwood, wrought untreated; 16mm thick 100mm wide boards	m^2	0.10	11.30	0.60	3.40	**15.30**	*3.29*
Z1.2.4.03	as above; Widths: over 150mm; Plywood external quality; 18mm thick	m^2	0.05	5.65	0.30	13.13	**19.08**	*9.87*
Z1.2.4.04	as above; Widths: over 225mm; Masterboard; 6mm thick	m^2	0.08	8.47	0.45	4.29	**13.21**	*4.67*
Z1.2.4.05	as above; Widths: over 225mm; Softwood, wrought untreated; 16mm thick 100mm wide boards	m^2	0.13	14.12	0.75	3.40	**18.27**	*3.35*
Z1.2.4.06	as above; Widths: over 225mm; Plywood external quality; 18mm thick	m^2	0.06	6.78	0.36	13.13	**20.27**	*9.89*
Z1.2.4.07	as above; Widths: over 300mm; Masterboard; 6mm thick	m^2	0.16	18.07	0.96	4.29	**23.32**	*4.86*
Z1.2.4.08	as above; Widths: over 300mm; Softwood, wrought untreated; 16mm thick 100mm wide boards	m^2	0.30	33.89	1.81	3.40	**39.10**	*3.74*
Z1.2.4.09	as above; Widths: over 300mm; Plywood external quality; 18mm thick	m^2	0.16	18.07	0.96	13.13	**32.16**	*10.11*
Z1.3	**Sheet boarding**							
Z1.3.1	Floors							
Z1.3.1.01	Thickness: 15mm; Plywood, butt jointed	m^2	0.11	12.43	0.66	4.15	**17.24**	*5.50*
Z1.3.1.02	Thickness: 18mm; Plywood, butt jointed	m^2	0.11	12.43	0.66	5.23	**18.32**	*8.12*
Z1.3.1.03	Thickness: 18mm; Chipboard, tongued and grooved jointed	m^2	0.06	6.78	0.36	3.14	**10.28**	*5.35*
Z1.3.1.04	Thickness: 22mm; Plywood, butt jointed	m^2	0.11	12.43	0.66	6.42	**19.51**	*11.18*
Z1.3.1.05	Thickness: 22mm; Chipboard, tongued and grooved jointed	m^2	0.06	6.78	0.36	4.63	**11.77**	*7.38*

Z1 Carpentry and Joinery continued...

		Unit	Labour Hours	Labour Net £	Plant Net £	Materials Net £	Unit Net £	CO_2 Kg
Z1.4	**Stairs and walkways**							
Z1.4.1	Stairways and landings							
Z1.4.1.01	Balustrade to one side, 900mm wide x 2600mm rise; stairs, 25mm treads, 19mm risers; 32mm strings each side; 75 x 75mm newel posts; balustrade, 38 x 38mm balusters at 150mm centres, 50 x 75mm handrail; fixing to masonry walls; no finishes; Wrought Softwood	Nr	4.00	451.84	24.08	438.90	914.82	*120.43*
Z1.4.1.02	as above; Wrought Softwood; Two flight with quarter landing	Nr	6.00	677.76	36.12	342.50	1,056.38	*120.16*
Z1.4.1.03	as above; Wrought Softwood; Two flight with half landing	Nr	7.00	790.72	42.14	357.63	1,190.49	*138.90*
Z1.4.3	Isolated balustrades							
Z1.4.3.01	Balustrades 1100mm high; 32 x 32mm balusters; 50 x 75mm moulded handrails; jointed to newel posts; Wrought Softwood; Balustrade to landing, 3000mm long	Nr	1.00	112.96	6.02	122.61	241.59	*40.24*
Z1.4.3.02	as above; Wrought Softwood; Balustrade to straight staircase, 2600mm rise	Nr	2.00	225.92	12.04	122.61	360.57	*42.49*
Z1.4.3.03	as above; Wrought Oak; Balustrade to landing, 3000mm long	Nr	1.00	112.96	6.02	714.88	833.86	*133.77*
Z1.4.3.04	as above; Wrought Oak; Balustrade to straight staircase, 2600mm rise	Nr	2.00	225.92	12.04	714.88	952.84	*136.02*
Z1.5	**Miscellaneous joinery**							
Z1.5.1	Skirtings							
Z1.5.1.01	Skirtings including sawn softwood grounds plugged and screwed to blockwork; Rounded Softwood, wrought: 19 x 100mm	m	0.03	3.01	0.10	0.98	4.09	*0.50*
Z1.5.1.02	as above; Rounded Softwood, wrought: 19 x 150mm	m	0.03	3.01	0.10	1.48	4.59	*0.73*
Z1.5.1.03	as above; Rounded Softwood, wrought: 19 x 175mm	m	0.03	3.01	0.10	1.74	4.85	*0.84*
Z1.5.1.04	as above; Rounded Softwood, wrought: 25 x 100mm	m	0.05	4.42	0.15	1.15	5.72	*0.65*
Z1.5.1.05	as above; Rounded Softwood, wrought: 25 x 150mm	m	0.05	4.42	0.15	1.73	6.30	*0.95*
Z1.5.1.06	as above; Rounded Softwood, wrought: 25 x 175mm	m	0.05	4.42	0.15	2.04	6.61	*1.10*
Z1.5.1.07	as above; Rounded Oak, wrought: 19 x 100mm	m	0.09	7.10	0.15	1.54	8.79	*0.70*
Z1.5.1.08	as above; Rounded Oak, wrought: 19 x 150mm	m	0.10	8.01	0.20	2.31	10.52	*1.05*
Z1.5.1.09	as above; Rounded Oak, wrought: 19 x 175mm	m	0.10	8.01	0.20	2.72	10.93	*0.74*
Z1.5.1.10	as above; Rounded Oak, wrought: 25 x 100mm	m	0.15	12.03	0.30	1.88	14.21	*0.96*
Z1.5.1.11	as above; Rounded Oak, wrought: 25 x 150mm	m	0.15	12.03	0.30	2.83	15.16	*1.38*

Z1 Carpentry and Joinery continued...

		Unit	Labour Hours	Labour Net £	Plant Net £	Materials Net £	Unit Net £	CO_2 Kg
Z1.5	**Miscellaneous joinery**							
Z1.5.1	Skirtings							
Z1.5.1.12	as previous item; Rounded Oak, wrought: 25 x 175mm	m	0.15	12.03	0.30	2.24	14.57	*1.59*
Z1.5.1.13	as above; Moulded Softwood, wrought: 19 x 100mm	m	0.05	4.42	0.15	0.98	5.55	*0.51*
Z1.5.1.14	as above; Moulded Softwood, wrought: 19 x 150mm	m	0.05	4.42	0.15	1.48	6.05	*0.74*
Z1.5.1.15	as above; Moulded Softwood, wrought: 19 x 175mm	m	0.05	4.42	0.15	1.74	6.31	*0.86*
Z1.5.1.16	as above; Moulded Softwood, wrought: 25 x 100mm	m	0.07	5.84	0.20	1.15	7.19	*0.67*
Z1.5.1.17	as above; Moulded Softwood, wrought: 25 x 150mm	m	0.07	5.84	0.20	1.73	7.77	*0.97*
Z1.5.1.18	as above; Moulded Softwood, wrought: 25 x 175mm	m	0.07	5.84	0.20	2.04	8.08	*1.12*
Z1.5.1.19	as above; Moulded Oak, wrought: 19 x 100mm	m	0.10	8.01	0.20	1.54	9.75	*0.72*
Z1.5.1.20	as above; Moulded Oak, wrought: 19 x 150mm	m	0.10	8.01	0.20	2.31	10.52	*1.05*
Z1.5.1.21	as above; Moulded Oak, wrought: 19 x 175mm	m	0.10	8.01	0.20	2.72	10.93	*1.21*
Z1.5.1.22	as above; Moulded Oak, wrought: 25 x 100mm	m	0.13	10.04	0.25	1.88	12.17	*0.94*
Z1.5.1.23	as above; Moulded Oak, wrought: 25 x 150mm	m	0.13	10.04	0.25	2.83	13.12	*1.36*
Z1.5.1.24	as above; Moulded Oak, wrought: 25 x 175mm	m	0.13	10.04	0.25	2.24	12.53	*1.57*
Z1.5.2	Architraves							
Z1.5.2.01	Rounded Softwood, wrought: 25 x 44mm	m	0.03	3.01	0.10	0.49	3.60	*0.30*
Z1.5.2.02	Rounded Softwood, wrought: 25 x 50mm	m	0.03	3.01	0.10	0.57	3.68	*0.34*
Z1.5.2.03	Rounded Softwood, wrought: 25 x 63mm	m	0.03	3.01	0.10	0.72	3.83	*0.41*
Z1.5.2.04	Rounded Softwood, wrought: 25 x 75mm	m	0.03	3.01	0.10	0.88	3.99	*0.49*
Z1.5.2.05	Rounded Oak, wrought: 25 x 44mm	m	0.07	5.84	0.20	0.81	6.85	*0.46*
Z1.5.2.06	Rounded Oak, wrought: 25 x 50mm	m	0.07	5.84	0.20	0.94	6.98	*0.51*
Z1.5.2.07	Rounded Oak, wrought: 25 x 63mm	m	0.07	5.84	0.20	1.18	7.22	*0.62*
Z1.5.2.08	Rounded Oak, wrought: 25 x 75mm	m	0.07	5.84	0.20	1.43	7.47	*0.73*
Z1.5.2.09	Moulded Softwood, wrought: 25 x 44mm	m	0.03	3.01	0.10	0.49	3.60	*0.30*
Z1.5.2.10	Moulded Softwood, wrought: 25 x 50mm	m	0.03	3.01	0.10	0.57	3.68	*0.34*
Z1.5.2.11	Moulded Softwood, wrought: 25 x 63mm	m	0.03	3.01	0.10	0.72	3.83	*0.41*
Z1.5.2.12	Moulded Softwood, wrought: 25 x 75mm	m	0.03	3.01	0.10	0.88	3.99	*0.49*
Z1.5.2.13	Moulded Oak, wrought: 25 x 44mm	m	0.07	5.84	0.20	0.81	6.85	*0.46*
Z1.5.2.14	Moulded Oak, wrought: 25 x 50mm	m	0.07	5.84	0.20	0.94	6.98	*0.51*
Z1.5.2.15	Moulded Oak, wrought: 25 x 63mm	m	0.07	5.84	0.20	1.18	7.22	*0.62*

Z1 Carpentry and Joinery continued...

		Unit	Labour Hours	Labour Net £	Plant Net £	Materials Net £	Unit Net £	CO_2 Kg
Z1.5	**Miscellaneous joinery**							
Z1.5.2	Architraves							
Z1.5.2.16	Moulded Oak, wrought: 25 x 75mm	m	0.07	5.84	0.20	1.43	7.47	*0.73*
Z1.5.3	Trims							
Z1.5.3.01	Rounded Softwood, wrought: 25 x 44mm	m	0.03	3.01	0.10	0.49	3.60	*0.30*
Z1.5.3.02	Rounded Softwood, wrought: 25 x 50mm	m	0.03	3.01	0.10	0.57	3.68	*0.34*
Z1.5.3.03	Rounded Softwood, wrought: 25 x 63mm	m	0.03	3.01	0.10	0.72	3.83	*0.41*
Z1.5.3.04	Rounded Softwood, wrought: 25 x 75mm	m	0.03	3.01	0.10	0.88	3.99	*0.49*
Z1.5.3.05	Rounded Oak, wrought: 25 x 44mm	m	0.07	5.84	0.20	0.81	6.85	*0.45*
Z1.5.3.06	Rounded Oak, wrought: 25 x 50mm	m	0.07	5.84	0.20	0.94	6.98	*0.50*
Z1.5.3.07	Rounded Oak, wrought: 25 x 63mm	m	0.07	5.84	0.20	1.18	7.22	*0.61*
Z1.5.3.08	Rounded Oak, wrought: 25 x 75mm	m	0.07	5.84	0.20	1.43	7.47	*0.71*
Z1.5.3.09	Moulded Softwood, wrought: 25 x 44mm	m	0.03	3.01	0.10	0.49	3.60	*0.30*
Z1.5.3.10	Moulded Softwood, wrought: 25 x 50mm	m	0.03	3.01	0.10	0.57	3.68	*0.34*
Z1.5.3.11	Moulded Softwood, wrought: 25 x 63mm	m	0.03	3.01	0.10	0.72	3.83	*0.41*
Z1.5.3.12	Moulded Softwood, wrought: 25 x 75mm	m	0.03	3.01	0.10	0.88	3.99	*0.49*
Z1.5.3.13	Moulded Oak, wrought: 25 x 44mm	m	0.07	5.84	0.20	0.81	6.85	*0.45*
Z1.5.3.14	Moulded Oak, wrought: 25 x 50mm	m	0.07	5.84	0.20	0.94	6.98	*0.50*
Z1.5.3.15	Moulded Oak, wrought: 25 x 63mm	m	0.07	5.84	0.20	1.18	7.22	*0.61*
Z1.5.3.16	Moulded Oak, wrought: 25 x 75mm	m	0.07	5.84	0.20	1.43	7.47	*0.71*
Z1.5.4	Shelves							
Z1.5.4.01	Shelving including bearers; Widths: 300mm; Softwood, wrought; 25mm thick	m	0.25	28.24	1.50	2.61	32.35	*1.32*
Z1.5.4.02	as above; Widths: 300mm; Softwood, wrought; slatted 25 x 50mm spaced at 75mm; 25mm thick	m	0.20	22.59	1.20	1.84	25.63	*2.27*
Z1.5.4.03	as above; Widths: 300mm; Blackboard, butt joints: 18mm thick	m	0.20	22.59	1.20	1.60	25.39	*3.40*
Z1.5.4.04	as above; Widths: 300mm; Blackboard, butt joints: 25mm thick	m	0.20	22.59	1.20	2.05	25.84	*4.32*
Z1.5.4.05	as above; Widths: 300mm; Chipboard, butt joints: 18mm thick	m	0.20	22.59	1.20	1.42	25.21	*2.60*
Z1.5.4.06	as above; Widths: 300mm; Chipboard, butt joints: 25mm thick	m	0.20	22.59	1.20	1.87	25.66	*3.21*
Z1.5.4.07	as above; Widths: 300mm; Plywood, butt joints: 18mm thick	m	0.20	22.59	1.20	2.05	25.84	*3.40*

Z1 Carpentry and Joinery continued...

		Unit	Labour Hours	Labour Net £	Plant Net £	Materials Net £	Unit Net £	CO_2 Kg
Z1.5	**Miscellaneous joinery**							
Z1.5.4	Shelves							
Z1.5.4.08	as previous item; Widths: 300mm; Plywood, butt joints: 25mm thick	m	0.20	22.59	1.20	2.40	**26.19**	*4.32*
Z1.5.4.09	as above; Widths: 300mm; Chipboard, faced both sides with white melamine; 15mm thick	m	0.20	22.59	1.20	1.45	**25.24**	*2.34*
Z1.5.4.10	as above; Widths: 450mm; Softwood, wrought; slatted 25 x 50mm spaced at 75mm; 25mm thick	m	0.25	28.24	1.50	2.76	**32.50**	*3.30*
Z1.5.4.11	as above; Widths: 450mm; Blackboard, butt joints: 18mm thick	m	0.25	28.24	1.50	2.39	**32.13**	*4.99*
Z1.5.4.12	as above; Widths: 450mm; Blackboard, butt joints: 25mm thick	m	0.25	28.24	1.50	3.07	**32.81**	*6.37*
Z1.5.4.13	as above; Widths: 450mm; Chipboard, butt joints: 18mm thick	m	0.20	22.59	1.20	2.13	**25.92**	*3.68*
Z1.5.4.14	as above; Widths: 450mm; Chipboard, butt joints: 25mm thick	m	0.20	22.59	1.20	2.80	**26.59**	*4.59*
Z1.5.4.15	as above; Widths: 450mm; Plywood, butt joints: 18mm thick	m	0.25	28.24	1.50	3.07	**32.81**	*4.99*
Z1.5.4.16	as above; Widths: 450mm; Plywood, butt joints: 25mm thick	m	0.25	28.24	1.50	3.60	**33.34**	*6.37*
Z1.5.4.17	as above; Widths: 450mm; Chipboard, faced both sides with white melamine; 15mm thick	m	0.30	33.89	1.81	2.17	**37.87**	*3.51*
Z1.5.4.18	as above; Widths: 600mm; Softwood, wrought; slatted 25 x 50mm spaced at 75mm; 25mm thick	m	0.30	33.89	1.81	3.67	**39.37**	*4.32*
Z1.5.4.19	as above; Widths: 600mm; Blackboard, butt joints: 18mm thick	m	0.30	33.89	1.81	3.19	**38.89**	*6.58*
Z1.5.4.20	as above; Widths: 600mm; Blackboard, butt joints: 25mm thick	m	0.30	33.89	1.81	4.09	**39.79**	*8.41*
Z1.5.4.21	as above; Widths: 600mm; Chipboard, butt joints: 18mm thick	m	0.25	28.24	1.50	2.84	**32.58**	*4.87*
Z1.5.4.22	as above; Widths: 600mm; Chipboard, butt joints: 25mm thick	m	0.25	28.24	1.50	3.73	**33.47**	*6.09*
Z1.5.4.23	as above; Widths: 600mm; Plywood, butt joints: 18mm thick	m	0.30	33.89	1.81	4.09	**39.79**	*6.58*
Z1.5.4.24	as above; Widths: 600mm; Plywood, butt joints: 25mm thick	m	0.30	33.89	1.81	4.81	**40.51**	*8.41*
Z1.5.4.25	as above; Widths: 600mm; Chipboard, faced both sides with white melamine; 15mm thick	m	0.35	39.54	2.11	2.90	**44.55**	*4.57*
Z1.5.4.26	as above; Widths: 900mm; Softwood, wrought; slatted 25 x 50mm spaced at 75mm; 25mm thick	m	0.35	39.54	2.11	4.83	**46.48**	*5.64*
Z1.5.4.27	as above; Widths: 900mm; Blackboard, butt joints: 18mm thick	m	0.35	39.54	2.11	4.79	**46.44**	*9.64*

Z1 Carpentry and Joinery continued...

		Unit	Labour Hours	Labour Net £	Plant Net £	Materials Net £	Unit Net £	CO_2 Kg
Z1.5	**Miscellaneous joinery**							
Z1.5.4	Shelves							
Z1.5.4.28	as previous item; Widths: 900mm; Blackboard, butt joints: 25mm thick	m	0.35	39.54	2.11	6.14	**47.79**	*12.40*
Z1.5.4.29	as above; Widths: 900mm; Chipboard, butt joints: 18mm thick	m	0.30	33.89	1.81	4.26	**39.96**	*7.14*
Z1.5.4.30	as above; Widths: 900mm; Chipboard, butt joints: 25mm thick	m	0.30	33.89	1.81	5.60	**41.30**	*8.96*
Z1.5.4.31	as above; Widths: 900mm; Plywood, butt joints: 18mm thick	m	0.35	39.54	2.11	6.14	**47.79**	*9.64*
Z1.5.4.32	as above; Widths: 900mm; Plywood, butt joints: 25mm thick	m	0.35	39.54	2.11	7.21	**48.86**	*12.40*
Z1.5.4.33	as above; Widths: 900mm; Chipboard, faced both sides with white melamine; 15mm thick	m	0.40	45.18	2.41	4.35	**51.94**	*6.58*
Z1.6	**Units and fittings**							
Z1.6.1	Base units							
Z1.6.1.01	Framed construction fixed to blockwork with screws, plugging; including ironmongery; plinth to base; no worktop; Finish: White Matt Melamine; Wall unit; single door, single shelf; 500 x 500 x 882mm high	Nr	1.00	112.96	6.02	34.00	**152.98**	*2.25*
Z1.6.1.02	as above; Finish: White Matt Melamine; Wall unit; single door, single shelf; 1000 x 500 x 882mm high	Nr	1.10	124.26	6.62	47.00	**177.88**	*2.48*
Z1.6.1.03	as above; Finish: White Matt Melamine; Wall unit; single door, single shelf; 500 x 300 x 600mm high	Nr	0.75	84.72	4.51	32.00	**121.23**	*1.69*
Z1.6.1.04	as above; Finish: White Matt Melamine; Wall unit; double door, single shelf; 1000 x 300 x 600mm high	Nr	1.00	112.96	6.02	42.00	**160.98**	*2.25*
Z1.6.1.05	as above; Finish: White Matt Melamine; Wall unit; double door, double shelf; 1000 x 300 x 900mm high	Nr	1.20	135.55	7.22	47.00	**189.77**	*2.70*
Z1.6.1.06	as above; Finish: Pine; Wall unit; single door, single shelf; 500 x 500 x 882mm high	Nr	1.50	169.44	9.03	66.00	**244.47**	*3.38*
Z1.6.1.07	as above; Finish: Pine; Wall unit; single door, single shelf; 1000 x 500 x 882mm high	Nr	1.60	180.74	9.63	102.00	**292.37**	*3.60*
Z1.6.1.08	as above; Finish: Pine; Wall unit; single door, single shelf; 500 x 300 x 600mm high	Nr	1.50	169.44	9.03	64.00	**242.47**	*3.38*
Z1.6.1.09	as above; Finish: Pine; Wall unit; double door, single shelf; 1000 x 300 x 600mm high	Nr	2.00	225.92	12.04	94.00	**331.96**	*4.50*
Z1.6.1.10	as above; Finish: Pine; Wall unit; double door, double shelf; 1000 x 300 x 900mm high	Nr	2.50	282.40	15.05	109.00	**406.45**	*5.63*

Z1 Carpentry and Joinery continued...

		Unit	Labour Hours	Labour Net £	Plant Net £	Materials Net £	Unit Net £	CO_2 Kg
Z1.6	**Units and fittings**							
Z1.6.1	Base units							
Z1.6.1.11	as previous item; Finish: Oak; Wall unit; single door, single shelf; 500 x 500 x 882mm high	Nr	2.00	225.92	12.04	76.00	**313.96**	*4.50*
Z1.6.1.12	as above; Finish: Oak; Wall unit; single door, single shelf; 1000 x 500 x 882mm high	Nr	2.20	248.51	13.24	132.00	**393.75**	*4.95*
Z1.6.1.13	as above; Finish: Oak; Wall unit; single door, single shelf; 500 x 300 x 600mm high	Nr	1.50	169.44	9.03	79.00	**257.47**	*3.38*
Z1.6.1.14	as above; Finish: Oak; Wall unit; double door, single shelf; 1000 x 300 x 600mm high	Nr	2.00	225.92	12.04	124.00	**361.96**	*4.50*
Z1.6.1.15	as above; Finish: Oak; Wall unit; double door, double shelf; 1000 x 300 x 900mm high	Nr	2.50	282.40	15.05	146.00	**443.45**	*5.63*
Z1.6.3	Work tops							
Z1.6.3.01	High density chipboard faced and lipped with melamine laminates; post formed edge; fixing with screws; Thickness: 25mm; 3000 x 500mm	Nr	0.25	28.24	1.50	30.00	**59.74**	*11.43*
Z1.6.3.02	as above; Thickness: 25mm; 3000 x 600mm	Nr	0.25	28.24	1.50	37.50	**67.24**	*13.60*
Z1.6.3.03	as above; Thickness: 25mm; 4100 x 600mm	Nr	0.25	28.24	1.50	51.25	**80.99**	*18.39*
Z1.6.3.04	as above; Thickness: 50mm; 3000 x 500mm	Nr	0.25	28.24	1.50	55.00	**84.74**	*22.30*
Z1.6.3.05	as above; Thickness: 50mm; 3000 x 600mm	Nr	0.25	28.24	1.50	60.00	**89.74**	*26.64*
Z1.6.3.06	as above; Thickness: 50mm; 4100 x 600mm	Nr	0.25	28.24	1.50	82.00	**111.74**	*36.21*

Z2 Insulation

		Unit	Labour Hours	Labour Net £	Plant Net £	Materials Net £	Unit Net £	CO_2 Kg
Z2.1	**Sheets**							
Z2.1.1	Floors							
Z2.1.1.01	Expanded polystyrene butt jointed, laid loose; to floors; Thickness: 25mm; Standard grade	m^2	0.02	1.92	-	3.65	**5.57**	*4.65*
Z2.1.1.02	as above; Thickness: 25mm; Non-inflammable	m^2	0.02	1.92	-	3.65	**5.57**	*4.65*
Z2.1.1.03	as above; Thickness: 50mm; Standard grade	m^2	0.02	1.92	-	5.08	**7.00**	*9.30*
Z2.1.1.04	as above; Thickness: 50mm; Non-inflammable	m^2	0.02	1.92	-	5.08	**7.00**	*9.30*
Z2.1.3	Walls							
Z2.1.3.01	Sheets; expanded polystyrene butt jointed, fixing with adhesive; to walls; Thickness: 25mm; Standard grade	m^2	0.02	1.87	-	3.65	**5.52**	*4.65*
Z2.1.3.02	as above; Thickness: 25mm; Non-inflammable	m^2	0.02	1.87	-	3.65	**5.52**	*4.65*
Z2.1.3.03	as above; Thickness: 50mm; Standard grade	m^2	0.02	1.87	-	8.87	**10.74**	*11.16*

Z2 Insulation continued...

		Unit	Labour Hours	Labour Net £	Plant Net £	Materials Net £	Unit Net £	CO_2 Kg
Z2.1	**Sheets**							
Z2.1.3	Walls							
Z2.1.3.04	as previous item; Thickness: 50mm; Non-inflammable	m^2	0.02	1.87	-	8.87	10.74	*11.16*
Z2.2	**Quilts**							
Z2.2.1	Floors							
Z2.2.1.01	Glass fibre insulation; laid loose; to floors; Thickness: 80mm; Pilkingtons 'Crown wool'	m^2	0.02	1.92	-	2.85	4.77	*25.20*
Z2.2.1.02	as above; Thickness: 100mm; Pilkingtons 'Crown wool'	m^2	0.02	1.92	-	2.85	4.77	*25.20*
Z2.2.1.03	as above; Thickness: 150mm; Pilkingtons 'Crown wool'	m^2	0.02	1.92	-	4.32	6.24	*37.80*
Z2.2.3	Walls							
Z2.2.3.01	Boards; 'Styrofoam', Floormate 500, butt jointed, fixing with insulation retaining ties; to walls; Thickness: 50mm; Cavity wall insulation	m^2	0.03	3.62	-	9.92	13.54	*21.93*
Z2.2.3.02	as above; Thickness: 80mm; Cavity wall insulation	m^2	0.05	5.49	-	11.24	16.73	*25.65*

Z3 Windows, Doors and Glazing

Note(s): Timber windows; softwood side hung casement windows without glazing bars consisting of frame, mullions, transom and 140mm wide softwood sill; opening lights and casements on rustproof hinges with casement stays and fasteners; fully glazed; frame bedded in cement mortar pointed one side with mastic; knotting and priming by manufacturuer prior to delivery, no decoration. Double glazing: 14mm overall; 4mm clear float, 6mm air gap + 4mm clear float.

		Unit	Labour Hours	Labour Net £	Plant Net £	Materials Net £	Unit Net £	CO_2 Kg
Z3.1	**Timber**							
Z3.1.1	Windows							
Z3.1.1.01	Softwood side hung reversible windows without glazing bars consisting of frame, mullions, transom and softwood sill; opening lights and casements on rustproof hinges with casement stays and fasteners; fully glazed; frame bedded in cement mortar pointed one side with mastic; knotting and priming by manufacturer prior to delivery, no decoration; 1200 x 1200mm Jeld Wen reference: LEC1212CFR	Nr	1.45	26.00	-	361.58	387.58	*18.52*
Z3.1.1.02	as above; Jeld Wen reference number: 1800 x 1500mm; reference LEC1815CFCR	Nr	2.05	36.76	-	588.23	624.99	*31.43*
Z3.1.1.03	Softwood top hung reversible windows without glazing bars; softwood sill; opening casements on rustproof hinges with casement stay and fastener; fully glazed in double glazing units; frame bedded in cement mortar pointed one side with mastic; knotting and by manufacturer prior to delivery, no decoration; 600 x 900mm Jeld Wen reference: LEC0609AR	Nr	1.00	17.93	-	238.27	256.20	*8.80*
Z3.1.1.04	as above; 600 x 1200 mm; Jeld Wen reference LEC0612AR	Nr	1.00	17.93	-	262.79	280.72	*11.02*

Z3 Windows, Doors and Glazing continued...

		Unit	Labour Hours	Labour Net £	Plant Net £	Materials Net £	Unit Net £	CO_2 Kg
Z3.1	**Timber**							
Z3.1.1	Windows							
Z3.1.1.05	as previous item; 900 x 750 mm; Jeld Wen reference number: LEC0907AR	Nr	1.00	17.93	-	247.16	**265.09**	*10.29*
Z3.1.1.06	as above; 1200 x 1200 mm; Jeld Wen reference number: LEC1212AFR	Nr	1.00	17.93	-	397.36	**415.29**	*18.62*
Z3.1.3	Doors							
Z3.1.3.01	Softwood interior flush doors; including frame and ironmongery; no decoration; Sizes: Single; 35mm thick: hardboard faced	Nr	1.50	26.90	-	90.34	**117.24**	*37.59*
Z3.1.3.02	as above; Sizes: Single; 35mm thick: sapele faced	Nr	1.50	26.90	-	111.34	**138.24**	*60.77*
Z3.1.3.03	as above; Sizes: Single; 40mm thick: hardboard faced	Nr	1.50	26.90	-	89.24	**116.14**	*43.50*
Z3.1.3.04	as above; Sizes: Single; 40mm thick: sapele faced	Nr	1.50	26.90	-	114.74	**141.64**	*71.23*
Z3.1.3.05	as above; Sizes: Double; 35mm thick: hardboard faced	Nr	1.65	29.58	-	180.04	**209.62**	*74.75*
Z3.1.3.06	as above; Sizes: Double; 35mm thick: sapele faced	Nr	1.65	29.58	-	222.04	**251.62**	*121.12*
Z3.1.3.07	as above; Sizes: Double; 40mm thick: hardboard faced	Nr	1.65	29.58	-	177.84	**207.42**	*86.56*
Z3.1.3.08	as above; Sizes: Double; 40mm thick: sapele faced	Nr	1.65	29.58	-	228.84	**258.42**	*142.04*
Z3.1.3.09	Interior panelled doors; including frame and ironmongery; no decoration; Sizes: Single; Softwood	Nr	1.65	29.58	-	125.88	**155.46**	*22.98*
Z3.1.3.10	as above; Sizes: Double; Softwood	Nr	1.85	33.17	-	251.12	**284.29**	*45.53*
Z3.2	**Metal**							
Z3.2.3	Doors							
Z3.2.3.01	Galvanised steel roller shutter doors; two hour rated fire resistance; including installation; Sizes: Single; Bolton Gate Co Fireroll E240 Rolling Shutters; opening sizes: 3050mm high, 3000mm wide	Nr	4.55	81.58	-	2,562.00	**2,643.58**	*725.87*
Z3.2.3.02	as above; Sizes: Single; Bolton Gate Co Fireroll E240 Rolling Shutters; opening sizes: 4800mm high, 5000mm wide	Nr	5.50	98.61	-	6,000.00	**6,098.61**	*1,935.65*
Z3.2.3.03	as above; Sizes: Double; Bolton Gate Co Fireroll E240 Rolling Shutters; opening sizes: 3050mm high, 3000mm wide	Nr	5.55	99.51	-	2,745.00	**2,844.51**	*769.86*
Z3.2.3.04	as above; Sizes: Double; Bolton Gate Co Fireroll E240 Rolling Shutters; opening sizes: 4800mm high, 5000mm wide	Nr	6.50	116.55	-	6,720.00	**6,836.55**	*2,023.63*

Z3 Windows, Doors and Glazing continued...

		Unit	Labour Hours	Labour Net £	Plant Net £	Materials Net £	Unit Net £	CO_2 Kg
Z3.3	**Plastics**							
Z3.3.1	Windows							
Z3.3.1.01	White UPVC tilt and turn windows; including ironmongery; 24mm low E factory double glazed units; clear glass; Frame fixed to masonry with screws, plugging; 620 x 1050mm	Nr	1.00	17.93	-	101.67	**119.60**	*17.19*
Z3.3.1.02	as above; Frame fixed to masonry with screws, plugging; 1200 x 1200mm	Nr	1.55	27.79	-	180.67	**208.46**	*33.44*
Z3.3.1.03	as above; Frame fixed to masonry with screws, plugging; 1200 x 1500mm	Nr	1.80	32.27	-	211.45	**243.72**	*40.60*
Z3.3.6	Roof lights							
Z3.3.6.01	Cox Trade rooflights; GRP factory glazed double skin polycarbonate dome; fixed to concrete with screws, plugging; Rooflight sizes: 600 x 600mm; Non-ventilating; base frame	Nr	1.00	17.93	-	240.55	**258.48**	*10.31*
Z3.3.6.02	as above; Rooflight sizes: 600 x 600mm; Ventilating; base frame	Nr	1.25	22.41	-	273.85	**296.26**	*13.93*
Z3.3.6.03	as above; Rooflight sizes: 600 x 600mm; Non-ventilating; base frame and kerb	Nr	1.00	17.93	-	470.90	**488.83**	*20.84*
Z3.3.6.04	as above; Rooflight sizes: 600 x 600mm; Ventilating; base frame and kerb	Nr	1.25	22.41	-	504.20	**526.61**	*24.46*
Z3.3.6.05	as above; Rooflight sizes: 950 x 950mm; Non-ventilating; base frame	Nr	1.00	17.93	-	378.25	**396.18**	*21.98*
Z3.3.6.06	as above; Rooflight sizes: 950 x 950mm; Ventilating; base frame	Nr	1.25	22.41	-	411.55	**433.96**	*25.59*
Z3.3.6.07	as above; Rooflight sizes: 950 x 950mm; Non-ventilating; base frame and kerb	Nr	1.00	17.93	-	625.60	**643.53**	*38.65*
Z3.3.6.08	as above; Rooflight sizes: 950 x 950mm; Ventilating; base frame and kerb	Nr	1.25	22.41	-	658.90	**681.31**	*42.27*
Z3.3.6.09	as above; Rooflight sizes: 1200 x 1200mm; Non-ventilating; base frame	Nr	1.25	22.41	-	496.40	**518.81**	*32.86*
Z3.3.6.10	as above; Rooflight sizes: 1200 x 1200mm; Ventilating; base frame	Nr	1.50	26.90	-	529.70	**556.60**	*36.48*
Z3.3.6.11	as above; Rooflight sizes: 1200 x 1200mm; Non-ventilating; base frame and kerb	Nr	1.25	22.41	-	766.70	**789.11**	*53.92*
Z3.3.6.12	as above; Rooflight sizes: 1200 x 1200mm; Ventilating; base frame and kerb	Nr	1.50	26.90	-	800.00	**826.90**	*57.54*
Z3.5	**Glazing**							
Z3.5.1	Glass							
Z3.5.1.01	Glazing; clear sheet glass; in panes not exceeding 4m2; Thickness: 4mm; To timber with bradded wood beads	m^2	0.65	11.56	-	44.36	**55.92**	*9.63*

Z3 Windows, Doors and Glazing continued...

		Unit	Labour Hours	Labour Net £	Plant Net £	Materials Net £	Unit Net £	CO_2 Kg
Z3.5	**Glazing**							
Z3.5.1	Glass							
Z3.5.1.02	as previous item; Thickness: 4mm; To metal with screwed metal beads	m^2	0.65	11.56	-	45.44	**57.00**	*12.15*
Z3.5.1.03	as above; Thickness: 6mm; To timber with bradded wood beads	m^2	0.65	11.56	-	63.96	**75.52**	*13.88*
Z3.5.1.04	as above; Thickness: 6mm; To metal with screwed metal beads	m^2	0.65	11.56	-	65.04	**76.60**	*16.40*
Z3.5.1.05	Glazing; rough cast patterned glass; in panes not exceeding $4m^2$; Thickness: 4mm; To timber with bradded wood beads	m^2	0.65	11.56	-	47.35	**58.91**	*13.83*
Z3.5.1.06	as above; Thickness: 4mm; To metal with screwed metal beads	m^2	0.65	11.56	-	48.43	**59.99**	*16.35*
Z3.5.1.07	as above; Thickness: 6mm; To timber with bradded wood beads	m^2	0.65	11.56	-	72.12	**83.68**	*20.18*
Z3.5.1.08	as above; Thickness: 6mm; To metal with screwed metal beads	m^2	0.65	11.56	-	73.20	**84.76**	*22.70*
Z3.5.1.09	Glazing; Georgian wired cast glass; in panes not exceeding $4m^2$; Thickness: 7mm; To timber with bradded wood beads	m^2	0.65	11.56	-	49.83	**61.39**	*23.35*
Z3.5.1.10	as above; Thickness: 7mm; To metal with screwed metal beads	m^2	0.65	11.56	-	50.91	**62.47**	*25.88*
Z3.5.3	Special glass							
Z3.5.3.01	Glazing; toughened safety glass; in panes not exceeding $4m^2$; Thickness: 4mm; To timber with bradded wood beads: pane size $1.00m^2$	Nr	0.65	11.56	-	67.46	**79.02**	*13.83*
Z3.5.3.02	as above; Thickness: 4mm; To metal with screwed metal beads: pane size $1.00m^2$	Nr	0.65	11.56	-	68.54	**80.10**	*16.35*
Z3.5.3.03	as above; Thickness: 6mm; To timber with bradded wood beads: pane size $1.00m^2$	Nr	0.80	14.22	-	100.19	**114.41**	*20.18*
Z3.5.3.04	as above; Thickness: 6mm; To metal with screwed metal beads: pane size $1.00m^2$	Nr	0.80	14.22	-	101.27	**115.49**	*22.70*
Z3.5.3.05	Glazing; clear laminated safety glass; in panes not exceeding $4m^2$; Thickness: 4.4mm; To timber with bradded wood beads; pane size $1.00m^2$	Nr	0.80	14.22	-	69.76	**83.98**	*13.83*
Z3.5.3.06	as above; Thickness: 6.4mm; To timber with bradded wood beads; pane size $1.00m^2$	Nr	0.80	14.22	-	80.63	**94.85**	*21.45*
Z3.5.3.07	Glazing; Lexan Exell 'D' Clear-112 safety glass; extruded polycarbonate sheet, proprietary ultraviolet resistant surface on one side; to metal with screwed metal beads; Thickness: 5mm; Pane size $1.00m^2$	Nr	0.75	13.34	-	296.98	**310.32**	*19.53*
Z3.5.3.08	as above; Thickness: 5mm; Pane size $2.00m^2$	Nr	1.05	18.67	-	593.47	**612.14**	*38.16*
Z3.5.3.09	as above; Thickness: 6mm; Pane size $1.00m^2$	Nr	0.75	13.34	-	341.06	**354.40**	*22.70*
Z3.5.3.10	as above; Thickness: 6mm; Pane size $2.00m^2$	Nr	1.05	18.67	-	681.63	**700.30**	*44.51*

Z3 Windows, Doors and Glazing continued...

		Unit	Labour Hours	Labour Net £	Plant Net £	Materials Net £	Unit Net £	CO_2 Kg
Z3.5	**Glazing**							
Z3.5.4	Hermetically sealed units							
Z3.5.4.01	Glazing; clear float double glazed units; to metal with screwed metal beads; nominal airspace 6mm; Thickness: 2 x 4mm; Unit size: 0.50m2	Nr	0.80	14.22	-	51.01	**65.23**	*11.32*
Z3.5.4.02	as above; Thickness: 2 x 4mm; Unit size: 1.00m2	Nr	0.94	16.71	-	100.64	**117.35**	*20.92*
Z3.5.4.03	as above; Thickness: 2 x 4mm; Unit size: 2.00m2	Nr	1.05	18.67	-	199.45	**218.12**	*39.67*
Z3.5.4.04	as above; Thickness: 2 x 4mm; Unit size: 3.00m2	Nr	1.15	20.45	-	297.68	**318.13**	*57.55*
Z3.5.4.05	as above; Thickness: 2 x 6mm; Unit size: 0.50m2	Nr	0.80	14.22	-	70.46	**84.68**	*15.57*
Z3.5.4.06	as above; Thickness: 2 x 6mm; Unit size: 1.00m2	Nr	0.94	16.71	-	139.54	**156.25**	*29.42*
Z3.5.4.07	as above; Thickness: 2 x 6mm; Unit size: 2.00m2	Nr	1.05	18.67	-	277.25	**295.92**	*56.67*
Z3.5.4.08	as above; Thickness: 2 x 6mm; Unit size: 3.00m2	Nr	1.15	20.45	-	414.38	**434.83**	*83.05*
Z3.5.4.09	as above; Thickness: 2 x 10mm; Unit size: 0.50m2	Nr	0.80	14.22	-	127.01	**141.23**	*24.07*
Z3.5.4.10	as above; Thickness: 2 x 10mm; Unit size: 1.00m2	Nr	0.94	16.71	-	252.64	**269.35**	*46.42*
Z3.5.4.11	as above; Thickness: 2 x 10mm; Unit size: 2.00m2	Nr	1.05	18.67	-	503.45	**522.12**	*90.67*
Z3.5.4.12	as above; Thickness: 2 x 10mm; Unit size: 3.00m2	Nr	1.15	20.45	-	753.68	**774.13**	*134.05*
Z3.5.4.13	Glazing; solar control double glazed units; to timber with bradded wood beads; bronze float glass to outside, clear glass to inside; nominal airspace 12mm; Thickness: 2 x 4mm; Unit size: 0.50m2	Nr	0.80	14.22	-	47.09	**61.31**	*9.56*
Z3.5.4.14	as above; Thickness: 2 x 4mm; Unit size: 1.00m2	Nr	0.94	16.71	-	93.21	**109.92**	*18.39*
Z3.5.4.15	as above; Thickness: 2 x 4mm; Unit size: 2.00m2	Nr	1.05	18.67	-	185.22	**203.89**	*36.11*
Z3.5.4.16	as above; Thickness: 2 x 4mm; Unit size: 3.00m2	Nr	1.15	20.45	-	276.76	**297.21**	*53.19*
Z3.5.4.17	as above; Thickness: 2 x 6mm; Unit size: 0.50m2	Nr	0.80	14.22	-	66.62	**80.84**	*13.81*
Z3.5.4.18	as above; Thickness: 2 x 6mm; Unit size: 1.00m2	Nr	0.94	16.71	-	132.26	**148.97**	*26.89*
Z3.5.4.19	as above; Thickness: 2 x 6mm; Unit size: 2.00m2	Nr	1.05	18.67	-	263.32	**281.99**	*53.11*
Z3.5.4.20	as above; Thickness: 2 x 6mm; Unit size: 3.00m2	Nr	1.15	20.45	-	393.91	**414.36**	*78.69*
Z3.5.4.21	as above; Thickness: 2 x 10mm; Unit size: 0.50m2	Nr	0.90	16.00	-	123.30	**139.30**	*22.31*
Z3.5.4.22	as above; Thickness: 2 x 10mm; Unit size: 1.00m2	Nr	1.05	18.67	-	245.62	**264.29**	*43.89*
Z3.5.4.23	as above; Thickness: 2 x 10mm; Unit size: 2.00m2	Nr	1.25	22.23	-	490.04	**512.27**	*87.11*
Z3.5.4.24	as above; Thickness: 2 x 10mm; Unit size: 3.00m2	Nr	1.50	26.67	-	733.99	**760.66**	*129.69*

Z3 Windows, Doors and Glazing continued...

		Unit	Labour Hours	Labour Net £	Plant Net £	Materials Net £	Unit Net £	CO_2 Kg
Z3.5	**Glazing**							
Z3.5.5	Mirrors							
Z3.5.5.01	Silver backed 6mm clear glass; fixing to masonry with chromium headed screws, plugging; Edges polished; 450 x 300mm	Nr	0.75	13.45	-	18.67	**32.12**	*2.58*
Z3.5.5.02	as above; Edges polished; 900 x 400mm	Nr	0.90	16.14	-	49.95	**66.09**	*6.86*
Z3.5.5.03	as above; Edges polished; 1500 x 1500mm	Nr	2.00	35.86	-	206.22	**242.08**	*42.87*
Z3.5.5.04	as above; Edges bevelled; 450 x 300mm	Nr	0.75	13.45	-	19.65	**33.10**	*2.58*
Z3.5.5.05	as above; Edges bevelled; 900 x 400mm	Nr	0.90	16.14	-	52.57	**68.71**	*6.86*
Z3.5.5.06	as above; Edges bevelled; 1500 x 1500mm	Nr	2.00	35.86	-	217.07	**252.93**	*42.87*
Z3.6	**Patent glazing**							
Z3.6.1	Roofs							
Z3.6.1.01	2000mm long aluminium alloy bars at 600mm centres; Georgian wired polished glazing 6mm thick	m^2	1.93	110.24	-	209.29	**319.53**	*66.12*
Z3.6.2	Opening lights							
Z3.6.2.01	2000mm long aluminium alloy bars at 600mm centres; Georgian wired polished glazing 6mm thick; 600 x 900mm; electric linear motor gear	Nr	2.01	114.83	-	687.90	**802.73**	*21.24*
Z3.6.3	Vertical surfaces							
Z3.6.3.01	2000mm long aluminium alloy bars at 600mm centres; Georgian wired polished glazing 6mm thick	m^2	2.25	128.63	-	209.59	**338.22**	*66.94*

Z4 Surface Finishes, Linings and Partitions

		Unit	Labour Hours	Labour Net £	Plant Net £	Materials Net £	Unit Net £	CO_2 Kg
Z4.1	**In situ finishes, beds and backings**							
Z4.1.1	Floors							
Z4.1.1.01	Trowelled finish, to concrete base; Thickness: 25mm; Cement and sand (1 : 3); surfaces of width: over 1m wide	m^2	0.04	1.17	0.68	5.72	**7.57**	*8.40*
Z4.1.1.02	as above; Cement and sand (1 : 3); surfaces of width: not exceeding 300mm	m	0.05	1.46	0.85	1.78	**4.09**	*2.68*
Z4.1.1.03	as above; Granolithic; surfaces of width: over 1m wide	m^2	0.04	1.17	0.68	11.37	**13.22**	*45.75*
Z4.1.1.04	as above; Granolithic; surfaces of width: not exceeding 300mm	m	0.05	1.46	0.85	3.54	**5.85**	*14.30*
Z4.1.1.05	as above; Thickness: 32mm; Cement and sand (1 : 3); surfaces of width: over 1m wide	m^2	0.04	1.17	0.68	7.37	**9.22**	*10.80*
Z4.1.1.06	as above; Thickness: 32mm; Cement and sand (1 : 3); surfaces of width: not exceeding 300mm	m	0.05	1.46	0.85	2.16	**4.47**	*3.23*
Z4.1.1.07	as above; Thickness: 32mm; Granolithic; surfaces of width: over 1m wide	m^2	0.04	1.17	0.68	14.66	**16.51**	*58.94*

Z4 Surface Finishes, Linings and Partitions continued...

		Unit	Labour Hours	Labour Net £	Plant Net £	Materials Net £	Unit Net £	CO_2 Kg
Z4.1	**In situ finishes, beds and backings**							
Z4.1.1	Floors							
Z4.1.1.08	as previous item; Thickness: 32mm; Granolithic; surfaces of width: not exceeding 300mm	m	0.05	1.46	0.85	4.30	6.61	*17.34*
Z4.1.1.09	as above; Thickness: 38mm; Cement and sand (1 : 3); surfaces of width: over 1m wide	m^2	0.04	1.17	0.68	8.65	10.50	*12.65*
Z4.1.1.10	as above; Thickness: 38mm; Cement and sand (1 : 3); surfaces of width: not exceeding 300mm	m	0.04	1.17	0.68	2.54	4.39	*3.77*
Z4.1.1.11	as above; Thickness: 38mm; Granolithic; surfaces of width: over 1m wide	m^2	0.04	1.17	0.68	14.66	16.51	*58.94*
Z4.1.1.12	as above; Thickness: 38mm; Granolithic; surfaces of width: not exceeding 300mm	m	0.05	1.46	0.85	5.05	7.36	*20.39*
Z4.1.1.13	as above; Thickness: 50mm; Cement and sand (1 : 3); surfaces of width: over 1m wide	m^2	0.05	1.46	0.85	11.44	13.75	*16.74*
Z4.1.1.14	as above; Thickness: 50mm; Cement and sand (1 : 3); surfaces of width: not exceeding 300mm	m	0.07	1.96	1.14	3.43	6.53	*5.11*
Z4.1.1.15	as above; Thickness: 50mm; Granolithic; surfaces of width: over 1m wide	m^2	0.05	1.46	0.85	22.74	25.05	*91.44*
Z4.1.1.16	as above; Thickness: 50mm; Granolithic; surfaces of width: not exceeding 300mm	m	0.07	1.96	1.14	6.82	9.92	*27.52*
Z4.1.3	Walls							
Z4.1.3.01	Rough case external render; cement and sand (1 : 3); trowelled finish with dry pebble dash coating, to brickwork base; surfaces of width; Thickness: Two coat 15mm; over 1m wide	m^2	0.33	9.74	0.87	4.15	14.76	*5.74*
Z4.1.3.02	as above; Thickness: Two coat 15mm; not exceeding 300mm	m	0.17	4.88	0.44	1.26	6.58	*1.83*
Z4.1.3.03	In situ finishes; plaster; pre-mixed Carlite; two coats 13mm thick; comprising 11mm floating coat of browning; 2mm finishing coat; steel trowelled; surfaces of width; Work to brickwork base; over 1m wide	m^2	0.17	4.88	0.44	6.02	11.34	*97.02*
Z4.1.3.04	as above; not exceeding 300mm	m	0.13	3.65	0.33	1.67	5.65	*28.82*
Z4.1.3.05	In situ finishes; plaster; pre-mixed Carlite; two coats 13mm thick; comprising 11mm floating coat of browning; 2mm finishing coat; steel trowelled; surfaces of width; Work to metal lathing base; over 1m wide	m^2	0.20	5.85	0.52	6.02	12.39	*97.08*
Z4.1.3.06	as above; not exceeding 300mm	m	0.10	2.92	0.26	1.67	4.85	*28.78*

Z4 Surface Finishes, Linings and Partitions continued...

		Unit	Labour Hours	Labour Net £	Plant Net £	Materials Net £	Unit Net £	CO_2 Kg
Z4.1	**In situ finishes, beds and backings**							
Z4.1.4	Soffits							
Z4.1.4.01	Insitu finishes; plaster; thistle Universal one coat 13mm thick; steel trowelled work to metal lathing base; surface of width; over 1m wide	m^2	0.10	2.92	0.26	7.65	10.83	3.90
Z4.1.4.02	as above; surfaces of width: not exceeding 300mm	m	0.07	1.96	0.17	2.22	4.35	1.20
Z4.2	**Tiles**							
Z4.2.1	Floors							
Z4.2.1.01	Butt joints straight both ways; fixing with adhesive to cement and sand base; Thickness: 2mm; Vinyl, Marleyflex Plus, 300 x 300mm units; surfaces of width: over 1m wide	m^2	0.25	7.31	-	24.79	32.10	7.19
Z4.2.1.02	as above; Thickness: 2mm; Vinyl, Marleyflex Plus, 300 x 300mm units; surfaces of width: not exceeding 300mm	m	0.13	3.65	-	8.26	11.91	2.39
Z4.2.1.03	as above; Thickness: 2.5mm; Vinyl, Marleyflex Plus, 300 x 300mm units; surfaces of width: over 1m wide	m^2	0.25	7.31	-	28.81	36.12	8.57
Z4.2.1.04	as above; Thickness: 2.5mm; Vinyl, Marleyflex Plus, 300 x 300mm units; surfaces of width: not exceeding 300mm	m	0.13	3.65	-	9.59	13.24	2.85
Z4.2.1.05	as above; cork 300 x 300mm units; Thickness: 3.2mm; surfaces of width: over 1m wide	m^2	0.13	3.65	-	17.46	21.11	9.04
Z4.2.1.06	as above; Thickness: 3.2mm; surfaces of width: not exceeding 300mm	m	0.13	3.65	-	5.81	9.46	3.01
Z4.2.1.07	as above; Thickness: 4.5mm; surfaces of width: over 1m wide	m^2	0.13	3.65	-	20.06	23.71	12.25
Z4.2.1.08	as above; Thickness: 4.5mm; surfaces of width: not exceeding 300mm	m	0.13	3.65	-	6.68	10.33	4.08
Z4.2.1.09	as above; Thickness: 6mm; surfaces of width: over 1m wide	m^2	0.25	7.31	-	21.60	28.91	15.47
Z4.2.1.10	as above; Thickness: 6mm; surfaces of width: not exceeding 300mm	m	0.13	3.65	-	7.19	10.84	5.15
Z4.2.1.11	as above; rubber Polysafe stud tile 500 x 500mm units; Thickness: 4mm; surfaces of width: over 1m wide	m^2	0.40	11.70	-	34.59	46.29	20.78
Z4.2.1.12	as above; Thickness: 4mm; surfaces of width: not exceeding 300mm	m	0.20	5.85	-	11.52	17.37	6.92
Z4.2.3	Walls							
Z4.2.3.01	White glazed ceramic, butt joints straight both ways; fixing with adhesive on plaster base; pointing with white cement; Size: 108 x 108 x 4mm; surfaces of width: over 1m wide	m^2	0.50	14.78	-	11.08	25.86	12.41
Z4.2.3.02	as above; surfaces of width: not exceeding 300mm	m	0.25	7.39	-	3.69	11.08	4.13
Z4.2.3.03	as above; Size: 152 x 152 x 5.5mm; surfaces of width: over 1m wide	m^2	0.50	14.78	-	15.54	30.32	14.18

Z4 Surface Finishes, Linings and Partitions continued...

		Unit	Labour Hours	Labour Net £	Plant Net £	Materials Net £	Unit Net £	CO_2 Kg
Z4.2	**Tiles**							
Z4.2.3	Walls							
Z4.2.3.04	as previous item; surfaces of width: not exceeding 300mm	m	0.25	7.39	-	5.17	**12.56**	*4.72*
Z4.2.3.05	Flexible sheet coverings; to floors; linoleum sheet; 3.2mm thick; butt joints; fixing with adhesive to cement and sand base; Plain; surfaces of width: over 1m wide	m^2	0.40	11.70	-	24.36	**36.06**	*6.34*
Z4.2.3.06	as above; surfaces of width: not exceeding 300mm	m	0.20	5.85	-	8.11	**13.96**	*2.11*
Z4.2.3.07	as above; Marbled patterns; surfaces of width: over 1m wide	m^2	0.40	11.70	-	24.93	**36.63**	*6.34*
Z4.2.3.08	as above; surfaces of width: not exceeding 300mm	m	0.20	5.85	-	8.30	**14.15**	*2.11*
Z4.2.3.09	Flexible sheet coverings; to floors; fitted carpeting and underlay; heavy duty contract grade carpet PC £32 per m2 underlay PC £2.95 per m2; Plain; surfaces of width: over 1m wide	m^2	0.40	11.70	-	28.60	**40.30**	*12.15*
Z4.2.3.10	as above; surfaces of width: not exceeding 300mm	m	0.20	5.85	-	9.52	**15.37**	*4.05*
Z4.2.3.11	as above; Patterned; surfaces of width: over 1m wide	m^2	0.40	11.70	-	28.60	**40.30**	*12.15*
Z4.2.3.12	as above; surfaces of width: not exceeding 300mm	m	0.20	5.85	-	9.52	**15.37**	*4.05*
Z4.2.3.13	Dry partitions and linings; walls; gypsum plasterboard; tapered edges fixed with galvanised nails to softwood studs; compound dabs, joints filled taped and finished flush; no decoration; Thickness: 9.5mm; surfaces of width: over 1m wide	m^2	0.05	5.65	0.30	1.97	**7.92**	*3.67*
Z4.2.3.14	as above; Thickness: 9.5mm; surfaces of width: not exceeding 300mm	m	0.03	2.82	0.15	0.66	**3.63**	*1.24*
Z4.2.3.15	as above; Thickness: 12.5mm; surfaces of width: over 1m wide	m^2	0.05	5.65	0.30	2.04	**7.99**	*4.76*
Z4.2.3.16	as above; Thickness: 12.5mm; surfaces of width: not exceeding 300mm	m	0.03	2.82	0.15	0.68	**3.65**	*1.60*
Z4.2.4	Soffits							
Z4.2.4.01	Dry partitions and linings; walls; gypsum plasterboard; tapered edges fixed with galvanised nails to softwood studs; compound dabs, joints filled taped and finished flush; no decoration; Thickness: 9.5mm; surfaces of width: over 1m wide	m^2	0.07	7.57	0.40	1.97	**9.94**	*3.71*
Z4.2.4.02	as above; Thickness: 9.5mm; surfaces of width: not exceeding 300mm	m	0.03	3.73	0.20	0.66	**4.59**	*1.26*
Z4.2.4.03	as above; Thickness: 12.5mm; surfaces of width: over 1m wide	m^2	0.07	7.57	0.40	2.04	**10.01**	*4.80*
Z4.2.4.04	as above; Thickness: 12.5mm; surfaces of width: not exceeding 300mm	m	0.03	3.73	0.20	0.68	**4.61**	*1.62*

Z4 Surface Finishes, Linings and Partitions continued...

		Unit	Labour Hours	Labour Net £	Plant Net £	Materials Net £	Unit Net £	CO_2 Kg
Z4.5	**Suspended ceilings**							
Z4.5.1	Depth of suspension system: not exceeding 150mm							
Z4.5.1.01	Armstrong Microlook Suspended Ceiling system, galvanised steel comprising; runners and cross tees; runners at 1200mm centres fixed to concrete soffit on hangers at 1250mm centres; including perimeter trim fixed to walls at 450mm intervals; Circus 600 x 60	m^2	0.16	18.07	0.96	38.78	**57.81**	*12.71*
Z4.5.1.02	Gyproc M/F suspended ceiling system, comprising 12.7mm thick Gyproc wallboard on metal suspension grid; including perimeter trim fixed to walls, strap hangers fixed to concrete soffit, primary support channels and cleats; no decoration; 900 x 1800 x 12.7m	m^2	0.12	13.56	0.72	11.00	**25.28**	*20.74*
Z4.5.2	Depth of suspension system: 150 - 500mm							
Z4.5.2.01	Armstrong Microlook Suspended Ceiling system, galvanised steel comprising; runners and cross tees; runners at 1200mm centres fixed to concrete soffit on hangers at 1250mm centres; including perimeter trim fixed to walls at 450mm intervals; Circus 600 x 60	m^2	0.17	19.20	1.02	38.78	**59.00**	*12.73*
Z4.5.2.02	Gyproc M/F suspended ceiling system, comprising 12.7mm thick Gyproc wallboard on metal suspension grid; including perimeter trim fixed to walls, strap hangers fixed to concrete soffit, primary support channels and cleats; no decoration; 900 x 1800 x 12.7m	m^2	0.13	14.68	0.78	11.00	**26.46**	*20.76*
Z4.5.3	Depth of suspension system: 500 - 1000mm							
Z4.5.3.01	Armstrong Microlook Suspended Ceiling system, galvanised steel comprising; runners and cross tees; runners at 1200mm centres fixed to concrete soffit on hangers at 1250mm centres; including perimeter trim fixed to walls at 450mm intervals; Circus 600 x 60	m^2	0.18	20.33	1.08	38.78	**60.19**	*12.75*
Z4.5.3.02	Gyproc M/F suspended ceiling system, comprising 12.7mm thick Gyproc wallboard on metal suspension grid; including perimeter trim fixed to walls, strap hangers fixed to concrete soffit, primary support channels and cleats; no decoration; 900 x 1800 x 12.7m	m^2	0.14	15.81	0.84	11.00	**27.65**	*20.78*

Z4 Surface Finishes, Linings and Partitions continued...

		Unit	Labour Hours	Labour Net £	Plant Net £	Materials Net £	Unit Net £	*CO_2 Kg*
Z4.5	**Suspended ceilings**							
Z4.5.4	Bulkheads							
Z4.5.4.01	Gyproc M/F suspended ceiling system, comprising 12.7mm thick Gyproc wallboard on metal suspension grid; including perimeter trim fixed to walls, strap hangers fixed to concrete soffit, primary support channels and cleats; no decoration; Vertical; 1000mm d	m	0.20	22.59	1.20	18.87	42.66	*33.24*
Z4.6	**Raised access floors**							
Z4.6.1	Full access system, comprising steel sheet panels with high density chipboard core on metal pedestals, including anti-static vinyl finish on panels							
Z4.6.1.01	Pedestal height: 300mm; Diamond 600 medium grade panels	m^2	0.24	27.11	1.44	73.92	102.47	*48.21*
Z4.6.1.02	as above; Diamond 600 heavy grade panels	m^2	0.24	27.11	1.44	80.27	108.82	*50.79*
Z4.6.1.03	Pedestal height: 500mm; Diamond 600 medium grade panels	m^2	0.24	27.11	1.44	77.22	105.77	*60.62*
Z4.6.1.04	as above; Diamond 600 heavy grade panels	m^2	0.24	27.11	1.44	83.58	112.13	*63.21*
Z4.7	**Proprietary system partitions**							
Z4.7.1	Solid							
Z4.7.1.01	Paramound dry partitions, with timber supports at vertical joints; tapered edges fixed with galvanised nails to softwood studs and floor and ceiling battens; joints filled, taped and finished flush; no decoration; Thickness: 57mm; Height of partition: 210	m	0.50	56.48	3.01	12.92	72.41	*69.71*
Z4.7.1.02	as above; Thickness: 57mm; Height of partition: 2400mm	m	0.75	84.72	4.51	14.57	103.80	*79.88*
Z4.7.1.03	as above; Thickness: 57mm; Height of partition: 2700mm	m	1.00	112.96	6.02	16.23	135.21	*90.05*
Z4.7.1.04	as above; Thickness: 63mm; Height of partition: 2100mm	m	0.50	56.48	3.01	20.17	79.66	*45.02*
Z4.7.1.05	as above; Thickness: 63mm; Height of partition: 2400mm	m	1.00	112.96	6.02	22.21	141.19	*51.60*
Z4.7.1.06	as above; Thickness: 63mm; Height of partition: 2700mm	m	1.00	112.96	6.02	24.70	143.68	*57.49*
Z4.8	**Framed panel cubicle sets**							
Z4.8.1	Komfort'; melamine faced high density chipboard doors, walls and dividers; lipped all round; thickness 18mm; including fibreboard lacquered pilaster, capping rails, aluminium wall fixings, channels, brackets and hinges; Blue / grey marble effect finish							
Z4.8.1.01	Sets made up from a combination of the following units: Dividers 1950 x 1500mm	Nr	0.50	56.48	3.01	166.77	226.26	*40.14*
Z4.8.1.02	as above; Doors 1800 x 750mm	Nr	0.50	56.48	3.01	159.36	218.85	*19.10*
Z4.8.1.03	as above; Doors 1800 x 950mm	Nr	0.50	56.48	3.01	159.36	218.85	*24.08*
Z4.8.1.04	as above; Pilaster 1810 x 97mm	Nr	0.25	28.24	1.50	60.00	89.74	*1.90*
Z4.8.1.05	as above; Pilaster 1810 x 110mm	Nr	0.25	28.24	1.50	77.00	106.74	*2.08*

Z4 Surface Finishes, Linings and Partitions continued...

		Unit	Labour Hours	Labour Net £	Plant Net £	Materials Net £	Unit Net £	CO_2 Kg
Z4.8	**Framed panel cubicle sets**							
Z4.8.1	Komfort'; melamine faced high density chipboard doors, walls and dividers; lipped all round; thickness 18mm; including fibreboard lacquered pilaster, capping rails, aluminium wall fixings, channels, brackets and hinges; Blue / grey marble effect finish							
Z4.8.1.06	as above; Pilaster 1810 x 214mm	Nr	0.25	28.24	1.50	97.29	**127.03**	*3.51*
Z4.8.1.07	as above; Head rails 1000mm	Nr	0.13	14.12	0.75	5.00	**19.87**	*0.66*
Z4.8.1.08	as above; Head rails 2000mm	Nr	0.25	28.24	1.50	10.00	**39.74**	*1.32*
Z4.8.1.09	as above; Head rails 3000mm	Nr	0.33	37.62	2.00	15.00	**54.62**	*1.89*

Z5 Piped Building Services

		Unit	Labour Hours	Labour Net £	Plant Net £	Materials Net £	Unit Net £	CO_2 Kg
Z5.1	**Pipework**							
Z5.1.1	Pipes							
Z5.1.1.01	LTHW heating installation; copper pipes Table X to BS EN 2871; including fittings, valves, cocks and connections; fixed to backgrounds, plugging; Nominal bore: 15mm; Without insulation	m	0.14	7.61	-	2.86	**10.47**	*2.74*
Z5.1.1.02	as above; Nominal bore: 15mm; With mineral fibre foil faced insulation	m	0.18	9.96	-	4.38	**14.34**	*2.83*
Z5.1.1.03	as above; Nominal bore: 20mm; Without insulation	m	0.14	7.61	-	4.50	**12.11**	*5.07*
Z5.1.1.04	as above; Nominal bore: 20mm; With mineral fibre foil faced insulation	m	0.18	9.96	-	6.39	**16.35**	*6.27*
Z5.1.1.05	as above; Nominal bore: 35mm; Without insulation	m	0.18	10.18	-	11.60	**21.78**	*14.38*
Z5.1.1.06	as above; Nominal bore: 35mm; With mineral fibre foil faced insulation	m	0.27	14.82	-	13.85	**28.67**	*16.18*
Z5.1.1.07	as above; Nominal bore: 54mm; Without insulation	m	0.23	12.70	-	18.55	**31.25**	*24.57*
Z5.1.1.08	as above; Nominal bore: 54mm; With mineral fibre foil faced insulation	m	0.35	19.69	-	22.63	**42.32**	*26.67*
Z5.1.1.09	In sprinkler installations; black steel pipes to BS EN 10255; including fittings, valves, storage pump and sprinkler heads; Fixed to backgrounds, plugging; Rate per sprinkler head	Nr	0.80	44.74	-	248.80	**293.54**	*59.19*
Z5.2	**Equipment**							
Z5.2.2	Bolier plant and ancillaries							
Z5.2.2.01	Hot water heaters with thermostatic safety features; insulated; plugged and screwed to walls; connected to rising main including for fittings; not including electrical work; Loading: 3kW; Point of use; ABS moulded casing; vented taps and spout: Capacity: 7 litres	Nr	3.00	167.79	-	70.31	**238.10**	*47.68*
Z5.2.2.02	as above; Multipoint Cistern type; copper casing; fitting for hot water outlet: Capacity: 25 litres	Nr	6.00	335.58	-	178.63	**514.21**	*137.74*

Z5 Piped Building Services continued...

		Unit	Labour Hours	Labour Net £	Plant Net £	Materials Net £	Unit Net £	CO_2 Kg
Z5.2	**Equipment**							
Z5.2.2	Bolier plant and ancillaries							
Z5.2.2.03	Domestic boiler plant and ancillaries; fully automatic, controlled by thermostat with electric controls; white stove enamelled finish; placing in position, balancing, assembly and connections; including electrical work; Gas fired: Floor standing; capacity: 11.80kW Rating	Nr	9.00	503.37	-	801.42	1,304.79	*410.15*
Z5.2.2.04	as above; Gas fired: Floor standing; capacity; 17.60 kW Rating	Nr	9.00	503.37	-	888.72	1,392.09	*433.52*
Z5.2.2.05	as above; Oil fired: Floor standing; capacity; 11.80 kW Rating	Nr	9.00	503.37	-	1,017.08	1,520.45	*357.85*
Z5.2.2.06	as above; Oil fired: Floor standing; capacity; 17.60 kW Rating	Nr	9.00	503.37	-	1,053.87	1,557.24	*376.12*
Z5.2.2.07	Heating coils; aluminium finned copper tubing; placing and fixing into 300mm deep slot; grille cover; connections for 120 degrees C flow temperature; L.P.H.W.; 75 x 50mm	m	-	-	-	-	187.00	-
Z5.2.2.08	as above; 108 x 108mm	m	-	-	-	-	218.00	-
Z5.2.2.09	Pressed steel complete with air cock and thermostatic radiator valves; fixing brackets to masonry with screws, plugging; Panels: Single; 450mm high; of length: 800mm	Nr	0.25	13.98	-	69.16	83.14	*157.87*
Z5.2.2.10	as above; 450mm high; of length: 1120mm	Nr	0.30	16.78	-	76.88	93.66	*207.57*
Z5.2.2.11	as above; 450mm high; of length: 1920mm	Nr	0.40	22.37	-	93.08	115.45	*331.83*
Z5.2.2.12	as above; 450mm high; of length: 2720mm	Nr	0.50	27.97	-	107.54	135.51	*456.08*
Z5.2.2.13	as above; 600mm high; of length: 800mm	Nr	0.30	16.78	-	76.79	93.57	*199.29*
Z5.2.2.14	as above; 600mm high; of length: 1120mm	Nr	0.40	22.37	-	87.58	109.95	*265.56*
Z5.2.2.15	as above; 600mm high; of length: 1920mm	Nr	0.50	27.97	-	111.67	139.64	*431.23*
Z5.2.2.16	as above; 600mm high; of length: 2720mm	Nr	0.60	33.56	-	136.49	170.05	*596.90*
Z5.2.2.17	as above; Double; 450mm high; of length: 800mm	Nr	0.30	16.78	-	93.27	110.05	*282.13*
Z5.2.2.18	as above; 450mm high; of length: 1120mm	Nr	0.35	19.58	-	103.57	123.15	*381.53*
Z5.2.2.19	as above; 450mm high; of length: 1920mm	Nr	0.45	25.17	-	147.43	172.60	*630.04*
Z5.2.2.20	as above; 450mm high; of length: 2720mm	Nr	0.55	30.76	-	196.88	227.64	*878.54*
Z5.2.2.21	as above; 600mm high; of length: 800mm	Nr	0.40	22.37	-	108.49	130.86	*364.96*
Z5.2.2.22	as above; 600mm high; of length: 1120mm	Nr	0.50	27.97	-	129.52	157.49	*497.50*
Z5.2.2.23	as above; 600mm high; of length: 1920mm	Nr	0.60	33.56	-	186.40	219.96	*431.23*

Z5 Piped Building Services continued...

		Unit	Labour Hours	Labour Net £	Plant Net £	Materials Net £	Unit Net £	CO_2 Kg
Z5.2	**Equipment**							
Z5.2.2	Bolier plant and ancillaries							
Z5.2.2.24	as previous item; 600mm high; of length: 2720mm	Nr	0.70	39.15	-	245.03	284.18	*596.90*
Z5.2.3	Pumps							
Z5.2.3.01	Centrifugal heating pump direct drive; 3 phase; 1450 rpm motor; max. temperature 110 degrees C; button starter; including electrical connections; Pump Size 40mm; Maximum Head 40kN per m2; Maximum Delivery 4 litre/sec	Nr	3.00	167.79	-	663.01	830.80	*233.39*
Z5.2.3.02	as above; Pump Size 50mm; Maximum Head 35kN per m^2; Maximum Delivery 7 litre/sec	Nr	3.00	167.79	-	763.01	930.80	*276.41*
Z5.2.3.03	as above; Pump Size 80mm; Maximum Head 50kN per m^2; Maximum Delivery 16 litre/sec	Nr	3.00	167.79	-	1,063.01	1,230.80	*570.38*
Z5.2.3.04	as above; Pump Size 100mm; Maximum Head 80kN per m^2; Maximum Delivery 28 litre/sec	Nr	3.00	167.79	-	1,363.02	1,530.81	*692.27*
Z5.2.3.05	as above; Pump Size 150mm; Maximum Head 120kN per m^2; Maximum Delivery 70 litre/sec	Nr	3.00	167.79	-	2,063.01	2,230.80	*814.16*
Z5.3	**Sanitary appliances and fittings**							
Z5.3.1	Including waste pipes and fittings, valves, fittings, traps; placing in position, assembly and connections							
Z5.3.1.01	WC suites; white vitreous china with pan, cistern, flush pipe and seat	Nr	3.00	167.79	-	73.52	241.31	*68.07*
Z5.3.1.02	Bowl urinals; white vitreous china with concealed hangers, cistern and flush pipe	Nr	1.00	55.93	-	296.75	352.68	*122.15*
Z5.3.1.03	Slab urinals; white glazed fireclay with cistern, flush pipes and spreaders waste fitting: 2 persons	Nr	2.00	111.86	-	618.85	730.71	*231.45*
Z5.3.1.04	as above; 3 persons	Nr	3.00	167.79	-	876.11	1,043.90	*314.18*
Z5.3.1.05	as above; 4 persons	Nr	4.00	223.72	-	1,188.75	1,412.47	*414.46*
Z5.3.1.06	Hand rinse basins; vitreous china with brackets chromium plated waste, pillar taps, plug and chain	Nr	2.00	111.86	-	61.60	173.46	*43.59*

Z6 Ducted Building Services

		Unit	Labour Hours	Labour Net £	Plant Net £	Materials Net £	Unit Net £	CO_2 Kg
Z6.2	**Rectangular ductwork**							
Z6.2.1	Straight							
Z6.2.1.01	Air supply system; galvanised sheet steel; low pressure including supports; fittings; 1nr taper; 1nr 90 degree bend; 2nr grilles; 1nr fire damper; DW 142; overall length 20m; Without insulation; 0.6mm thick: sum of both sides 200mm	m	0.05	2.35	0.74	117.85	120.94	*25.07*
Z6.2.1.02	as above; 0.6mm thick: sum of both sides 400mm	m	0.05	2.54	0.80	145.09	148.43	*48.49*

Z6 Ducted Building Services continued...

		Unit	Labour Hours	Labour Net £	Plant Net £	Materials Net £	Unit Net £	CO_2 Kg
Z6.2	**Rectangular ductwork**							
Z6.2.1	Straight							
Z6.2.1.03	as previous item; 0.6mm thick: sum of both sides 500mm	m	0.05	2.54	0.80	163.97	**167.31**	*57.50*
Z6.2.1.04	as above; 0.6mm thick: sum of both sides 600mm	m	0.05	2.54	0.80	185.99	**189.33**	*72.43*
Z6.2.1.05	as above; 0.8mm thick: sum of both sides 700mm	m	0.05	2.54	0.80	198.89	**202.23**	*95.29*
Z6.2.1.06	as above; 0.8mm thick: sum of both sides 900mm	m	0.06	2.73	0.86	295.94	**299.53**	*138.41*
Z6.2.1.07	as above; 0.8mm thick: sum of both sides 1100mm	m	0.06	2.73	0.86	362.64	**366.23**	*156.15*
Z6.2.1.08	as above; 0.8mm thick: sum of both sides 1500mm	m	0.07	3.15	0.99	427.56	**431.70**	*218.04*
Z6.2.1.09	as above; 1.0mm thick: sum of both sides 2000mm	m	0.08	3.52	1.11	485.56	**490.19**	*229.58*
Z6.2.1.10	as above; 1.0mm thick: sum of both sides 2400mm	m	0.08	3.90	1.23	571.56	**576.69**	*316.66*
Z6.2.1.11	as above; 1.0mm thick: sum of both sides 2800mm	m	0.10	4.70	1.48	665.56	**671.74**	*428.63*
Z6.2.1.12	as above; 1.0mm thick:: sum of both sides 3200mm	m	0.12	5.50	1.73	727.56	**734.79**	*540.05*
Z6.2.1.13	as above; Rigid mineral fibre foil faced insulation; 0.6mm thick: sum of both sides 200mm	m	0.05	2.54	0.80	120.75	**124.09**	*26.57*
Z6.2.1.14	as above; 0.6mm thick: sum of both sides 400mm	m	0.06	2.73	0.86	150.89	**154.48**	*51.47*
Z6.2.1.15	as above; 0.6mm thick: sum of both sides 500mm	m	0.06	2.73	0.86	171.22	**174.81**	*61.22*
Z6.2.1.16	as above; 0.6mm thick: sum of both sides 600mm	m	0.06	2.73	0.86	194.69	**198.28**	*76.90*
Z6.2.1.17	as above; 0.8mm thick: sum of both sides 700mm	m	0.06	2.96	0.93	209.04	**212.93**	*100.52*
Z6.2.1.18	as above; 0.8mm thick: sum of both sides 900mm	m	0.07	3.15	0.99	308.99	**313.13**	*145.13*
Z6.2.1.19	as above; 0.8mm thick: sum of both sides 1100mm	m	0.07	3.15	0.99	378.59	**382.73**	*164.35*
Z6.2.1.20	as above; 0.8mm thick: sum of both sides 1500mm	m	0.08	3.52	1.11	449.31	**453.94**	*229.22*
Z6.2.1.21	as above; 1.0mm thick: sum of both sides 2000mm	m	0.08	3.90	1.23	514.56	**519.69**	*244.48*
Z6.2.1.22	as above; 1.0mm thick: sum of both sides 2400mm	m	0.09	4.32	1.36	606.36	**612.04**	*334.53*
Z6.2.1.23	as above; 1.0mm thick: sum of both sides 2800mm	m	0.12	5.50	1.73	706.16	**713.39**	*449.50*
Z6.2.1.24	as above; 1.0mm thick:: sum of both sides 3200mm	m	0.13	6.25	1.96	773.96	**782.17**	*563.89*
Z6.3	**Equipment**							
Z6.3.1	Conditioning and handling units							
Z6.3.1.01	Roof mounted air handling unit, air supply system; steel trays; insulation; mixing box filter; 240V centrifugal fan; attenuator; plenum box; heater battery; chiller; flexible connections; commissioning; Air volume: 0.3 m3/sec; Heating Capacity 14.5 kW; Cooling capacity 7.1kW	Nr	15.00	749.55	168.60	1,750.58	**2,668.73**	*438.43*

Z6 Ducted Building Services continued...

		Unit	Labour Hours	Labour Net £	Plant Net £	Materials Net £	Unit Net £	CO_2 Kg
Z6.3	**Equipment**							
Z6.3.1	Conditioning and handling units							
Z6.3.1.02	as previous item; Air volume: 0.6 m3/sec; Heating Capacity 25.8 kW; Cooling Capacity 12.4 kW	Nr	15.00	749.55	168.60	2,303.58	**3,221.73**	*526.93*
Z6.3.1.03	as above; Air volume: 1.4 m3/sec; Heating Capacity 54.8 kW; Cooling Capacity 25.8 kW	Nr	18.00	899.46	202.32	3,227.02	**4,328.80**	*670.22*
Z6.3.3	Fans							
Z6.3.3.01	Ceiling mounted encased fan coil unit, air supply system; variable speed fan; filter; coils; grilles; condensate drip tray; fresh air capacity; including electrical connections; Heating capacity: 5.0kW; Cooling Capacity 2.3kW	Nr	2.00	102.92	22.48	362.58	**487.98**	*244.93*
Z6.3.3.02	as above; Heating capacity: 9.0kW; Cooling Capacity 4.7kW	Nr	2.00	102.92	22.48	412.58	**537.98**	*312.68*

Z7 Cabled Building Services

		Unit	Labour Hours	Labour Net £	Plant Net £	Materials Net £	Unit Net £	CO_2 Kg
Z7.1	**Cables**							
Z7.1.1	Laid or drawn into conduits; trunking or ducts							
Z7.1.1.01	Type: Two core; PVC insulated; S.W.A.; PVC sheathed copper: 1.5mm^2	m	0.05	2.80	-	0.66	**3.46**	*0.73*
Z7.1.1.02	as above; PVC insulated; S.W.A.; PVC sheathed copper: 2.5mm^2	m	0.05	2.80	-	0.82	**3.62**	*0.87*
Z7.1.1.03	as above; PVC insulated; S.W.A.; PVC sheathed copper: 4.0mm^2	m	0.07	3.75	-	1.10	**4.85**	*1.02*
Z7.1.1.04	as above; PVC insulated; S.W.A.; PVC sheathed copper: 6.0mm^2	m	0.10	5.59	-	1.48	**7.07**	*1.21*
Z7.1.1.05	as above; PVC insulated; S.W.A.; PVC sheathed copper: 10.0mm^2	m	0.15	8.39	-	2.14	**10.53**	*1.58*
Z7.1.1.06	as above; PVC insulated; S.W.A.; PVC sheathed copper: 16.0mm^2	m	0.17	9.34	-	2.94	**12.28**	*2.21*
Z7.1.1.07	as above; XLPE insulated; S.W.A.; PVC sheathed copper: 25mm^2	m	0.25	13.98	-	3.86	**17.84**	*2.57*
Z7.1.1.08	as above; XLPE insulated; S.W.A.; PVC sheathed copper: 35mm^2	m	0.33	18.62	-	5.00	**23.62**	*3.59*
Z7.1.1.09	as above; XLPE insulated; S.W.A.; PVC sheathed copper: 70mm^2	m	0.42	23.32	-	10.00	**33.32**	*5.58*
Z7.1.1.10	Type: Three core; PVC insulated; S.W.A.; PVC sheathed copper: 1.5mm^2	m	0.05	2.80	-	0.70	**3.50**	*0.83*
Z7.1.1.11	as above; PVC insulated; S.W.A.; PVC sheathed copper: 2.5mm^2	m	0.05	2.80	-	0.94	**3.74**	*0.98*
Z7.1.1.12	as above; PVC insulated; S.W.A.; PVC sheathed copper: 4.0mm^2	m	0.07	3.75	-	1.29	**5.04**	*1.20*
Z7.1.1.13	as above; PVC insulated; S.W.A.; PVC sheathed copper: 6.0mm^2	m	0.10	5.59	-	1.71	**7.30**	*1.46*
Z7.1.1.14	as above; PVC insulated; S.W.A.; PVC sheathed copper: 10.0mm^2	m	0.15	8.39	-	2.79	**11.18**	*2.18*
Z7.1.1.15	as above; PVC insulated; S.W.A.; PVC sheathed copper: 16.0mm^2	m	0.17	9.34	-	3.98	**13.32**	*2.62*
Z7.1.1.16	as above; XLPE insulated; S.W.A.; PVC sheathed copper: 25mm^2	m	0.25	13.98	-	5.85	**19.83**	*4.25*
Z7.1.1.17	as above; XLPE insulated; S.W.A.; PVC sheathed copper: 35mm^2	m	0.33	18.62	-	7.25	**25.87**	*5.10*

Z7 Cabled Building Services continued...

		Unit	Labour Hours	Labour Net £	Plant Net £	Materials Net £	Unit Net £	CO_2 Kg
Z7.1	**Cables**							
Z7.1.1	Laid or drawn into conduits; trunking or ducts							
Z7.1.1.18	as previous item; XLPE insulated; S.W.A.; PVC sheathed copper: 70mm²	m	0.42	23.32	-	14.00	**37.32**	*7.64*
Z7.1.1.19	Type: Four core; PVC insulated; S.W.A.; PVC sheathed copper: 1.5mm²	m	0.07	3.75	-	0.84	**4.59**	*0.95*
Z7.1.1.20	as above; PVC insulated; S.W.A.; PVC sheathed copper: 2.5mm²	m	0.08	4.64	-	1.18	**5.82**	*1.13*
Z7.1.1.21	as above; PVC insulated; S.W.A.; PVC sheathed copper: 4.0mm²	m	0.13	7.44	-	1.64	**9.08**	*1.41*
Z7.1.1.22	as above; PVC insulated; S.W.A.; PVC sheathed copper: 6.0mm²	m	0.17	9.34	-	2.36	**11.70**	*1.99*
Z7.1.1.23	as above; PVC insulated; S.W.A.; PVC sheathed copper: 10.0mm²	m	0.20	11.19	-	3.49	**14.68**	*2.65*
Z7.1.1.24	as above; PVC insulated; S.W.A.; PVC sheathed copper: 16.0mm²	m	0.25	13.98	-	5.26	**19.24**	*3.40*
Z7.1.1.25	as above; XLPE insulated; S.W.A.; PVC sheathed copper: 25mm²	m	0.25	13.98	-	7.30	**21.28**	*5.10*
Z7.1.1.26	as above; XLPE insulated; S.W.A.; PVC sheathed copper: 35mm²	m	0.33	18.62	-	9.99	**28.61**	*6.26*
Z7.1.1.27	as above; XLPE insulated; S.W.A.; PVC sheathed copper: 70mm²	m	0.33	18.62	-	18.65	**37.27**	*10.44*
Z7.1.1.28	Type: Single core; PVC insulated cable copper; Single Strand; 1.5mm²	m	0.02	0.95	-	0.18	**1.13**	*0.73*
Z7.1.1.29	as above; PVC insulated cable copper; Single Strand; 2.5mm²	m	0.02	0.95	-	0.24	**1.19**	*0.87*
Z7.1.1.30	as above; PVC insulated cable copper; Multi Strand; 1.5mm²	m	0.02	0.95	-	0.16	**1.11**	*0.73*
Z7.1.1.31	as above; PVC insulated cable copper; Multi Strand; 2.5mm²	m	0.02	0.95	-	0.22	**1.17**	*0.87*
Z7.1.1.32	as above; PVC insulated cable copper; Multi Strand; 4.0mm²	m	0.02	0.95	-	0.36	**1.31**	*1.02*
Z7.1.1.33	as above; PVC insulated cable copper; Multi Strand; 6.0mm²	m	0.02	0.95	-	0.49	**1.44**	*1.21*
Z7.1.3	Fixed to surfaces							
Z7.1.3.01	Mineral Insulated; copper sheathed with copper conductors; Type: bare; Light duty 600 volt grade; 2L 1.0	m	0.03	1.40	-	3.58	**4.98**	*0.04*
Z7.1.3.02	as above; Light duty 600 volt grade; 2L 1.5	m	0.03	1.40	-	4.22	**5.62**	*0.06*
Z7.1.3.03	as above; Light duty 600 volt grade; 2L 2.5	m	0.03	1.40	-	5.48	**6.88**	*0.09*
Z7.1.3.04	as above; Light duty 600 volt grade; 2L 4.0	m	0.03	1.40	-	8.31	**9.71**	*0.09*
Z7.1.3.05	as above; Heavy duty 1000 volt grade; 1H 6.0	m	0.03	1.85	-	8.55	**10.40**	*0.33*
Z7.1.3.06	as above; Heavy duty 1000 volt grade; 1H 10.0	m	0.03	1.85	-	9.13	**10.98**	*0.74*
Z7.1.3.07	as above; Heavy duty 1000 volt grade; 2H 2.5	m	0.05	2.80	-	9.52	**12.32**	*3.47*
Z7.1.3.08	as above; Heavy duty 1000 volt grade; 2H 6.0	m	0.05	2.80	-	15.96	**18.76**	*1.34*
Z7.1.3.09	as above; Type: PV sheathed; Light duty 600 volt grade; 2L 1.0	m	0.03	1.40	-	4.17	**5.57**	*0.04*
Z7.1.3.10	as above; Light duty 600 volt grade; 2L 1.5	m	0.03	1.40	-	4.63	**6.03**	*0.06*

Z7 Cabled Building Services continued...

		Unit	Labour Hours	Labour Net £	Plant Net £	Materials Net £	Unit Net £	CO_2 Kg
Z7.1	**Cables**							
Z7.1.3	Fixed to surfaces							
Z7.1.3.11	as previous item; Light duty 600 volt grade; 2L 2.5	m	0.03	1.40	-	5.85	7.25	*0.09*
Z7.1.3.12	as above; Light duty 600 volt grade; 2L 4.0	m	0.03	1.40	-	8.80	10.20	*0.14*
Z7.1.3.13	as above; Heavy duty 1000 volt grade; 1H 6.0	m	0.03	1.85	-	9.35	11.20	*0.33*
Z7.1.3.14	as above; Heavy duty 1000 volt grade; 1H 10.0	m	0.03	1.85	-	9.93	11.78	*0.74*
Z7.1.3.15	as above; Heavy duty 1000 volt grade; 2H 2.5	m	0.05	2.80	-	10.36	13.16	*3.47*
Z7.1.3.16	as above; Heavy duty 1000 volt grade; 2H 6.0	m	0.05	2.80	-	17.30	20.10	*1.34*
Z7.1.4	Laid in trenches							
Z7.1.4.01	PVC sheathed; S.W.A; PVC insulated copper; Type: Two core; 4mm2	m	0.08	4.64	-	1.10	5.74	*1.02*
Z7.1.4.02	as above; 6mm²	m	0.08	4.64	-	1.48	6.12	*1.21*
Z7.1.4.03	as above; 10mm²	m	0.10	5.59	-	2.14	7.73	*1.58*
Z7.1.4.04	as above; 16mm²	m	0.17	9.34	-	2.94	12.28	*2.21*
Z7.1.4.05	as above; Type: Three core; 4mm²	m	0.08	4.64	-	1.29	5.93	*1.20*
Z7.1.4.06	as above; 6mm²	m	0.12	6.54	-	1.71	8.25	*1.46*
Z7.1.4.07	as above; 10mm²	m	0.17	9.34	-	2.79	12.13	*2.18*
Z7.1.4.08	as above; 16mm²	m	0.20	11.19	-	3.98	15.17	*2.62*
Z7.1.4.09	as above; Type: Four core; 4mm²	m	0.15	8.39	-	1.64	10.03	*1.41*
Z7.1.4.10	as above; 6mm²	m	0.20	11.19	-	2.36	13.55	*1.99*
Z7.1.4.11	as above; 10mm²	m	0.20	11.19	-	3.49	14.68	*2.65*
Z7.1.4.12	as above; 16mm²	m	0.25	13.98	-	5.26	19.24	*3.40*
Z7.1.4.13	XLPE insulated; S.W.A; PVC sheathed copper; Type: Two core; 25mm²	m	0.17	9.34	-	3.86	13.20	*2.57*
Z7.1.4.14	as above; 35mm²	m	0.25	13.98	-	5.00	18.98	*3.59*
Z7.1.4.15	as above; 70mm²	m	0.25	13.98	-	10.00	23.98	*5.58*
Z7.1.4.16	as above; 120mm²	m	0.33	18.62	-	20.00	38.62	*9.22*
Z7.1.4.17	as above; 240mm²	m	0.33	18.62	-	35.00	53.62	*17.67*
Z7.1.4.18	as above; Type: Three core; 25mm²	m	0.17	9.34	-	5.85	15.19	*4.25*
Z7.1.4.19	as above; 35mm²	m	0.25	13.98	-	7.25	21.23	*5.10*
Z7.1.4.20	as above; 70mm²	m	0.25	13.98	-	14.00	27.98	*7.64*
Z7.1.4.21	as above; 120mm²	m	0.25	13.98	-	21.00	34.98	*12.74*
Z7.1.4.22	as above; 240mm²	m	0.33	18.62	-	40.00	58.62	*24.63*
Z7.1.4.23	as above; Type: Four core; 25mm²	m	0.08	4.64	-	7.30	11.94	*5.10*
Z7.1.4.24	as above; 35mm²	m	0.17	9.34	-	9.99	19.33	*6.26*
Z7.1.4.25	as above; 70mm²	m	0.17	9.34	-	18.65	27.99	*10.44*
Z7.1.4.26	as above; 120mm²	m	0.17	9.34	-	27.00	36.34	*17.35*
Z7.1.4.27	as above; 240mm²	m	0.17	9.34	-	36.00	45.34	*31.55*
Z7.3	**Trunking**							
Z7.3.1	Plain							
Z7.3.1.01	Fixed to backgrounds; fittings included in the running length; Type: Single compartment; Galvanised steel; 3m lengths: 50 x 50mm	m	0.17	9.34	-	4.30	13.64	*13.20*

Z7 Cabled Building Services continued...

		Unit	Labour Hours	Labour Net £	Plant Net £	Materials Net £	Unit Net £	CO_2 Kg
Z7.3	**Trunking**							
Z7.3.1	Plain							
Z7.3.1.02	as previous item; Galvanised steel; 3m lengths: 75 x 75mm	m	0.17	9.34	-	7.10	**16.44**	*19.80*
Z7.3.1.03	as above; Galvanised steel; 3m lengths: 100 x 75mm	m	0.25	13.98	-	7.83	**21.81**	*23.10*
Z7.3.1.04	as above; Galvanised steel; 3m lengths: 150 x 150mm	m	0.33	18.62	-	8.30	**26.92**	*39.59*
Z7.3.1.05	as above; PVC; grey finish; clip on lid: 50 x 50mm	m	0.17	9.34	-	2.16	**11.50**	*2.24*
Z7.3.1.06	as above; PVC; grey finish; clip on lid: 75 x 75mm	m	0.20	11.19	-	4.33	**15.52**	*3.37*
Z7.3.1.07	as above; PVC; grey finish; clip on lid: 100 x 75mm	m	0.25	13.98	-	5.00	**18.98**	*3.93*
Z7.3.1.08	as above; PVC; grey finish; clip on lid: 150 x 150mm	m	0.33	18.62	-	14.63	**33.25**	*6.73*
Z7.3.1.09	as above; Type: Double compartment; Galvanised steel; 3m lengths: 50 x 50mm	m	0.20	11.19	-	6.45	**17.64**	*16.50*
Z7.3.1.10	as above; Galvanised steel; 3m lengths: 75 x 75mm	m	0.20	11.19	-	10.65	**21.84**	*24.75*
Z7.3.1.11	as above; Galvanised steel; 3m lengths: 100 x 75mm	m	0.25	13.98	-	11.75	**25.73**	*28.05*
Z7.3.1.12	as above; Galvanised steel; 3m lengths: 150 x 150mm	m	0.33	18.62	-	12.45	**31.07**	*49.49*
Z7.3.1.13	as above; PVC; grey finish; clip on lid: 50 x 50mm	m	0.25	13.98	-	3.49	**17.47**	*2.81*
Z7.3.1.14	as above; PVC; grey finish; clip on lid: 75 x 75mm	m	0.33	18.62	-	5.62	**24.24**	*4.21*
Z7.3.1.15	as above; PVC; grey finish; clip on lid: 100 x 75mm	m	0.42	23.32	-	6.99	**30.31**	*4.77*
Z7.3.1.16	as above; PVC; grey finish; clip on lid: 150 x 150mm	m	0.50	27.97	-	16.62	**44.59**	*7.85*
Z7.3.1.17	as above; Type: Triple compartment; Galvanised steel; 3m lengths: 75 x 75mm	m	0.17	9.34	-	15.97	**25.31**	*29.70*
Z7.3.1.18	as above; Galvanised steel; 3m lengths: 100 x 75mm	m	0.20	11.19	-	15.97	**27.16**	*29.70*
Z7.3.1.19	as above; Galvanised steel; 3m lengths: 150 x 150mm	m	0.33	18.62	-	15.97	**34.59**	*29.70*
Z7.3.1.20	as above; PVC; grey finish; clip on lid: 75 x 75mm	m	0.33	18.62	-	7.28	**25.90**	*5.05*
Z7.3.1.21	as above; PVC; grey finish; clip on lid: 100 x 75mm	m	0.42	23.32	-	8.98	**32.30**	*5.61*
Z7.3.1.22	as above; PVC; grey finish; clip on lid: 150 x 150mm	m	0.50	27.97	-	18.62	**46.59**	*8.98*
Z7.5	**Trays**							
Z7.5.1	Plain							
Z7.5.1.01	Cable tray; fittings included in the running length; Galvanised steel; 2.4m lengths: 50mm wide tray	m	0.17	9.34	0.68	1.50	**11.52**	*3.30*
Z7.5.1.02	as above; Galvanised steel; 2.4m lengths: 100mm wide tray	m	0.25	13.98	1.01	3.10	**18.09**	*6.60*
Z7.5.1.03	as above; Galvanised steel; 2.4m lengths: 300mm wide tray	m	0.33	18.62	1.35	9.00	**28.97**	*19.80*
Z7.5.1.04	as above; Galvanised steel; 2.4m lengths: 600mm wide tray	m	0.75	41.95	3.04	13.33	**58.32**	*39.59*

Z7 Cabled Building Services continued...

		Unit	Labour Hours	Labour Net £	Plant Net £	Materials Net £	Unit Net £	CO_2 Kg
Z7.5	**Trays**							
Z7.5.1	Plain							
Z7.5.1.05	Cable tray with return flange; fittings included in the running length; Galvanised steel; 2.4m lengths: 50mm wide tray	m	0.25	13.98	1.01	2.46	**17.45**	*3.63*
Z7.5.1.06	as above; Galvanised steel; 2.4m lengths: 100mm wide tray	m	0.50	27.97	2.02	8.76	**38.75**	*7.26*
Z7.5.1.07	as above; Galvanised steel; 2.4m lengths: 300mm wide tray	m	0.75	41.95	3.04	14.66	**59.65**	*19.80*
Z7.5.1.08	as above; Galvanised steel; 2.4m lengths: 600mm wide tray	m	1.00	55.93	4.05	26.67	**86.65**	*43.55*
Z7.6	**Earthing and bonding**							
Z7.6.1	Tapes							
Z7.6.1.01	In accordance with the IEE Wiring Regulations; Copper tapes; PVC insulated single core cable; earth clamps; fixings; Rate per m	m	0.16	8.95	-	1.00	**9.95**	*1.45*
Z7.6.1.02	In lightning protection; Earth rods; strike points; 25 x 3mm copper tape; bonding links; test clamps; commissioning; Rate per m2 of gross floor area	m^2	0.05	2.45	0.33	2.78	**5.56**	*2.52*
Z7.7	**Final circuits**							
Z7.7.2	Cable and conduit							
Z7.7.2.01	With equipment and fittings to internal lighting; 2.5mm2 PVC singles cable; galvanised heavy gauge mild steel conduit; luminaires; diffusers; control gear; switches; fixings; 1800mm 70W single batten fluorescents	Point	2.00	111.86	8.10	42.90	**162.86**	*36.29*
Z7.7.2.02	as above; 1200mm 36W twin batten fluorescents	Point	2.00	111.86	8.10	50.50	**170.46**	*37.17*
Z7.7.2.03	as above; 1200mm 36W twin batten fluorescents, Zone 2 Hazard rated	Point	2.00	111.86	8.10	94.90	**214.86**	*43.37*
Z7.7.2.04	as above; 1200 x 600mm 36W recessed modular fluorescent	Point	3.00	167.79	12.15	70.25	**250.19**	*40.71*
Z7.7.2.05	as above; 1200 x 600mm 36W recessed modular fluorescent with emergency inverter / charger module and 3 hour battery pack	Point	4.00	223.72	16.20	121.35	**361.27**	*45.14*
Z7.7.2.06	With equipment and fittings to external lighting installations; 4 core 6mm2 PVC/SWA/PVC cable in trenches; luminaires; control gear; brackets; columns; fixings; 250W SON XL floodlight and 7 metre column	Point	4.25	234.49	32.63	1,293.63	**1,560.75**	*1,455.45*
Z7.7.2.07	as above;	Point	3.12	172.96	7.89	352.94	**533.79**	*811.59*
Z7.7.2.08	With equipment and fittings to suspended track lighting; Suspensions; brackets; 2.5mm2 PVC single cable; galvanised conduit; control gear; switches; fixings; 58W single linear track (anodised finish)	Point	1.00	55.93	-	74.70	**130.63**	*52.46*

Z7 Cabled Building Services continued...

		Unit	Labour Hours	Labour Net £	Plant Net £	Materials Net £	Unit Net £	CO_2 Kg
Z7.7	**Final circuits**							
Z7.7.2	Cable and conduit							
Z7.7.2.09	as previous item; 58W twin linear track (anodised finish)	Point	1.20	67.12	-	127.95	195.07	*73.06*
Z7.7.2.10	with equipment and fittings in emergency lighting installation; Luminaires; illuminated signs; MICC cable; galvanised cable tray; control gear; fixings; 11W Bulkhead	Point	1.20	67.12	-	87.10	154.22	*36.93*
Z7.7.2.11	as above; 11W Bulkhead Zone 2 Hazard rated	Point	1.50	83.89	-	171.45	255.34	*37.78*
Z7.7.2.12	as above; 24W 'EXIT' Bulkhead sign	Point	1.20	67.12	-	183.45	250.57	*38.94*
Z7.7.2.13	as above; 24W 'EXIT' Bulkhead sign Zone 2 Hazard rated	Point	1.50	83.89	-	321.45	405.34	*39.83*
Z7.7.2.14	with equipment and fittings in security alarm installation; Infra red detectors; card access system; perimeter intruder alarms; control alarms; control and mimic panels; PVC singles cable; galvanised conduit and cable trunking; fixings; Rate per point	Nr	0.33	18.62	-	150.13	168.75	*31.76*
Z7.7.2.15	with equipment and fittings in fire alarm installation; Smoke detectors; heat detectors; alarm sounders; break glass units; control panel; MICC cable; galvanised steel cable tray; fixings; Rate per point	Nr	0.25	13.98	-	286.88	300.86	*12.62*
Z7.7.2.16	with equipment and fittings to trace heating to internal pipework; Parallel circuit heater cables; fibreglass wrap-a-round tape; connection glands; junction boxes; Rate per m	m	0.20	11.19	-	0.74	11.93	*1.03*
Z7.8	**Equipment and fittings**							
Z7.8.1	Equipment							
Z7.8.1.01	Distribution boards; sheet steel case; fully shrouded; fixing of plates; supports; fixings; connections to equipment; fixed to masonry; Rate: SP & N; 500V 1nr 2-20 Amp HRC fuses: 4 way	Nr	2.00	111.86	-	220.00	331.86	*69.69*
Z7.8.1.02	as above; 500V 1nr 2-20 Amp HRC fuses: 6 way	Nr	2.00	111.86	-	275.00	386.86	*85.55*
Z7.8.1.03	as above; 500V 1nr 2-20 Amp HRC fuses: 8 way	Nr	2.00	111.86	-	330.00	441.86	*101.95*
Z7.8.1.04	as above; 500V 6nr 63 Amp MCBs: 4 way	Nr	3.00	167.79	-	165.00	332.79	*54.64*
Z7.8.1.05	as above; 500V 6nr 63 Amp MCBs: 8 way	Nr	3.00	167.79	-	192.50	360.29	*64.33*
Z7.8.1.06	as above; 500V 6nr 63 Amp MCBs: 12 way	Nr	3.00	167.79	-	220.00	387.79	*73.21*
Z7.8.1.07	as above; Rate: TP & N; 500V 1nr 2-20 Amp HRC fuses: 4 way	Nr	3.00	167.79	-	330.00	497.79	*104.28*
Z7.8.1.08	as above; 500V 1nr 2-20 Amp HRC fuses: 6 way	Nr	3.00	167.79	-	440.00	607.79	*131.78*

Z7 Cabled Building Services continued...

		Unit	Labour Hours	Labour Net £	Plant Net £	Materials Net £	Unit Net £	CO_2 Kg
Z7.8	**Equipment and fittings**							
Z7.8.1	Equipment							
Z7.8.1.09	as previous item; 500V 1nr 2-20 Amp HRC fuses: 8 way	Nr	3.00	167.79	-	495.00	662.79	*147.81*
Z7.8.1.10	as above; 500V 6nr 63 Amp MCBs: 4 way	Nr	4.00	223.72	-	220.00	443.72	*75.81*
Z7.8.1.11	as above; 500V 6nr 63 Amp MCBs: 8 way	Nr	4.00	223.72	-	385.00	608.72	*116.73*
Z7.8.1.12	as above; 500V 6nr 63 Amp MCBs: 12 way	Nr	4.00	223.72	-	495.00	718.72	*149.43*
Z7.8.2	Switches							
Z7.8.2.01	Type: 1 gang; Fused Connection Unit 13 Amp; BS 5733: metal clad	Nr	0.25	13.98	-	8.50	22.48	*3.77*
Z7.8.2.02	as above; Fused Connection Unit 13 Amp; BS 5733: moulded plastic	Nr	0.25	13.98	-	4.55	18.53	*2.53*
Z7.8.2.03	Type: 1 gang; Switch 10 Amp; 1 way; weatherproof	Nr	0.33	18.62	-	28.30	46.92	*4.07*
Z7.8.2.04	as above; Switch 15 Amp; 2 way: metal clad	Nr	0.17	9.34	-	3.10	12.44	*5.42*
Z7.8.2.05	as above; Switch 15 Amp; 2 way: moulded plastic	Nr	0.17	9.34	-	0.95	10.29	*5.42*
Z7.8.2.06	as above; Switch 20 Amp: metal clad	Nr	0.25	13.98	-	5.45	19.43	*6.78*
Z7.8.2.07	as above; Switch 20 Amp: moulded plastic	Nr	0.25	13.98	-	3.30	17.28	*6.78*
Z7.8.2.08	Type: 2 gang; Fused Connection Unit 13 Amp; BS 5733: metal clad	Nr	0.25	13.98	-	12.75	26.73	*5.02*
Z7.8.2.09	Type: 2 gang; Switch 15 Amp; 2 way: moulded plastic	Nr	0.33	18.62	-	4.20	22.82	*5.42*
Z7.8.2.10	as above; Switch 20 Amp: metal clad	Nr	0.33	18.62	-	8.18	26.80	*6.78*
Z7.8.2.11	as above; Switch 20 Amp: moulded plastic	Nr	0.33	18.62	-	4.95	23.57	*6.78*
Z7.8.4	Sockets							
Z7.8.4.01	Type: 1 gang; Socket outlet 13 Amp metal clad; BS 1363: switched	Nr	0.33	18.62	-	6.31	24.93	*1.46*
Z7.8.4.02	as above; Socket outlet13 Amp metal clad; BS 1363: switched with neon indicator	Nr	0.33	18.62	-	7.31	25.93	*2.19*
Z7.8.4.03	as above; Socket outlet 13 Amp; BS 1363; white moulded plastic: switched	Nr	0.33	18.62	-	5.59	24.21	*1.36*
Z7.8.4.04	as above; Socket outlet 13 Amp; BS 1363; white moulded plastic: switched with neon indicator	Nr	0.33	18.62	-	6.59	25.21	*2.03*
Z7.8.4.05	as above; Socket outlet 16 Amp industrial; BS 4343: 1P44; 415V	Nr	1.00	55.93	-	6.50	62.43	*2.92*
Z7.8.4.06	as above; Socket outlet 16 Amp industrial; BS 4343: 1P67; 240V	Nr	0.50	27.97	-	1.98	29.95	*1.46*
Z7.8.4.07	Type: 2 gang; Socket outlet 13 Amp metal clad; BS 1363: switched	Nr	0.42	23.32	-	8.03	31.35	*2.92*
Z7.8.4.08	as above; Socket outlet 13 Amp metal clad; BS 1363: switched with neon indicator	Nr	0.50	27.97	-	12.03	40.00	*4.38*

Z7 Cabled Building Services continued...

		Unit	Labour Hours	Labour Net £	Plant Net £	Materials Net £	Unit Net £	CO_2 Kg
Z7.8	**Equipment and fittings**							
Z7.8.4	Sockets							
Z7.8.4.09	as previous item; Socket outlet 13 Amp; BS 1363; white moulded plastic: switched	Nr	0.50	27.97	-	6.72	**34.69**	*2.71*
Z7.8.4.10	as above; Socket outlet 13 Amp; BS 1363; white moulded plastic: switched with neon indicator	Nr	0.58	32.61	-	10.72	**43.33**	*4.07*
Z7.8.4.11	as above; Socket outlet 16 Amp industrial; BS 4343: 1P44; 415V	Nr	1.50	83.89	-	9.75	**93.64**	*5.84*
Z7.8.4.12	as above; Socket outlet 16 Amp industrial; BS 4343: 1P67; 240V	Nr	0.75	41.95	-	2.97	**44.92**	*2.19*

CLASS ZZ:
ALTERATIONS

Calculations used throughout Class ZZ - Alterations

Labour

		Qty		Rate		Total
L A0120ICE	**General Earthworks Labour Gang**					
	Ganger	1	x	16.99	=	£16.99
	Labourer (General Operative)	1	x	12.56	=	£12.56
	Banksman	1	x	13.53	=	£13.53
	Total hourly cost of gang				**=**	**£43.08**
L A0123ICE	**Landscape Labour Gang**					
	Labourer (Skill Rate 3)	1	x	14.34	=	£14.34
	Labourer (General Operative)	1	x	12.56	=	£12.56
	Total hourly cost of gang				**=**	**£26.90**
L A0130ICE	**Formwork (make, fix and strike) Labour Gang**					
	Craftsman WRA	1	x	16.68	=	£16.68
	Labourer (Skill Rate 3)	1	x	14.34	=	£14.34
	Carpenter (charge hand)	1	x	17.93	=	£17.93
	Total hourly cost of gang				**=**	**£48.95**
L A0140ICE	**Steel fixing Labour Gang**					
	Craftsman WRA	2	x	16.68	=	£33.37
	Labourer (General Operative)	1	x	12.56	=	£12.56
	Total hourly cost of gang				**=**	**£45.93**
L A0150ICE	**Provision of concrete Labour Gang**					
	Labourer (Skill Rate 3)	1	x	14.34	=	£14.34
	Labourer (General Operative)	1	x	12.56	=	£12.56
	Banksman	0.5	x	13.53	=	£6.77
	Total hourly cost of gang				**=**	**£33.67**
L A0155ICE	**Placing of concrete Labour Gang**					
	Labourer (Skill Rate 3)	1	x	14.34	=	£14.34
	Labourer (General Operative)	4	x	12.56	=	£50.24
	Banksman	0.25	x	13.53	=	£3.38
	Ganger	1	x	16.99	=	£16.99
	Craftsman WRA	0.5	x	16.68	=	£8.34
	Total hourly cost of gang				**=**	**£93.29**
L A0184ICE	**Small bore pipes in shallow trenches Labour Gang**					
	Banksman	1	x	13.53	=	£13.53
	Ganger	1	x	16.99	=	£16.99
	Pipelayer (standard rate)	1	x	14.34	=	£14.34
	Labourer (General Operative)	5	x	12.56	=	£62.80
	Total hourly cost of gang				**=**	**£107.66**
L A0300ICE	**Brickwork Labour Gang**					
	Bricklayer (chargehand)	1	x	17.93	=	£17.93
	Bricklayer	4	x	16.68	=	£66.73
	Labourer (General Operative)	2	x	12.56	=	£25.12
	Total hourly cost of gang				**=**	**£109.78**
L A0310ICE	**Painting Labour Gang**					
	Painter (chargehand)	1	x	17.93	=	£17.93
	Painter	2	x	16.68	=	£33.37
	Brush hand (labourer)	1	x	12.56	=	£12.56
	Total hourly cost of gang				**=**	**£63.86**
L A0330ICE	**Clearance Labour Gang**					

	Ganger	1	x	16.99	=	£16.99
	Labourer (General Operative)	2	x	12.56	=	£25.12
	Total hourly cost of gang				**=**	**£42.11**
L K0200ICE	**Manholes Labour Gang**					
	Ganger	1	x	16.99	=	£16.99
	Labourer (General Operative)	3	x	12.56	=	£37.68
	Craftsman WRA	1	x	16.68	=	£16.68
	Total hourly cost of gang				**=**	**£71.35**
L Z0100ICE	**Concrete Drilling Labour Gang**					
	Labourer (General Operative)	1	x	12.56	=	£12.56
	Labourer (Skill Rate 3)	2	x	14.34	=	£28.68
	Total hourly cost of gang				**=**	**£41.24**
L S2070ICE	**Brickwork cleaning Labour Gang**					
	Labourer (General Operative)	1	x	12.56	=	£12.56
	Labourer (Skill Rate 3)	2	x	14.34	=	£28.68
	Total hourly cost of gang				**=**	**£41.24**

Plant

P A1040ICE	**Formwork (make) Plant Gang**					
	Saw Bench - 24 inch Diesel / Electric	1	x	1.89	=	£1.89
	Kango Type Tool - Electric Power Woodauger	1	x	0.57	=	£0.57
	Kango Type Tool - Electric Nut Runner	1	x	0.48	=	£0.48
	Total hourly cost of gang				**=**	**£2.94**
P A1035ICE	**Formwork (fix and strike) Plant Gang**					
	Kango Type Tool - Electric Power Woodauger	1	x	0.57	=	£0.57
	Kango Type Tool - Electric Nut Runner	1	x	0.48	=	£0.48
	Cranes Crawler - NCK 305B - 20t	0.25	x	45.36	=	£11.34
	Total hourly cost of gang				**=**	**£12.39**
P A1124ICE	**General excavation Plant Gang**					
	Hydraulic Excavator - Cat 166kW	1	x	41.41	=	£41.41
	Crawler Tractor / Dozer - Cat D6 LGP 160 Hp	0.5	x	48.61	=	£24.30
	Total hourly cost of gang				**=**	**£65.71**
P A1125ICE	**Trimming Plant Gang / preparation Plant Gang / spread and level Plant Gang**					
	Crawler Tractor / Dozer - Cat 16H Grader	0.34	x	82.10	=	£27.92
	Hydraulic Excavator - Cat 320 96kW	0.34	x	33.98	=	£11.55
	Crawler Tractor / Dozer - Cat D6 LGP 160 Hp	0.34	x	48.61	=	£16.53
	Total hourly cost of gang				**=**	**£56.00**
P A1126ICE	**General spoil haulage Plant Gang**					
	Dumper Truck - Volvo A25C 25t 6x6	3	x	56.35	=	£169.04
	Total hourly cost of gang				**=**	**£169.04**
P A1127ICE	**General compaction Plant Gang**					
	Roller - Bomag 90 900mm	1	x	3.27	=	£3.27
	Crawler Tractor / Dozer - Dresser 1004 48kW	1	x	28.68	=	£28.68
	Total hourly cost of gang				**=**	**£31.95**
P A1140ICE	**Steel fixing Plant Gang**					
	Cranes Crawlers - NCK 305C 19t	0.25	x	43.26	=	£10.81
	Total hourly cost of gang				**=**	**£10.81**
P A1330ICE	**Clearance Plant Gang**					

	Crawler Tractor / Dozer - Dresser 1004 48kW	1	x	28.68	=	£28.68
	Tipping Waggon - 16t 6-Wheel (24t Gr)	1	x	47.97	=	£47.97
	Compressor - 2-Tool (Complete)	1	x	4.86	=	£4.86
	Rock Drill	3	x	0.89	=	£2.66
	Total hourly cost of gang				**=**	**£84.17**
P A1331ICE	**Demolition Plant Gang**					
	Crawler Tractor / Dozer - Dresser 1004 48kW	1	x	28.68	=	£28.68
	Tipping Waggon - 16t 6-Wheel (24t Gr)	1	x	47.97	=	£47.97
	Compressor - 2-Tool (Complete)	1	x	4.86	=	£4.86
	Rock Drill	3	x	0.89	=	£2.66
	Cutting and Burning Gear	1	x	3.52	=	£3.52
	Hydraulic Excavator - Cat 320 96kW	1	x	33.98	=	£33.98
	Total hourly cost of gang				**=**	**£121.67**
P K1200ICE	**Precast concrete manholes (shallow) Plant Gang**					
	Hydraulic Excavator - Cat 320 96kW	1	x	33.98	=	£33.98
	Pump - Godwin ET50 23m3/h 4 inches	1	x	2.74	=	£2.74
	Wheeled Tractor / Grader - Ford 3190H	1	x	23.52	=	£23.52
	Trailer - Massey Tipping	1	x	1.69	=	£1.69
	Dumper - 1.50t 2WD	1	x	2.75	=	£2.75
	Trench Sheets	72	x	0.08	=	£5.72
	Acrow Props	50	x	0.08	=	£3.97
	Concrete Mixer - 4/3 Petrol	1	x	2.04	=	£2.04
	Total hourly cost of gang				**=**	**£76.41**
P Z0200ICE	**Concrete drilling Plant Gang**					
	Kango Type Tool - Electric Power Drill 19mm	1	x	1.04	=	£1.04
	Total hourly cost of gang				**=**	**£1.04**
P Z0202ICE	**Compressor Plant Gang**					
	Compressor - 480 cfm	1	x	18.85	=	£18.85
	Total hourly cost of gang				**=**	**£18.85**

Class ZZ - Alterations

ZZ1 Alterations to Existing Works

Note(s): 1) The rates in this section are for alteration works to an existing plant where the value of the alteration works is in the order of £250,000 to £500,000.

2) The rates in this section assume open and unrestricted access for the movement of labour and plant.

3) No costs have been included for the cost of disruption and loss of production that may occur to existing plant.

4) No costs have been included in the disposal rates due to the wide variatio in prices from tip to tip.

5) Landfill Tax has not been included in the disposal rates as this is dependent on the nature of the material and statutory adjustment.

		Unit	Labour Hours	Labour Net £	Plant Net £	Materials Net £	Unit Net £	CO_2 Kg
ZZ1.1	**Buildings and other structures**							
ZZ1.1.1	Diamond drilling to reinforced concrete walls							
ZZ1.1.1.01	125mm diameter holes 500mm deep	Nr	1.00	41.24	1.04	-	**42.28**	*0.69*
ZZ1.1.1.02	125mm diameter holes 750mm deep	Nr	1.25	51.55	1.30	-	**52.85**	*0.86*
ZZ1.1.1.03	200mm diameter holes 500mm deep	Nr	3.00	123.72	3.12	-	**126.84**	*2.07*
ZZ1.1.2	Forming holes in brickwork walls including making good to all edges and installation of lintel size 1.0 x 1.0m							
ZZ1.1.2.01	Thickness: 102.5mm	Nr	1.00	109.79	-	-	**109.79**	-
ZZ1.1.2.02	Thickness: 215mm	Nr	1.00	109.79	-	-	**109.79**	-
ZZ1.1.2.03	Thickness: 265mm cavity wall	Nr	2.00	219.58	-	-	**219.58**	-
ZZ1.2	**Pipelines and other services**							
ZZ1.2.1	Alterations to existing manholes							
ZZ1.2.1.01	Raising manhole cover 150mm high internal size of manhole 900 x 675mm with fair faced engineering bricks class B 215mm thick in cement mortar 1:3	Nr	4.80	342.48	366.80	25.46	**734.76**	*248.87*
ZZ1.2.1.02	Raising manhole cover 300mm high internal size of manhole 900 x 675mm with fair faced engineering bricks class B 215mm thick in cement mortar 1:3	Nr	7.20	513.72	550.22	51.19	**1,115.13**	*433.04*
ZZ1.2.1.03	Forming new 100mm diameter vitrified clay branch (including alteration of benching)	Nr	0.40	28.54	30.57	47.85	**106.96**	*12.61*
ZZ1.2.1.04	Take up and remove manhole cover and install new cover and frame 600 x 450mm grade B single seal cast iron	Nr	0.40	28.54	30.57	127.61	**186.72**	*131.36*
ZZ1.2.1.06	Filling in redundant manhole internal size 900 x 675mm 1m deep with granular sub base DTp type 1	Nr	1.00	71.35	76.42	14.25	**162.02**	*32.57*
ZZ1.3	**Blocking up openings**							
ZZ1.3.1	Blocking up openings in brick walls with common bricks in cement mortar 1:3 fair face both sides including cut tooth and bond into existing brickwork							
ZZ1.3.1.01	102.5mm thick in stretcher bond	m^2	0.85	93.32	-	15.42	**108.74**	*97.04*

ZZ1 Alterations to Existing Works continued...

		Unit	Labour Hours	Labour Net £	Plant Net £	Materials Net £	Unit Net £	CO_2 Kg
ZZ1.3	**Blocking up openings**							
ZZ1.3.1	Blocking up openings in brick walls with common bricks in cement mortar 1:3 fair face both sides including cut tooth and bond into existing brickwork							
ZZ1.3.1.02	215mm thick in English bond	m^2	1.45	159.20	-	30.84	190.04	*194.07*
ZZ1.3.1.03	265mm thick in two 102.5mm stretcher bond including 50mm cavity	m^2	1.80	197.62	-	30.84	228.46	*194.07*

ZZ2 Repairs and Renovation

		Unit	Labour Hours	Labour Net £	Plant Net £	Materials Net £	Unit Net £	CO_2 Kg
ZZ2.1	**Buildings and other structures**							
ZZ2.1.1	Pressure cleaning brickwork, masonry or concrete surfaces to receive treatment							
ZZ2.1.1.01	Vertical	m^2	0.15	6.19	2.83	-	9.02	*3.51*
ZZ2.1.1.02	Horizontal (Bases)	m^2	0.15	6.19	2.83	-	9.02	*3.51*
ZZ2.1.1.03	Horizontal (Soffits)	m^2	0.20	8.25	3.77	-	12.02	*4.67*
ZZ2.1.2	Scabble concrete surfaces 12mm deep to receive treatment, new works or repair (new works or repair measure separately)							
ZZ2.1.2.01	Vertical	m^2	0.71	29.28	19.79	5.78	54.85	*24.81*
ZZ2.1.2.02	Horizontal (Bases)	m^2	0.52	21.44	14.51	-	35.95	*17.99*
ZZ2.1.2.03	Horizontal (Soffits)	m^2	1.00	41.24	26.39	-	67.63	*32.72*
ZZ2.1.3	Cut out cracks in concrete not exceeding 25 x 50mm and fill with approved polymer cement repair mortar							
ZZ2.1.3.01	Vertical	m	0.35	14.43	-	6.13	20.56	*0.29*
ZZ2.1.3.02	Horizontal (Bases)	m	0.31	12.78	-	6.13	18.91	*0.29*
ZZ2.1.3.03	Horizontal (Soffits)	m	0.45	18.56	-	6.13	24.69	*0.29*
ZZ2.1.4	Cut out half brick thick spalled brickwork and replace with common bricks in cement mortar 1:3							
ZZ2.1.4.01	Vertical	m^2	1.80	197.62	-	15.42	213.04	*97.04*
ZZ2.1.4.02	Horizontal	m^2	2.80	307.41	-	15.42	322.83	*97.04*
ZZ2.1.5	Rake out brickwork joints to a minimum depth of 25mm and point with cement mortar 1:3 flush							
ZZ2.1.5.01	Vertical	m^2	1.50	164.69	-	0.48	165.17	*2.81*
ZZ2.1.5.02	Horizontal	m^2	0.35	38.43	-	0.48	38.91	*2.81*
ZZ2.2	**Pipelines and other services**							
ZZ2.2.1	Dry grit blast (lead free) corroded pipework							
ZZ2.2.1.01	300mm diameter	m	0.75	21.51	14.14	-	35.65	*17.53*
ZZ2.2.1.02	450mm diameter	m	1.13	32.41	21.30	-	53.71	*26.41*
ZZ2.2.1.03	750mm diameter	m	1.88	53.92	35.44	-	89.36	*43.94*
ZZ2.2.1.04	1000mm diameter	m	2.44	69.98	45.99	-	115.97	*57.02*
ZZ2.2.2	Bituminous heavy duty paint in two coats to pipework							
ZZ2.2.2.01	300mm diameter	m	0.27	17.24	-	4.07	21.31	*3.56*
ZZ2.2.2.02	450mm diameter	m	0.41	26.18	-	6.11	32.29	*5.34*
ZZ2.2.2.03	750mm diameter	m	0.68	43.42	-	10.18	53.60	*8.90*
ZZ2.2.2.04	1000mm diameter	m	0.88	56.20	-	13.23	69.43	*11.57*

ZZ3 Miscellaneous Earthworks

		Unit	Labour Hours	Labour Net £	Plant Net £	Materials Net £	Unit Net £	CO_2 Kg
ZZ3.1	**Excavation**							
ZZ3.1.1	Excavation for foundations							
ZZ3.1.1.01	Topsoil maximum depth: not exceeding 250mm	m^3	0.03	1.46	2.23	-	3.69	*1.24*

ZZ3 Miscellaneous Earthworks continued...

		Unit	Labour Hours	Labour Net £	Plant Net £	Materials Net £	Unit Net £	CO_2 Kg
ZZ3.2	**Material other than topsoil, rock or artificial hard material**							
ZZ3.2.1	Maximum depth							
ZZ3.2.1.01	not exceeding 250mm	m^3	0.04	1.90	2.89	-	4.79	*1.61*
ZZ3.2.1.02	250 - 500mm	m^3	0.05	2.15	3.29	-	5.44	*1.83*
ZZ3.2.1.03	500mm - 1m	m^3	0.05	2.28	3.48	-	5.76	*1.94*
ZZ3.3	**Disposal of excavated material**							
ZZ3.3.1	Generally							
ZZ3.3.1.01	Topsoil off site (transporting to skip distance not exceeding 5km)	m^3	0.06	2.58	10.14	-	12.72	*6.80*
ZZ3.3.1.02	Topsoil on site (adjacent to excavation)	m^3	0.02	0.65	2.54	-	3.19	*1.70*
ZZ3.3.1.03	Material other than topsoil, rock or artificial hard material off site (transporting to tip distance not exceeding 5km)	m^3	0.06	2.58	10.14	-	12.72	*6.80*
ZZ3.3.1.04	Material other than topsoil, rock or artificial hard material off site (adjacent to excavation)	m^3	0.03	1.29	5.07	-	6.36	*3.40*
ZZ3.4	**Filling**							
ZZ3.4.1	Generally							
ZZ3.4.1.01	Excavated topsoil	m^3	0.01	0.47	0.62	-	1.09	*0.47*
ZZ3.4.1.02	Excavated material other than topsoil or rock	m^3	0.03	1.42	1.67	-	3.09	*0.83*
ZZ3.4.1.03	Imported material other than topsoil of rock	m^3	0.02	1.03	3.24	14.43	18.70	*35.56*
ZZ3.4.1.04	Imported DTp type 1	m^2	0.01	0.47	1.67	22.80	24.94	*8.83*
ZZ3.4.1.05	Grass seeding n.e. 10°	m^2	0.00	0.11	-	2.50	2.61	-
ZZ3.4.1.06	Grass seeding 10° - 45°	m^2	0.00	0.11	-	2.50	2.61	-

ZZ4 Miscellaneous Concrete Works

		Unit	Labour Hours	Labour Net £	Plant Net £	Materials Net £	Unit Net £	CO_2 Kg
ZZ4.1	**In situ concrete**							
ZZ4.1.1	Generally							
ZZ4.1.1.01	Provide Grade 20 (10mm aggregate)	m^3	-	-	-	91.37	91.37	*312.00*
ZZ4.1.1.02	Provide Grade 30 (20mm aggregate)	m^3	-	-	-	94.92	94.92	*312.00*
ZZ4.1.1.03	Place blinding concrete 80mm thick	m^3	0.55	35.17	-	-	35.17	-
ZZ4.1.1.04	Place reinforced ground slabs 150 - 300mm thick	m^3	0.67	42.40	-	-	42.40	-
ZZ4.1.1.05	Place reinforced ground slabs 300 - 500mm thick	m^3	0.62	39.10	-	-	39.10	-
ZZ4.1.1.06	Place reinforced walls 150 - 300mm thick	m^3	0.73	46.21	-	-	46.21	-
ZZ4.1.1.07	Place reinforced walls 300 - 500mm thick	m^3	0.61	38.59	-	-	38.59	-
ZZ4.2	**Formwork**							
ZZ4.2.1	Fair finish							
ZZ4.2.1.01	Fair finish: vertical 0.2 - 0.4m	m^2	0.76	37.21	4.66	5.21	47.08	*2.27*
ZZ4.2.1.02	Fair finish: vertical 0.4 - 1.22m	m^2	1.16	56.79	7.16	6.24	70.19	*2.96*
ZZ4.2.1.03	Fair finish: vertical exc. 1.22m	m^2	1.52	74.42	9.50	10.42	94.34	*4.56*

ZZ4 Miscellaneous Concrete Works continued...

		Unit	Labour Hours	Labour Net £	Plant Net £	Materials Net £	Unit Net £	CO_2 Kg
ZZ4.2	**Formwork**							
ZZ4.2.1	Fair finish							
ZZ4.2.1.04	Fair worked finish: vertical 0.2 - 0.4m	m^2	0.76	37.21	4.66	9.32	**51.19**	*3.50*
ZZ4.2.1.05	Fair worked finish: vertical 0.4 - 1.22m	m^2	1.16	56.79	7.16	11.21	**75.16**	*4.45*
ZZ4.2.1.06	Fair worked finish: vertical exc. 1.22m	m^2	1.52	74.42	9.50	18.79	**102.71**	*7.07*
ZZ4.3	**Reinforcement**							
ZZ4.3.1	Fair finish							
ZZ4.3.1.01	High yield steel reinforcement 12mm diameter	Tonne	16.00	734.88	172.96	648.27	**1,556.11**	*1,741.30*
ZZ4.3.1.02	High yield steel reinforcement 16mm diameter	Tonne	14.00	643.02	151.34	612.65	**1,407.01**	*1,737.38*
ZZ4.3.1.03	Mesh reinforcement: A193	m^2	0.10	4.78	-	1.98	**6.76**	*7.58*
ZZ4.3.1.04	Mesh reinforcement: C385	m^2	0.15	6.89	-	2.23	**9.12**	*8.56*
ZZ4.3.1.05	Mesh reinforcement: A393	m^2	0.20	9.19	2.16	4.00	**15.35**	*15.85*

ZZ5 Site clearance

		Unit	Labour Hours	Labour Net £	Plant Net £	Materials Net £	Unit Net £	CO_2 Kg
ZZ5.1	**Clearance of trees (including stumps) and backfilling void with suitable material**							
ZZ5.1.1	Girth							
ZZ5.1.1.01	100mm - 500mm	Nr	0.50	21.06	42.09	-	**63.15**	*27.44*
ZZ5.1.1.02	1m - 2m	Nr	1.00	42.11	84.17	-	**126.28**	*54.88*
ZZ5.1.1.03	500mm - 1m	Nr	1.25	52.64	105.21	-	**157.85**	*68.59*
ZZ5.2	**Demolition of buildings and other structures**							
ZZ5.2.1	Demolition brick building to ground slab level and dispose of material off site							
ZZ5.2.1.01	Volume: not exceeding 100m3	Nr	6.60	277.93	803.02	-	**1,080.95**	*459.10*
ZZ5.2.1.02	100 - 250m3	Nr	10.50	442.15	1,277.54	-	**1,719.69**	*730.39*
ZZ5.2.1.03	250 - 500m3	Nr	12.25	515.85	1,490.46	-	**2,006.31**	*852.12*
ZZ5.2.1.04	500 - 1000m3	Nr	18.50	779.03	2,250.90	-	**3,029.93**	*1,286.88*
ZZ5.2.2	Demolition steel framed building with sheet cladding and dispose of material off site (including credit for scrap steel)							
ZZ5.2.2.01	Volume: not exceeding 100m3	Nr	7.75	326.35	942.94	-	**1,269.29**	*539.10*
ZZ5.2.2.02	100 - 250m3	Nr	12.25	515.85	1,490.46	-	**2,006.31**	*852.12*
ZZ5.2.2.03	250 - 500m3	Nr	15.00	631.65	1,825.05	-	**2,456.70**	*1,043.42*
ZZ5.2.2.04	500 - 1000m3	Nr	23.00	968.53	2,798.41	-	**3,766.94**	*1,599.90*
ZZ5.2.3	Demolish walls to foundation level and dispose off site							
ZZ5.2.3.01	Reinforced concrete wall, thickness: 150 - 300mm	m^2	2.00	84.22	168.34	-	**252.56**	*109.75*
ZZ5.2.3.02	Brick wall, thickness 225mm	m^2	0.50	21.06	42.09	-	**63.15**	*27.44*
ZZ5.2.4	Take down fencing (including grubbing up foundations) and dispose off site							
ZZ5.2.4.01	Chestnut pale fencing 1200mm high (with posts)	m	0.25	10.53	-	-	**10.53**	-
ZZ5.2.4.02	Chain link fencing 1800mm high (with posts)	m	0.50	21.06	-	-	**21.06**	-
ZZ5.3	**Removal and grouting of services**							
ZZ5.3.1	Removal of redundant services							
ZZ5.3.1.01	Clay sewer or drain, diameter 100mm	m	1.00	28.68	-	-	**28.68**	-

ZZ5 Site clearance continued...

		Unit	Labour Hours	Labour Net £	Plant Net £	Materials Net £	Unit Net £	CO_2 Kg
ZZ5.3	**Removal and grouting of services**							
ZZ5.3.1	Removal of redundant services							
ZZ5.3.1.02	Ductile iron sewer or drain, diameter: 300mm	m	1.50	43.02	-	-	**43.02**	-
ZZ5.3.2	Grouting redundant drains or sewers							
ZZ5.3.2.01	Clay sewer or drain, diameter 100mm	m	1.00	107.66	-	0.86	**108.52**	*3.16*
ZZ5.3.2.02	Ductile iron sewer or drain, diameter: 300mm	m	1.75	188.41	-	7.49	**195.90**	*27.41*

SECTION 2:
APPROXIMATE ESTIMATING

SECTION 2: APPROXIMATE ESTIMATING

The prices contained in this section are intended to assist in the preparation of estimates for work where an outline design has been formulated and for comparative pricing of various alternative design proposals.

Prices are based on the same sources of information used in the 'Unit Pricing' section. The prices do not include for any Preliminary type items nor for any incidental items of mechanical plant or equipment but do include normal services. Suitable percentage additions should be made to cover these and General Items. The latter is commonly covered by 15% of the measured work.

Costing by individual unit can be found in the 'Unit Pricing' section.

		Amount £	Unit
	EARTHWORKS		
	Excavation		
	General excavation in a large pit or into a large embankment with no restriction of movement of the machine or wagons; in moderately hard illy sandy clay ground conditions.		
a)	Plant; 2m^3 hydraulic face shovel excavator; rear dump wagons; D6 tractor and blade	3.40	m^3
b)	add for disposal on site not exceeding 100m	2.67	m^3
c)	add for disposal off-site distance not exceeding 15km	13.43	m^3
	Excavating foundations; not exceeding 500m^3; in moderately hard dry sandy clay ground conditions		
d)	Plant; 2m^3 hydraulic face shovel excavator; rear dump wagons; D6 tractor and blade	4.61	m^3
e)	add for disposal on site not exceeding 100m	2.67	m^3
f)	add for disposal off-site distance not exceeding 15km	13.43	m^3
	Trunk road cutting; in moderately hard dry sandy clay ground conditions; material deposited on site within 1km		
g)	Plant; 2m motorised scrapers; pusher tractor; blade tractor and grader	2.97	m^3
	Filling and compacting excavated material on site		
	General excavation; deposited in layers and compacted in open areas		
h)	Plant; 0.5m^3 hydraulic excavator; tractor with blade; compactor; grader	2.66	m^3
	Trunk road embankment; deposited in layers and compacted in open areas		
i)	Plant; tractor with blade; compactor; grader	0.97	m^3
	CONCRETE STRUCTURES		
	Concrete including blinding, mass and reinforced concrete used in a typical civil engineering structure such as tanks and biological filters including miscellaneous metal work and related pipework but not mechanical and electrical plant and equipment.		
a)	Biological filters; per cubic metre of filter media		
	20,000 - 30,000 m^3	76.42	m^3
	10,000 -20,000 m^3	101.56	m^3
	2,000 -10,000 m^3	119.80	m^3
	Less than 2,000 m^3	139.77	m^3
b)	Humus tanks; per cubic metre of capacity		
	1,500 m3 and above	172.55	m^3
	500 -1,500 m^3	207.06	m^3
	Less than 500 m^3	463.42	m^3

		Amount £	Unit
Bridges			
c)	Reinforced in situ concrete; per square metre of deck area	1,331.10	m^2
d)	Reinforced in situ deck with precast prestressed beams; per square metre of deck area	1,257.15	m^2
e)	Reinforced in situ deck; with steel beams; per square metre of deck area	1,168.41	m^2

OTHER STRUCTURES

Conventional single storey brick and block structure including earthworks, foundations, normal services, fixtures and fittings but excluding mechanical and electrical work.

Expressed as price per square metre of floor area measured between external walls and over internal walls.

		Amount £	Unit
f)	Pumping Station including sump pump	1,510 - 2315	m^2
g)	Administration building Typical water or sewage treatment works portal frame with cladding superstructure including earthworks, concrete and associated pipework, excluding mechanical and electrical work	1,340 - 1640	m^2
h)	Inlet building	1,195 - 1780	m^2

DAMS

Typical mass concrete gravity dam; overall length 200x40m high; consisting of abutment blocks, main embankment and central intake block, single carriage. Crest roadway comprising precast concrete beams, parapets, insitu deck and piers, excluding external works, approach roads and Hydro electric works.

	Amount £	Unit
Ground stabilization	1,212,000	
Concrete	4,890,560	
Formwork	1,168,830	
Reinforcement	403,200	
Precast concrete	452,725	
Metalwork	149,526	
Brickwork	200,070	
Miscellaneous	212,100	
	8,689,011	
Contingencies @ 10%	868,901	
	9,557,912	
Volume of concrete 54,000m³: cost per cubic metre	**£177**	per m^3

ROADWORKS

Road Construction Excluding Earthworks and Structures

Trunk road pavement construction; alternative combinations in accordance with DTp specification for Road and Bridge Works assumes three lane dual carriageway road 4km in length with hard shoulders total width 33m. Prices derived from information supplied by specialist subcontractors.

		Amount £	Unit
a)	Hot rolled asphalt Rolled asphalt - 911 40 Wearing course Rolled asphalt - 905 60 Base course	8.27	m^2
	Rolled asphalt - 904 205 Road base	25.82	m^2
	Granular subbase material 803 150 Sub base +804 +805	6.16	m^2
	TOTAL	£40.25	m^2

Road Construction Excluding Earthworks and Structures continued/...

		Amount £	Unit
b)	**Dense Bitumen macadam**		
	Rolled asphalt - 911 40 Wearing course		
	Rolled asphalt - 906 60 Base course	7.59	m^2
	Rolled asphalt - 903 205 Road base	28.88	m^2
	Granular subbase		
	material 803 150 Sub base	6.16	m^2
	804		
	805		
	TOTAL	£42.63	m^2
c)	**Lean mix concrete**		
	Rolled asphalt - 911 40 Wearing course	8.11	m^2
	Dense Bitumen - 906 60 Base course		
	Dense Bitumen - 906 100 Base course	12.04	m^2
	Lean Concrete - 1030 210 Road base	17.03	m^2
	Granular subbase material 803 150 Sub base	6.16	m^2
	TOTAL	£43.34	m^2
d)	**Rigid pavement**		
	Concrete pavement - 1000 280	39.14	m^2
	Granular subbase material - 803 170 Sub base	6.97	m^2
	TOTAL	£46.11	m^2
e)	**Typical Trunk Road costs; 4km in length and 33m wide**		
	Average cost of pavement:	£44.00	per m^2
	Total width of pavement: 33m, therefore cost per metre run of pavement	1,451.70	
	Site clearance, soiling, seeding and hedging	25.25	
	Lighting and telephones	46.46	
	Fencing including safety barriers	112.85	
	Signs and marking	28.28	
	Associated drainage	329.26	
	PC kerbs and channels	22.89	
		2,016.69	
	Earthworks (assume value of £2,800,000)	700.00	
		2,716.69	
	Contingencies @10%	271.67	
	Cost of Trunk Road per m run (excluding structures and profits and overheads)	**£2,988.36**	**per m**

BRIDGES

		Amount £	Unit
a)	Typical single span road bridge with two abutments carrying dual carriageway trunk road over two track rail line comprising precast concrete beams and in situ deck; excluding excavation and piling		
	Formwork	161,109	
	Steel reinforcement	162,960	
	In situ concrete	259,318	
	Precast concrete	224,870	
	Bearings	35,693	
	Joints	18,180	
	Parapets	35,820	
	Finishings	3,012	
	Waterproofing	61,306	
		962,268	
	Contingencies @10%	96,227	
		1,058,495	
	Deck area of bridge 928 m2: cost per square metre	**£1,141**	**per m**

Bridges continued/...

b) Single span railway bridge with two abutments carrying two track main line trains and sidings over a proposed new road including partially constructing abutments beneath existing bridge with demolition of existing bridge and slide/roll of superstructure deck during weekend possession; excluding excavation and piling

Demolition	27,608	
Formwork	56,862	
Steel reinforcement	73,080	
In situ concrete	120,292	
Structural steel deck	246,440	
Brickwork	69,768	
Waterproofing	19,026	
Miscellaneous	63,630	
Slide/roll operation	97,970	
	774,676	
Contingencies @ 10%	77,468	
	852,144	
Deck area of bridge = 332 m²: cost per square metre	**£2,567**	per m²

PIPEWORK

The tables shown on the following pages indicate approximate guide prices for the constituent elements for pipework.

Access for delivery of large quantities of materials will probably warrant the construction of a temporary access road at an approximate cost of £33 per metre run. Smaller quantities will warrant an appropriate gang to deliver the materials along the line.

UNDERGROUND CHAMBERS

1 Precast Concrete Manholes

Excavation and backfilling in natural material; in situ concrete grade 20 in 300mm base; 300mm diameter half round channel: 300/l50mm branch junction channel; 150mm half round bend channel; cement mortar benching (1:3); precast concrete manhole rings, taper section and cover slab to BS 5911 150mm in situ concrete grade 20/20 surround to rings and taper section, 600mm diameter heavy duty cast iron access cover and frame; galvanised malleable step irons to BS EN13101 at 305mm centres cast into side of chamber rings.

		Nominal diameter:			
		1200mm	1350mm	1500mm	Unit
		£	£	£	
a)	Depth; not exceeding 2m	1,857	2,077	2,541	nr
b)	2-3m	2,179	2,475	3,003	nr
c)	3-4m	2,629	3,053	3,622	nr
d)	4-5m	3,128	3,637	4,219	nr

2 Shafts

Vertical shafts formed out of precast concrete segmental bolted rings, including excavating in sand, silts and clays, disposal off site, reinstatement of ground, benching, landings, reducing slabs, ladders, handrails, flooring, chains and cover.

		Amount £	Unit
	Depth 4 -8m		
a)	Internal diameter: 2.74m	5,808	m
b)	Internal diameter: 3.97m	8,646	m

PIPEWORK

Supply and installation (including earthworks and 10% allowance for fittings)

	300mm £	375mm £	450mm £	600mm £	750mm £	900mm £	1200mm £	UNIT
a) Vitrified clay pipes, BS 65, spigot and socket flexible joints								
Depth: not exceeding 1.5m	85.55	152.74	233.13	-	-	-	-	m
1.5-2m	87.31	154.61	240.65	-	-	-	-	m
2-3m	95.77	167.98	249.68	-	-	-	-	m
3-4m	140.01	217.86	308.37	-	-	-	-	m
4-5m	225.50	308.59	398.15	-	-	-	-	m
b) Ductile spun iron pipes; concrete lined, BS EN598, spigot and socket Tyton joints								
Depth: not exceeding 1.5m	114.92	-	184.98	-	-	-	-	m
1.5-2m	116.89	-	189.52	276.60	-	-	-	m
2-3m	123.81	-	195.92	284.78	-	-	-	m
3-4m	147.08	-	222.72	317.12	-	-	-	m
4-5m	182.75	-	260.41	349.91	-	-	-	m
c) UPVC pipes; BS EN1452 and BS 3506; compression joints with rubber rings								
Depth: not exceeding 1.5m	173.13	-	-	-	-	-	-	m
1.5-2m	177.16	-	-	-	-	-	-	m
2-3m	184.20	-	-	-	-	-	-	m
3-4m	210.00	-	-	-	-	-	-	m
4-5m	260.16	-	-	-	-	-	-	m

Supply and installation (including earthworks and 10% allowance for fittings)

	74mm £	102mm £	131mm £	204mm £	258mm £	290mm £	327mm £	UNIT
d) Blue MDPE (SDR 11) pipe to WIS 4-32-03 butt welded joints								
Depth: not exceeding 1.5m	20.82	28.34	37.44	44.51	66.76	93.39	113.60	m
1.5-2m	23.38	33.48	45.15	49.44	71.90	98.54	116.17	m
2-3m	33.68	43.77	52.87	57.37	80.91	107.54	127.74	m
3-4m	49.08	60.76	72.33	78.52	104.91	134.01	155.01	m
4-5m	69.26	87.66	107.63	112.93	151.99	192.86	220.58	m

Supply and installation (including earthworks and 10% allowance for fittings)

	300mm £	375mm £	450mm £	600mm £	750mm £	900mm £	1200mm £	UNIT
Concrete pipes; BS 5911; rebated flexible joints with mastic sealant to internal faces								
e) Class 120								
Depth: not exceeding 1.5m	-	49.67	56.41	-	-	-	-	m
1.5-2m	-	53.99	61.68	78.80	115.38	146.55	192.23	m
2-3m	-	60.11	69.48	87.07	122.25	154.82	206.40	m
3-4m	-	85.68	100.36	119.59	155.35	191.70	254.40	m
4-5m	-	121.68	131.61	159.63	190.14	231.76	304.06	m

PIPEWORK continued/...

	300mm £	375mm £	450mm £	600mm £	750mm £	900mm £	1200mm £	UNIT
Trench Support								
f) Depth: 1.5-2m	63.87	63.87	63.87	63.87	63.87	63.87	63.87	m
g) 2-3m	94.64	94.64	94.64	94.64	94.64	94.64	94.64	m
h) 3-4m	121.07	121.07	121.07	121.07	121.07	121.07	121.07	m
i) 4-5m	156.19	156.19	156.19	156.19	156.19	156.19	156.19	m

Excavation Through Obstructions

	300mm £	375mm £	450mm £	600mm £	750mm £	900mm £	1200mm £	UNIT
j) Extra for breaking through rock (say 0.5m depth of rock in trench)	26.04	28.49	30.92	35.81	40.69	45.58	63.47	m

Beds, Haunches and Surrounds

	300mm £	375mm £	450mm £	600mm £	750mm £	900mm £	1200mm £	UNIT
k) Sand; thickness 150mm								
Bed	9.98	11.22	12.15	14.67	16.81	18.50	23.45	m
Surround (incl bed)	25.83	29.53	32.71	39.86	47.09	55.01	81.10	m
l) Selected excavated granular material; thickness 150mm								
Bed	9.29	10.77	11.75	14.69	17.13	18.61	22.03	m
Surround (incl bed)	20.46	22.99	24.47	27.89	31.80	36.22	41.11	m
m) Imported granular material; thickness 150mm								
Bed	9.42	10.64	11.47	13.51	15.96	17.54	22.11	m
Surround (incl bed)	23.98	27.43	30.17	36.60	43.21	50.27	72.88	m
n) Mass concrete; grade 15, 20mm aggregate; thickness 150mm								
Bed	19.54	21.70	23.74	28.35	32.54	36.16	46.73	m
Haunches (incl bed)	31.29	37.85	44.78	62.11	90.70	119.70	160.33	m
Surround (incl bed)	53.01	63.16	72.78	92.08	122.94	152.81	238.44	m
o) Reinforced concrete; grade 25, 20mm aggregate; 1 layer A252 mesh reinforcement; thickness 150mm								
Bed	24.19	26.58	29.37	34.93	39.40	44.23	58.11	m
Haunches (incl bed)	36.43	43.65	51.40	70.67	100.71	131.80	177.54	m
Surround (incl bed)	59.97	70.91	81.75	103.15	135.62	167.68	262.18	m

PIPEWORK continued/...

Reinstatement

Breaking up and temporary reinstatement of roads

	300mm £	375mm £	450mm £	600mm £	750mm £	900mm £	1200mm £	UNIT
p) Break up 150mm flexible pavement and reinstate with 150mm lean mix, 40mm base course and 10mm wearing course; in bituminous macadam	54.48	-	-	65.46	-	78.28	91.91	m
q) Break up 325mm flexible pavement and reinstate with 200mm lean mix, 85mm base course and 15mm wearing course; in bituminous macadam	81.94	-	-	100.20	-	122.25	145.79	m
r) Break up 250mm rigid pavement and reinstate with 150mm. lean mix and 150mm concrete grade 20	65.99	-	-	80.81	-	99.84	120.01	m
s) Break up 300mm reinforced rigid pavement and reinstate with 200mm lean mix and 150mm concrete grade 20, reinforced (1 layer A252)	79.13	-	-	89.13	-	120.53	144.55	m

SECTION 3:

PLANT HIRE RATES AND OUTPUTS

SECTION 3: PLANT HIRE RATES AND OUTPUTS

PLANT HIRE RATES

The first part of this section details a comprehensive list of hire rates of plant, likely to be used in Civil Engineering and has been calculated on the basis of a 39 hour week.

Rates for plant hire vary considerably between hire companies depending upon many factors and readers are advised to enquire widely to obtain the most competitive rates. The rates quoted in this section have been obtained from several companies and show significant differences and the rates given will be strongly influenced by the availability of plant and by the duration of hire – longer hire periods giving rise to noticeably lower charges. Readers must allow for transporting plant to and from the site and for movement around the site as required.

Readers may wish to substitute different plant items in lieu of those detailed in the plant gang build-ups at the front of the Unit Pricing Sections. It is important to note, that the cost of plant operators has been based on the following, where applicable, which are 'average' plus rates under the W.R.A classified into 4 categories in order to simplify the wide range of plus rates for estimating purposes.

Plant Operator	Class 1	£17.34 per hour
	Class 2	£16.71 per hour
	Class 3	£15.63 per hour
	Class 4	£14.75 per hour

Fuel has been included in the total rate at the following Prime Cost sums:

Gas Oil (Red)	40.0p per litre
Diesel	120.0p per litre
Unleaded petrol	120.0p per litre

The reader can substitute current fuel costs when fine tuning the rates, to suit his own circumstances.

Fuel consumption has been based on the assumption of 75% utilization over 39 hours per week, other than the following:

Crawler cranes	= 25%
Cable excavators/bulldozer	= 85%
Mobile cranes	= 40%
Vans	= 20%
Dumpers	= 90%
Mixers, generators, pumps	= 100%
Waggons	= 112%

The second part of this section provides details of likely outputs which may be expected from commonly used Civil Engineering Plant.

Price Code	Description	Weekly Hire Charges	Consumables percent	Operator cost per hour	Fuel cost per hour	TOTAL COST PER HOUR
		£	%	£	£	£
Air Tools and Fittings						
PA0401ICE	Thor 16D/Maco SK8 Medium Duty Breaker	30.00	-	-	-	0.77
PA0402ICE	CP9 Air Breaker drill	16.50	-	-	-	0.42
PA0403ICE	CP222 Clay Digger	13.20	-	-	-	0.34
PA0404ICE	Rock Drill	34.60	-	-	-	0.89
PA0405ICE	Air Vibrating Poker up to 75mm	48.60	-	-	-	1.25
PA0406ICE	Scabbler - Single Headed Hand	35.60	-	-	-	0.91
PA0407ICE	Scabbler - Three Headed Hand	41.20	-	-	-	1.06
PA0408ICE	Scabbler - Floor - 3 Headed	96.20	-	-	-	2.47
PA0409ICE	Scabbler - Floor - 5 Headed	137.40	-	-	-	3.52
PA0410ICE	Air Pump	40.20	-	-	-	1.03
PA0411ICE	Air Hose - 3/4 inch - 15m length	5.60	-	-	-	0.14
PA0412ICE	Air Hose - 1 inch - 15m length	13.70	-	-	-	0.35
PA0413ICE	Air Hose - 1.5 inch - 15m length	19.30	-	-	-	0.49
PA0414ICE	Points and Chisels	2.00	-	-	-	0.05
PA0415ICE	Tarmac Cutters	6.90	-	-	-	0.18
PA0416ICE	Clay Spades	6.90	-	-	-	0.18
PA0417ICE	Piling Attachment	17.80	-	-	-	0.46
PA0418ICE	Vertical Rammer - 2 Stroke	60.00	-	-	-	1.54
PA0420ICE	Waggon Drill with Steel & Bits	178.60	-	-	-	4.58
PA0421ICE	Exploder with curcuit Tester	96.20	-	-	-	2.47
Bar Benders and Croppers						
PA0426ICE	Bar Bender - Manual	20.90	-	-	-	0.54
PA0427ICE	Bar Bender - Electric (to 40mm capacity)	137.40	-	-	-	3.52
PA0431ICE	Bar Croppers - Manual	20.90	-	-	-	0.54
PA0432ICE	Bar Croppers - Electric (to 40mm capacity)	137.40	-	-	-	3.52
Bowsers						
PA0441ICE	Bowsers (200 gallon water/fuel)	27.50	-	-	-	0.71
PA0442ICE	Bowsers (250 gallon water/fuel)	34.30	-	-	-	0.88
PA0443ICE	Bowsers (400 gallon water/fuel)	48.10	-	-	-	1.23
PA0444ICE	Bowsers (500 gallon water/fuel)	55.00	-	-	-	1.41
Cars and Vans						
PA1021ICE	Ford Transit 18v	151.10	-	-	4.54	8.41
PA1022ICE	Ford Escort Van 9v	123.60	-	-	3.24	6.41
PA1023ICE	Landrover 4WD	412.10	-	-	4.54	15.10
PA1024ICE	Minibus 12-seater	267.90	-	-	4.54	11.41
PA1026ICE	1300 Saloon	109.90	-	-	1.51	4.33
PA1027ICE	1500 Saloon	206.10	-	-	1.94	7.23
PA1028ICE	2000 Saloon	219.80	-	-	2.38	8.01
PA1029ICE	2000 Ghia	233.50	-	-	2.38	8.36

Price Code	Description	Weekly Hire Charges	Consumables percent	Operator cost per hour	Fuel cost per hour	TOTAL COST PER HOUR
		£	%	£	£	£
Compressors						
PA0451ICE	Compressor - Single Tool (Complete)	60.00	7.5	-	1.10	2.76
PA0452ICE	Compressor - 2 Tool (Complete)	69.20	7.5	-	2.95	4.86
PA0453ICE	Compressor - 100 cfm	74.30	7.3	-	2.30	4.35
PA0454ICE	Compressor - 180 cfm	121.10	7.5	-	3.82	7.15
PA0455ICE	Compressor - 200 cfm	181.10	7.5	-	4.31	9.30
PA0456ICE	Compressor - 250 cfm	189.30	7.5	-	5.59	10.81
PA0457ICE	Compressor - 375 cfm	250.30	7.5	-	8.05	14.95
PA0458ICE	Compressor - 480 cfm	304.20	7.5	-	10.46	18.85
PA0459ICE	Compressor - 600 to 630 cfm	380.60	7.5	-	13.10	23.59
Concrete Equipment						
PA0461ICE	Hose & Breaker 7 3 Steels	13.70	-	-	-	0.35
PA0471ICE	Power Float 900mm etrol (Blades extra)	56.00	-	-	0.53	1.97
PA0472ICE	Cement Silo 30t	68.70	-	-	-	1.76
PA0473ICE	Cement Silo 50t	96.20	-	-	-	2.47
PA0476ICE	Concrete Skip	27.50	-	-	-	0.71
Cranes Transit						
PA0481ICE	Cranes Transit - 25t	711.20	6.0	17.19	19.75	56.27
PA0482ICE	Cranes Transit - 12/15t	539.30	6.0	17.19	14.70	46.55
PA0483ICE	Cranes Transit - 10t	494.50	6.0	17.19	13.02	43.65
PA0484ICE	Cranes Transit - 8t	319.00	6.0	17.19	11.88	37.74
Cranes Wheeled						
PA0491ICE	Cranes Wheeled - Jones Iron Fairy - 8t	322.60	6.0	15.50	1.30	25.56
PA0492ICE	Cranes Wheeled - Jones Iron Fairy - 10t	368.30	6.0	15.50	1.91	27.42
PA0493ICE	Cranes Wheeled - Jones Iron Fairy - 12t	453.80	6.0	15.50	1.91	29.74
PA0494ICE	Cranes Wheeled - Jones Iron Fairy - 15t	541.30	6.0	15.50	1.91	32.12
Cranes Crawler						
PA0502ICE	Cranes Crawler - NCK 605C - 42t	1,404.20	6.0	17.19	2.96	58.32
PA0503ICE	Cranes Crawler - NCK 407C - 32t	1,329.90	6.0	17.19	2.96	56.30
PA0505ICE	Cranes Crawler - NCK 406C - 30t	1,089.80	6.0	17.19	1.74	48.55
PA0506ICE	Cranes Crawler - NCK - 26t	966.60	6.0	17.19	2.24	45.71
PA0507ICE	Cranes Crawler - NCK 305B - 20t	980.90	6.0	17.19	1.51	45.36
PA0508ICE	Cranes Crawler - NCK - 20t Pentland	966.60	6.0	17.19	1.75	45.21
PA0509ICE	Cranes Crawler - NCK 305C - 19t	829.30	6.0	17.19	3.53	43.26
PA0510ICE	Cranes Crawler - 30RB - 35t	1,154.90	6.0	17.19	1.68	50.26
PA0511ICE	Cranes Crawler - 22RB - 15t	717.40	6.0	17.19	1.68	38.37

Price Code	Description	Weekly Hire Charges	Consumables percent	Operator cost per hour	Fuel cost per hour	TOTAL COST PER HOUR
		£	%	£	£	£
Dumpers						
PA0541ICE	Dumper - 0.60t 2WD	40.70	6.0	-	0.48	1.59
PA0542ICE	Dumper - 0.75t 2WD	45.80	6.0	-	0.56	1.81
PA0543ICE	Dumper - 1.25t 2WD	61.10	6.0	-	0.56	2.22
PA0544ICE	Dumper -1.50t 2WD	61.10	4.0	-	1.12	2.75
PA0545ICE	Dumper - 1.75t 2WD	66.10	4.0	-	1.30	3.06
PA0546ICE	Dumper - 2.0t 2WD	81.40	4.0	-	1.45	3.62
PA0547ICE	Dumper - 2.0t 4WD	91.60	4.0	15.50	1.80	19.74
PA0548ICE	Dumper - 2.25t 4WD	101.80	4.0	15.50	2.40	20.61
PA0549ICE	Dumper - 2.5t 4WD	111.90	4.0	15.50	3.00	21.48
PA0550ICE	Dumper - 3.0t 4WD	152.60	4.0	15.50	4.20	23.77
PA0551ICE	Dumper - 4.0t 4WD	203.50	4.0	15.50	5.41	26.34
PA0552ICE	Dumper - 5.0t 4WD	81.40	4.0	16.57	6.05	24.79
PA0553ICE	Dumper - 1.25t Swivel Skip	127.20	4.0	16.57	3.00	22.96
PA0554ICE	Dumper - 2.0t 4WD Swivel Skip	101.80	4.0	16.57	1.80	21.08
Dump Trucks						
PA1011ICE	Dumper Truck - Volvo A25C 25t 6x6	933.10	-	15.50	16.92	56.35
PA1012ICE	Dumper Truck - Volvo A35	1,201.70	-	15.50	19.92	66.23
Excavators Cable						
PA0522ICE	Excavators Cable - NCK 6052C 1.34m^3	1,284.10	6.0	17.19	7.38	59.47
PA0523ICE	Excavators Cable - NCK 407 0.60m^3	1,236.30	6.0	17.19	7.62	58.41
PA0526ICE	Excavators Cable - NCK 305A 0.67m^3	686.80	6.0	17.19	5.93	41.78
PA0527ICE	Excavators Cable - 30RB 1.34m^3	1,071.40	6.0	17.19	11.88	58.19
PA0528ICE	Excavators Cable - 22RB ICD 0.72m^3	659.40	6.0	17.19	5.71	40.82
PA0529ICE	Excavators Cable - 22RB HD 1.00m^3	659.40	6.0	17.19	5.71	40.82
Fork Lift Trucks						
PA0561ICE	Fork Lift Truck - 1.0t 2WD	137.40	3.0	15.50	2.21	21.34
PA0562ICE	Fork Lift Truck - 2.5t 2WD	206.10	3.0	15.50	3.70	24.64
PA0563ICE	Fork Lift Truck - 2.0t 4WD	226.70	3.0	15.50	3.70	25.18
PA0564ICE	Fork Lift Truck - 2.5t 4WD	247.30	3.0	16.57	3.70	26.80
Generators						
PA0571ICE	Generator - 1.5 kvA Petrol	27.50	3.0	-	0.29	1.02
PA0572ICE	Generator - 2.5 kvA Petrol	34.30	3.0	-	0.29	1.20
PA0573ICE	Generator - 3 kvA Petrol	48.10	3.0	-	0.29	1.56
PA0574ICE	Generator - 4kvA Diesel	55.00	3.0	-	0.36	1.81
PA0575ICE	Generator - 5kvA Diesel	68.70	3.0	-	0.49	2.31
PA0576ICE	Generator - 6kvA Diesel	92.60	3.0	-	0.56	3.01
PA0577ICE	Generator - 7kvA Diesel	89.30	3.0	-	0.61	2.97
PA0578ICE	Generator - 10 kvA Diesel	96.20	3.0	-	1.01	3.55
PA0579ICE	Generator - 57 kvA Diesel	467.00	3.0	-	2.35	14.69
PA0580ICE	Generator - 150 kvA 3-Phase Skid Mounted Silenced	1,201.90	3.0	-	12.19	43.93
PA0581ICE	Generator - 250 kvA 3-Phase Skid Mounted Silenced	1,673.80	3.0	-	19.58	63.79

Price Code	Description	Weekly Hire Charges	Consumables percent	Operator cost per hour	Fuel cost per hour	TOTAL COST PER HOUR
		£	%	£	£	£
Hydraulic Excavators						
PA0592ICE	Hydraulic Excavator - Cat 320 96kW	386.70	3.0	17.19	6.58	33.98
PA0594ICE	Hydraulic Excavator - JCB 3CX Sitemaster	249.30	3.0	17.19	3.24	27.01
PA0595ICE	Hydraulic Excavator - JCB 803 R/T	305.30	3.0	17.19	1.82	27.08
PA0596ICE	Hydraulic Excavator - JCB 803 S/T	330.70	3.0	17.19	1.82	27.75
PA0597ICE	Hydraulic Excavator - JCB 802 R/T	239.10	3.0	17.19	1.82	25.33
PA0598ICE	Hydraulic Excavator - JCB 801 R/T	244.20	3.0	17.19	6.48	30.12
PA0605ICE	Hydraulic Excavator - Cat 166kW	544.40	3.0	17.19	9.84	41.41
PA0606ICE	Hydraulic Excavator - Case 588A	559.60	3.0	17.19	7.54	39.51
PA0607ICE	Hydraulic Excavator - Samsung SE130W-4	636.00	3.0	17.19	7.54	41.52
PA0608ICE	Hydraulic Excavator - Komatsu PC130	686.80	3.0	17.19	7.54	42.86
PA0609ICE	Hydraulic Excavator - Komatsu PW130	686.80	3.0	17.19	7.54	42.86
PA0610ICE	Hydraulic Excavator - Hyundai 210	747.90	3.0	17.19	5.42	42.37
PA0611ICE	Hydraulic Excavator - Cat 215	381.60	3.0	17.19	5.42	32.69
Hoists						
PA0641ICE	Scaffold Hoist 5 cut	40.70	-	-	-	1.04
PA0642ICE	Platform Hoist 10 Cut Friction	96.70	-	-	-	2.48
PA0643ICE	Platform Hoist 10 Cut Geared	96.70	-	-	-	2.48
PA0644ICE	Wyselift Hoist GL75	96.70	-	-	-	2.48
PA0645ICE	Elephante hoist 6 East	99.00	-	-	-	2.54
PA0646ICE	5 Omers Bocker Hoist	117.00	-	-	-	3.00
PA0647ICE	Elevator CEDA Hoist	101.80	-	-	-	2.61
Hydraulic Breakers - as attachments						
PA0661ICE	Hydraulic Breaker - BRH40	226.70	-	-	-	5.81
PA0662ICE	Hydraulic Breaker - BRH125	302.20	-	-	-	7.75
PA0663ICE	Hydraulic Breaker - BRH250	384.60	-	-	-	9.86
PA0664ICE	Hydraulic Breaker - BRH501	439.60	-	-	-	11.27
Hydraulic Breakers - Independent						
PA0671ICE	Hydraulic Breaker - Single Tool Static Breaker	56.00	-	-	1.22	2.66
PA0672ICE	Hydraulic Breaker - Single Tool Towable Breaker	61.10	-	-	0.67	2.24
PA0673ICE	Hydraulic Breaker - Two Tool Towable Breaker	68.70	-	-	0.98	2.75
PA0674ICE	Hydraulic Breaker - Single Tool-metreater Breaker	86.50	-	-	1.97	4.19
Kango Type Tools						
PA0701ICE	Kango Type Tool - 950 Kango	48.30	-	-	-	1.24
PA0702ICE	Kango Type Tool - Electric Power Drill 19mm	40.70	-	-	-	1.04
PA0703ICE	Kango Type Tool - Electric Power Woodauger	22.40	-	-	-	0.57
PA0704ICE	Kango Type Tool - Electric Nut Runner	18.80	-	-	-	0.48
PA0705ICE	Kango Type Tool - Electric Screwdriver	18.80	-	-	-	0.48
Lighting Towers						
PA0711ICE	Towable Lighting Tower 10m Diesel	96.20	-	-	-	2.47
PA0712ICE	Towable Lighting Tower 20m Diesel	109.90	-	-	-	2.82
PA0713ICE	Lighting Tower - Lighting the Works	193.30	-	-	-	4.96

Price Code	Description	Weekly Hire Charges	Consumables percent	Operator cost per hour	Fuel cost per hour	TOTAL COST PER HOUR
		£	%	£	£	£
Concrete Mixers						
PA0721ICE	Cement Mixer - 3/2 Petrol	37.70	2.0	-	0.99	1.97
PA0722ICE	Cement Mixer - 4/3 Petrol	40.20	2.0	-	0.99	2.04
PA0723ICE	Cement Mixer - 5/3 Petrol	69.20	2.0	-	0.80	2.61
PA0724ICE	Cement Mixer - 5/3.5 Diesel Road Tow	79.40	2.0	-	0.80	2.88
PA0725ICE	Cement Mixer - 7/5 Diesel	83.40	2.0	-	0.80	2.99
PA0729ICE	Cement Mixer - 10/7 Diesel	93.60	2.0	-	3.02	5.47
PA0730ICE	Cement Mixer - Mortar Pan Mixer	140.90	2.0	-	0.80	4.49
PA0735ICE	Cement Mixer - Liner Rolpanit	686.80	2.0	17.19	2.21	37.36
PA0737ICE	Cement Mixer - Schwing BP1000R Concrete Pumps	910.70	2.0	17.19	2.28	43.29
PA0738ICE	Cement Mixer - 18/12 Diesel	144.50	2.0	17.19	3.31	24.28
Tunneling Equipment						
PA1049ICE	Micro Tunneling Equipment (rock) 1.2m dia	10,910.40	20.0	-	-	335.70
PA1050ICE	Micro Tunneling Equipment (rock) 1.5m dia	11,239.60	20.0	-	-	345.83
PA1051ICE	Micro Tunneling Equipment (rock) 1.8m dia	11,944.90	20.0	-	-	367.54
PA1052ICE	Micro Tunneling Equipment (rock) 3.0m dia	15,754.00	20.0	-	-	484.74
PA1053ICE	Micro Tunneling Equipment (soil) 1.2m dia	9,734.60	20.0	-	-	299.53
PA1054ICE	Micro Tunneling Equipment (soil) 1.5m dia	9,828.60	20.0	-	-	302.42
PA1055ICE	Micro Tunneling Equipment (soil) 1.8m dia	10,063.80	20.0	-	-	309.66
PA1056ICE	Micro Tunneling Equipment (soil) 3.0m dia	12,932.30	20.0	-	-	397.92
Piling Equipment						
PA1046ICE	Pile Jetting Pump and Accessories	528.20	30.0	-	16.42	34.02
PA1047ICE	Pile Testing Rig and Equipment	4,702.80	45.0	17.19	27.28	219.32
PA1066ICE	Driven Piling Rig Large	4,326.40	45.0	17.19	27.28	205.32
PA1067ICE	Driven Piling Rig Medium	2,953.40	45.0	17.19	27.28	154.27
PA1062ICE	Bored Piling Rig Large	4,326.40	45.0	17.19	27.28	205.32
PA1063ICE	Bored Piling rig Medium	2,953.40	45.0	17.19	27.28	154.27
PA1079ICE	Sheet Piling Rig Large	4,326.40	45.0	17.19	27.28	205.32
PA1080ICE	Sheet Piling rig Medium	2,953.40	45.0	17.19	27.28	154.27
Drilling Equipment						
PA1060ICE	Anchor Drilling Rig (rock)	797.20	45.0	17.19	32.84	79.67
PA1061ICE	Anchor drilling Rog (soil)	637.70	45.0	17.19	32.84	73.74
Pipework and Plumbing Equipment						
PA1083ICE	Vactor Unit for Sewer Cleaning	152.10	10.0	-	3.65	7.94
PA1084ICE	Pipe Thrust Boring Equipment	6,398.00	25.0	-	-	205.06
PA1085ICE	Pipe Jacking Equipment	12,736.60	20.0	-	-	391.90
PA1041ICE	Pressure Testing Equipment	528.20	30.0	-	16.42	34.02
PA1065ICE	CCTV unit for Sewer Inspection	2,708.80	10.0	15.50	3.65	95.55
Fencing Equipment						
PA1335ICE	Fence Post Rammer	29.80	-	-	-	0.76
PA1336ICE	Post Hole Borer: Two Man	104.80	20.0	-	1.08	4.30
PA1059ICE	Agricultural Tractor: Fencing Auger	152.10	10.0	15.50	3.65	23.44

Price Code	Description	Weekly Hire Charges	Consumables percent	Operator cost per hour	Fuel cost per hour	TOTAL COST PER HOUR
		£	%	£	£	£
Sheet Piling Equipment (Excluding Compressors)						
PA0752ICE	160 cfm - Air Hammer	165.40	-	-	-	4.24
PA0753ICE	250 cfm - Air Hammer	224.90	-	-	-	5.77
PA0754ICE	480 cfm - Air Hammer	271.20	-	-	-	6.95
PA0755ICE	600 cfm - Air Hammer	304.20	-	-	-	7.80
PA0761ICE	BSP 300 - Air Hammer	224.90	-	-	-	5.77
PA0762ICE	BSP 500 - Air Hammer	251.30	-	-	-	6.44
PA0763ICE	BSP 600 - Air Hammer	277.80	-	-	-	7.12
PA0764ICE	Zeneth 20 Sheet Pile Extractor	238.10	-	-	-	6.11
PA0765ICE	Zeneth 80 Sheet Pile Extractor	264.60	-	-	-	6.78
PA0766ICE	Zeneth 120 Sheet Pile Extractor	555.60	-	-	-	14.25
PA0767ICE	HD7 Sheet Pile Extractor	496.00	-	-	-	12.72
PA0768ICE	HD10 Sheet Pile Extractor	595.30	-	-	-	15.26
PA0769ICE	HD15 Sheet Pile Extractor	727.50	-	-	-	18.65
Air Hoses						
PA0781ICE	Air Hose - 3/4 inch x 15m length	5.50	-	-	-	0.14
PA0782ICE	Air Hose - 1.5 inch x 15m length	19.20	-	-	-	0.49
PA0783ICE	Air Hose - 2 inch x 15m length	20.60	-	-	-	0.53
PA0784ICE	Air Hose - 2.5 inch x 15m length	27.50	-	-	-	0.71
Diesel Hammers						
PA0792ICE	Diesel Hammer up to 1500kg	463.00	-	-	2.96	14.84
PA0793ICE	Diesel Hammer up to 2500kg	553.50	-	-	4.80	18.99
PA0794ICE	Diesel Hammer up to 5000kg	932.10	-	-	6.14	30.04
PA0795ICE	Diesel Hammer up to 7500kg	1,543.60	-	-	6.14	45.72
Quick Release Shackles						
PA0801ICE	Quick Release Shackles - Larssen Single	24.40	-	-	-	0.63
PA0802ICE	Quick Release Shackles - Frodingham Double	43.80	-	-	-	1.12
Trench Supports						
PA0803ICE	Trench Sheets	3.10	-	-	-	0.08
PA0804ICE	Acrow Props	3.10	-	-	-	0.08
PA0805ICE	Timber Baulks	23.80	-	-	-	0.61
Pumps						
PA0811ICE	Godwin ET50 23m^3/h 4 inches	76.30	20.0	-	0.40	2.74
PA0812ICE	Godwin ET75 74m^3/h 4 inches	111.90	20.0	-	0.67	4.12
PA0813ICE	Godwin Univac 4 inches 500 gpm	170.90	20.0	-	2.16	7.42
PA0814ICE	Godwin Univac 6 inches 1000 gpm	228.90	20.0	-	3.53	10.57
PA0815ICE	Godwin HL4 200m^3/h	325.60	20.0	-	2.96	12.98
PA0816ICE	Godwin HL5 150/100mm 1200m^3/h	381.60	20.0	-	3.53	15.27
PA0817ICE	Godwin HL8 200mm 2000 gpm	325.60	20.0	-	7.82	17.84
PA0818ICE	Godwin HL6 200/150mm 1250 gpm	473.20	20.0	-	6.16	20.72
PA0819ICE	Flygt B2050 2 inch Discharge	72.20	20.0	-	1.58	3.81
PA0820ICE	Flygt B2066 3 inch Discharge	88.50	20.0	-	2.46	5.18
PA0821ICE	Flygt B2102 4 inch Discharge	107.90	20.0	-	3.07	6.39
PA0822ICE	Flygt B2125 6 inch Discharge	162.80	47.0	-	8.18	14.32
PA0823ICE	Flygt B2151 6 inch Discharge	193.30	41.0	-	12.29	19.28

Price Code	Description	Weekly Hire Charges	Consumables percent	Operator cost per hour	Fuel cost per hour	TOTAL COST PER HOUR
		£	%	£	£	£
Pumps continued/...						
PA0824ICE	Flygt C53085MT 3 inch Discharge	86.50	10.0	-	2.46	4.90
PA0825ICE	Flygt CS3102 4 inch Discharge	152.60	30.0	-	3.22	8.30
PA0826ICE	Flygt CS3126MT 6 inch Discharge	180.00	50.0	-	8.18	15.11
PA0827ICE	Weda 2 inches L154 30m^3/h	68.20	10.0	-	1.60	3.52
PA0828ICE	Weda 3 inches L262/4 87m^3/h	81.40	50.0	-	3.26	6.39
PA0829ICE	Weda 4 inches L502 107m^3/h	137.00	45.0	-	4.06	9.15
PA0830ICE	Weda 4 inches L554 180m^3/h	137.00	50.0	-	6.48	11.75
PA0832ICE	Godwin Heidra 100mm Pump (Hydrosubmersible) Complete with 10m Hoses and Power Pack on Site Trolley	210.00	40.0	-	4.06	11.59
PA0833ICE	Pump - Godwin Heidra 100mm Pump Sewer Cleaner (Hydrosubmersible) Complete with 10m Hoses and Power Pack on Site Trolley	240.00	40.0	-	4.61	13.22
PA0834ICE	Pump - Godwin Hycon 100mm Pump (Hydrosubmersible) Complete with 10m Hoses, Strainer and Power Pack on Site Trolley	265.00	40.0	-	4.61	14.12
PA1081ICE	Shotcrete Pump	470.10	20.0	-	14.26	28.72
PA1334ICE	Pump 100mm 1500 l/min	104.40	10.0	-	1.20	4.14
PA1077ICE	Screed Pump	470.10	20.0	-	-	14.46
Diaphragm Pumps						
PA0836ICE	Petrol Pump c/w 6m 50mm Suction Hose and 6m 75mm Delivery Hose	66.10	20.0	-	0.19	2.22
PA0837ICE	Diesel Pump 75mm c/w 6m Suction Hose and 6m Delivery Hose	96.70	20.0	-	0.38	3.36
PA0838ICE	Extra for Additonal 50mm x 6m Suction Hose	10.20	-	-	-	0.26
PA0839ICE	Extra for Additonal 75mm x 6m Delivery Hose	6.10	-	-	-	0.16
Rammers and Compacters						
PA0851ICE	Vibrating Plate Light	40.70	-	-	0.28	1.32
PA0852ICE	Vibrating Plate Light Medium	45.80	-	-	0.28	1.45
PA0853ICE	Vibrating Plate Diesel 24kN	81.40	-	-	0.28	2.36
PA0854ICE	Vibrating Plate Diesel 33.5kN	96.70	-	-	0.28	2.76
Rollers						
PA0861ICE	Single Drum - 28 inch Pedestrian	51.90	2.0	-	0.44	1.80
PA0862ICE	Single drum - 28 inch Roller Breaker c/w Trailer	88.50	2.0	-	0.44	2.76
PA0863ICE	28 inch Vibratory Roller 0.37t	61.10	2.0	-	0.44	2.04
PA0864ICE	Bomag (Trench) 350mm	74.30	2.0	-	0.34	2.28
PA0865ICE	Bomag 55 550mm	56.00	2.0	-	0.44	1.91
PA0866ICE	Bomag 60 600mm	58.50	2.0	-	0.55	2.08
PA0867ICE	Bomag 75 750mm	71.20	2.0	-	0.79	2.65
PA0868ICE	Bomag 90 900mm	86.50	2.0	-	1.01	3.27
PA0869ICE	800mm Ride on Roller	189.80	2.0	-	1.10	6.07
PA0870ICE	1000mm Ride on Roller	223.90	3.0	-	3.31	9.23
PA0871ICE	1200mm Ride on Roller	258.50	3.0	-	3.31	10.14

Price Code	Description	Weekly Hire Charges	Consumables percent	Operator cost per hour	Fuel cost per hour	TOTAL COST PER HOUR
		£	%	£	£	£
Rollers continued/...						
PA0872ICE	1300mm Ride on Roller	269.60	3.0	-	3.31	10.43
PA0874ICE	Aveling Barford DCI2 8.5t	223.90	3.0	-	3.31	9.23
PA0876ICE	Two Drum Ride On	154.70	3.0	-	3.31	7.40
PA0878ICE	Case Vibromax W651	158.70	3.0	-	2.93	7.12
Sawing						
PA0891ICE	Saw Bench - 24 inch Diesel/Electric	62.60	3.0	-	0.24	1.89
PA1058ICE	9" Circular Saw	34.60	10.0	-	-	0.98
Road Plant						
PA0900ICE	Tar Sprayer	48.30	-	-	-	1.24
PA0901ICE	Barber Greene BGP 255 Paver	3,240.80	3.0	17.19	-	102.78
PA0902ICE	Barber Greene BGP 200 Paver	1,297.30	3.0	17.19	-	51.45
PA1048ICE	Road Marking Vehicle	554.60	10.0	-	28.56	44.21
Wheeled Tractors/Graders						
PA0911ICE	Ford 3190H	173.00	4.0	15.50	3.41	23.52
PA0912ICE	Ford 4610H	198.40	2.0	15.50	3.65	24.34
PA0913ICE	Ford 5610H	211.60	2.0	15.50	4.27	25.31
PA0914ICE	Ford 6610H	231.50	2.0	15.50	3.65	25.20
PA0916ICE	Massey Ferguson MF20B 35kW	137.40	2.0	15.50	3.65	22.74
PA0917ICE	Massey Ferguson MF50E 52kW	152.10	4.0	15.50	3.65	23.20
Crawler Tractors/Dozers						
PA0931ICE	Cat D3C LGP 52kW	478.20	4.0	17.19	4.66	34.60
PA0932ICE	Cat D4C LGP 60kW	480.80	4.0	17.19	5.66	35.68
PA0933ICE	Cat D5M LGP 82kW	574.90	4.0	17.19	7.97	40.49
PA0934ICE	Cat D6R LGP 138kW	671.60	4.0	17.19	10.66	45.76
PA0935ICE	Cat D8R LGP	1,271.90	4.0	17.19	20.54	71.65
PA0937ICE	Cat 302kW Pusher	1,628.00	4.0	17.19	23.65	84.26
PA0938ICE	Cat 931	427.40	4.0	17.19	4.66	33.24
PA0939ICE	Cat 941	452.80	4.0	17.19	6.10	35.36
PA0940ICE	Cat 951	498.60	4.0	17.19	6.10	36.58
PA0941ICE	Cat 621F 246kW 153m^3	1,195.10	4.0	17.19	25.10	74.16
PA0942ICE	Cat 631F 365kW 23.7m^3	1,359.90	4.0	17.19	31.25	84.70
PA0943ICE	Cat D6 LGP 160Hp	686.80	4.0	17.19	13.10	48.61
PA0944ICE	Cat D456kW	478.20	4.0	17.19	5.66	35.61
PA0945ICE	Dresser 1004 48kW	288.50	4.0	17.19	3.79	28.68
PA0946ICE	Cat 561 Sideboom	610.50	4.0	17.19	7.97	41.44
PA0953ICE	Fiatallis FD145 93kW	617.60	-	17.19	18.48	51.51
PA0956ICE	Terex TS14 D Scraper (Wheeled) 10.7m^3	1,246.50	3.0	17.19	18.43	68.54
PA0957ICE	Terex TS24 C Scraper (Wheeled) 18.4m^3	1,653.50	2.5	17.19	35.62	96.26
PA0958ICE	Cat 633E Scraper	1,339.30	2.5	17.19	37.73	90.12
PA0959ICE	Tractor D8 Blade	1,071.40	2.5	17.19	18.24	36.59
PA0960ICE	Cat 16H Grader	1,070.90	2.5	17.19	36.77	82.10
Tipping Wagon						
PA1001ICE	10t 4-Wheel (16t Gr)	554.60	-	15.50	12.22	41.94

Price Code	Description	Weekly Hire Charges	Consumables percent	Operator cost per hour	Fuel cost per hour	TOTAL COST PER HOUR
		£	%	£	£	£
Tipping Wagon continued/...						
PA1002ICE	16t 6-Wheel (24t Gr)	689.90	-	15.50	14.78	47.97
PA1003ICE	20t 8-Wheel (30t Gr)	889.30	-	15.50	16.13	54.43
Trailers						
PA0961ICE	Massey Tipping	66.10	-	-	-	1.69
PA0962ICE	28 inch Vib Roller Trailer	25.40	-	-	-	0.65
PA0963ICE	D/D Vib Roller Trailer	40.70	-	-	-	1.04
PA0964ICE	Road Sweeper	127.20	-	-	-	3.26
Traffic Lights						
PA0971ICE	Main Generator 2-Way with 100m Cables	117.00	-	-	-	3.00
PA0981ICE	Petrol up to 75mm	37.70	-	-	0.36	1.33
PA0982ICE	Diesel up to 75mm	40.70	-	-	0.14	1.19
Welding Sets						
PA0991ICE	300 amp Diesel Electric Start Sil	120.10	-	-	1.10	4.18
PA0992ICE	250 amp Diesel Electric Start Sil	99.70	-	-	0.96	3.52
PA0993ICE	200 amp Petrol Recoil Start	60.00	-	-	0.96	2.50
PA0994ICE	Plastic Pipe Welding (Small)	249.30	-	-	-	6.39
PA0995ICE	Plastic Pipe Welding (Large)	330.70	-	-	-	8.48
Miscellaneous						
PA0740ICE	12m Hydraulic Platform	377.50	-	-	-	9.68
PA0741ICE	Asphalt Boiler	75.80	-	-	-	1.94
PA0742ICE	Towered Brush - Canline	70.20	-	-	-	1.80
PA0744ICE	Shotblast Equipment - 160 (1.5 Bag Pot)	75.60	-	-	-	1.94
PA0745ICE	Shotblast Equipment - 350 (3.0 Bag Pot)	89.30	-	-	-	2.29
PA0746ICE	Shotblast Equipment (3.0 Bag Pot) with 250 cfm compressor	130.80	-	-	-	3.35
PA0747ICE	Paint Spray Equipment - HD 1 Gun	80.40	-	-	0.80	2.87
PA0730ICE	Rammer Benjo	58.00	-	-	-	1.49
PA0731ICE	Cutting and Burning Gear	137.40	-	-	-	3.52
PA0739ICE	Bentonite Plant	1,760.70	30.0	-	49.25	107.94
PA1044ICE	Articulated Lorry	933.10	25.0	17.19	16.92	64.02
PA1045ICE	Low Loader Trailer	508.80	-	-	-	13.05
PA1064ICE	Cable Percussion Rig	184.20	45.0	-	1.21	8.06
PA1068ICE	Ground Anchor Drilling Rig	1,913.20	25.0	17.19	32.84	111.35
PA1069ICE	Grouting Rig (Anchorage Items)	264.60	45.0	-	-	9.84
PA1073ICE	Robotic Sewer Repair Unit	1,316.70	20.0	-	28.56	69.08
PA1074ICE	Rotary Borehole Rig	290.50	45.0	-	1.51	12.31
PA1076ICE	Scissor Lift - 2032	131.70	20.0	-	-	4.05
PA1078ICE	Self Propelled Chip Spreader	343.10	10.0	15.50	3.65	28.83

TYPICAL PLANT OUTPUTS

The information used in this section has been derived from generally available information published by certain manufacturers but in assessing capacities and outputs readers are advised to consult the makers of the equipment being assessed to confirm capacities and outputs.

Civil engineering activities often require large quantities of material to be excavated and removed. The types of excavation determine the type of machine used assuming it to be available. The most common types are:

Trenches
Pits
Cuttings/Banks
Foundations
each can vary considerably in size.

To illustrate the calculation of machine outputs a reasonable sized task has been chosen for each operation.

Excavation to:

Trenches
A trench 7 metres deep and 2 metres wide at the bottom in stiff sandy clay with battered sides. The material is dumped by the side of the trench ready for backfilling.

Use: Case Poclain 170B.

Output which can be expected depends on the following factors:

1)	Activity	(A)	The type of activity can vary from very difficult restricted work to straight forward unrestrained work. Factors vary from 0.5 to 1.0.
2)	Cycle time	(C)	Comprises four movements, dig, slew loaded, dump and slew empty.

The movements are affected by:
a) the nature of the material being dug; see table I.
b) the position of the point of dig in relation to the point of dump; see table 2.

3)	Bucket capacity	(B)	The nature of the material affects the makers rated capacity. This is normally expressed as a CECE* rating.
4)	Job Efficiency	(E)	This takes into account the actual time in a shift that its machine is usefully engaged. A normal rating is 0.83%.

Applying these factors to this task.

1) Activity (A) The machine has to move frequently otherwise straight forward. Use factor 0.9 (A2).

2) Cycle time

apply factors to theoretical timing.
dig 4.0 seconds from table 1 apply factor of 1.42 (D3)

4.0 x 1.42	= 5.68 sec.
slew loaded 5.0 sec from table 2 use factor of 1.5 (S3)	
5.0 x 1.50	= 7.50 sec.
dump 1.5 seconds	= 1.50 sec.
slew empty	= 4.00 x 1.42 (S3)
	= 5.68 sec.
TOTAL	20.36 secs.
Equals	176 cycles per hour.

3) Bucket capacity

CECE rating 1.6m^3 apply factor from table 3 for stiff clay 0.85 (B3).
Capacity = 1.60 x 0.85 = 1.36m^3.

NOTE: *CECE - Committee on European Construction Equipment

TYPICAL PLANT OUTPUTS continued/...

Trenches continued/...

4) Job Efficiency use 0.83 (E2).

Thus:	Activity	= 0.9
	Cycles	= 176 per hour
	Bucket Capacity	= 1.36 m^3
	Efficiency	= 0.83
	Output equals	= 0.9 x 176 x 1.36 x 0.83
		= 178m^3 per hour

Output equals 178m^3 per hour. This is loose material. Apply bulking factor of 0.85 from table 4. Output measured in the solid equals 178 x 0.85 = 152m^3 per hour.

This is excavation only, no allowance has been made for fairing up the bottom of the trench or backfilling or double handling.

Excavation to:

Pits

Assume a large cut excavation on an open cast coal site. Typical coal measure overburden – loose shale and sandy clay.

Use Caterpillar 245 Excavator with face shovel equipment, bottom dump bucket rated capacity 3.1m^3 loading into dump-trucks. Unrestricted space for trucks to manoeuvre.

Activity	Straight forward assuming adequate number of trucks. Use factor 1.0 (AI).	
Cycle	Makers theoretical rated cycle times.	
	Dig 9 seconds x 1.3 (D2)	11.7
	Slew loaded 4.0 x 1.3 (S2)	5.2
	This allows for digging from track level and slewing 45 degrees to load into dump-truck 4m high.	
	Dump 2.5 sec	2.5
	Slew empty 4.0 x 1.3 (S2)	5.2
		24.6 secs.
	24.6 secs. equals 146 cycles per hour.	
Bucket Capacity	3.1m^3. Bucket fill factor 0.85 (B2)	= 2.65
Job Efficiency		= 0.83
Output		= 1 x 146 x 2.65 x 0.83
		= 321m3 per hour

This is loose cubic metres per hour allowing a bulking factor of 0.75 (from table 4) the solid measure equals 321 x 0.75 = 240m^3 per hour.

Excavation to:

Cuttings

Assume a motorway cut and fill operation. The average length of haul is 500 metres. Material stiff, sandy, clay, dry. Haul grade no more than 4 per cent.

A typical plant spread for this operation would consist of:

4/6 motorized scrapers
Tractor D9 pusher
Tractor D8 blade
Grader Caterpillar

TYPICAL PLANT OUTPUTS continued/...

Cuttings continued/...

The production units being the scrapers; the output of one scraper is examined here.

Use a Cat 631E.

Activity	The task is a normal one and a factor of 1.0 (A1) is used.	
Cycle	Load 36 secs. Use factor of 0.9 (DI)	
	36 x 0.9	= 32 secs.
	Haul loaded	= 84 secs.
	Use factor of 1.0 (S1)	= 84 secs.
	Spread and manoeuvre 42 secs.	= 42 secs.
	Haul empty 60 secs.	
	Use factor of 1.0 (S1)	= 60 secs.
	TOTAL	= 218 secs.
Cycle	equals 218 secs.	
	equals 16.5 per hour.	
Capacity	rated capacity average $20m^3$	
	$20m^3$ loose. Use factor 0.85 (B2).	
	Capacity equals 20 x 0.85 = $17m^3$.	
Efficiency	use 0.83.	
Output	Activity	= 1.0
	Cycle	= 16.5 per hour
	Capacity	= 17.0 m^3
	Efficiency	= 0.83
	output equals 1 x 16.5 x 17 x 0.83	= $232m^3$

To convert to solid cubic metres refer to table 4 use a bulking factor of 0.79.
Output in solid m^3 equals 232 x 0.79 = $183m^3$ per hour

Excavation to:

Pile Caps

1) Type of activity	Use a JCB 3CX Sitemaster. This means a lot of travel is required by the machine and a set up at each position. Use an activity factor of 0.5 (A4)	
2) Cycle Time	Dig will be slower because of much higher proportion of squaring off and cleaning bottom.	
	Use factor (D5) 2.5.	
	Use factor (S3) 1.67.	
	Dig 2.6 x 2.50	= 6.5
	Slew 2.1 x 1.67	= 3.5
	Dump 1.5	= 1.5
	Slew 1.7 x 1.67	= 2.8
	Total cycle time	14.3 seconds
	= 251 cycles per hour	
3) Bucket	Capacity slightly less than before because of obstructions of pile heads and steel. Use factor (B4) 0.6.	
4) Job Efficiency	This will be low because of constant moving. Use factor 0.75.	

Output is calculated as follows:
activity x cycles x bucket x job efficiency
= 0.5 (A4) x 251 x 0.24 x 0.6 (B4) x 0.75 = $13.55m^3$ per hour

TYPICAL PLANT OUTPUTS continued/...

Loading excavated materials

Load, excavated, medium hard clay spoil into 3 tipper wagons. Use Drott International Crawler Loader.

1) Activity — No impediment to movement. Use activity factor 1.0 of (A1).

2) Cycle time — Use factors shown:

Load	3 x (D2) 1.3	= 3.9
Manoeuvre	4 x (S2) 1.3	= 5.2
Dump	1.5	= 1.5
Manoeuvre	3 x (S2) 1.3	= 3.9
Total cycle time		14.5 seconds

= 248 cycles per hour

3) Bucket — CECE rated capacity 1m3. Use factor 0.85 (B2).

4) Job Efficiency — = 0.83
Output — 1.0 (A1) x 248 cycles x bucket
0.85 (B2) x efficiency 0.83
1.0 x 248 x 0.85 x 0.83
175m^3 per hour
Weight of material bulked; see table 4
Medium hard clay dry. 1.480 tonne m^3
= 175 x 1.480 = 259 tonne per hour.

Tables to be used for excavation output calculations

Table 1 - Dig Factors

(DI)	0.9 to 1.0	Soft soil or sand
(D2)	1.0 to 1.3	Medium hard clay or gravel with cobbles
(D3)	1.3 to 2.0	Hard clay with some boulders
(D4)	2.0 to 2.5	Well blasted rock
(D5)	2.5 to 4.0	Frequent obstructions, working with trench shield

Table 2 -Slew Factors

(S1)	0.9 to 1.0	Trench not less than 2m deep. Spoil can be dumped on the ground by the trench
(S2)	1.0 to 1.3	Trench up to 3m deep. Spoil dump on ground or into wagons not more than 3m above track level. Slew not more than 900.
(S3)	1.3 to 2.0	Trench up to 4m deep. Spoil to be dumped into wagons at rear of m/c.
(S4)	2.0 to 2.5	Trench over 4m deep. Spoil to be dumped into wagon.

Table 3 - Bucket Fill Factors

The Committee on European Construction Equipment (CECE) rates heaped bucket pay loads on a 2:1 angle of repose.

CECE capacity times

(BI)	1.0	Soft soil
(B2)	0.85 to 1.0	Medium hard clay or gravel
(B3)	0.7 to 0.85	Hard clay
(B4)	0.5 to 0.75	Well blasted rock
(B5)	0.4 to 0.5	Poorly blasted rock

TYPICAL PLANT OUTPUTS continued/...

Table 4 - Bulking Factors

WEIGHT OF MATERIALS*	LOOSE		SOLID		BULKING FACTOR
	kg/m³	lb/yd³	kg/m³	lb/yd³	
Basalt	1960	3300	2970	5000	0.67
Bauxite, Kaolin	1420	2400	1900	3200	0.75
Caliche	1250	2100	2260	3800	0.55
Carnotite, uranium ore	1630	2750	2200	3700	0.74
Cinders	560	950	860	1450	0.66
Clay - Natural bed	1660	2800	2020	3400	0.82
Dry	1480	2500	1840	3100	0.81
Wet	1660	2800	2080	3500	0.80
Clay & Gravel - Dry	1420	2400	1660	2800	0.85
Wet	1540	2600	1840	3100	0.85
Coal - Anthracite Raw	1190	2000	1600	2700	0.74
Washed	1100	1850			0.74
Ash, Bituminous Coal	540-650	900-1100	590-890	1000-1500	0.93
Bituminous, Raw	950	1600	1280	2150	0.74
Washed	830	1400			0.74
Decomposed rock -					
75% Rock, 25% Earth	1960	3300	2790	4700	0.70
50% Rock, 50% Earth	1720	2900	2280	3850	0.75
25% Rock, 75% Earth	1570	2650	1960	3300	0.80
Earth - Dry packed	1510	2550	1900	3200	0.80
Wet excavated	1600	2700	2020	3400	0.79
Loam	1250	2100	1540	2600	0.81
Granite - Broken	1660	2800	2730	4600	0.61
Gravel - Pitrun	1930	3250	2170	3650	0.89
Dry	1510	2550	1690	2850	0.89
Dry 6-50mm (0.25" - 2")	1690	2850	1900	3200	0.89
Wet 6-50mm (0.25" - 2")	2020	3400	2260	3800	0.89
Gypsum - Broken	1810	3050	3170	5350	0.57
Crushed	1600	2700	2790	4700	0.57
Hematite, iron ore, high grade	1810-2450	4000-5400	2130-2900	4700-6400	0.85
Limestone - Broken	1540	2600	2610	4400	0.59
Crushed	1540	2600	-	-	-
Magnetite, iron ore	2790	4700	3260	5500	0.85
Pyrite, iron ore	2580	4350	3030	5100	0.85
Sand - Dry loose	1420	2400	1600	2700	0.89
Damp	1690	2850	1900	3200	0.89
Wet	1840	3100	2080	3500	0.89

* Varies with moisture content, grain size, degree of compaction, etc. Tests must be made to determine exact material characteristics.

TYPICAL PLANT OUTPUTS continued/...

Table 4 - Bulking Factors continued/...

WEIGHT OF MATERIALS*	LOOSE		SOLID		BULKING FACTOR
	kg/m³	lb/yd³	kg/m³	lb/yd³	
Sand and clay - Loose	1600	2700	2020	3400	0.79
Compacted	2400	4050	-	-	-
Sand & Gravel - Dry	1720	2900	1930	3250	0.89
Wet	2020	3400	2230	3750	0.91
Sandstone	1510	2550	2520	4250	0.60
Shale	1250	2100	1660	2800	0.75
Slag - broken	1750	2950	2940	4950	0.60
Snow - Dry	130	220	-	-	-
Wet	520	860	-	-	-
Stone - Crushed	1600	2700	2670	4500	0.60
Taconite	1630-1900	3600-4200	2360-2700	5200-6100	0.58
Top Soil	950	1600	1370	2300	0.70
Traprock - broken	1750	2950	2610	4400	0.67

* Varies with moisture content, grain size, degree of compaction, etc. Tests must be made to determine exact material characteristics.

Summary of Tables 1, 2 and 3

	Factors	1	2	3	4	5
(A)	Activity	1.0	0.85	0.75	0.6	0.5
(D)	Dig	0.9 - 1.0	1.0 - 1.3	1.3 - 2.0	2.0 - 2.5	2.5 - 4.0
(S)	Slew	0.9 - 1.0	1.0 - 1.3	1.3 - 2.0	2.0 - 2.5	-
(B)	Bucket	1.1 - 1.0	1.0 - 0.85	0.85 - 0.70	0.7 - 0.5	-
(E)	Efficiency	0.9	0.83	0.75	0.6	-

Output in cubic metres per hour equals:
Activity factor (A) x Cycles per hour x Bucket CECE rating x factor (B) x Efficiency factor (E)

TYPICAL PLANT OUTPUTS continued/...

Compaction by vibrating roller – light

Bomag BW 655 width 650rnm double vibrating roller pedestrian controlled Mass 600kg.
Speed 1st gear 0.875mph = 1.4km/h

Compaction is specified as: mass per metre width of roll. Number of passes depends on the thickness of material.

Compact granular material on footpath formation 75rnm thick 2m wide 100m long.
Use Bomag BW 655. DTp clause 802 requires 6 passes of this mass of double roller.

Factors affecting this output. Uneven surface – 0.75 to 1.0.
Job efficiency normal 0.83.

Area to be consolidated 2 x 100 = 200m^2 width of roll .65m length to be rolled
200 divided by 0.65m = 308m @ 1.4km per hr. x .75 surface factor x 0.83
efficiency factor = 0.87km hour.

308m @0.870kmlh = 0.35 hr. 6 passes 2.12 hr

100m^2 75mm granular material consolidated in 0.69 hr

Compaction by vibrating roller – heavy

Bomag BW 90S width .90m

Double vibrating roller	
Pedestrian controlled.	
Mass	= 1300kg
Speed 1st gear .67mph	= 1.08km/hr
2nd gear 1.75	= 2.82

Compaction is specified as:

Mass per metre width of roll
Number of passes for varying thickness of material

BW90S Bomag Example 2.

Compact granular material in road formation.
li0rnm thick 5m wide 100m long.

Mass	= 1300kg per .90m
	= 1440kg per m

DTp clause 802 requires 3 passes of this mass of a double roller. Factors affecting this output.

Uneven surface, factors vary .75 to 1.0	
Job efficiency normal	= 0.83
Area to be consolidated	= 100 x 5 = 500m^2
Width of roll = .9m	
Length to be rolled 500 divided by .9	= 555m

555m @ 1.08km/h x .75 surface factor	
x 0.83 efficiency factor	
	= 0.67km/h
555 @ 670m/hr	= 0.828 hr
3 passes	= 2.484 hr

100m^2, 110mm granular material consolidated in **0.45 hours**

SECTION 4:
ECONOMIC FORECAST

SECTION 4 - ECONOMIC FORECAST

The UK economy is tentatively stepping out of the shadow of the recession that was experienced in 2008 until the second quarter of 2009. Gross Domestic Product (GDP) has risen for the last three quarters and has increased by 2.7% from this time last year. The British Chamber of Commerce expects this growth to continue with an annual growth rate of 1.3% predicted for 2010 and a figure of 2% for 2011.

The Bank of England has maintained a base interest rate of 0.5% since 5 March 2009. This is the lowest rate of interest since the Bank of England came into existence over three centuries ago. The intention was to stimulate the economy and from looking at the figures quoted above it is evident that this has had some success. However, with this success there appears to be a lack of balance developing in the economy.

The Consumer Price Index (CPI) is running at an annual change of 3.2% for the month of June. This is well above the current government target of 2%. One of the reasons for the increase stems from the rise in the price of housing and household services, both key goods in the CPI basket. The government have issued their inflation projections for the next three years and believe that overall inflation for 2010 will be 2.7%, inflation for the year 2011 will be 2.4% and for the year 2012, 1.9%. The Bank of England's reluctance to increase the interest rate despite the above target inflation indicates that they do not believe that the economic recovery is robust enough to deal with any negative monetary policy.

One of the key indicators concerning the UK economy is the housing market. Figures from the Office for National Statistics show that from April 2009 to April 2010 house prices rose by 10%. Forecasts indicate that prices are likely to remain at this level with little chance of a fall in price. There still appears to be a problem with commercial banks passing on the low interest rates to end buyers or developers. Bank of England mortgage approvals stayed static for May 2010 at 49,815. However, this is an increase of three thousand approvals in comparison with May 2009.

Unemployment is still a source of concern for the economy. The current level of 7.8% accounts for 2.47 million jobless. This figure is predicted to continue to rise with forecasts suggesting that the figure will peak in the second quarter of 2013 and stand at 2.9 million jobless people. Whilst the economy in general is growing the labour market is lagging behind in its recovery.

A big change that will affect the future of the economy is the new government, formed in May 2010. The Conservative Liberal Democrat coalition has outlined a new austerity package designed to decrease the deficit that the UK is currently burdened with. Amongst these measures are huge public expenditure cuts, to be finally decided with a comprehensive spending review on 20th October 2010, and a rise in the level of VAT from 17.5% to 20% with effect from 4 January 2011. The main area of concern within the construction trade with regard to these measures comes from infrastructure projects. Whilst 60% of spending is private in this area a reduction in government spending would clearly have a considerable impact on overall figures. Despite this the sector is likely to continue to outperform the rest of the construction industry.

In the first quarter of 2010 construction output was down 3.7% on last year and 18% down from the first quarter of 2008. Forecasts suggest that this figure will continue to fall in the future particularly when taking into account some of the new government's measures such as the scrapping of the Building Schools for the Future initiative. The Construction Products Association predicts a contraction of 3% this year followed by increases of 1% for the years 2011, 2012 and 2013. Construction continues to be hit hard by the problems of 2008-2009 and it seems that there is still some way to go until a full recovery is seen.

Building tender prices in the UK were down by 0.5% in the first quarter of 2010 in comparison to the previous quarter. They are predicted to continue falling until the third quarter of 2010 before stagnating and starting to rise in the first quarter of 2011. This rise in 2011 is likely to be in part due to rising input costs which contractors will have difficulty in absorbing. Civil engineering tender prices are predicted to fall this year by 0.7% before rising by 3% from second quarter of 2011 and the second quarter of 2012. Civil engineering input cost indices have been more robust against the economic problems of the past and have been continually rising since November 2009. At the time of writing provisional figures indicate that there has been a 7.4% increase in this index between May 2009 and May 2010.

Input costs have risen by 3.5% between March 2009 and March 2010. This upward pressure is likely to lead to an increase in tender prices over time but will certainly lead to pressures for contractors whilst the tender market is so competitive. The biggest increase has come from plant costs which have risen by 7.7% over the year 2009 to 2010.

Oil prices are expected to rise throughout 2010 and by December it is predicted that the price will have reached $95 per barrel with the price at $75.35 in June 2010. With oil being one of the key components of the construction trade either profit margins will have to be trimmed even further or tender prices will have to rise. These price rises in commodities illustrate the tension which contractors face between maintaining their skilled staff base by winning contracts at low prices and being able to make it through to better times in the industry.

With many other commodities such as steel, a 18.2% rise from June 2009 to June 2010, also beginning to increase in price due to the waking global economy it remains to be seen whether the market can respond to increased demand for products with an increased supply or if it will lead to more inflationary pressure. The signs are that there could be increasing prices over the next year and this will have to be managed effectively in order for project costs to stay within budget.

SECTION 5:
WORKING RULE AGREEMENT

SECTION 5 - WORKING RULE AGREEMENT

The employment of labour within the civil engineering industry in Great Britain is governed by the Working Rule Agreement - often abbreviated to WRA – produced by the Construction Industry Joint Council. This Council is made up of representatives from Unions, Trade bodies and Employers and meets regularly to modify and amend the WRA from time to time.

This section summarises some of the WRA that commonly has an impact upon the rates of wages paid to operatives.

The WRA is available from the Construction Industry Joint Council (at the address shown in Section 6: Professional, Government and Trade Bodies).

The current edition of the WRA is effective from 30 June 2010. The following selected extracts are reproduced with kind permission of the Construction Industry Joint Council who holds the copyright.

Scope of these Extracts

The total scope and coverage of the WRA is best derived from an appraisal of the Index of the Agreement which is reproduced in full below.

Those sections which are reproduced are marked with an asterisk.

INDEX

SCHEDULE 1*

Specified Work

- Bar Benders
- Concrete
- Drilling and Blasting
- Dry Liners
- Fonnwork Carpenters
- Gangers and Trade Chargehands
- Gas Distribution
- Linesmen - Erectors
- Linesmen - Erectors' Mate

Mechanical Plant

- Banksmen
- Compressors and Generators
- Concrete Placing Equipment
- Derricks (Stationery or Travelling)
- Drag Shovel
- Dumpers and Dump Trucks
- Excavators (360 degree slewing, rope or hydraulic)
- Fork Lift Trucks
- Locos
- Miscellaneous Cranes, etc.
- Mixers
- Mobile Cranes, Hoist or Fork Lift Trucks
- Motor Graders
- Motor Vehicles (Road Licensed Vehicles with the Construction and Use Regulations)
- Motorised Scrapers
- Power Driven Tools
- Power Rollers
- Pumps
- Shovel Loaders, Wheeled or Tracked
- Smooth or Rough Terraine (Fork Lift Trucks)
- Tower Cranes (including travelling or climbing)
- Tractors (Agricultural)
- Tractors (Wheeled or Tracked - with or without equipment such as buckets, blades, loaders, backhoes)
- Trenching Machine (Multi Bucket)
- Winches

Pavoirs, Masons, etc

Piling

Pipe Jointers

Pipelayers

Plate Layer

Post Tensioning and Pre-Stressing Concrete

Qualified Bar Benders and Reinforcement Fixers

Rolled Asphalt Road Surfacing Work, Tar and/or Bitumen Macadam Surfacing Work

- Chipper
- Leveller on Mechanical Spreader
- Mixing Platform Chargehand
- Power Roller
- Operator of Mechanical Spreader
- Raker
- Tamperman

Scaffolders (See WR.26)

Skilled Mechanics

Maintenance Mechanic
Contractors' Plant Mechanic
Contractors' Plant Mechanic's Mate
Greaser
Tyre Fitter

Steelwork Construction

Tar Spraying, Manual or Mechanical

Timberman

Tunnels

Welders

Opencast Coal Washeries and Screening Plants
(where work is ancillary to civil engineering works)

Young Workers

SCHEDULE 2*

Entitlement to additional rates of pay for intermittent skill, responsibility or working in adverse conditions

- Stone Cleaning
- Tunnels
- Sewer work
- Working at height

WR.1 ENTITLEMENT TO BASIC AND ADDITIONAL RATES OF PAY

Operatives employed to carry out work in the Building and Civil Engineering Industry are entitled to basic pay in accordance with this Working Rule (W.R.1.), Rates of pay are set out in a separate schedule, published periodically by the Council.

Classification of basic and additional pay rates of operatives:

General Operative
Skilled Operative Rate:- 4
3
2
1
Craft Operative

1.1 General Operatives

1.1.1 General Operatives employed to carry out general building and/or civil engineering work are entitled to receive the "General Operatives Basic Rate of Pay".

Payment for Occasional Skilled Work

1.1.2 General Operatives, employed as such, who are required to carry out building and/or civil engineering work defined in Schedule 1, on an occasional basis, are entitled to receive the "General Operative Basic Rate of Pay" increased to the rate of pay specified in Schedule 1 for the hours they are engaged to carry out the defined work.

1.2 Skilled Operatives

1.2.1 Skilled Operatives engaged and employed whole time as such, who are required to carry out skilled building and/or civil engineering work defined in Schedule 1 on a continuous basis, are entitled to the "Basic Rate of Pay" specified in Schedule 1.

1.3 Craft Operatives

Craft operatives employed to carry out craft building and/or civil engineering work are entitled to receive the "Craft Operative Basic Rate of Pay".

1.4 Additional Payments for Intermittent Skill, Responsibility or Working in Adverse Conditions.

1.4.1. While carrying out duties specified in Schedule 2 of the Working Rule Agreement, an operative shall be entitled, during the hour he is so engaged, to an additional payment as specified in Schedule 2.

Note: **Normal hourly rate**
The expression "normal hourly rate" in this agreement means the craft, skilled or general operatives' weekly basic rate of pay as above, divided by the hours defined in Working Rule. 3 "Working Hours". Additional payments for intermittent skill or responsibility, occasional skilled work, work at heights, work in adverse conditions or bonus payments are not taken into account for calculating the "normal hourly rate".

WR.1 ENTITLEMENT TO BASIC AND ADDITIONAL RATES OF PAY

Classification	Basic pay (pence per hour)	Weekly Rates based on 39 hours £
General Operative	(775p)	302.25
Skill Rate 4	(835p)	325.65
3	(885p)	345.15
2	(946p)	368.94
1	(982p)	382.98
Craft Rate	(1030p)	401.70

WR. 1.2.2 Additional Payment for Skilled Work
Skilled Operative Additional Rate

A	(17p)	6.63
B	(28p)	10.92
C	(37p)	14.43
D	(42p)	16.38
E	(64p)	24.96

WR.2 BONUS

It shall be open to employers and employees on any job to agree a bonus scheme based on measured output and productivity for any operation or operations on that particular job.

SCHEDULE 1

Specified Work Establishing Entitlement to the Skilled Operative Pay Rate 4, 3, 2, 1 or Craft Rate

	Rates of Pay Basic	Additional
QUALIFIED BAR BENDERS AND REINFORCEMENT FIXERS	Craft rate	
Bender and fixer of Concrete Reinforcement capable of reading and understanding drawings and bending schedules and able to set out work Craft Rate		
CONCRETE	4.	
Concrete Leveller or Vibrator Operator.......		
Screeder and Concrete Surface Finisher man working off forms or other datum (e.g. road-form or concrete haunch, or edge beam or wire) man required by his employer to use trowel or hand or powered float to produce high quality finished concrete		
DRILLING AND BLASTING		
Drills, rotary or percussive: mobile rigs, operator of....	3.	
Operative attending drill rig..........	4.	
Shotfirer, operative in control of and responsible for explosives, including placing, connecting and detonating charges.	3.	
Operatives attending on shotfirer, including stemming	4.	
FORMWORK CARPENTERS		
1st year trainee.....	4.	
2nd year trainee....	3.	
Formwork Carpenters	Craft Rate	
Craft Rate		
GANGERS AND TRADE CHARGEHANDS		
(Higher Grade payments may be made at the employer's discretion).....	4.	
GAS DISTRIBUTION		
Operatives who have successfully completed approved training to the standard of: Gas Distribution Operative		
Category 1 and 2....	4.	
Category 3.....	3.	
Team Leader - Service layer....	2.	
Team Leader - Main Layer....	1.	
Team Leader - Main and Service Layer....	1.	
LINESMEN - ERECTORS		
1st Grade	2.	
(Skilled in all works associated with the erection of O.H. Transmission Lines including Assembly and Erection of Steel Towers; Concrete and Wood Poles of all types; Insulators and O.H. Line Switchgear; Stringing, tensioning, sagging, jointing, clamping and making off all types of O.H. conductors; making off stay wires; also similar structures and other works appertaining thereto.)		
2nd Grade	3.	
(As above but lesser degree of skill - or competent and fully skilled either in assembly and erection of all types of supports or assembly and erection of the insulators, conductors, stay wires - all as specified above.)		
LINESMEN - ERECTORS' MATE		
(Semi-skilled in works specified above and a general helper.)	4.	
SKILLED MECHANICS		
Maintenance Mechanic on site, i.e. man capable of carrying out field service, maintenance, and minor repairs ancillary to civil engineering works....	2.	
Contractors' Plant Mechanic in shop, depot or on site, i.e. man capable of carrying out major repairs and overhauls including welding work, operating turning lathe or similar machine and/or carrying out highly skilled work ancillary to civil engineering works....	1.	
Contractors' Plant Mechanics' Mate on site or in depot...	4.	
Greaser on site, servicing machines...	4.	
Tyre Fitter, heavy earthmover tyres...	2.	

MECHANICAL PLANT	
Compressors and Generators	
Air compressors diesel or petrol or generators over 10 KW operator or Driver of...	4.
Concrete Placing Equipment	
Portable or static concrete pumps; pneumatic concrete placers; concrete placing booms; operator of...	4.
Self-propelled Mobile Concrete Pump, with or without boom, mounted on lorry or lorry chassis; driver/operator of...	3.
Mobile Cranes, Hoists or Fork-Lift Trucks	
Self-propelled Mobile Crane on road wheels or caterpillar tracks including lorry mounted:	
Capacity up to and including 5 tons (or metric tonnes); driver of...	4.
Capacity up to and including 10 tons (or metric tonnes); driver of...	3.
Capacity over 10 tons (or metric tonnes)	
Where grabs are attached to Cranes the next higher skilled basic rate of pay applies except over 10 tons (or metric tonnes) where the rate is at the employer's discretion.	Craft Rate
Tower Cranes (including travelling or climbing)	
Up to and including 2 tons (or metric tonnes) maximum lifting capacity at minimum radius; driver of...	4.
Over 2 tons (or metric tonnes) up to and including 10 tons (or metric tonnes) lifting capacity at minimum radius; driver Of.....	3.
Over 10 tons (or metric tonnes) up to and including 20 tons (or metric tonnes) lifting capacity at minimum radius; driver Of.....	2.
Over 20 tons (or metric tonnes) lifting capacity at minimum radius; driver of.....	1.
Miscellaneous Cranes, etc.	
Overhead traveller or gantry up to and including 10 tons (or metric tonnes) capacity; driver of....	3.
Loco traveller up to and including 10 tons (or metric tonnes) capacity; driver of....	3.
Power driven Hoist/crane; driver of.....	4.
Where grabs are attached to Cranes....	3.
Derricks (Stationary or Travelling)	
Power-driven derrick: capacity up to and including 20 tons (or metric tonnes); driver of....	3.
Capacity over 20 tons (or metric tonnes); driver of....	2.
Where grabs are attached to Derricks the next higher skilled Operative Basic Rate of pay applies.	
Banksmen appointed to attend Crane, hoist or Derrick and to be responsible for fastening or slinging loads and generally to direct Crane hoist or Derrick Driver....	4.
Smooth or Rough Terrain fork lift trucks or side loader up to and including 3 tons (or metric tonnes) capacity driver of......	4.
Over 3 tons (or metric tonnes) capacity driver of....	3.
Dumpers and Dump Trucks	
Up to and including 7 tons (or metric tonnes) carrying capacity; driver of....	4.
Over 7 tons (or metric tonnes) and up to and including 16 tons (or metric tonnes) carrying capacity; driver of....	3.
Over 16 tons (or metric tonnes) and up to and including 60 tons (or metric tonnes) carrying capacity; driver of....	2.
Over 60 tons (or metric tonnes) and up to and including 125 tons (or metric tonnes) carrying capacity; driver of.....	1.
Over 125 tons (or metric tonnes) carrying capacity; driver of....	Craft Rate
Excavators (360 degree slewing, rope or hydraulic)	
Excavators with rated bucket capacity up to and including - cu. yd. (0.6 cu. metres); driver of....	3.
Excavator with rated bucket capacity over - cu. yd. (0.6 cu. metres) and up to and including 5 cu. yds (3.85 cu. metres); driver of....	2.
Excavator with rated bucket capacity over 5 cu. yds. (3.85 cu. metres)	1.
Operative attending excavator or responsible for positioning vehicles during loading of tipping....	4.
Shovel Loaders, Wheeled or Tracked	
See Tractors and Equipments.	
Locos	
Loco all; driver of....	4.

Mixers	
Mortar Pan or Concrete Mixer up to but not including 21/4 (or 400 litres) wet capacity, to apply to one man only per machine; man employed on, and actually responsible for, operating....	4.
Mixer Concrete 21/14 and up to and including 2 cu. yds. (or 400 litres and up to but not including 1,500 litres) wet capacity, to apply to one man only per machine; man employed on, and actually responsible for, operating....	3.
Mixer Concrete of over 2 cu. yds. (or 1,500 litres) wet capacity, to apply to one man only per machine; man employed on, and actually responsible for, operating....	2.
Mixer Concrete, mobile self-loading and batching up to 2,500 litres wet capacity, to apply to one man only per machine; man employed on, and actually responsible for, operating....	2.
Drag Shovel: operative of...	4.
Motor Graders	
Motor Grader; driver of....	2.
Motor Vehicles (Road Licensed Vehicles within the Construction and Use Regulations)	
Vehicle up to and including 7.5 tons (or metric tonnes); driver of....	4.
Operations requiring a LGV Licence of either or both Classes C & E; driver of....	1.
Motorised Scrapers	
Motorised Scraper; driver of....	2.
Power Driven Tools	
Operatives using power-driven tools such as breakers, percussive drills, picks and spades, rammers and tamping machines....	4.
Pumps	
Power-driven pump(s); attendant of....	4.
Power Rollers	
Roller up to but not including 4 tons (or metric tonnes); driver of....	4.
Roller, 4 tons (or metric tonnes) and upwards; driver of....	3.
Tractors (Agricultural)	
Tractor, rubber-tyred agricultural type, when used to tow trailer and/or with mounted compressor; driver of....	4.
Tractors (Wheeled or Tracked - with or without equipment such as buckets, blades, loaders, backhoes)	
Tractor, up to and including 100 h.p.; driver of....	3.
Tractor, over 100 h.p. up to and including 400 h.p.; driver of....	2.
Tractor, over 400 h.p. up to and including 650 h.p. driver of....	1.
Tractor, over 650 h.p.; driver of....	Craft Rate
Trenching Machine (Multi Bucket)	
Trenching Machine, up to and including 30 h.p.; driver of....	4.
Trenching Machine, over 30 h.p. and up to and including 70 h.p.; driver of....	3.
Trenching Machine, over 70 h.p.; driver of....	2.
Winches	
Power driven winch; driver of....	4.
PAVIORS, MASONS, ETC.	
Paviors Rammerman...	4.
Kerb & Paving Jointer....	4.
Operative engaged in face pitching or dry walling....	3.
PILING	
General; Skilled Piling Operative....	4.
Piling Ganger/Chargehand....	3.
Pile Frame Winch Driver....	3.
Rotary or Specialist Mobile Piling Rig Driver....	2.
PIPE JOINTERS	
Jointers, Stoneware or Concrete Pipes....	4.
Jointers working on flexible joints or setting up or caulking lead joints under 12 in. (or 300 mm,) dia....	4.
Jointers working on flexible joints or setting up or caulking lead joints of 12in. (or 300 mm.) dia and over....	4.
Jointers, Cast Iron or Steel Pipes using lead....	4.

EXCEPT
(a) in mains of 12 in. dia. up to and including 21 in. dia (or 300 rom. dia. up to and including 535 mm. dia.) when experienced in all or any of the following operations: 3.
i) Jointing with run lead
ii) Jointing with cold strip lead, wool or similar type
(b) on mains of over 21 in. (or 535 mm.) dia. when so experienced.... 2.

PIPELAYERS
Men preparing the bed and laying pipes up to 12 in. (or 300 mm.) dia... 4.

PLATE LAYER
not labourer in gang.... 3.

POST TENSIONING AND PRE-STRESSING CONCRETE
Operative in control of and responsible for hydraulic jacks and other tensioning devices engaged in post-tensioning and/or pre-stressing whilst so employed (not labourer in gang).... 3.

SCAFFOLDERS
See WR.26

STEELWORK CONSTRUCTION
Men fully skilled in and engaged in the assembly erection and fixing of steel-framed construction of a permanent nature ancillary to civil engineering works.... 1.
Operative capable of and engaged in fixing simple steelwork and structures ancillary to civil engineering works.... 3.

TAR SPRAYING, MANUAL OR MECHANICAL
Chargehand.... 4.
Spraybar Operators.... 4.
Gritter Operators.... 4.

TIMBERMAN
Timberman.... 3.
Except in cases where the timbering required calls for a special degree of skill, as, for example, in running sand and/or cofferdams, or where walings, struts and/or rakers are of 10 in. by 5 in. (or 250 mm, by 125 mm.) nominal or large timbers, in which cases the rates shall be.... 2.
Operative attending.... 4.

TUNNELS
Operative working below ground on the construction or reconstruction of Tunnels or sinking shafts for Tunnels in hard rock or soft ground:
Face Tunnelling machine; operator of.... 2.
Tunnel Miner (the skilled operative working at the face, or machineman working a drifter type of machine).... 3.
Tunnel Miner's mates (the operative who assists the miner at the face or break-up, including such men who work pneumatic tools or breakers, and/or in a soft tunnel, prepare the timber).... 4.
(The above tunnel rates are exclusive of plus rate payments prescribed for work in active foul or surface water sewers but inclusive of any other plus rate payment for conditions which might otherwise apply.)
Other operatives engaged in driving headings over 2 metres in length from the entrance, in connection with drain cable and main laying.... 4.

WELDERS
Gas or electric arc welder capable of welding mild steel and building up to normal welds, ancillary to civil engineering work, when so required.... 2.
Electric arc welder able and required to weld to highest standards for structural fabrication and simple pressure vessels (air receivers), including C02 processes, ancillary to civil engineering works.... 1.
Electric arc welder able and required to undertake all welding processes on all weldable materials, ancillary to civil engineering works, including working on his own initiative from drawings.... Craft Rate

Opencast Coal Washeries and Screening Plants (where work is ancillary to civil engineering works).
Screening Plant Machine Operators, Operatives employed and responsible for controlling:
Mechanical equipment in a dry coal plant, or a washing plant machine.... 4.

ROLLED ASPHALT ROAD SURFACING WORK, TAR AND/OR BITUMEN MACADAM SURFACING WORK
Operatives employed on this class of work to be paid as follows:

Raker....	3.
Tamperman....	4.
Chipper....	4.
Mixing Platform Chargehand....	4.
Power Roller, 4 tons (or metric tonnes) and upwards driver of....	3.
Operator of Mechanical Spreader of the Barber-Greene or similar type....	3.
Leveller on Mechanical Spreader of the Barber-Greene or similar type....	3.

(3) The hours of work as set in this Working Rule Agreement shall apply to this class of work, subject to the proviso that due to the exceptional circumstances of the work and the desirability of keeping work going continuously, it is necessary to limit intervals for meals to a period of half-hour each.

*(4) In the event of a breakdown of plant (including haulage plant) or of conditions arising which make it necessary or desirable in the interests of the job to cease work on the job for any period exceeding one hour, the following arrangements shall apply:

(a) If the operatives who have to cease work are given alternative work, hours worked either on that work, or on Rolled Asphalt Road Surfacing Work after the end of the normal working day they shall be paid at the over time rates in accordance with WR. 4 Overtime Rates,

(b) If the operatives who have to cease work are not given alternative work but are notwithstanding paid for the period of such stoppage, work may be continued beyond what would otherwise be the normal working day for a period equal to the total of the periods of such stoppages, but not exceeding three hours at ordinary hourly rates, and after a period of three hours, at the overtime rate prescribed by WR.4 Overtime Rates as if the day had ended at the time at which ordinary hourly rates cease to be payable.

*NOTE - Para 4 does not apply to Tar Macadam Surfacing Work.

Operatives below 18 years of age will receive payment 60% of the General Operatvies basic rate or relevant rate.

Dry-liners

Operatives undergoing approved training in dry-lining operations....	4.
Operatives who can produce a certificate of training achievement indicating satisfactory completion of approved dry-lining training module (iii) (iv) or (v)....	3.

SCHEDULE 2

Entitlement to additional rates of pay for intermittent skill, responsibility or working in adverse conditions.

			Extra Rate
1.4.1	STONE CLEANING	Operatives other than craft operatives employed on dry-cleaning stone-work by mechanical process for the removal of protective material and/or discoloration....	E
1.4.2	TUNNELS	Operatives (other than Tunnel Machine Operators, Tunnel Miners and Tunnel Miners' Mates) wholly or mainly engaged in work of actual construction including the removal and dumping of mined materials but excluding operatives whose employment in the tunnel is occasional and temporary:	
		In unlined tunnels....	A
		(The above tunnels are exclusive of extra payments prescribed for work in active foul or surface water sewers, but inclusive of any other extra payment for conditions which might otherwise apply).	
1.4.3	SEWER WORK	Operatives working within a totally enclosed active foul sewer of any nature or condition....	D
		Operatives working within a totally enclosed active surface water sewer of any nature or condition.	B
		Operatives working outside existing sewers excavating or removing foul materials emanating from existing sewers....	C
1.4.4	WORKING AT HEIGHT	Operatives (including drivers of tower cranes, but excluding the drivers of power driven derricks on high stages and linesmen-erectors and their mates and scaffolders) employed on "detached work" shall receive in respect of conditions extra payments on the following scale calculated from the "point of departure".	
		Above 45m and up to 90m....	C
		Thereafter a further extra payment at the same rate for each additional 45metres....	
		For the purpose of this rule "detached work" shall be deemed to comprise work on detached "tower like structures" whether completely detached or rising above and being connected to a main structure. In the latter case the "point of departure" shall be the level at which the detached structure leaves the top of the main structure.	

SCHEDULE 2

Extra Rate	(pence per hour)	Weekly Rates based on 39 hours (£)
A	(17p)	6.63
B	(28p)	10.92
C	(37p)	14.43
D	(42p)	16.38
E	(64p)	24.96

SECTION 6:
PROFESSIONAL, GOVERNMENT AND TRADE BODIES

SECTION 6 - PROFESSIONAL, GOVERNMENT & TRADE BODIES

List below are some of the organisations in central and local government, public utilities, trade and professional bodies which are most relevant to the Civil Engineering Industry.

Advisory, Conciliation and Arbitration Service
Brandon House
180 Borough High Street
London
SE1 1LW
Telephone: 0207 210 3613

The Architect and Surveyors Institute
St Mary House
15 St. Mary Street
Chippenham
Wiltshire
SN15 3WD
Telephone: 0124 944 4505
Fax: 0124 944 3602

Association of Consulting Engineers
Alliance House
12 Caxton Street
London
SW1H 9QL
Telephone: 0207 222 6557
Fax: 0207 222 0750

Association of Cost Engineers
Lea House
5 Middlewich Road
Sandbach
Cheshire
CW11 1XL
Telephone: 0127 076 4798
Fax: 0127 076 6180

British Board of Agreement
P O Box No 195
Bucknalls Lane
Garston
Watford
Hertfordshire
WD2 7NG
Telephone: 0192 366 5300
Fax: 0192 366 5301

British Cement Association
Century House
Telford Avenue
Crowthorne
Berks
RG45 6YS
Telephone: 0134 476 2676
Fax: 0134 476 1214

British Constructional Steelwork Association
4 Whitehall Court
Westminster
London
SW1A 2ES
Telephone: 0207 839 8566
Fax: 0207 976 1634

British Geotechnical Society
Administered by the BGS Secretary at the Institution of Civil Engineers

British Precast Concrete Federation
60 Charles Street
4th Floor
Leicester
Leicestershire
LE1 1FB
Telephone: 0116 253 6161
Fax: 0116 251 4568

British Railway Board
Whittles House
14 Pentonville Road
LONDON
N1 9HF
Telephone: 0207 904 5079

British Road Federation
Pillar House 194-202 Old Kent Road
London
SE1 5TG
Telephone: 0207 703 9769
Fax: 0207 701 0029

British Standards Institute (BSI)
389 Chiswick High Road
London
W4 4AL
Telephone: 0208 996 9000
Fax: 0208 996 7001

British Waterways Board
Willow Grange
Church Road
Watford
WD17 4QA
Hertfordshire
Telephone: 0192 320 1120
Fax: 0192 320 1304

Building Research Establishment
Bucknalls Lane
Garston
Watford
Herts
WD25 9XX
Telephone: 0192 366 4000
Fax: 0192 366 4010

Building Services Research and Information Association
Old Bracknell Lane West
Bracknell
Berkshire
RG12 7AH
Telephone: 0134 446 5600
Fax: 0134 446 5626

Chartered Institute of Building
Englemere
King's Ride
Ascot
Berkshire
SL5 7TB
Telephone: 0134 463 0700
Fax: 0134 463 0777

The Chartered Institution of Building Services Engineers
222 Balham High Road
Balham
London
SW12 9BS
Telephone: 0208 675 5211
Fax: 0208 675 5449

Clay Pipe Development Association Limited
Copsham House
53 Broad St
Chesham
Buckinghamshire
HP5 3EA
Telephone: 0149 479 1456
Fax: 0149 479 2378

The Concrete Society
Riverside House
4 Meadows Business Park
Station Approach
Blackwater, Camberley
Surrey
GU17 9AB
Telephone: 0127 660 7140
Fax: 0127 660 7141

Construction Confederation
55 Tufton Street
Westminster
London
SW1P 3QL
Telephone: 0870 898 9090
Fax: 0870 898 9095

Construction Industry Computing Association
National Computing Centre
Oxford House
Oxford Road
Manchester
M1 7ED
Telephone: 0161 242 2262

Construction Federation
55 Tufton Street
London
SW1P 3QL
Telephone: 0207 227 4500
Fax: 0207 227 4501

Construction Industry Research and Information Association (CIRIA)
Classic House
174 - 180 Old Street
London
EC1V 9BP
Telephone: 0207 549 3300
Fax: 0207 253 0523

Construction Industry Training Board
Bircham Newton
Kings Lynn
Norfolk
PE31 6RH
Telephone: 0148 557 7577
Fax: 0148 557 7793

Construction Plant Hire Association (CPA)
27/28 Newbury Street
Barbican
London
EC1A 7HU
Telephone: 0207 796 3366
Fax: 0207 796 3399

Department for Environment, Food & Rural Affairs (Defra)
Eastbury House
30 - 34 Albert Embankment
London
SE1 7TL
Telephone: 0207 238 2188
Fax: 0207 238 2188

Department for Business, Innovation & Skills
1 Victoria Street
London
SW1H 0ET
Telephone: 0207 215 5000
Fax: 0207 215 0105

Ductile Iron Pipe Association (DIPA)
The National Metalforming Centre
47 Birmingham Road
West Bromwich
West Midlands
B70 6PY
Telephone: 0121 601 6390
Fax: 0121 601 6391

Health and Safety Executive
Rose Court
2 Southwark Bridge
London
SE1 9HS
Telephone: 0207 556 2100
Fax: 0207 556 2102

Heating and Ventilating Contractors' Association
HVCA Head Office
Esca House
34 Palace Court
London
W2 4JG
Telephone: 0207 313 4900
Fax: 0207 727 9268

Centre for Ecology and Hydrology (CEH)
CEH Wallingford
Maclean Building
Benson Lane
Crowmarsh Gifford
Wallingford
Oxfordshire
OX10 8BB
Telephone: 0149 183 8800
Fax: 0149 169 2424

Chartered Management Institute
3rd Floor
2 Savoy Court
Strand
London
WC2R 0EZ
Telephone: 0207 497 0580
Fax: 0207 497 0463

Institute of Measurement and Control
87 Gower Street
London
WC1E 6AF
Telephone: 0207 387 4949
Fax: 0207 388 8431

The Chartered Quality Institute
12 Grosvenor Crescent
London
SW1X 7EE
Telephone: 0207 245 6722
Fax: 0207 245 6788

Institution of Civil Engineering Surveyors (ICES)
Dominion House
Sibson Road
Sale
Cheshire
M33 7PP
Telephone: 0161 972 3100
Fax: 0161 972 3118

Institution of Civil Engineers (ICE)
One Great George Street
Westminster
London
SW1P 3AA
Telephone: 0207 222 7722

The Institution of Engineering Designers
Courtleigh
Westbury Leigh
Westbury
Wiltshire
BA13 3TA
Telephone: 0137 382 2801
Fax: 0137 385 8085

Institution of Gas Engineers and Managers
Charnwood Wing
Holywell Park
Ashby Road
Loughborough
Leicestershire
LE11 3GH
Telephone: 0150 928 2728
Fax: 0150 928 3110

Institution of Mechanical Engineers
1 Birdcage Walk
Westminster
London
SW1H 9JJ
Telephone: 0207 222 7899
Fax: 0207 222 4557

Institute of Materials, Minerals and Mining
Danum House
South Parade
Doncaster
DN1 2DY
Telephone: 0130 232 0486
Fax: 0130 238 0900

The Institution of Nuclear Engineers
Allan House
1 Penerley Road
London
SE6 2LQ
Telephone: 0208 698 1500
Fax: 0208 695 6409

Institution of Plant Engineers (IPlantE)
22 Greencoat Place
Westminster London
SW1P 1PR
Telephone: 0207 630 1111
Fax: 0207 630 6677

The Institution of Structural Engineers
11 Upper Belgrave Street
London
SW1X 8BH
Telephone: 0207 235 4535
Fax: 0207 235 4294

Chartered Institution of Water and Environmental Management (CIWEM)
15 John Street
London
WC1N 2EB
Telephone: 0207 831 3110
Fax: 0207 405 4967

International Arbitration Centre
24 Angel Gate
London
EC IV 2RS
Telephone: 0207 837 4483
Fax: 0207 837 4185

Laboratory of the Government Chemist (LGC)
Queens Road
Teddington
Middlesex
TW11 0LY
Telephone: 0208 943 7000
Fax: 0208 943 2767

Meteorological Office (Met Office)
FitzRoy Road
Exeter
Devon
EX1 3PB
Telephone: 0139 288 5680
Fax: 0139 288 5681

National Assembly for Wales
Cardiff Bay
Cardiff
CF99 1NA
Telephone: 0845 010 5500

National Association of Scaffolding Contractors
18 Mansfield Street
London
W1M 9FG
Telephone: 0207 580 5404

National Federation of Painting & Decorating Contractors
18 Mansfield Street
London
W1M 9FG
Telephone: 0207 580 5404
Fax: 0207 636 5984

OFGEM (Office of Gas and Electricity Markets)
9 Millbank
London
SW1P 3GE
Telephone: 0207 901 7000
Fax: 0207 901 7066

OFRR
Office of Rail Regulation
One Kemble Street
London
WC2B 4AN
Telephone: 0207 282 2000
Fax: 0207 282 2040

OFCOM (Office of Communications)
Riverside House
2a Southwark Bridge Road
London
SE1 9HA
Telephone: 0207 981 3000
Fax: 0207 981 3333

OFWAT (Office of Water Services)
Centre City Tower
7 Hill Street
Birmingham
B5 4UA
Telephone: 0121 625 1300 / 1373
Fax: 0121 625 1400

Ordnance Survey
Customer Service Centre
Romsey Road
Southampton
SO16 4GU
Telephone: 0845 605 0505
Fax: 0238 079 2615

Pipe Jacking Association
10 Greycoat Place
London
SW1P 1SB
Telephone: 0845 070 5201
Fax: 0845 070 5202

The Pipeline Industries Guild
14/15 Belgrave Square
London
SW1X 8PS
Telephone: 0207 235 7938
Fax: 0207 235 0074

Property Services Agency
Carillion Head Office
24 Birch Street
Wolverhampton
West Midlands
WV1 4HY
Telephone: 0190 242 2431

Quarry Products Association
Gillingham House
38-44 Gillingham Street
London
SW1V 1HU
Telephone: 0207 963 8000
Fax: 0207 963 8001

Royal Institute of British Architects
66 Portland Place
London
W1B 1AD
Telephone: 0207 580 5533
Fax: 0207 255 1541

Royal Institution of Chartered Surveyors
12 Great George Street
Parliament Square
London
SW1P 3AD
Telephone: 0870 333 1600
Fax: 0207 334 3811

The Royal Town Planning Institute
41 Botolph Lane
London
EC3R 8DL
Telephone: 0207 929 9494
Fax: 0207 929 9490

Quarry Products Association
Gillingham House
38-44 Gillingham Street
London
SW1V 1HU
Telephone: 0207 963 8000
Fax: 0207 963 8001

Scottish Executive Development Department
Victoria Quay
Edinburgh
EH6 6QQ
Telephone: 0131 556 8400
Fax: 0139 779 5001

Society of Construction Law
67 Newbury Street
Wantage
Oxon
OX12 8DJ
Telephone: 0123 577 0606
Fax: 0123 577 0580

Society of Surveying Technicians
Surveyor Court
Westwood Way
Coventry
CV4 8JE
Telephone: 0207 222 7000

Water UK
1 Queen Anne's Gate
London
SW1H 9BT
Telephone: 0207 344 1844
Fax: 0207 344 1866

WRc Plc (Water Research Centre plc)
Frankland Road
Blagrove
Swindon
Wiltshire
SN5 8YF
Telephone: 0179 386 5000
Fax: 0179 386 5001

SECTION 7:
TECHNICAL INFORMATION

SECTION 7 - TECHNICAL INFORMATION

Generally

Metric Conversion Factors

	Metric	Imperial	Imperial	Metric
LENGTH	1 mm	= 0.0394 inches	1 inch	= 25.4 (exact) mm
	1 m	= 3.2808 feet	1 foot	= 0.3048 m
	1 m	= 1.0936 yards	1 yard	= 0.9144 m
	1 km	= 0.6214 miles	1 mile	= 1.6093 km
AREA	1 mm^2	= 0.0016 sq inches	1 sq inch	= 645.1600 mm^2
	1 m^2	= 10.7639 sq feet	1 sq foot	= 0.0929 m^2
	1 m^2	= 1.1960 sq yards	1 sq yard	= 0.8361 m^2
	1km^2	= 0.3861 sq mile	1 sq mile	= 2.5900 km^2
	1ha	= 2.4711 acres	1 acre	= 0.4047 ha
VOLUME	1 m^3	= 35.3147 cubic feet	1 cubic foot	= 0.0283 m^3
	1 m^3	= 1.3080 cubic yards	1 cubic yard	= 0.7646 m^3
	1 litre	= 1.7598 pints	1 pint	= 0.5683 litres
	1 litre (UK)	= 0.2200 gallons (UK)	1 gallon	= 4.5461 litres
	NOTE: 1 litre	= 1000 cm^3	1m^3	= 1000 litres
WEIGHT	1 kg	= 2.2046 pounds	1 pound	= 0.4536 kg
	1 kg	= 0.0197 hundredweight	1 hundredweight	= 50.8024 kg
	1 tonne	= 0.9842 ton	1 ton	= 1.0161 tonnes
FORCE	1 N	= 0.2248 lbf	1 pdf	= 4.4482 N
	1 kN	= 225 lbf	1 lbf	= 0.0044 kN
	1 MN	= 9.3197 tonf	1 tonf	= 0.1073 MN
	NOTE: Standard gravity (Gn) = 9.80665 m/s^2 (exactly)			
PRESSURE	1 kpa	= 0.1450 lbf/sq inch	1 lbf/sq inch	= 6.8948 kpa
	NOTE: 1 kpa = 1 kN/m^2 = 1 N/mm^2			
ENERGY (work and heat)	1 kJ	= 0.9478 Btu		
	1 Btu	= 1.055 kJ		
POWER	1 W	= 3.4121 Btu	1 Btu	= 0.2931 W
	1 kW	1.3410 hp	1 hp	= 0.7457 kW

Conversion to Metric

On the following page is a set of Conversion Tables – metres to yards (Linear, square and cubic). Readers who either by choice or compulsion are estimating in Imperial measurements may use the Metric analysis detail and convert to Imperial by using these tables, or if more convenient, the following 'rule of thumb' formula may be used for quick calculation where exact accuracy is not essential.

To convert	Deduct from metric cost
Linear metre cost to linear yard cost	one eleventh
Square metre cost to square yard cost	one sixth
Cubic metre cost to cubic yard cost	one quarter

Worked examples:

1) If the Unit Price of a cubic metre item = £9.00 per cubic metre, then the cubic yard rate = £9.00 less one quarter = £6.75. Referring to the tables, the equivalent is £6.885.

2) If the Unit Price of a square metre item = £3.40 per square metre then the square yard rate = £3.40 less one sixth = £2.83. Referring to the tables, the equivalent is £2.839.

3) If the Unit Price of a linear metre item = £1.26 per linear metre, then the linear yard rate = £1.26 less one eleventh = £1.145. Referring to the tables, the equivalent is £1.153.

Cost Conversion Tables Metres to Yards

LINEAR		SQUARE		CUBIC	
£ Metre	£ Yard	£ Metre	£ Yard	£ Metre	£ Yard
0.01	0.01	0.01	0.01	0.01	0.01
0.02	0.02	0.02	0.02	0.02	0.015
0.03	0.025	0.03	0.025	0.03	0.025
0.04	0.035	0.04	0.03	0.04	0.03
0.05	0.045	0.05	0.04	0.05	0.04
0.06	0.055	0.06	0.05	0.06	0.045
0.07	0.065	0.07	0.06	0.07	0.055
0.08	0.075	0.08	0.065	0.08	0.06
0.09	0.085	0.09	0.075	0.09	0.07
0.10	0.09	0.10	0.08	0.10	0.075
0.11	0.10	0.11	0.09	0.11	0.085
0.12	0.11	0.12	0.10	0.12	0.09
0.13	0.12	0.13	0.11	0.13	0.10
0.14	0.13	0.14	0.12	0.14	0.11
0.15	0.135	0.15	0.125	0.15	0.115
0.16	0.145	0.16	0.135	0.16	0.12
0.17	0.155	0.17	0.14	0.17	0.13
0.18	0.165	0.18	0.15	0.18	0.14
0.19	0.175	0.19	0.16	0.19	0.145
0.20	0.185	0.20	0.17	0.20	0.155
0.25	0.23	0.25	0.21	0.25	0.19
0.30	0.275	0.30	0.25	0.30	0.23
0.35	0.32	0.35	0.29	0.35	0.27
0.40	0.365	0.40	0.33	0.40	0.305
0.45	0.41	0.45	0.375	0.45	0.345
0.50	0.46	0.50	0.42	0.50	0.38
0.60	0.55	0.60	0.50	0.60	0.46
0.70	0.64	0.70	0.585	0.70	0.53
0.80	0.73	0.80	0.67	0.80	0.61
0.90	0.825	0.90	0.75	0.90	0.69
1.00	0.915	1.00	0.835	1.00	0.765
1.50	1.37	1.50	1.255	1.50	1.145
2.00	1.83	2.00	1.67	2.00	1.53
2.50	2.285	2.50	2.09	2.50	1.91
3.00	2.745	3.00	2.505	3.00	2.295
3.50	3.20	3.50	2.925	3.50	2.675
4.00	3.66	4.00	3.34	4.00	3.06
4.50	4.115	4.50	3.765	4.50	3.44
5.00	4.575	5.00	4.185	5.00	3.825
6.00	5.49	6.00	5.02	6.00	4.59
7.00	6.405	7.00	5.855	7.00	5.355
8.00	7.32	8.00	6.69	8.00	6.13
9.00	8.235	9.00	7.525	9.00	6.895
10.00	9.15	10.00	8.36	10.00	7.65

MEASUREMENT FORMULAE

Perimeters or circumferences of planes

Circle: 3.14159 x Diameter

Ellipse: 3.14159 x $\frac{\textit{(major axis; minor axis)}}{2}$

Sector: $\frac{\textit{Radius x Degrees in Arc}}{57.3}$

Surface areas of planes and solids

Circle: 3.14159 x Radius Sq

Sphere: 3.14159 x Diameter Sq

Ellipse: 0.7854 *(major axis x minor axis)*

Cylinder: *(circumference x length)* + *(2 x area of end)*

Cone: Area of base + $\frac{\textit{(circumference x slant height)}}{2}$

Frustum of cone: 3.14159 x *slant height (radius at top +radius at bottom) + area of top + area of bottom*

Pyramid: $\frac{\textit{(sum of base perimeters)}}{2}$ *slant height + area of base*

Sector of circle: $\frac{\textit{3.14159 x Degrees in Arc x Radius Sq}}{360}$

Segment of circle: Area of sector less area of triangle

Segment of arc: 2 (chord x rise) + $\frac{rise^3}{2 \times chord}$

Bellmouth at road junction: *Area 'A'* = $\frac{3}{14}$ x *Radius*^{2}

Volume of solids

Sphere: 4.1888 x *Radius*^{3}

Cone: $\frac{height}{3}$ *(area of base)*

Frustum of cone: $\frac{height}{3}$ (3.14159 x $R^2 + r^2 + Rr$) where R and r are radius of base and top

Pyramid: $\frac{height}{3}$ *(area of base)*

Frustum of pyramid: $\frac{height}{3}$ ($A + B + vAB$) where A and B are areas of base and top

Volumes of earthworks

a) Simpsons Rule for Volumes (Prismoidal formula)

The volume must be divided into an even number of prisms by an odd number of cross-sectional areas.
(V = Volume, d = constant distance between sections, A = Area)

$$V = \frac{d}{3} [(A1 + An) + 2 (A3 + A5 + \ldots + A(n-2) + 4 (A2 + A4 + \ldots + A(n-l)]$$

i.e.

$$V = \frac{d}{3} [\textit{1st + last Area + 2 (Sum of odd Areas) + 4 (Sum of even Areas)}]$$

b) End Areas Formula (Trapezoidal rule)

The total volume is divided into any number of equal portions by cross-sectional planes

$$V = \frac{d}{2} [(A1 + An) + A2 + A3 + \ldots + A(n-1)]$$

i.e.

$$V = \frac{d}{2} [\textit{(1st + last Area) + Sum of other Areas}]$$

GENERALLY

Weights of Building Materials

Material	Weight	Unit
Aggregates:		
Coarse, natural materials	1500.00	kg/m³
Coarse, natural sands:		
dry	1600.00	kg/m³
moist	1280.00	kg/m³
Aluminium:		
Cast and wrought	2770.00	kg/m³
Corrugated sheets; thickness:		
0.87mm	1.70	kg/m²
1.10mm	2.40	kg/m²
1.42 mm	2.70	kg/m²
1.89mm	3.70	kg/m²
Flat sheets; thickness:		
0.87mm	1.50	kg/m²
1.10mm	2.00	kg/m²
1.42 mm	2.40	kg/m²
1.89mm	3.40	kg/m²
Asphalt:		
damp proofing; thickness:		
20mm	42.40	kg/m²
25mm	53.00	kg/m²
30mm	63.60	kg/m²
flooring; thickness:		
20mm	42.40	kg/m²
roofing; thickness:		
20mm	43.90	kg/m²
Bitumen:		
damp proof courses BS, 743:		
type A, hessian base	3.80	kg/m²
type B, fibre base	3.30	kg/m²
type C, asbestos base	3.80	kg/m²
type D, hessian base and lead	4.40	kg/m²
type E, fibre base and lead	4.40	kg/m²
type F, asbestos base and lead	4.90	kg/m²
Bitumen macadam:		
per 25 mm thickness	57.70	kg/m²
Blockwork, per 25 mm thickness:		
clay, hollow	25.50	kg/m²
concrete, natural aggregate:		
cellular	39.90	kg/m²
hollow	34.20	kg/m²
solid	53.80	kg/m²
concrete, lightweight aggregate:		
cellular	28.30	kg/m²
hollow	25.50	kg/m²
solid	31.70	kg/m²
Blackboard	450.00	kg/m³
Brass	8500.00	kg/m³
Brickwork, per 25 mm thickness:		
clay solid:		
low density	50.00	kg/m²
medium density	53.80	kg/m²
high density	58.20	kg/m²

Weights of Building Materials continued/...

Material	Weight	Unit
clay perforated, 20% voids:		
low density	40.10	kg/m^2
medium density	43.00	kg/m^2
high density	46.10	kg/m^2
concrete solid	57.70	kg/m^2
calcium silicate, solid	50.00	kg/m^2
Cast stone	2240.00	kg/m^3
Cement	1440.00	kg/m^3
Concrete, plain:		
natural aggregates	2300.00	kg/m^3
lightweight aggregates	1760.00	kg/m^3
Concrete reinforced:		
natural aggregates	2450.00	kg/m^3
lightweight aggregates	1900.00	kg/m^3
Copper:		
cast	8730.00	kg/m^3
wrought	8940.00	kg/m^3
sheet and strip; thickness:		
0.87mm	4.90	kg/m^2
1.10 mm	6.30	kg/m^2
1.42 mm	8.30	kg/m^2
1.89mm	10.80	kg/m^2
Lead:		
cast	11325.00	kg/m^3
sheet, code:		
3	14.20	kg/m^2
4	20.40	kg/m^2
5	25.40	kg/m^2
6	28.40	kg/m^2
7	35.70	kg/m^2
8	40.30	
Lime, hydrated	720.00	kg/m^3
Plywood, per 25 mm thickness	15.00	kg/m^2
Rendering, cement and sand (1:3):		
12 mm thick	27.70	kg/m^2
18 mm thick	41.60	kg/m^2
Sand:		
dry	1600.00	kg/m^3
moist	1280.00	kg/m^3
Screeds, cement and sand (I :3):		
25mm	57.70	kg/m^2
50mm	115.40	kg/m^2
Soil, compact:		
sands and gravels	2080.00	kg/m^3
silts and clays	2000.00	kg/m^3
Steel, mild and cast	7850.00	kg/m^3
Stone, natural:		
Bath	2080.00	kg/m^3
Darley Dale	2320.00	kg/m^3
Granite, Cornish	2640.00	kg/m^3
Mantle	2720.00	kg/m^3
Portland	2240.00	kg/m^3
Terrazo paving:		
per 25mm thickness	49.50	kg/m^2
Timber:		
softwoods	500.00	kg/m^3
hardwoods	800.00	kg/m^3
Water:	1000.00	kg/m^3

EARTHWORKS

Bearing Capacities of Soils

Nature of soil:	Approximate bearing capacity; kN/m^2
Peat and bog	0 - 20
Clay, marl, loam	330 - 750
Solid chalk	110 - 450
Solid rock (unweathered)	220 - 2000
Gravel, coarse	660 - 900
Gravel, fine	450 - 660
Sand	220 - 550

Bulkage of Soils after Excavation

Nature of soil:	Approximate bulkage of 1m^3 after excavation
Vegetable soil and loam	1.25 - 1.30 m^3
Soft clay, marl	1.30 - 1.40 m^3
Sand	1.10 - 1.15 m^3
Gravel	1.20 - 1.25.m^3
Chalk	1.40 - 1.50 m^3
Stiff clay	1.40 - 1.50 m^3
Rock, weathered	1.30 - 1.40 m^3
Rock, unweathered	1.50 - 1.60 m^3

Shrinkage of Materials

NOTE: Materials increase in bulk when excavated and, on being deposited, shrink. Wet soils shrink more than dry. Rock increases in bulk when broken up and does not settle to less than its original volume. The increase in bulk is dependant on the size of the broken pieces, and varies between 40 and 60 per cent.

Nature of material	Percentage shrinkage
Clay	10%
Gravel	8%
Gravel and sand	9%
Loam and light sandy soils	12%
Loose vegetable soils	15%

Cubic metres of solid material hauled per load by various types of transporting plant

NOTES:

1) In transporting by dumpers or wagons the bulkage of the material should be taken into account. Such vehicles are rated on a volume basis, their struck measured capacity being stated. The vehicles, however, have a Heaped Capacity, the load being heaped in the vehicle. In the table the cubic metres hauled per cubic metre of Struck Measured Capacity allow for normal heaping of the loads and the bulkage of the various materials. Thus a 2 cubic metre dumper hauls 2 x 0.80 = 1.60 cubic metre of stiff clay (solid) per load.

2) In hauling excavated materials by lorry, the weight of load carried should not exceed that which the vehicle is designed to carry.

Nature of material hauled	Weight of the material in the solid. m^3 per tonne	Haulage by lorries. Cubic metres of material (solid) matrial hauled per load						The cubic metres of solid material hauled by dumpers or in wagons per m^3 of struck measured capacity
		1 tonne lorry	2 tonne lorry	3 tonne lorry	4 tonne lorry	5 tonne lorry	6 tonne lorry	
Chalk	0.44	0.44	0.88	1.32	1.76	2.20	2.64	0.70
Soft or Sandy Clay	0.57	0.57	0.14	1.71	2.28	2.85	3.42	0.85
Stiff Clay	0.53	0.53	1.06	1.59	2.12	2.65	3.18	0.80
Gravel	0.57	0.57	1.14	1.71	2.28	2.85	3.42	1.14
Loam	0.67	0.67	1.34	2.01	2.68	3.35	4.02	0.92
Marl	0.57	0.57	1.14	1.71	2.28	2.85	3.42	0.98
Sand	0.67	0.67	1.34	2.01	2.68	3.35	4.02	1.09
Soil	0.63	0.63	1.26	1.89	2.52	3.15	3.78	0.90

CONCRETE WORK

Quantities of Materials per 1m^3 **Hardened Concrete**

NOTE: The following quantities allow for the increase in bulk of moist sand and moist all-in aggregate.

Nominal mix by volume	Cement tonnes	Moist sand m^3	Gravel m^3
1:3:6	0.215	0.55	0.88
1:2:4	0.304	0.53	0.84
1:1.5:3	0.389	0.50	0.80
		Moist all-in aggregate (m^3)	
1:6	0.304	0.45	
1:9	0.214	0.52	
1:12	0.167	0.55	
Nominal mix by weight	Cement tonnes	Moist sand tonnes	Gravel tonnes
1:3:6	0.216	0.81	1.31
1:2:4	0.312	0.81	1.24
1:1.5:3	0.391	0.74	1.17
	Cement tonnes	Moist all-in aggregate (tonnes)	
1:6	0.312	2.15	
1:9	0.217	2.26	
1:12	0.172	2.38	

Quantities of Material per 1m^3 of Concrete

Grade	Quantity/m3 including waste (in tonnes)	Material
20/20	0.320	Cement
	0.630	Sand
	1.170	Gravel
25/20	0.360	Cement
	0.612	Sand
	1.137	Gravel
30/20	0.400	Cement
	0.595	Sand
	1.105	Gravel
7/40 All-in	0.180	Cement
	1.950	Aggregate
20/20 All-in	0.320	Cement
	0.180	Aggregate
25/20 All-in	0.360	Cement
	1.750	Aggregate

Quantities of Materials for Prescribed Mix Concrete

Prescribed Mix	Workability medium/high	Aggregate	Cement	(kg per m^3) Aggregate	Sand
C7.5P	Medium	20mm	235	1272	848
C7.5P	High	20mm	268	1252	835
C7.5P	Medium	40mm	240	1400	754
C7.5P	High	40mm	231	1381	743
C10P	Medium	20mm	271	1251	834
C10P	High	20mm	302	1250	833
C10P	Medium	40mm	235	1378	742
C10P	High	40mm	262	1361	733
C15P	Medium	20mm	302	1232	821
C15P	High	20mm	346	1205	804
C15P	Medium	40mm	268	1370	741
C15P	High	40mm	298	1338	718
C20P	Medium	10mm	386	1081	888
C20P	High	10mm	421	967	967
C20P	Medium	14mm	357	1070	714
C20P	High	14mm	413	1066	876
C20P	Medium	20mm	336	1312	706
C20P	High	20mm	374	1189	793

Quantities of Material for Prescribed Mix Concrete

Prescribed Mix	Workability medium/high	Aggregate	Cement	(kg per m³) Aggregate	Sand
C20P	Medium	40mm	310	1432	614
C20P	High	40mm	336	1312	706
C25P	Medium	10mm	428	1177	749
C25P	High	10mm	501	927	927
C25P	Medium	14mm	399	1134	822
C25P	High	14mm	462	1039	855
C25P	Medium	20mm	386	1278	691
C25P	High	20mm	421	1161	775
C25P	Medium	40mm	357	1399	600
C25P	High	40mm	386	1278	691
C30P	Medium	10mm	491	1026	840
C30P	High	10mm	512	1014	829
C30P	Medium	14mm	471	1159	725
C30P	High	14mm	512	1014	829
C30P	Medium	20mm	421	1257	678
C30P	High	20mm	471	1130	754
C30P	Medium	40mm	380	1356	619
C30P	High	40mm	421	1257	678

Cubic Metres of Concrete Hauled per Load Using Various Sized Lorries and Dumpers, etc.

NOTE: The data shown are based on concrete weighing 2.242 tonnes per cubic metre

Type of plant used to transport concrete	Cubic metres of concrete hauled per load or per wagon
1 tonne lorry	0.46
2 tonne lorry	0.92
3 tonne lorry	1.38
4 tonne lorry	1.83
5 tonne lorry	2.29
6 tonne lorry	2.75
1.5 m³ dumper	1.22
2m³ dumper	1.83
0.5 m³ Decauville wagon	0.46
0.7 m³ Decauville wagon	0.61

Aggregates, Cement, etc. - Approximate Average Properties

Material	Loose weight				Voids	Absorption by Weight
	Per m3 kg	Per cu. ft. lb	Per cu. yd. cwt	tons	%	%
Sand	1862					
Bone dry		116	28	1.40	30	0.4
Average	1595	100	24	1.20	39	-
Moist	1277	80	19	0.96	52	-
Gravel						
10mm to sand	1408	88	21	1.06	47	1.0
20mm to sand	1461	91	22	1.10	45	1.0
25mm to sand	1488	93	22	1.12	44	1.0
38mm to sand	1530	95	23	1.15	42	1.0
50mm to sand	1556	97	23	1.17	41	1.0
75mm to sand	1595	100	24	1.20	39	1.0
150mm to sand	1635	102	25	1.23	38	1.0
38 to 20mm	1635	102	25	1.23	38	1.0
75 to 38mm	1556	97	23	1.17	41	1.0
150 to 75mm	1461	91	22	1.10	45	1.0
225 to 150mm	1382	86	21	1.04	48	1.0
Broken stone						
10mm to sand	1250	78	19	0.94	53	2.0
20mm to sand	1303	81	20	0.98	51	2.0
25mm to sand	1330	83	20	1.00	50	2.0
38mm to sand	1370	85	20	1.03	49	2.0
50mm to sand	1382	86	21	1.04	48	2.0
Granite						
6mm to sand	1330	83	20	1.00	51	0.5
10mm to sand	1370	85	20	1.08	50	0.5

20mm to sand	1408	88	21	1.06	48	0.5
25mm to sand	1435	90	22	1.08	47	0.5
38mm to sand	1435	90	22	1.08	47	0.5
50mm to sand	1461	91	22	1.10	46	0.5
'All-in' Ballast	1795	112	27	1.35	32	0.6
Brick Hardcore	1197	75	18	0.90	35	25
Brick Aggregate						
Coarse	878	55	13	0.66	52	25
Fine	1118	70	17	0.84	39	25
Breeze Clinker						
Coarse	18	45	11	0.54	50	-
Fine	878	55	13	0.66	45	-
Foamed Slag						
Coarse	557	35	8	0.42	-	30
Fine	718	45	11	0.54	-	30
Pumice	557	35	8	0.42	-	-
Vermiculite	66	4	1	0.05	80	-
Portland Cement	1436	90	22	1.08	54	-
Chalk Lime						
Lump	718	54	11	0.45	73	-
Ground	798	50	12	0.45	70	-
Slaked	557	35	8	0.42	60	-
Gypsum Plaster						
Heavy	1000	62	15	0.75	57	-
Light	798	50	12	0.60	65	-
Plaster of Paris	918	56	14	0.69	66	-

Curing Times (at 10C)

Type of Cement	Wet curing time after completion of placing concrete (not less than)
Ordinary Portland	4 days
Sulphate-resisting Portland	4 days
Portland blast-furnace	4 days
Super-Sulphated	4 days
Rapid hardening Portland	3 days

Formwork Stripping Times

Minimum time in days	Normal weather (about 60F/16C)		*Cold weather (about 35F/2C)	
before stripping	Portland cement	Rapid hardening	Portland cement	Rapid hardening
Sides of beams, columns or walls	1	1	6	5
Soffits (props left under)				
of slabs	3	2	10	7
of beams	7	4	12	10
Removal of props				
from slabs	7	4	14	14
from beams	16	8	28	21

*These curing periods may be reduced when the materials are heated and the concrete is insulated.

Weight of Steel Bar Reinforcement

Diameter	kg/m	m/tonne	Cross-sectional area mm^2
6mm	0.222	4505	28.3
8mm	0.395	2532	50.3
10mm	0.616	1624	78.5
12mm	0.888	1126	113.1
16mm	1.579	634	201.1
20mm	2.466	406	314.2
25mm	3.854	260	490.9
32mm	6.313	158	804.2
40mm	9.864	101	1256.6
50mm	15.413	65	1963.3

Weights of steel bar reinforcement in various percentages of $1m^3$ **of concrete**

Percentage of reinforcement

Weights	0.50	0.75	1.00	1.25	1.50	1.75	2.00	2.50	3.00	3.50	4.00	4.50	5.00
kg/m³	39.00	59.00	79.00	98.00	118.00	137.00	157.00	196.00	236.00	275.00	314.00	353.00	393.00

Weights of Stainless Steel Bar Reinforcement

Diameter	kg/m	m/tonne	Cross-sectional area mm^2
10mm	0.667	1499	78.5
12mm	0.938	1066	113.1
16mm	1.628	614	201.1
20mm	2.530	395	314.2
25mm	4.000	250	490.9
32mm	6.470	155	804.2

Weights of steel fabric reinforcement

Fabric reinforcement to BS 4483

Square Mesh Fabric BS reference	Mesh Size		Wire Size		Weight/m^2 kg
	Main mm	Cross mm	Main mm	Cross mm	
A393	200	200	10	10	6.16
A252	200	200	8	8	3.95
AI93	200	200	7	7	3.02
AI42	200	200	6	6	2.22
A98	200	200	5	5	1.54

Structural Mesh Fabric BS reference	Mesh Size		Wire Size		Weight/m^2 kg
	Main mm	Cross mm	Main mm	Cross mm	
B1131	100	200	12	8	10.90
B785	100	200	10	8	8.14
B503	100	200	8	8	5.93
B385	100	200	7	7	4.53
B283	100	200	6	7	3.73
BI96	100	200	5	7	3.05

Long Mesh Fabric BS reference	Mesh Size		Wire Size		Weight/m^2 kg
	Main mm	Cross mm	Main mm	Cross mm	
C785	100	400	10	6	6.72
C503	100	400	8	5	4.34
C385	100	400	7	5	3.41
C283	100	400	6	5	2.61

Wrapping Fabric BS reference	Mesh Size		Wire Size		Weight/m^2 kg
	Main mm	Cross mm	Main mm	Cross mm	
D98	200	200	5	5	1.54
D49	100	100	2.5	2.5	0.77

Carriageway Fabric BS reference	Mesh Size		Wire Size		Weight/m² kg
	Main mm	Cross mm	Main mm	Cross mm	
C636	80-130	400	8-10	6	5.55

Floor Finishes

Description	Thickness (mm)	kg/m² (including waste) Cement	Grano-Chippings
Granolithic paving (1:2:5) to floors	12	6.6	24.8
	25	13.8	51.7
	32	17.7	66.2
	38	21.0	78.6
	50	27.7	103.4

Description	Thickness (mm)	kg/m² (including waste) Cement	Sand
Cement and sand (1:3) to floors	10	4.5	20.1
	25	11.3	50.3
	32	14.4	64.4
	38	17.1	76.5
	50	22.6	100.7

PIPEWORK

Beds, Haunches and Surrounds

100mm Concrete to Pipes – m³ per linear metre

Pipe diameter (mm)	Bed only (m³)	Bed and haunched (m³)	Bed and surround (m³)
100	0.036	0.061	0.108
150	0.041	0.074	0.133
225	0.049	0.095	0.172
300	0.057	0.118	0.213
450	0.075	0.175	0.321
600	0.093	0.237	0.442
750	0.110	0.301	0.563
900	0.127	0.371	0.699
1200	0.163	0.538	1.026
1500	0.197	0.715	1.375

150mm Concrete to Pipes – m³ per linear metre

Pipe diameter (mm)	Bed only (m³)	Bed and haunched (m³)	Bed and surround (m³)
100	0.070	0.105	0.191
150	0.077	0.125	0.226
225	0.090	0.156	0.282
300	0.100	0.188	0.340
450	0.128	0.264	0.483
600	0.155	0.346	0.635
750	0.180	0.427	0.791
900	0.206	0.528	0.960
1200	0.259	0.729	1.361
1500	0.311	0.953	1.798

225mm Concrete to Pipes – m³ per linear metre

Pipe diameter (mm)	Bed only (m³)	Bed and haunched (m³)	Bed and surround (m³)
100	0.139	0.192	0.353
150	0.152	0.225	0.402
225	0.169	0.271	0.483
300	0.187	0.318	0.562
450	0.227	0.432	0.760
600	0.268	0.547	0.970
750	0.305	0.661	1.170
900	0.343	0.782	1.395
1200	0.423	1.052	1.900
1500	0.500	1.338	2.435

Pipe Trench Excavation - Battered Sides

Based on OG Pipes (m^3 per linear metre)

Invert depth metres	Pipe Diameter (mm) Not exceeding 225	300	450	600	750	900	1200	1500
0.60	0.57	0.62	0.73	0.87	0.99	1.11	1.37	1.64
0.80	0.84	0.90	1.04	1.22	1.39	1.53	1.86	2.20
1.00	1.14	1.22	1.39	1.62	1.82	1.99	2.39	2.81
1.25	1.58	1.68	1.90	2.17	2.42	2.63	3.08	3.61
1.50	2.09	2.20	2.47	2.78	3.08	3.33	3.90	4.48
1.75	2.65	2.78	3.09	3.45	3.79	4.09	4.73	5.40
2.00	3.27	3.42	3.78	4.17	4.57	4.90	5.63	6.39
2.50	4.83	4.90	5.37	5.84	6.32	6.76	7.64	8.57
3.00	6.39	6.62	7.15	7.74	8.31	8.80	9.88	10.98
3.50	8.34	8.56	9.22	9.91	10.57	11.13	12.38	13.65
4.00	10.52	10.82	11.53	12.30	13.06	13.70	15.12	16.56
5.00	15.64	16.02	16.90	17.87	18.80	19.60	21.36	23.15
6.00	21.77	22.22	23.28	24.43	25.60	26.56	28.60	30.73
7.00	28.83	29.42	30.65	31.98	33.34	34.46	36.85	39.32

Pipe Trench Excavation – Vertical Sides

OG Pipes with Light or Medium Timber (m^3 per linear metre)

Invert depth metres	Pipe Diameter (mm) Not exceeding 225	300	450	600	750	900	1200	1500
0.60	0.47	0.52	0.62	0.75	0.87	1.00	1.24	1.50
0.80	0.62	0.68	0.82	0.98	1.14	1.30	1.60	1.93
1.00	0.77	0.85	1.01	1.21	1.40	1.60	1.96	2.36
1.25	0.96	1.05	1.26	1.50	1.74	1.98	2.41	2.90
1.50	1.15	1.26	1.50	1.79	2.07	2.35	2.86	3.44
1.75	1.33	1.47	1.74	2.07	2.40	2.73	3.31	3.97
2.00	1.52	1.67	1.99	2.36	2.73	3.10	3.76	4.51
2.50	1.90	2.09	2.48	2.94	3.39	4.85	4.56	5.59
3.00	2.27	2.50	2.96	3.51	4.05	4.60	5.56	6.66
3.50	2.85	3.11	3.65	4.29	4.92	5.55	6.66	7.94
4.00	3.42	3.72	4.33	5.06	5.78	6.50	7.76	9.21
5.00	4.57	4.95	5.70	6.61	7.50	8.40	9.95	11.76
6.00	5.72	6.17	7.08	8.16	9.22	10.30	12.15	14.31
7.00	7.17	7.70	8.75	10.01	11.25	12.50	14.65	17.16

OG Pipes with Medium-heavy/Heavy Timber (m^3 per linear metre)

Invert depth metres	Pipe Diameter (mm) Not exceeding 225	300	450	600	750	900	1200	1500
0.60	0.52	0.56	0.67	0.79	0.92	1.04	1.28	1.55
0.80	0.68	0.74	0.88	1.04	1.20	1.36	1.66	1.99
1.00	0.84	0.92	1.09	1.28	1.48	1.69	2.03	2.44
1.25	1.05	1.15	1.35	1.59	1.83	2.07	2.50	2.99
1.50	1.26	1.37	1.62	1.90	2.18	2.46	2.92	3.55
1.75	1.46	1.60	1.88	2.20	2.53	2.85	3.45	4.11
2.00	1.67	1.82	2.14	2.51	2.88	3.25	3.91	4.66
2.50	2.08	2.27	2.67	3.12	3.58	4.04	4.85	5.78
3.00	2.49	2.72	3.19	3.73	4.28	4.82	5.78	6.89
3.50	3.10	3.37	3.88	4.54	5.17	5.81	6.92	8.20
4.00	3.71	4.01	4.52	5.35	6.07	6.79	8.05	9.51
5.00	4.94	5.32	6.00	6.98	7.87	8.77	10.32	12.13
6.00	6.16	6.62	7.52	8.60	9.67	10.74	12.60	14.76
7.00	7.69	8.22	9.27	10.53	11.77	13.02	15.17	17.68

Lay and Joint

Concrete Pipes

Pipe Diameter (mm)	Lay only per linear metre (hrs)	Per Joint Ogee Pipes (hrs)
150	0.27	0.20
225	0.33	0.24
300	0.49	0.32
450	0.88	0.64
600	1.10	0.87
750	1.65	1.52
900	2.75	1.96
1200	5.09	3.85
1500	7.53	5.63

Where pipes are laid in battered trenches take 0.66 of the above allowances for lay and joint. For porous concrete pipes take the lay only labour allowances.

Spun Iron Pipes

Pipe Diameter (mm)	Lay only per linear metre (hrs)	Tyton Joints per Joint (hrs)	Mechanical Joints per Joint (hrs)
102	0.22	0.12	0.36
150	0.36	0.17	0.50
225	0.55	0.28	0.83
300	0.90	0.37	1.10
450	1.49	0.62	1.87
600	2.09	0.83	2.50
750	3.08	1.05	3.15
900	3.85	1.25	3.75
1200	5.67	1.67	5.00

The above figures are for short lengths of sewers. For long runs of sewers or rising mains (more akin to gas and water works) take 0.66 of the allowances. For awkward lengths such as in sewage works take 1.5 times the allowances.

Trench Reinstatement

OG Pipes (super metres per linear metre)

Pipe diameter (mm)	Depth 0-3m	Depth 3-6m	Depth 6-8m
225	0.750	1.150	1.450
300	0.825	1.225	1.525
450	0.975	1.375	1.675
600	1.150	1.550	1.850
750	1.325	1.725	2.025
900	1.500	1.900	2.200
1200	1.800	2.200	2.500
1500	2.150	2.550	2.850

Above is for trenches with light or medium timbering

a) For medium-heavy or heavy timber add 0.08 m^2
b) In road with heavy traffic over 3 m deep add 0.37 m^2
c) For final coat or permanent reinstatement add 0.15 m^2

Weights of Pipes

Weight of concrete pipes

NOTE: The data show average weights, as there is slight variation in weight between the pipes supplied by various manufacturers. The data shown are for unreinforced pipes. If pipes are reinforced add 2.5 percent to weights shown, and reduce the metres of pipes per tonne accordingly.

Internal Diameter of Pipe (mm)	Ogee joints Metres per tonne	Tonnes per metre
300	11.89	0.083
375	8.74	0.115
450	6.93	0.144
525	5.07	0.197
600	4.15	0.240
675	3.52	0.283
750	2.82	0.355
825	2.48	0.402
900	2.12	0.473
975	1.89	0.529
1050	1.64	0.610
1125	1.36	0.732
1200	1.26	0.796
1350	0.99	1.100
1500	0.82	1.222

Nominal Internal Diameter (mm)	Nominal Wall thickness (mm)
150	25
225	29
300	32
375	35
450	38
600	48

Nominal Internal Diameter (mm)	Nominal Wall thickness (mm)
750	54
900	60
1200	76
1500	89
1800	102
2100	127

Wall thickness will vary, depending on type of pipe required.

The particulars shown above represent a selection of available diameters and are applicable to strength class 1 pipes with flexible rubber ring joints.

Tubes with Ogee joints are also available.

Weight of clayware pipes

Internal Diameter of Pipe (mm)	Metres per tonne	Tonnes per metre
100	51.0	0.012
150	49.0	0.020
225	27.7	0.036
300	16.5	0.060
375	11.2	0.091
450	7.3	0.137
525	5.4	0.183
600	4.1	0.244
675	3.2	0.310
750	2.7	0.366
900	1.8	0.515

Clayware gully pots

Size of gully pots in mm

Diameter	Depth	Number of gully pots per tonne
300	750	17.0
300	900	16.0
375	750	12.0
375	900	10.0
375	1050	9.5
450	750	9.0
450	900	8.0
450	1050	6.5
450	1200	6.0

Weight of Stanton Socket and Spigot Spun Iron Pipes

Weights of Standard Lengths

PIPES 5.4m LONG

Test pressure nominal bore mm	Class B 120m head kg	Class C 180m head kg	Class D 240m head kg
100	116	119	132
150	186	206	235
225	332	369	420
300	494	572	651
375	630	794	904
450	832	1043	1190
525	1072	1275	1476
600	1277	1598	1795
675	1629	2005	2296

Weights of Standard Lengths

PIPES 3.6m LONG

Test pressure nominal bore mm	Class B 120m head kg	Class C 180m head kg	Class D 240m head kg
75	60	60	61
100	80	83	91
150	128	140	161
225	214	254	288
250	249	293	336
300	318	394	446
375	435	547	620
450	574	718	816

Weight of Steel Pipes

Pipe		Class A		Class B		Class C		Class D	
Inside diameter (mm)	Outside diameter (mm)	Weight kg/m	Gauge and thickness (mm)	Weight kg/m	Gauge and thickness (mm)	Weight kg/m	Gauge and thickness (mm)	Weight kg/m	Gauge and thickness (mm)
50	59	3.81	12g	4.20	11g	4.60	109	5.14	9g
75	87	6.29	11g	7.84	9g	9.37	7g	10.17	6g
100	112	8.99	10g	10.05	9g	12.19	7g	13.26	6g
150	162	14.67	9g	17.83	7g	19.41	6g	21.36	5g
225	237	28.63	6g	31.05	5g	37.05	6.3	41.50	7.1
300	312	37.86	6g	41.75	5g	49.05	6.3	54.06	7.1
450	462	56.32	6g	64.06	5.5	73.11	6.3	91.06	7.9
600	612	97.14	6.4	121.11	7.9	133.05	8.7	144.95	9.5
750	768	153.00	7.9	168.00	8.7	198.00	9.5	195.00	10.3
900	918	183.00	7.9	219.00	9.5	237.00	10.3	255.00	11.1
1200	1225	292.00	9.5	340.00	11.1	389.00	12.7	436.00	14.3
1500	1525	485.00	12.7	544.00	14.3	605.00	15.9	665.00	17.5

Circular Sewers

Discharge through 225mm diameter pipe in litres per minute

	Depth of flow in proportion to diameter of pipe			
Gradient	One-eighth	One-quarter	One-half	Seven-eighths
1 in 20	264	1012	3432	6978
1 in 30	218	887	2796	5660
1 in 40	182	718	2409	4932
1 in 50	168	650	2160	4432
1 in 80	136	509	1714	3491
1 in 100	118	455	1500	3100

Discharge through 300mm diameter pipe in litres per minute

	Depth of flow in proportion to diameter of pipe			
Gradient	One-eighth	One-quarter	One-half	Seven-eighths
1 in 30	446	1727	5796	11730
1 in 40	391	1500	5000	10164
1 in 50	345	1327	4455	9092
1 in 80	273	1068	3296	7182
1 in 100	241	963	3136	6418
1 in 200	173	659	2227	4546

Discharge through 375mm diameter pipe in litres per minute

	Depth of flow in proportion to diameter of pipe			
Gradient	One-eighth	One-quarter	One-half	Seven-eighths
1 in 40	682	2682	8637	17729
1 in 50	614	2387	7728	15819
1 in 80	478	1887	6090	12500
1 in 100	432	1690	5478	11183
1 in 200	305	1205	4036	7887
1 in 440	205	796	2591	5295
1 in 660	164	660	2114	4523
1 in 880	145	568	1818	3751

Discharge through 450mm diameter pipe in litres per minute

	Depth of flow in proportion to diameter of pipe			
Gradient	One-eighth	One-quarter	One-half	Seven-eighths
1 in 50	955	3773	12201	25003
1 in 66	827	3114	10820	21707
1 in 80	745	2841	9637	19710
1 in 100	668	2614	8651	17761
1 in 200	478	1882	6100	12480
1 in 440	318	1236	4123	8388
1 in 880	227	873	2909	5919

Manholes

Concrete to manhole chamber rings

150mm concrete to chamber rings

Internal diameter (mm)	Concrete m^3/linear metre	Shutter m^2/linear metre	m^2/ m^3
675	0.474	3.59	7.57
750	0.511	3.84	7.51
900	0.584	4.34	7.43
975	0.619	4.55	7.35
1050	0.656	4.80	7.32
1200	0.730	5.26	7.21
1350	0.802	5.77	7.19
1500	0.875	6.23	7.12
1650	0.947	6.72	7.10
1800	1.020	7.19	7.05
2400	1.486	10.38	7.02

Weight of precast concrete manhole parts

Diameter of manhole (mm)	Precast concrete bases 600mm high Weight per base (kg)	Tapers		Cover slabs 150mm thick	
		Height of taper (mm)	Weight per taper (kg)	Diameter of cover slab	Weight per cover slab (kg)
900	600	600	265	1050	225
1050	900	600	350	1200	300
1200	1300	600	500	1350	425
1350	1750	600	615	1500	625
1500	2000	900	775	1800	915
1800	2500	900	975	2000	1100

Weight of precast concrete manhole rings

Diameter of ring (mm)	Weight per metre (kg)
675	281
900	467
1050	624
1200	760
1350	869
1500	1036
1800	1449

METALWORK

Weight of metals in kg/m²

	Thickness in mm								
Type of metal	1.6	3.2	6.4	9.5	12.7	15.9	19.1	22.2	25.0
Brass	13.9	27.7	55.4	83.2	108.9	139.0	168.0	190.4	222.0
Cast iron	11.5	22.1	45.7	68.7	91.8	114.4	137.0	161.0	191.2
Copper	14.1	28.2	56.4	84.6	112.8	141.0	169.2	197.4	225.6
Lead, cast	18.1	36.2	72.4	108.6	144.8	181.0	217.2	253.4	289.6
Steel	12.5	25.0	50.0	75.0	100.0	125.0	150.0	175.0	200.0
Wrought iron	12.2	24.4	48.8	73.2	97.4	121.9	146.4	170.8	193.8

Type of material	Weight in tonnes/m³
Cast brass	8.474
Cast copper	8.769
Cast iron	7.348
Cast lead	11.566
Gun-metal	8.618
Milled lead	11.643
Sheet copper	8.981
Steel	7.894
Tin	7.304
Wrought iron	7.668
Zinc	7.048

TIMBER

Lengths of timber per m³

Dimensions (mm)	m/m³	Dimensions (mm)	m/m³
25 x 25	1600	50 x 50	400
50	800	75	267
75	533	100	200
100	400	125	160
125	320	150	133
150	267	175	114
		200	100
		225	89
		250	80
		300	67
75 x 75	178	100 x 100	100
100	133	150	67
125	107	200	50
150	89	250	40
175	76	300	33
200	67		
225	59		
250	53		
300	44		
150 x 200	33	200 x200	25
250	27	250 x 250	16
300	22	300 x 300	11

m^3 per tonne of timber

Wood	m³ per tonne Air dry (15%)	Shipping dry (20%)	Green
Ash, European	1.47	1.41	1.24
Beech	1.44	1.38	1.06
Redwood	2.01	1.96	1.7
Elm, Common	1.84	1.78	0.98
Mahogany, Honduras	1.9	1.84	1.44
Oak, European	1.44	1.38	0.95

Drying times

Species	Time (weeks)	Species	Time (weeks)
Oak	10-12	Ash	4-5
Elm	4-5	Pitch pine	3-4
Beech	5-6	Scots pine	1-2

Drying times are for 50mm timber from freshly felled to 12% moisture content in a moderately efficient fan kiln.

m^2 per m^3 and m^3 per 100 m^2 for timber of various thicknesses

Thickness of timber (mm)	m² per m³	m³ per 100 m²	Thickness of timber (mm)	m² per m³	m³ per 100 m²
12	83.3	120	50	20.0	500
19	52.6	190	57	17.6	570
25	40.0	250	63	15.9	630
32	31.2	320	75	13.5	750
40	25.0	400	89	11.3	890
45	22.2	450	100	10.0	1000

Number of nails per kilogramme

Oval Wire Nails

Length	18mm	25mm	31mm	38mm	44mm	50mm	63mm	75mm	88mm	100mm
No. nails per kg	4500	2425	1365	880	620	375	240	110	100	70

Cut Clasp Nails

Length	25mm	38mm	50mm	63mm	75mm	88mm	100mm	112mm	125mm	150mm
No. nails per kg	1455	550	310	175	110	90	55	45	33	27

Round Wire Nails

Length	25mm	31mm	38mm	50mm	63mm	75mm	88mm	100mm	112mm	125mm	175mm
Gauge	14	13	12	10	10	8	8	8	8	6	5
No. nails per kg	1322	1145	620	265	200	130	110	100	90	65	34

ROADS AND PAVINGS

Weight of road foundation materials

NOTE: The data shown are based on 45 percent voids

Nature of the material	Weight in the solid kg per m^3	Weight in the loose as delivered on the site	
		Tonnes per m^3	m^3 per tonne
Ashes	-	0.96	1.04
Clinker	-	0.8	1.24
Gravel	-	1.52	0.66
Hardcore, brick	2123	1.16	0.86
Hardcore, chalk	2286	1.24	0.81
Hardcore, concrete	2286	1.24	0.81
Pitching, granite	2711	1.48	0.68
Pitching, limestone	2367	1.29	0.78
Pitching, sandstone	2449	1.33	0.75
Pitching, whinstone	2804	1.53	0.65

Weight of road surfacing materials

Nature of the material	Weight in the solid kg per m^3	Weight in the loose as delivered on the site	
		Tonnes per m^3	m^3 per tonne
Asphalt, bottom course	-	2.12	0.51
Asphalt, top course	-	2.24	0.45
Asphalt, mastic	2711	2.33	0.43
Tarred granite	-	1.53	0.62
Tarred gravel	2449	1.53	0.65
Tarred limestone	2531	1.57	0.64
Tarred slag	2804	1.4	0.70
Tarred whinstone	-	1.56	0.61

Stone pitching (m^2 covered by one tonne of material)

Weight of stone in the solid tonnes per m^3	Consolidated thickness laid in mm and m^2 covered by 1 tonne of material				
	150mm	175mm	200mm	225mm	300mm
2.082	4.3	3.69	3.22	2.86	2.15
2.162	4.18	3.59	3.14	2.78	2.08
2.242	4.06	3.49	3.06	2.71	2.03
2.322	3.95	3.39	2.97	2.63	1.98
2.402	2.84	3.29	2.89	2.56	1.92
2.482	3.73	3.2	2.81	2.48	1.87
2.562	3.61	3.1	2.72	2.41	1.81
2.643	3.5	3.01	2.65	2.33	1.76
2.724	3.39	2.91	2.56	2.26	1.7
2.803	3.28	2.82	2.47	2.18	1.65
2.883	3.16	2.72	2.39	2.11	1.59

Surface dressing roads (m^2 covered by various sizes of chippings, gravel or sand per m^3 and per tonne)

		Square metres covered per tonne			
Size in mm	per m^3	Sand	Granite chips	Gravel	Limestone chips
Sand	242	168	-	-	-
3	198	-	148	152	165
6	176	-	130	133	144
9	154	-	111	114	123
13	121	-	85	87	95
19	99	-	68	71	78

Weight of kerb per metre

	Type of kerb and weight in tonnes per metre	
Size of kerb in mm	Concrete	Granite
125 x 50	0.011	0.013
175 x 50	0.022	0.025
250 x 100	0.066	0.077
250 x 125	0.077	0.088
250 x 150	0.088	0.099
250 x 200	0.11	0.132
300 x 150	0.099	0.121
300 x200	0.132	0.165

Weight of artificial stone paving

Thickness of stone	Tonnes per m^2
50mm	0.12
63mm	0.15

Weight of York and Purbeck stone paving

	m^2 per tonne	
Thickness in mm	York	Purbeck
50	7.8	7.5
63	6.4	6
75	5.3	5
100	3.9	3.7

Number of paving flags per m^2

Paving Flags	Number/m^2 (incl. waste)
600 x 450mm	3.527
600 x 600mm	2.646
600 x 750mm	2.116
600 x 900mm	1.764

Asphalt Work

Weight of asphalt per m^2

Description	Thickness (mm)	Tonnes of asphalt/m^2
Single coat cold asphalt	13	0.029
	25	0.058
	50	0.115
	75	0.173
Two coats cold asphalt	88	0.194
	100	0.222
Single coat hot asphalt	25	0.062
	50	0.125
	75	0.187
Two coats hot asphalt	88	0.206
	100	0.238
Mastic asphalt	25	0.060
	50	0.120

BRICKWORK, BLOCKWORK AND MASONRY

Bricks and mortar required per m^2

Bricks 215 x 102.5 x 65mm with 10mm joints:

Wall thickness	Number of bricks (no waste allowance)	Mortar (m^3) no frogs	one frog	two frogs
102.5mm (half brick)	59.25	0.017	0.024	0.031
215mm (one brick)	118.50	0.045	0.059	0.073
327.5mm (one and a half brick)	177.75	0.072	0.093	0.114
440mm (two brick)	237.00	0.101	0.128	0.155

Extra over common brickwork for facing and pointing one side in:

		Length of pointing to one face per m^2		
	Number of bricks (no waste allowance)	Horizontal joints	Vertical joints	Combined
English bond	89	13.3m	5.8m	19.1m
Flemish bond	79	13.3m	5.1m	18.4m
English garden wall bond	74	13.3m	4.8m	18.1m
Flemish garden wall bond	68	13.3m	4.4m	17.7m

Blocks and mortar required per m^2

Blocks 440 x 215mm on face with 10mm joints require 9.88 blocks per m^2 (exclusive of waste)

Wall thickness (mm)	50	60	70	75	90	100	115	125
Mortar (m^3/m^2)	0.003	0.004	0.005	0.005	0.006	0.007	0.008	0.008

Wall thickness (mm)	140	150	190	215	220	250	275	305
Mortar (m^3/m^2)	0.009	0.010	0.013	0.014	0.015	0.017	0.019	0.020

Approximate weight of brickwork

Type of brick	Approximate weight of brickwork in kg/m^3
Facing bricks	2025
Flettons	1602
Staffordshire blue wirecuts	2123
Staffordshire blue pressed facing bricks	2188
Stocks	1945
Wirecuts	2091
Heavy engineering bricks	2286

Approximate weight of blockwork

Thickness of blocks in mm	Weight per m^2 in kg	m^2 of blocks per tonne
50	43	23
63	54	18
75	65	16
100	87	12

Quantity of brickwork (laid in mortar) and number of bricks per metre of sewer or culvert

Diameter in metres	Half a brick thick		One brick thick	
	No. of bricks	m^3 of brickwork	No. of bricks	m^3 of brickwork
0.3	72	0.15	181	0.39
0.6	127	0.26	303	0.61
0.9	177	0.37	415	0.83
1.2	240	0.48	524	1.07
1.5	279	0.59	633	1.26
1.8	353	0.7	746	1.46
2.1	406	0.81	858	1.70
2.4	462	0.92	963	1.93
2.7	514	1.03	1075	2.15
3.0	574	1.14	1188	2.37

Basic compressive strengths of bricks

Type of brick	N/mm^2 compressive strength
Clay bricks	
Engineering types	
BS 3921: 1985 engineering bricks:	
Class A	100 upwards
Class B	70 upwards
Sand-lime bricks	
Range	
BS 187: 1978 classes:	
Special purposes	
Class 3	20.5
Class 4	27.5
Class 5	34.5
Class 6	41.5
Class 7	48.5
Concrete bricks	
Range with natural aggregates	
BS 6073, Pt 1: 1981	7-40

Random rubble walling: weight per m^2

Thickness of wall (mm)	Average stone thickness (mm)	Tonnes of stone/m^2	m^3 of mortar/m^2
300	75	0.615	0.143
300	150	0.64575	0.121
300	225	0.661	0.099
300	300	0.6765	0.077
600	75	1.23	0.297
600	150	1.2915	0.231
600	225	1.322	0.187
600	300	1.353	0.165
900	75	1.845	0.44
900	150	1.93725	0.352
900	225	1.98338	0.297
900	300	2.0295	0.231

PAINTING

Average coverages of paint per coat

Coating (m² per litre)	Type of Surface						
	Smooth concrete/ Cement	Fair-faced Brickwork	Blockwork	Roughcast/ pebble-dash	Structural Steelwork	Metal Sheeting	Joinery
Woodprimer (oil based)	-	-	-	-	-	-	8-11
Metal primer: conventional	-	-	-	-	7-10	10-13	-
Alkali resistant primer	7-11	6-8	4-6	2-4	-	-	-
External wall primer sealer	6-8	6-7	4-6	2-4	-	-	-
Undercoat	7-9	6-8	6-8	3-4	10-12	10-12	10-12
Gloss finish	8-10	7-9	6-8	-	10-12	10-12	10-12
Emulsion Paint:							
standard	11-14	8-12	6-10	2-4	-	-	10-12
contract	10-12	7-10	5-9	2-4	-	-	10-12
Masonry paint	5-7	4-6	3-5	2-4	-	-	-
Cement based paint	6-7	3-6	3-6	2-3	-	-	-

WATERPROOFING

Quantities of material per m²

Material	Quantity per m²
1 layer 1200 gauge polythene sheet	0.01237 Number (rolls 25 x 4m)
2 coats RIW solution	0.2120 litres
2 coats synthaprufe horizontally	1.6545 litres
3 coats synthaprufe vertically	1.4320 litres

		kg per m² (including waste)		
Wall Renders	Thickness (mm)	Sand	Cement	Lime
Cement and sand	12	24.2	5.4	-
(1:3) to brickwork,	18	36.0	8.1	-
blockwork or concrete				
Cement, lime and sand	12	25.5	2.8	1.5
1: 1:6) external rendering to walls	18	38.2	4.2	2.2

INDEX

How to activate your 3-month period of access to CapIT: Online Carbon & Cost Estimator

As a purchaser of the CESMM3 Carbon & Price Book you are entitled to a free 3-month period of access to the CapIT online carbon and price estimator (see introduction and back cover for more details).

To activate your account, please follow the three simple steps below. The account can be activated any time between September 2010 and September 2011.

1. Go to www.capit-online.com/cesmm

2. Enter the account activation code at the bottom of this page.

3. Click on "activate".

For technical support please contact eru@franklinandrews.com
For information on CapIT: Online Carbon & Cost Estimator visit www.capit-online.com

0u21Hf-205524